THE SCIENTIFIC BASIS
OF
ILLUMINATING ENGINEERING

THE SCIENTIFIC BASIS

OF

ILLUMINATING ENGINEERING

BY

PARRY MOON
Professor of Electrical Engineering
Massachusetts Institute of Technology

REVISED EDITION

DOVER PUBLICATIONS, INC.

NEW YORK   NEW YORK

Library of Congress Catalog Card Number: 61-19883

Manufactured in the United States of America

Dover Publications, Inc.
180 Varick Street
New York 14, N. Y.

PREFACE TO DOVER EDITION

It is gratifying to find that a textbook written more than two decades ago should be deemed worthy of republication. The present edition is essentially that of 1936, but with a few corrections. Most of the book is still pertinent: the text deals primarily with basic principles, and these principles have changed very little since 1936. Moreover, the practical importance of light to the human race is undiminished; and the desirability of a scientific approach to radiation engineering is as valid as ever. Whether we call the subject "illuminating engineering," "photic engineering," or "applied optics" is immaterial. The fact remains that the need for radiation experts becomes greater each year, while the facilities for adequate training in this field are now even less satisfactory than in 1936.

If *Scientific Basis* were rewritten today, the principal difference would be in the radiometric and photometric nomenclature. As pointed out in Appendix B, the nomenclature advocated by the Illuminating Society and the American Standards Association is quite inadequate for a general treatment of the subject. Consequently, the notation used in *Scientific Basis* was necessarily unorthodox. The improved notation that I would use today is also unorthodox, though it has been employed in the *Encyclopædia Britannica, Collier's Encyclopedia, Lighting Design,** and in numerous scientific papers. A short bibliography is given at the end of this preface (Table 4).

The improved system would differ from that employed in this book as follows:

a. Instead of a separate symbol and name for radiation incident on a surface and radiation reflected from a surface (as in the book), the two would be taken as a single concept.

b. The concept of *helios* would replace the antiquated and unsatisfactory concept of "brightness." The simple concept of *luminosity*, as used in the book, is an adequate substitute for

* Moon and Spencer, *Lighting Design*, Addison-Wesley, Reading, Mass., 1948.

"brightness" in most practical cases, but it fails for imperfectly diffusing surfaces and for scattering media.

c. Names and symbols would be altered to effect greater simplicity and better correlation between radiometric and photometric quantities.

d. The mks system of units would replace the combination of cgs and English units employed in the book.

Table 1 will allow the reader to translate the ideas of *Scientific Basis* into the improved notation if he feels that such a change is advantageous. The basic radiometric measurement deals with radiant power per unit area (watt m^{-2}), so this can be taken as the fundamental concept. In the new system it is called *radiant pharosage* (pronounced *far-o-sazh'*) and is denoted by D_r. For a continuous spectrum, we need also the watts per unit area, per unit wavelength band. This is called *phengosage J* (λ); and

$$D_r = \int J(\lambda)\, d\lambda \tag{1}$$

The corresponding quantities used in the text are *irradiation G*, *radiosity J*, *spectral irradiation* G_λ, *and spectral radiosity* J_λ, with

$$G = \int G_\lambda\, d\lambda \tag{1a}$$

Geometrically related concepts are *radiant pharos* F_r, defined as

$$F_r = \int D_r\, d\mathscr{A} \tag{2}$$

and *radiant phos* Q_r:

$$Q_r = \int F_r\, dt \tag{3}$$

The corresponding quantities used in the book are *radiant power* Φ,

$$\Phi = \int G\, d\mathscr{A} \tag{2a}$$

and *radiant energy U*:

$$U = \int \Phi\, dt \tag{3a}$$

Also included in the new system is *radiant helios* H_r. Helios at an arbitrary point P is a scalar function of five independent variables—three specifying the position of point P and two specifying direction. The concept is defined by the equation

$$H_r = \pi \lim_{\Omega \to 0} \left(\frac{D_r}{\Omega}\right) \tag{4}$$

where Ω is the solid angle of a lightcone with apex at P. The mks unit of radiant helios is the *herschel*. In fog and other scattering media, *heliosent* G_r may also be helpful:

$$G_r = \frac{dH_r}{ds} \tag{5}$$

The foregoing are physical quantities, measured by means of radiation thermocouple, bolometer, or other physical instruments.

Photometric quantities are obtained by evaluating radiometric quantities with respect to the eye (Table 2). Employing the internationally standardized *lamprosity* $\bar{y}(\lambda)$ as weighting function, one obtains the *luminous pharosage*:

$$D = \int \bar{y}(\lambda)\, J(\lambda)\, d\lambda \quad \text{(young m}^{-2}\text{)} \tag{6}$$

By use of an experimentally determined conversion factor, one may express luminous pharosage also in lumen m^{-2}.

Other photometric quantities are *luminous pharos F*,

$$F = \int D\, d\mathscr{A} \quad \text{(lumen)} \tag{7}$$

luminous phos Q,

$$Q = \int F\, dt \quad \text{(lumen-sec)} \tag{8}$$

and *luminous helios H*,

$$H = \pi \lim_{\Omega \to 0} \left(\frac{D}{\Omega}\right) \quad \text{(blondel)} \tag{9}$$

Corresponding concepts in *Scientific Basis* are indicated in Table 2. By use of other weighting functions $w_i(\lambda)$, one can obtain analogous quantities associated with photoelectric, photographic, erythemal, or other effects of radiation:

$$D_i = \int w_i(\lambda)\, J(\lambda)\, d\lambda \tag{10}$$

For most purposes, the complete set of concepts is not required, and the improved system reduces to the very simple arrangement of Table 3.

CAMBRIDGE, MASS.,
January, 1961.

PARRY MOON

TABLE 1

RADIOMETRIC CONCEPTS

Scientific Basis			Improved System		
Name	Symbol	Unit	Name	Symbol	Unit
Irradiation........	G	watt cm^{-2}			
			Radiant pharosage.	D_r	watt m^{-2}
Radiosity.........	J	watt cm^{-2}			
Spectral irradiation.	G_λ	watt cm$^{-2}\mu^{-1}$			
			Phengosage	$J(\lambda)$	watt m^{-2} μ^{-1}
Spectral radiosity..	J_λ	watt cm$^{-2}\mu^{-1}$			
Radiant power.....	Φ	watt	Radiant pharos ...	F_r	watt
Radiant energy....	U	watt-sec	Radiant phos	Q_r	watt-sec
			Radiant helios	H_r	herschel
			Radiant heliosent..	G_r	herschel m^{-1}
Spectral reflection factor	ρ_λ	numeric	Spectral reflectance	$\rho(\lambda)$	numeric
Spectral transmission factor	τ_λ	numeric	Spectral transmittance	$\tau(\lambda)$	numeric

TABLE 2

PHOTOMETRIC CONCEPTS

Scientific Basis			Improved System		
Name	Symbol	Unit	Name	Symbol	Unit
Illumination.......	E	lumen ft^{-2}			
			Pharosage........	D	lumen m^{-2}
Luminosity........	L	lumen ft^{-2}			
Luminous flux.....	F	lumen	Pharos..........	F	lumen
Light............	Q	lumen-sec	Phos.............	Q	lumen-sec
			Helios	H	blondel
			Heliosent........	G	blondel m^{-1}
Reflection factor...	ρ	numeric	Reflectance.......	ρ	numeric
Transmission factor	τ	numeric	Transmittance....	τ	numeric
Visibility..........	$v(\lambda)$	$\dfrac{\text{lightwatt}}{\text{watt}}$	Spectral lamprosity	$\bar{y}(\lambda)$	young/ watt
Luminous efficacy..	η_l	lumens per radiated watt	Total lamprosity ..	y	youngs per radiated watt
Over-all efficacy....	η_0	lumens per input watt	Actance..........	η	lumens per input watt

TABLE 3

IMPROVED SYSTEM FOR ORDINARY USE

Radiometric			Photometric		
Name	Symbol	Unit	Name	Symbol	Unit
Pharosage (radiant)	D_r	watt m^{-2}	Pharosage (luminous)	D	lumen m^{-2}
Phengosage	$J(\lambda)$	watt m$^{-2}\,\mu^{-1}$			
Pharos (radiant) ...	F_r	watt	Pharos (luminous) .	F	lumen
Phos (radiant)	Q_r	watt-sec	Phos (luminous)...	Q	lumen-sec
Helios (radiant)	H_r	herschel	Helios (luminous)..	H	blondel

$\bar{y}(\lambda)$ lamprosity (young watt^{-1})

TABLE 4

SUPPLEMENTARY PAPERS BY THE AUTHOR

1937

"A Table of Planck's Function from 3500 to 8000°K," *J. Math. Phys.*, Vol. 16 (1937), p. 133.

1938

"Reflection Characteristics of Road Surfaces," *J. Franklin Inst.*, Vol. 225 (1938), p. 1 (with R. M. Hunt).

"The Dielectric Bolometer," *J. Opt. Soc. Am.*, Vol. 28 (1938), p. 148 (with L. R. Steinhart).

"On the Reflection Factor of Clothing," *J. Opt. Soc. Am.*, Vol. 28 (1938), p. 277 (with M. S. Cettei).

1939

"Some Tests on Radiation-mixing Enclosures," *J. Opt. Soc. Am.*, Vol. 28 (1939), p. 20 (with D. P. Severance).

"Basic Principles of Illumination Calculations," *J. Opt. Soc. Am.*, Vol. 29 (1939), p. 108.

"The Light Field," *J. Math. Phys.*, Vol. 18 (1939), p. 51 (Translation, with G. S. Timoshenko, from the Russian book by A. Gershun).

"The Design of Photoelectric Flicker Photometers," *I.E.S. Trans.*, Vol. 34 (1939), p. 801 (with D. P. Severance).

1940

"A Table of Fresnel Reflection," *J. Math. Phys.*, Vol. 19 (1940), p. 1.

"On Interreflections," *J. Opt. Soc. Am.*, Vol. 30 (1940), p. 195.

"Proposed Standard Solar-radiation Curves for Engineering Use," *J. Franklin Inst.*, Vol. 230 (1940), p. 583.

1941

"Construction and Test of a Goniophotometer," *J. Opt. Soc. Am.*, Vol. 31 (1941), p. 130 (with J. Laurence).

"Interreflections in Finite Cylinders," *J. Opt. Soc. Am.*, Vol. 31 (1941), p. 223.

"Interreflections in Lightwells," *J. Opt. Soc. Am.*, Vol. 31 (1941), p. 301.

"Optical Reflection Factors of Acoustical Materials," *J. Opt. Soc. Am.*, Vol. 31 (1941), p. 317.

"Interreflections in Rooms," *J. Opt. Soc. Am.*, Vol. 31 (1941), p. 374.

"Color Determination," *Illum. Eng.*, Vol. 36 (1941), p. 313.

"Colors of Ceramic Tiles," *J. Opt. Soc. Am.*, Vol. 31 (1941), p. 482.

"Wall Materials and Lighting," *J. Opt. Soc. Am.*, Vol. 31 (1941), p. 723.

1942

"Reflection Factors of Floor Materials," *J. Opt. Soc. Am.*, Vol. 32 (1942), p. 238.

"Reflection Factors of Some Materials Used in Schoolrooms," *J. Opt. Soc. Am.*, Vol. 32 (1942), p. 243.

"Colors of Furniture," *J. Opt. Soc. Am.*, Vol. 32 (1942), p. 293.

"The Names of Physical Concepts," *Am. J. Phys.*, Vol. 10 (1942), p. 134.

"A System of Photometric Concepts," *J. Opt. Soc. Am.*, Vol. 32 (1942), p. 348.

"Illumination from a Non-uniform Sky," *Illum. Eng.*, Vol. 37 (1942), p. 707 (with D. E. Spencer).

1943

"New Methods of Calculating Illumination," *J. Opt. Soc. Am.*, Vol. 33 (1943), p. 115.

(With Domina Eberle Spencer)

"Analytical Representation of Standard Response Curves," *J. Opt. Soc. Am.*, Vol. 33 (1943), p. 89.

"A Metric for Colorspace," *J. Opt. Soc. Am.*, Vol. 33 (1943), p. 260.

"A Metric Based on the Composite Color Stimulus," *J. Opt. Soc. Am.*, Vol. 33 (1943), p. 270.

"The Specification of Foveal Adaptation," *J. Opt. Soc. Am.*, Vol. 33 (1943), p. 444.

"Photometrics in General Physics," *Am. J. Phys.*, Vol. 11 (1943), p. 200.

1944

(Papers with Domina Eberle Spencer)

"Geometric Formulation of Classical Color Harmony," *J. Opt. Soc. Am.*, Vol. 34 (1944), p. 46.

"Area in Color Harmony," *J. Opt. Soc. Am.*, Vol. 34 (1944), p. 93.

"Aesthetic Measure Applied to Color Harmony," *J. Opt. Soc. Am.*, Vol. 34 (1944), p. 234.

"On the Stiles-Crawford Effect," *J. Opt. Soc. Am.*, Vol. 34 (1944), p. 319.

"Brightness and Helios," *Ill. Eng.*, Vol. 39 (1944), p. 507.

"Visual Data Applied to Lighting Design," *J. Opt. Soc. Am.*, Vol. 34 (1944), p. 605.

"The Transient Stiles-Crawford Effect," *J. Opt. Soc. Am.*, Vol. 34 (1944), p. 744.

"Color Space and Color Harmony," *Inter-Society Color Council News Letter*, No. 54, p. 6, July, 1944.

1945

(Papers with Domina Eberle Spencer)

"A Modified Photochemical Theory of Vision," *J. Opt. Soc. Am.*, Vol. 35 (1945), p. 43.

"The Visual Effect of Non-uniform Surrounds," *J. Opt. Soc. Am.*, Vol. 35 (1945), p. 233.

"Analytical Representation of Trichromatic Data," *J. Opt. Soc. Am.*, Vol. 35 (1945), p. 399.

"Visual Dark Adaptation: A Mathematical Formulation," *J. Math. Phys.*, Vol. 24 (1945), p. 65.

"Polynomial Representation of Reflectance Curves," *J. Opt. Soc. Am.*, Vol. 35 (1945), p. 597.

1946

(Papers with Domina Eberle Spencer)

"Units in the Trichromatic System," *J. Opt. Soc. Am.*, Vol. 36 (1946), p. 120.

"It Seems to Me," *Illum. Eng.*, Vol. 41 (1946), p. 180.

"Discussion of Illuminating Engineering as a Profession," *Illum. Eng.*, Vol. 41 (1946), p. 253.

"Maintenance Factors," *Illum. Eng.*, Vol. 41 (1946), p. 211.

"Light Flux Distribution in a Rectangular Parallelepiped and Its Simplifying Scale," *Illum. Eng.*, Vol. 41 (1946), p. 232 (Translation of a paper by K. Hisano. Translated by H. Shiramizu, edited by P. Moon).

"Light Distribution from Rectangular Sources," *J. Franklin Inst.*, Vol. 241 (1946), p. 195.

"Analytic Expressions in Photometry and Colorimetry," *J. Math. Phys.*, Vol. 25 (1946), p. 111.

"Approximations to Planckian Distributions," *J. Appl. Phys.*, Vol. 17 (1946), p. 506.

"International Names in Colorimetry," *J. Opt. Soc. Am.*, Vol. 36 (1946), p. 427.

"Light Distributions in Rooms," *J. Franklin Inst.*, Vol. 242 (1946), p. 111.

"Brillo y Helios," *Revista Electrotecnica*, Vol. 32 (1946), p. 353.
"Internationality in the Names of Scientific Concepts: A Method of Naming Concepts," *Am. J. Phys.*, Vol. 14 (1946), p. 285.
"A Study of Photometric Nomenclature," *J. Opt. Soc. Am.*, Vol. 36 (1946), p. 666.
"A Proposed International Photometric System," *Am. J. Phys.*, Vol. 14 (1946), p. 431.
"Lighting Design by the Interreflection Method," *J. Franklin Inst.*, Vol. 242 (1946), p. 465.

1947
(Papers with Domina Eberle Spencer)

"Comparison of Photometric Systems," *Am. J. Phys.*, Vol. 15 (1947), p. 84.
"A Simple Criterion for Quality in Lighting," *Illum. Eng.*, Vol. 42 (1947), p. 325.
"Pri la defino e nomizo di ciencala koncepti," *Progresso*, Vol. 23 (1947), p. 13.
"Photometric Nomenclature for the Post-war World," *Illum. Eng.*, Vol. 42 (1947), p. 611.
"Analytic Representation of Experimental Spectroradiometric Curves," *J. Franklin Inst.*, Vol. 244 (1947), p. 441.

1948
(Papers with Domina Eberle Spencer)

"Utilizing the MKS System," *Am. J. Phys.*, Vol. 16 (1948), p. 25.
"Modern Terminology for Physics," *Am. J. Phys.*, Vol. 16 (1948), p. 100.
"A Table of Planckian Radiation," *J. Opt. Soc. Am.*, Vol. 38 (1948), p. 291.
"The Color of Unstained Wood," *J. Opt. Soc. Am.*, Vol. 38 (1948), p. 405.
"Visual Performance and the Surround," *J. Opt. Soc. Am.*, Vol. 38 (1948), p. 651.
"Languages for Science," *J. Franklin Inst.*, Vol. 246 (1948), p. 1.
Lighting Design, Addison-Wesley Press, Reading, Mass., 1948.
A Table of Planck's Function, 2000 to 3500°K, Addison-Wesley Press, Reading, Mass., 1948.

1949, 1950
(Papers with Domina Eberle Spencer)

"An Engineering Correlation of Room Colors," *J. Franklin Inst.*, Vol. 247 (1949), p. 117.
"The New Approach to Room Lighting," *Illum. Eng.*, Vol. 44 (1949), p. 221.
Sections on "Photometry" and "Candlepower" in *Encyclopœdia Britannica*.
"Luminous Ceiling Lighting," *Illum. Eng.*, Vol. 44 (1949), p. 465.
"A Survey of Colors for Industry," *Illum. Eng.*, Vol. 45 (1950), p. 39.
"Interflections in Coupled Enclosures," *J. Franklin Inst.*, Vol. 250 (1950), p. 151.

1951
(Papers with Domina Eberle Spencer)

"Simplified Interflection Calculations," *J. Franklin Inst.*, Vol. 251 (1951), p. 215.
"A Slide Rule for Lighting Calculations," *J. Opt. Soc. Am.*, Vol. 41 (1951), p. 98.
"Modeling with Light," *J. Franklin Inst.*, Vol. 251 (1951), p. 453.
"How to Design Your Luminous Ceilings," *Illum. Eng.*, Vol. 46 (1951), p. 295.
"Interflection Calculations for Various Luminaires," *J. Franklin Inst.*, Vol. 252 (1951), p. 11.
"Electric Lighting" (Article in *Collier's Encyclopedia*, P. F. Collier and Son, New York, Vol. 7, p. 170).

1952 to date
(Papers with Domina Eberle Spencer)

"Theory of the Photic Field," *J. Franklin Inst.*, Vol. 255 (1953), p. 33.

"Some Applications of Photic-field Theory," *J. Franklin Inst.*, Vol. 255 (1953), p. 113.

"L'environnement lumineux," *Ann. d'Optique Oculaire*, Vol. 1 (1953), p. 169.

"Calculation of Camera Exposure," *J. Franklin Inst.*, Vol. 258 (1954), p. 113.

"Photometrics in Astronomy," *J. Franklin Inst.*, 258 (1954), p. 461.

"On Photographic Exposure Meters," *J. Soc. Mot. Pic. Engrs.*, Vol. 63 (1954), p. 233.

"The Photometric Range of Outdoor Scenes," *J. Soc. Mot. Pic. Engrs.*, Vol. 63 (1954), p. 237.

Lighting Design (Japanese translation), Gihodo, Tokyo, 1956.

PREFACE TO 1936 EDITION

This book is an outgrowth of mimeographed notes which have been used for a number of years in teaching illuminating engineering at Massachusetts Institute of Technology. The endeavor to teach the subject as a true branch of engineering showed clearly the necessity for a radically different kind of text than any hitherto available. Many excellent books on optics are obtainable, as well as numerous texts dealing with lighting as an *art*. But apparently there has been nothing suitable as an introductory text on the *engineering* of lighting, based on physics, and comparable with the really fine texts which have been available in electrical engineering.

"The Scientific Basis of Illuminating Engineering" was written in an endeavor to fill this gap. Stress is laid throughout on the *quantitative* aspects, which are so important in all forms of engineering. No attempt is made to treat the whole field of illuminating engineering—practical applications, artistic aspects, and psychological effects are hardly touched. As the name implies, the book is designed as a scientific introduction to the basic ideas underlying illuminating engineering. It is felt that the mastery of these basic ideas will not only free the young engineer from the necessity of learning by rote many of the details of present practice, but will allow him to exercise his originality in going far beyond the methods of today.

A rereading of the manuscript discloses a number of rather violent statements having a decidedly dogmatic ring. I hope they will not annoy the reader unduly. As a matter of fact, these statements were made purposely, with the idea of provoking discussion and jarring the student out of his placid belief that illuminating engineering, having attained perfection in some past era, is now permanently embalmed in all its glory. In destroying such an attitude, even violent means seem justifiable.

The book is so written that it can be used either for a one-term subject or for a more thorough treatment. Chapters and sections marked with an asterisk may be omitted in an introductory course without interfering with the understanding of the remainder. Thus, Chapters IV, X, XII, XIII, and XIV may be omitted. In some cases, the study of Chapter VII directly after Chapter III may be advisable to bring the classroom work more closely in touch with the laboratory investigations.

In writing the book, I am indebted to many. In particular, I wish to thank Dr. Dugald C. Jackson, whose insistence on a scientific treatment of the subject and whose help and inspiration have been most valuable. To Dr. J. L. Barnes, Dr. L. J. Buttolph, Dr. W. E. Forsythe, Prof. A. C. Hardy, Dr. S. Hecht, and Mr. W. F. Little, who kindly read and criticized portions of the manuscript, I am deeply grateful. I appreciate also the help of Messrs. J. P. Connor, A. Herzenberg, and N. D. Kenney in the computation of tables and the preparation of graphs, and of Messrs. K. L. Blaisdell and S. Q. Duntley in the reading of the galley proof. Numerous data were obtained from the literature and from theses, acknowledgments of which are given in the text. Not least do I wish to thank Dean H. E. Clifford, editor of the "Electrical Engineering Texts," for his very careful reading of the entire manuscript and for his many suggestions.

PARRY MOON.

CAMBRIDGE, MASS.,
August, 1936.

CONTENTS

CONTENTS

ABBREVIATIONS USED IN BIBLIOGRAPHICAL REFERENCES

Akad. Wiss. Wien, Ber.	Sitzungsberichte der Akademie der Wissenschaften in Wien. Mathematisch-naturwissenschaftliche Klasse. Vienna
Am. Acad. Sci., Proc.	Proceedings of the American Academy of Arts and Sciences, Boston.
Am. Architect	American Architect, New York.
Am. Electrochem. Soc., Trans.	Transactions of the American Electrochemical Society, New York.
A.I.E.E. Trans.	Transactions of the American Institute of Electrical Engineers, New York.
Am. Inst. Min. and Met. Engrs.	Transactions of the American Institute of Mining and Metallurgical Engineers, New York.
Am. J. Physiol.	American Journal of Physiology, Boston.
Am. J. Sci.	American Journal of Science, New Haven, Conn.
Ann. d. Physik	Annalen der Physik, Leipzig.
Astrophys. J.	Astrophysical Journal, Chicago.
Brit. J. Phot.	British Journal of Photography, London.
B.S.T.J.	Bell System Technical Journal, New York.
Bu. Stds. Bull.	Bulletin of the Bureau of Standards, Washington, D.C.
Bu. Stds. J. R.	Bureau of Standards Journal of Research. National Bureau of Standards, Washington, D.C.
Bu. Stds. Misc. Pub.	Miscellaneous Publications of the Bureau of Standards, Washington, D.C.
Bu. Stds. Sci. Paper	Scientific Papers of the Bureau of Standards, Washington, D.C.
Bu. Stds. Tech. Paper	Technical Papers of the Bureau of Standards.
C.I.E. Proc.	Proceedings of the Commission Internationale de l'Éclairage. (Also called Proceedings of the International Illumi-

nation Congress and Proceedings of the International Congress on Illumination.)

Comptes Rendus	Comptes Rendus Hebdomadaires des Séances de l'Académie des Sciences, Paris.
Dept. of Sci. and Ind. Res. Tech. Paper	Illumination Research Technical Paper, the Department of Scientific and Industrial Research, London.
Elect. Engineering	Electrical Engineering. Journal of the American Institute of Electrical Engineers, New York.
El. World	Electrical World, New York.
E.T.Z.	Elektrotechnische Zeitschrift, Berlin.
Electrot. Lab. Tokyo, Researches	Researches of the Electrotechnical Laboratory, Tokyo, Japan.
Elettrotecnica	L'Elettrotecnica. Giornale ed Atti dell' Associazione Elettrotecnica Italiana, Milan.
Ergeb. Physiol.	Ergebnisse der Physiologie, Wiesbaden.
Frank. Inst., J.	Journal of the Franklin Institute, Philadelphia.
G.E. Res. Lab. Reprints	Reprints of the General Electric Research Laboratory, Schenectady, N.Y.
G.E.Rev.	General Electric Review, Schenectady, N.Y.
I.E.E., J.	Journal of the Institution of Electrical Engineers, London.
I.E.S. Trans.	Transactions of the Illuminating Engineering Society, New York.
J. Cell. and Comp. Physiol.	Journal of Cellular and Comparative Physiology, Philadelphia.
J. Exp. Psychol.	Journal of Experimental Psychology, Princeton, N.J.
J. Gen. Physiol.	Journal of General Physiology, New York
J.O.S.A.	Journal of the Optical Society of America. The American Institute of Physics, New York.
J. Physiol.	Journal of Physiology, London.

K. Akad. Amsterdam, Proc.	Proceedings of the Koninklijke Akademie van Wetenschappen te Amsterdam, Amsterdam, Holland.
Mag. of Light	The Magazine of Light, General Electric Co., Cleveland, Ohio.
M.I.T. Thesis	Thesis submitted in partial fulfillment of a degree at the Massachusetts Institute of Technology.
Med. Res. Council, Spec. Rep.	Privy Council, Medical Research Council, Reports of the Committee upon the Physiology of Vision, Special Report Series, London.
M.P.E. Trans.	See *Soc. M.P.E., Trans.*
Nat. Acad. Sci., Proc.	Proceedings of the National Academy of Sciences, Washington, D.C.
Nature	Nature, London.
Naturwiss.	Naturwissenschaften, Berlin.
Opt. Inst. Trans., Leningrad	Transactions of the Optical Institute, Leningrad.
Opt. Soc. Trans.	Transactions of the Optical Society, London.
Phil. Mag.	The London, Edinburgh and Dublin Philosophical Magazine and Journal of Science, London.
Phil. Science	Philosophy of Science, Baltimore, Md.
Physica	Physica. The Hague, Holland.
Phys. Rev.	The Physical Review. American Institute of Physics, New York.
Phys. Rev. Supp.	Physical Review Supplement. (Later published as Reviews of Modern Physics.)
Phys. Soc., Proc.	Proceedings of the Physical Society, London.
Physics	Physics. The American Institute of Physics, New York.
Physiol. Rev.	Physiological Review, Baltimore, Md.
Phys. Zeits.	Physikalische Zeitschrift, Leipzig.
Phys. Zeits. d. Sowjetunion	Physikalische Zeitschrift der Sowjetunion, Clarkow, U.S.S.R.

Preuss. Akad. Wiss. Berlin	Abhandlungen der Preussischen Akademie der Wissenschaften, Berlin.
Proc. Roy. Soc.	Proceedings of the Royal Society of London.
Psychol. Bull.	Psychological Bulletin, Lancaster, Pa.
Psychol. Rev.	Psychological Review, Princeton, N.J.
Rev. d'Optique	Revue d'Optique Théorique et Instrumentale, Paris.
R.G.E.	Revue Générale de l'Électricité, Paris.
Rev. Modern Physics	Reviews of Modern Physics. The American Institute of Physics, New York.
R.S.I.	Review of Scientific Instruments. The American Institute of Physics, New York.
Roy. Soc. Phil. Trans.	Philosophical Transactions of the Royal Society of London, London.
Roy. Soc., Proc.	See Proceedings Royal Society.
Russ. Phys. Chem. Soc., J.	Journal of the Russian Physico-Chemical Society.
Smithsonian Inst. Astrophys. Obs., Ann.	Annals of the Astrophysical Observatory of the Smithsonian Institution, Washington, D.C.
Smithsonian Misc. Coll.	Smithsonian Miscellaneous Collection, the Smithsonian Institution, Washington, D.C.
Soc. M.P.E., Trans.	Transactions of the Society of Motion Picture Engineers, Washington, D.C.
U. Mich., Dept. of Eng. Res.	Bulletin of the Department of Engineering Research of the University of Michigan, Ann Arbor, Mich.
Verh. d. D. phys. Ges.	Verhandlungen der Deutsche physikalische Gesellschaft, Leipzig.
Wied. Ann.	See Ann. d. Physik.
World Power	World Power, London.
Zeits. f. Phys.	Zeitschrift für Physik, Berlin.
Zeits. psychol. u. physiol. Sinnes.	Zeitschrift für Psychologie und Physiologie der Sinnesorgane, Hamburg.
Zeits. f. techn. Physik	Zeitschrift für technische Physik, Leipzig.

THE SCIENTIFIC BASIS
OF
ILLUMINATING ENGINEERING

ILLUMINATING ENGINEERING

CHAPTER I

FUNDAMENTALS

Various professions have arisen from time to time, owing to the increasing complexity of modern civilization and the economic need for further specialization. Such professions as theology, law, and medicine have descended to us from the ancients. Others, such as engineering, are of fairly recent origin. Of the engineering professions, the latest to arrive is that of illuminating engineering; in fact, it is still in the throes of arriving.

The basic difference between a trade and a profession lies in the training required in the two cases. A craft or trade requires a much less severe period of training—particularly less severe intellectually—than a profession. In the Middle Ages, engineering was of some value to society, but since it was almost entirely empirical it had not risen to the dignity of a profession and remained for a long time as a trade, like plumbing or carpentry today. Illuminating engineering still remains more of a trade than a true profession, though the recent rapid development of the subject and the awakening of society to the importance of correct lighting are gradually creating a need for illuminating engineers equipped with a thorough fundamental training.

A graphical representation of the relations between illuminating engineering and the other professions is shown in Fig. 1.01.* The outstanding difference between illuminating engineering and all other forms of engineering is evident. Other branches deal largely with the exact sciences of mathematics, physics, and chemistry, with the economic factor always kept in mind, but have practically nothing to do with physiology or art. Illuminating engineering, on the other hand, is vitally concerned with all these subjects. The illuminating engineer should not

---

* *Cf.* A. E. Kennelly, *I.E.S. Trans.*, **6**, 1911, p. 73.

only interest himself in the exact sciences and in economics but should also be thoroughly conversant with the physiology of the eye, the peculiarities of our seeing process, and psychological effects. In most cases, he must also understand something of art and architecture in order to produce pleasing results.

Obviously, a single text cannot give a thorough treatment of all the subjects indicated in Fig. 1.01. It has seemed best in the

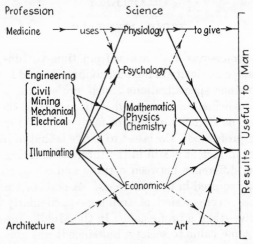

Fɪɢ. 1.01.—Professions.

present volume, therefore, to confine the material to such limits as will be of the greatest use in an introductory course in illuminating engineering. We shall limit ourselves largely to the *scientific basis* of the subject and shall attempt to develop a suitable foundation of applied physics on which the student may build his own superstructure. A great many of the details of modern practice as well as the aesthetic factors have been purposely omitted in favor of a more thorough treatment of the scientific fundamentals without which illuminating engineering must necessarily fail to reach its true place as a profession.

Without question, the most important of our senses is sight, and thus the problems of the illuminating engineer are of vital concern to mankind. In the remote past when human beings spent most of their waking moments out of doors, their lighting was provided on a satisfactory and lavish scale by nature. One would expect the human organism to evolve in harmony with such lighting. Civilized man, however, spends most of his time in buildings lighted either through windows or by artificial illumination. Thus practically all of his seeing, both by night and by day, is done under man-made conditions, which may be good or bad according to the skill and understanding of the illuminating engineer.

Considering the extremely deleterious effects caused by poor lighting—the eye strain, headaches, impairment of vision, accidents due to insufficient light or to glare—it is astounding how little attention is paid to the subject. The average person is peculiarly uncritical as regards lighting, being satisfied with inadequate illumination as well as with atrociously ugly luminaires. If a transmission line or a bridge is to be built, an engineer is consulted without question; but if an important public building is to be lighted, the design is usually entrusted to a salesman who may have nothing to guide him but a catalogue of fixtures and an itching palm. Windows are still placed in buildings in such positions as give a pleasing exterior effect and with no analysis of the interior illumination that they will provide. Desks and benches are still arranged so that workers must face the light. Artificial sources of high luminosity are placed directly in the field of vision or so placed that reflected glare will be experienced from polished table tops or parts of machines. Annoying shadows are so common as to be practically universal.

The blame for this state of affairs may be laid upon the so-called "practical" men who design most lighting installations, using rule-of-thumb methods instead of scientific analysis. The horrible examples of their labors are only too evident. Moreover, the quality of their work has not been notably improved by the recent astonishing development of new high-pressure sales methods parading under such names as the "newest science of vision"; while their ethics have fallen to a new low, in deplorable contrast to the high ideals generally expected of members of a profession. The public is deluged by an immense wave of lighting propaganda. Clever but bogus visual tests, combined with a great mess of doubtful statistics and pseudoscientific conclusions, may produce the desired result—*viz.*, the sale of fixtures, lamps, and power—but an unfavorable reaction on the part of the public seems inevitable.

Such charlatanism and such crude empirical methods of design were present in the very early stages of the development of other branches of engineering but have been largely supplanted by sound methods based upon fundamental scientific research. Traces of similar improvements are evident—to the optimist—even in illuminating engineering. The last few years have seen important developments in light sources. The sodium-vapor lamp and the high-pressure mercury lamps give much greater luminous output per watt than did any of the older types of light sources. The radical improvement in interior illumination by built-in lighting and the introduction of photoelectric methods of measurement and control are other examples of real progress. And we are only beginning to tap the possibilities of the subject. Thus illuminating engineering is a very promising field for men with adequate scientific training and enough originality to apply their knowledge. Such men can raise illuminating engineering to the level of a true profession.

1.02. The Nature of Radiation.—A question that has puzzled man since the earliest time is *What is light?*

The invaluable agent of our best knowledge of the environing world, and yet itself unknown except by inference; the intermediary between matter and the finest of our senses, and yet itself not material; intangible, and yet able to press, to strike blows, and to recoil; impalpable, and yet the vehicle of the energies that flow to the earth from the sun—light in all times has been a recognized and conspicuous feature of the physical world, a perpetual reminder that the material, the tangible, the palpable substances are not the only real ones.[8]*

The ancient Greeks thought of light as consisting of a stream of extremely minute corpuscles which were shot off from heated bodies and which, upon entering the eye, had the property of evoking a sensation. Such a view was generally held by physicists up to about 1850, though Huygens introduced the idea of light as a wave motion in about 1690. A heated controversy between the advocates of the corpuscular theory and the advocates of the wave theory finally led to the complete victory of the wave theory.[5] Subsequent work of Maxwell, Hertz, and others showed that light can be considered as an electromagnetic-wave phenomenon and that radiations that produce the visual

* See Bibliography at end of chapter.

sensation are of exactly the same nature as those that we term radio waves, Hertzian waves, infrared waves, and ultraviolet waves. All these radiations can be classed together. A large group of new results obtained since 1900 has now caused another revolution in our thought and has resulted in the quantum theory and the wave mechanics, which again stress the corpuscular nature of radiation.[6]

To understand more clearly the present status of the subject, let us consider briefly some of the experimental data on which our ideas of the nature of radiation are based. In the first place, it must be realized that we have no knowledge of the existence of light waves comparable with our knowledge of the existence of waves on the surface of water or of sound waves. Radiation can be detected only when it is absorbed by matter to raise the temperature of a body, to eject electrons from a metal surface, to affect the retina of the eye. Radiant energy streams from the sun; it manifests itself on the earth by

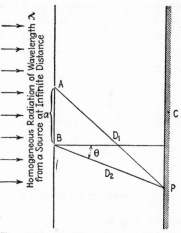

Fig. 1.02.—A diffraction experiment.

numerous heating, lighting, and photochemical effects; but who can say how it gets across the intervening space? We know only that somehow there is a transference of energy. It seems to be a peculiarity of man's present mode of thought that he can conceive of energy transfer through space in only two ways: Either the source shoots out particles whose kinetic energy is absorbed when they strike a surface, or the energy is transmitted by a wave motion.

The old corpuscular theory explained the transfer of energy in a satisfactory manner, also the fact that radiation passes through a homogeneous medium in straight lines. It gave a satisfactory picture of reflection, for if the corpuscles are assumed to be perfectly elastic spheres, they will bounce off a polished surface with the angle of reflection equal to the angle of incidence. The corpuscular theory, however, was unable to explain the phenomena of interference, where the addition of two lights may produce total darkness. A source of radiation of wavelength λ illuminates two tiny slits A and B in an opaque plate (Fig. 1.02). It is true that in the work with which an illuminating engineer ordinarily deals, light travels in straight lines. In the case shown, however, because of the narrowness of the slits, each slit radiates in all directions; and some parts of the wall C will be found to be brightly lighted while others are not lighted at all. The wave theory explains this interference phenomenon very easily. If the lengths of the paths AP and BP are such that the two waves are in phase at P, the resulting illumination will have a maximum value; but if the two waves arrive at P 180 deg out of phase, darkness results.

In reaching P, the radiation from A travels a distance

$$D_1 = \sqrt{D_2{}^2 + a^2 + 2aD_2 \sin \theta} \qquad (1.01)$$

Thus

$$D_1 - D_2 = \sqrt{D_2{}^2 + a^2 + 2aD_2 \sin \theta} - D_2$$

If $a << D_2$, a^2 is negligible in comparison with $D_2{}^2$, and

$$D_1 - D_2 \cong \sqrt{D_2{}^2 + 2aD_2 \sin \theta} - D_2$$

Expanding in a series,

$$D_1 - D_2 \cong (D_2 + a \sin \theta + \cdots) - D_2$$
$$= a \sin \theta$$

If P is a spot of maximum illumination, the two waves must be in phase at P, and $(D_1 - D_2)$ must be equal to an integral number of wavelengths. Thus

$$D_1 - D_2 = q\lambda = a \sin \theta \qquad (1.02)$$

where $q = 0, 1, 2, \cdots$
Thus the wavelength λ of the homogeneous radiation is easily obtained from a measurement of a and θ.

Many other facts were explained by the wave theory. As Darrow says:[3]

The history of optics in the nineteenth century, from Fresnel and Young to Michelson and Rayleigh, is the tale of a brilliant series of beautiful and striking demonstrations of the wave theory, of experiments which were founded upon the wave theory as their basis and would have failed if the basis had not been firm, of instruments which were designed and competent to make difficult and delicate measurements of all sorts—from the thickness of a sheet of molecules to the diameter of a star—and would have been useless had the theory been fallacious.

But the wave theory had its troubles. To account for a wave that could travel through free space, physicists postulated a medium—the ether. The ether has been defined, rather cynically, as a medium invented by man for the purpose of propagating his misconceptions from one place to another. Mathematical analysis showed that such a hypothetical medium must have quite contradictory properties, and the idea of its existence was gradually abandoned, leaving the alarming conception of a wave being propagated in nothing. Indeed, the wave and its medium were shorn of their material aspects until nothing remained but a sort of disembodied spirit represented by a set of equations: the electromagnetic equations of Maxwell.

More glaring faults were also found. The photoelectric effect could not be explained on the wave basis. It was found that radiations of certain wavelengths caused electrons to be ejected from a metal surface, the velocity of the electrons being independent of the intensity of the radiation; but if longer waves were used, it might happen that no electrons were ejected, no matter how strong the radiation. An analogous case is a lake with short water waves lapping a pebble beach. Suppose we should find that, owing to the action of the waves, a pebble would occasionally spring high into the air as if the energy of all the waves were suddenly concentrated at that point. Suppose that the height to which the pebble sprang were discovered to be the same whether we used hardly perceptible ripples or waves of great height. Suppose that we used longer waves and found that no pebbles were thrown into the air, no matter how high the waves were. Such results would be astonishing, to say the least. Yet exactly analogous behavior was observed for radiant energy falling on metal surfaces. The wave theory was also unable to account quantitatively for radiation from hot bodies, radiation from atoms, and a number of other phenomena.

It was found necessary to introduce a new fundamental principle which always applies when radiation is emitted or absorbed by matter: *energy is emitted and absorbed only in discrete quanta of magnitude hv.*

h = Planck's constant[11] = 6.547×10^{-27} erg-sec.

v = frequency (cycles/sec).

This principle comes into play whenever radiant energy is produced in a lamp and whenever this energy interacts with matter to be converted into heat, to darken a photographic plate, to affect the retina of the eye, to eject electrons in a photoelectric cell. During the last few years, an overwhelming mass of evidence has piled up for the existence of these discrete bundles or quanta of energy, these corpuscles, these photons. Radiant energy is always emitted and absorbed in "hunks," not continuously as in the wave theory. On the other hand, the photons are not able to explain the action of radiation in space any more than the old corpuscular theory was. Wave mechanics, introduced in 1925 by Schrödinger, attempts to harmonize the dualistic nature of radiation. Qualitatively, a satisfactory viewpoint seems to be that radiation consists of photons and that the wave theory is merely a convenient mathematical fiction which tells where the photons will go. In Fig. 1.02, for instance, according to the above viewpoint there are no waves, and the wave theory is merely a device which tells us where the photons will hit the wall C and where they will not. Swann[7] says:

Our electromagnetic equations are analogous to a scaffolding. The scaffolding itself was put up by the builders. It need not even exist in the final structure at all, but nevertheless its introduction . . . might serve as a convenient help. . . . When in science we meet things which have few of the attributes of the things around us, when the molecule carries no semblance of color, when the aether has no means whereby to freeze, we must not be alarmed.

One may feel cheated by such an explanation and by such a procedure: he may feel that the quantum theory is silly because it does not appeal to our intuition and common sense which we have formed as the result of everyday experience with macroscopic affairs. However, we cannot fail to accept the fundamental quantum principle, since it is a well-established fact which applies to the microscopic world. We must merely recognize that in the region of atomic dimensions our intuitive macroscopic concepts are inapplicable.

1.03. Wavelength and Frequency.—Each photon may be thought to have associated with it a wave which predicts how the photon will travel. By analogy with other waves, such as water waves and sound waves, we consider this fictitious wave to have the three attributes *frequency, wavelength,* and *velocity.* Consider the waves caused by dropping a stone in a pool of calm water. Evidently, a sort of energy conversion has taken place. The energy imparted to the stone by gravity has been converted into the energy of a set of waves. A cork on the surface of the pool bobs up and down and is capable of operating a light mechanical device and thus utilizing some of the original energy. The ripples spread out in ever widening circles. If one selects some particular crest or trough and follows it as it travels outward, he finds it to be going at a definite *velocity v.* If one measures the distance between successive crests, he finds the *wavelength* λ. A cork, bobbing up and down as the wave passes, enables the *frequency* in complete oscillations per second to be measured. Obviously, the three quantities are related by the equation

$$v = \lambda \nu \tag{1.03}$$

Though there seems to be little similarity between waterwaves and radiation from a light source, except that a transmission of energy takes place in both cases, the foregoing terms have been taken over to the latter case, and we speak of v, λ, and ν of the radiation. The wavelength can be measured by some scheme as in Fig. 1.02, the distance between dark spaces being a measure of λ. The diffraction grating is essentially such an instrument, and it allows the determination of wavelength with a precision that can hardly be approached by any other physical measurement. Measurements can also be made on the velocity of light, which in a vacuum is found to be[11]

$$c = 2.99796 \times 10^{10} \text{ cm/sec}$$

Thus the frequency is

$$\nu = \frac{2.99796 \times 10^{10}}{\lambda}$$

or very nearly $\dfrac{3.0 \times 10^{10}}{\lambda}$ where λ is expressed in *centimeters.*

In matter, light travels at a velocity lower than in a vacuum, as shown in Table I. It is usual to express the velocity by means of the index of refraction n defined as the ratio of the velocity in free space to that in the medium considered:

$$n = \frac{v_{\text{free space}}}{v_{\text{medium}}} \tag{1.04}$$

Table I shows that the velocity of light in air or in other gases is almost the same as in a vacuum, but the velocity in glass, water, etc., is greatly reduced.

In a specification of a given radiation, we evidently meet a rather peculiar condition. According to Eq. (1.03), since v changes with the medium, evidently either (or both) ν or λ must change. But the frequency ν is a constant of a given radiation, being determined by the constants of an oscillatory circuit (for radio waves) or by the constants of an atom or molecule (for light waves). Thus λ must be different for each medium that the radiation traverses. It would seem more logical to specify *frequency* rather than *wavelength*. This is sometimes done, a convenient unit being the *fresnel:*

$$1 \text{ fresnel} = 10^{12} \text{ cycles/sec}$$

On the other hand, fundamental measurements with the diffraction grating always give wavelength, not frequency. For this reason, it is almost universal to specify wavelength, as will be done in the present volume.

TABLE I.—INDEX OF REFRACTION FOR SODIUM D-LINES ($\lambda = 0.589\mu$)

Material	n_D	v
Free space	1.0000	2.99796×10^{10} cm/sec
Air (760 mm pressure, zero degrees centigrade)	1.000293	2.99708
Fused silica	1.4585	2.05551
Glass, ordinary crown	1.5125	1.98212
Glass, ordinary flint	1.6160	1.85517
Water	1.3330	2.24903
Carbon disulphide	1.628	1.84150

Wavelength is measured in various units. In radio telephony it is usually measured in meters, with commercial limits of about

1 to 20,000 meters. The wavelengths used by illuminating engineers are so short that even the cm is too large a unit, so several smaller ones are used:

$$1 \text{ meter} = 10^6 \mu \quad \text{(microns)}$$
$$= 10^9 m\mu \quad \text{(millimicrons)}$$
$$= 10^{10} A \quad \text{(angstrom units)}$$

All of these units are used in the literature, and the student will have no trouble with them if he remembers that the visual region

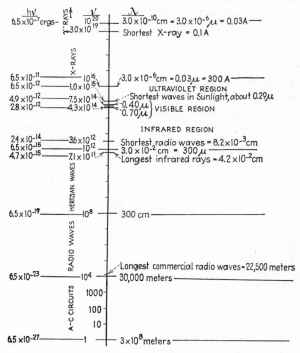

FIG. 1.03.—Spectrum of radiant energy.

extends from about 0.40 to 0.70μ, or 400 to 700mμ, or 4000 to 7000A. In the present book, we shall use the micron almost exclusively.

The complete spectrum of radiant energy extends over a tremendous range of frequency as shown in Fig. 1.03, where a logarithmic scale has been used. Ordinary electric circuits send out waves of the same nature as light waves but invisible to the eye.   These waves may be of the commercial frequencies of 60 or 25 cycles or even lower.   As the value of the inductance and capacitance in an oscillatory circuit is decreased, the frequency increases according to the relation

$$\nu = \frac{1}{2\pi\sqrt{LC}} \tag{1.05}$$

In this way, the ordinary radio range of about 10^4 to 10^8 cycles/sec is obtained.   Still higher frequencies may be obtained by reducing the values of the inductance and capacitance in the oscillatory circuit to a minimum.   With the capacitance reduced to that between two small metal spheres, and the inductance merely that of a short, gaseous conductor between them, the Hertzian range of approximately 10^8 to 10^{12} cycles/sec is obtained. Nichols and Tear,[9] using oscillations produced between two metal cylinders 0.02 cm in diameter and 0.02 cm long, produced frequencies as high as 1.4×10^{12} ($\lambda = 2.2 \times 10^{-2}$ cm), higher than the infrared radiations ($\nu = 0.71 \times 10^{12}$ cycles/sec) obtained from the mercury arc.   Arkadiewa[10] has produced even higher frequencies from an oscillating circuit—values up to

$$\nu = 0.36 \times 10^{13},$$

corresponding to a wavelength of 8.2×10^{-3} cm.

Beyond the range possible with the tiniest oscillating circuits, we must depend upon molecular and atomic phenomena.   The frequencies from about 10^{12} to 10^{16} cycles/sec, including the infrared, the visible, and the ultraviolet regions, may be considered as due to movements of atoms in the molecule or of electrons in the outer orbits of the atoms.   The frequencies above 10^{16} are caused by deep-seated changes in the atom and even in the tiny nucleus of the atom.   Thus the highest section of the chart (Fig. 1.03) embraces X rays that extend to a frequency of about 3×10^{19} and γ rays that extend upward from about this value to 10^{21} cycles/sec.   Still farther up the scale are the cosmic rays.

The column on the extreme left in Fig. 1.03 gives the energy contained in one photon at different frequencies.   With X rays, the energy may reach 10^{-7} or 10^{-8} erg, which though small is still capable of being measured.   At the still higher frequencies of

γ rays, the energy quanta are even larger, and the corpuscular nature of radiation is even more pronounced. At radio frequencies, on the other hand, $h\nu$ is of the order of 10^{-20} erg, which is so extremely small that hardly a trace of the granularity of radiation can be detected, and a pure wave phenomenon seems to exist. Actually, we believe that there is no fundamental difference between X rays and radio waves, but only a difference in degree.

In our daily life we are being bombarded constantly by radiations over this immense range of frequency, but in most cases we are entirely oblivious to them. Except for a heating effect in some cases, we are generally unconscious of all radiations except those in the very narrow region that affects the eye: the visible region extending from approximately 4.3×10^{14} to 7.5×10^{14} cycles/sec. Different frequencies in this region produce varied sensations: Wavelengths from about 0.40 to 0.45μ evoke the sensation of violet; those from 0.45 to 0.49μ give the sensation of blue; 0.49 to 0.55μ, green; 0.55 to 0.59μ, yellow; 0.59 to 0.63μ, orange; 0.63 to 0.70μ, red. The limits are not sharply defined, nor are the limits 0.40 and 0.70μ exact. If the radiation is strong enough, the eye can detect radiations slightly beyond these limits in both directions. It must be remembered that radiations, whether visible or not, are of the same nature; and that it is only because of a limitation of the eye that we single out a special region and call it the visible region. It should also be noted that the infrared radiations, which are often called "heat rays," are actually no more heat rays than radiations in the visible regions, in the ultraviolet, or elsewhere. All radiations have the property of heating anything that absorbs them.

We have considered radiations of a single frequency, like that produced by a sharply tuned radio transmitter which is delivering an unmodulated carrier wave. Strictly speaking, there is no such thing as a radiation of one frequency, though for all practical purposes many radiations may be considered as monofrequency radiations. They are sometimes called monochromatic radiations, but a better term is probably *homogeneous radiations*. Many sources, such as the sun and other heated bodies, send out radiations of all frequencies over a wide range. We shall study such radiations in some detail in later chapters.

Bibliography

1. HARDY and PERRIN: The Principles of Optics, Chap. I., McGraw-Hill Book Company, Inc., New York, 1932.
2. W. BRAGG: The Universe of Light, The Macmillan Company, New York, 1933.
3. A. E. KENNELLY: The Profession of Illuminating Engineering, *I.E.S. Trans.* **6**, 1911, p. 73.
4. W. E. WICKENDEN: Report on Engineering Education, Society for the Promotion of Engineering Education, **1**, 1930, p. 975.
5. H. CREW: Thomas Young's Place in the History of the Wave Theory of Light, *J.O.S.A.*, **20**, 1930, p. 3.
6. N. F. MOTT: An Outline of Wave Mechanics, Cambridge University Press, London, 1930.
7. W. F. G. SWANN: Contemporary Theories of Light, *J.O.S.A.*, **20**, 1930, p. 484.
   Architecture of the Universe, The Macmillan Company, New York, 1934.
8. K. K. DARROW: Some Contemporary Advances in Physics, *B.S.T.J.*, **3**, 1924, p. 268; **3**, 1924, p. 468; **4**, 1925, p. 280.
9. NICHOLS and TEAR: Joining the Infra-red and Electric-wave Spectra, *Astrophys. J.*, **61**, 1925, p. 17.
10. A. GLAGOLEWA-ARKADIEWA: Short Electromagnetic Waves of Wavelength up to 82 Microns, *Nature*, **113**, 1924, p. 640.
11. R. T. BIRGE: Values of the General Physical Constants, *Phys. Rev. Supp.*, **1**, 1929, p. 1.

CHAPTER II

THE SPECTRORADIOMETRIC CURVE

After the brief review of Chap. I, we can proceed advantageously to a study of the measurement of radiation. All such measurements entail a conversion of energy from one form to another, so a brief treatment of energy conversions comes first in this chapter. The measurement of radiant power or of radiant power per unit area as a function of wavelength gives a *spectroradiometric curve*. Most of this chapter is devoted to a study of the various kinds of spectroradiometric curves obtained from light sources and of the methods of calculating, from the spectroradiometric curve, the effects of radiant power.

2.02. Energy Conversions.—The electrical engineer is often concerned with the conversion of energy from one form to another. In the power field, mechanical energy is transformed into electrical energy (with as little by-product of thermal energy as possible) and is sent over transmission lines and distribution systems to the customer. There it may be transformed into thermal energy in heating appliances, mechanical energy in motors, chemical energy in various chemical transformations, and radiant energy in lamps. The communication engineer is interested in the transformation of mechanical energy in a vibrating telephone diaphragm into electrical energy, its transmission over long distances either by wire or by radio waves, and its final conversion into mechanical energy in the form of sound waves. The illuminating engineer is interested in the conversion of electrical energy into radiant energy of such frequencies as to be visible to the human eye and in the reciprocal conversion of radiant energy into electrical energy by photocells or by thermocouples.

Of the many possible energy transformations, the electrical engineer is concerned primarily with those that deal with electricity. A table of such transformations (Table II) may be found interesting. For generating electrical energy, he generally

15

uses mechanical energy and converts it in an alternator or a d-c generator.   If both input and output are expressed in watts, the efficiency of conversion is

$$\eta = \frac{\text{output (watts)}}{\text{input (watts)}} \qquad (2.01)$$

or if the input is measured in horse power, it is merely necessary to use the conversion factor: 746 watts = 1 hp.   The efficiencies are high, values of over 90 per cent being common.   The other

TABLE II.—ENERGY CONVERSIONS

Transformation	Examples	Approximate efficiency, per cent
Electrical to electrical.......	(Synchronous converters, static transformers, etc.)	90–99
Electrical to mechanical.....	{ Motors	85–95
	Telephone receiver, loud-speaker, etc.	3–30
Electrical to thermal........	Electric heaters	Approaches 100
Electrical to chemical........	Charging storage batteries, etc.	10–80
Electrical to radiant energy..	Radio transmitters	
	Radiant heaters	90
	Lamps	90
	X ray tubes	
Mechanical to electrical......	Generators	85–95
Chemical to electrical........	{ Primary cells	
	Storage cells	80
Thermal to electrical........	Thermopile	low
Radiant energy to electrical..	{ Barrier-layer photoelectric cell	1
	Thermopile	0.0001

transformations can be effected with various efficiencies running almost to 100 per cent in a few cases.   The efficiency is always expressible as in Eq. (2.01), where the only requirement is that numerator and denominator be expressed in the same units, either of power or of energy.   It would seem most consistent always to express energy in ergs, but other units of energy such as the *calorie* are often used.

Table II shows that most of the transformations can be accomplished with fairly high efficiency. Note, in particular, that the conversion from electrical energy to radiant energy in incandescent lamps is made customarily with an efficiency in the neighborhood of 90 per cent. Ordinary incandescent lamps are efficient radiators, *but they are not effective light sources*, since most of their radiation is at such wavelengths that it does not affect the eye. As will be shown in Chap. VI, the best of modern incandescent lamps produce only about 3 per cent of the visual effect that would be produced by an ideal source. Evidently, however, *the relative ability of a source to affect the retina should not be called an efficiency* (as is usually done). In Table II, therefore, there are no conversions dealing with *light* but only with *radiant energy*.

In the measurement of radiant energy, the illuminating engineer frequently uses the conversions indicated at the bottom of the table. In the barrier-layer photoelectric cell (Chap. VII) and other devices of this kind, electrons are emitted and an electric current flows through an external circuit when radiant energy falls upon the sensitive surface of the cell. Since the sun provides the earth with over a kilowatt of radiant power per square meter of surface perpendicular to the rays, or 2,000,000 kw/sq mi, one might expect a possibility of generating electric power by the use of photoelectric cells. However, the efficiencies rarely exceed 1 per cent and reach this value only at certain wavelengths, so the commercial photoelectric generation of electric power does not seem promising. The thermocouple method is also used in the measurement of radiant power. A thermocouple makes use of *two* transformations of energy, first from radiant to thermal energy and then from thermal to electrical energy. As might be expected, this double transformation is extremely inefficient, the best vacuum thermopiles having an efficiency of only about one ten-thousandth of 1 per cent.

Problem 1. For measuring radiant power, Rubens used 20 thermocouples in series.[7] The resistance of the complete thermopile was about 10 ohms, and one microvolt was obtained with a radiant power of 80 ergs/sec. With a galvanometer of 10 ohms resistance, what was the efficiency of energy conversion?

Problem 2. A certain barrier-layer cell is found to give a current of 3.9 microamps per erg/sec of radiant power when illuminated by radiation of sunlight quality and when used with an external circuit of 6.5 ohms resistance. How many watts of electrical power can be obtained at noon on a clear day (0.120 watt/sq cm radiant power from the sun at sea level), if it is assumed that the cells have a total area of 10 sq ft?

What is the efficiency of energy conversion?

2.03. Detection of Radiant Power.—We have seen that wavelength can be measured by a diffraction grating. For the visible and near-by regions, the grating may consist of fine lines ruled on metal or glass with a spacing of five to ten times the wavelength. For radio waves, a set of parallel wires can be used. For X rays, the spacing between lines must be so small that atomic distances between layers of atoms in a crystal are necessary.

Another important measurement is the measurement of radiant power. This is done by converting radiant power to some other form and measuring the effect. There is a variety of such effects—visual, thermal, photochemical, photoelectric. One method was used by Herschel in 1800 when he placed a thermometer in the spectrum obtained by passing sunlight through a prism and found that the thermometer was heated not only in the visible spectrum but also in the space beyond the red where the eye could detect no radiation whatsoever. This is one of the most general methods of detecting radiation. All forms of energy have a tendency to degenerate into the thermal form; and thus if radio, infrared, ultraviolet, or visible waves or X rays are absorbed by matter, a conversion to thermal energy will occur, the temperature will rise, and this temperature rise will be directly proportional to the radiant power. Instead of using a thermometer as Herschel did, much more delicate instruments, such as the bolometer and the vacuum thermocouple, are now used. If radiant power falls on a blackened target and the resulting temperature rise is measured electrically, a rise as small as one-millionth of a degree can be detected.

For long wavelengths, such as radio waves, it is more convenient to set up a resonant circuit tuned to the particular frequency of the radiation. Here the photons are so small that to detect them one by one is impossible. But if the individual quanta or photons are large enough, an ionization method is applicable. An argon atom, for instance, requires an energy of 2.5×10^{-11} erg to ionize it. A photon having an energy equal to or greater than this will be able to ionize the atom upon collision. Turning to Fig. 1.03, we find that a frequency of about

$10^{16}(\lambda = 0.03\mu)$ is necessary in order that the photon may have sufficient energy for this feat. Because of the large energies in the photons of X rays, the ionization method is often used in their measurement.

Since a metal, unlike a gas, contains a large number of free electrons, one might expect that a photon, even though its energy was small, would be able to set free an electron from the metal surface. It is found, however, that the energy of the photon must still be above a certain minimum, or no electrons will be freed. A definite amount of work W_p, called the work function, must be done by the electron in freeing itself from the surface, so

$$h\nu = W_p + \frac{1}{2}mv^2 \qquad (2.02)$$

where $\frac{1}{2}mv^2$ = the kinetic energy of the electron as it leaves the surface.

This phenomenon is the photoelectric effect. Modern technique has made possible the production of photoelectric cells which respond to photons with energies as low as 1.6×10^{-12} erg corresponding to a wavelength of 1.2μ, in the near infrared. Thus the photoelectric cell is a very useful tool in detecting and measuring radiation in the visible region or in the ultraviolet and near infrared.

The photographic method is an example of a great number of photochemical processes which function with photons possessing energies greater than a definite minimum. A photon with sufficient energy striking a silver-bromide grain is capable of affecting it so that a developing process changes the grain to metallic silver. The effect is obtained in the ultraviolet and in the short waves of the visible region and by the use of certain dyes can be extended into the red or even the infrared. It is now possible, for instance, to photograph in complete darkness by means of the infrared radiation from an ordinary hot flatiron. The photographic method is often used where the wavelengths are not too great. The density of the silver deposit is determined after the plate or film is developed and is a measure of the radiant power.

In detecting radiation the method to which we are most accustomed is the visual one. This, like most of the others, is a selective method; *i.e.*, it operates with photons of certain frequencies but not with others. Photons having a narrow range of energy, upon entering the eye, are capable of stimulating the retina to give a sensation of light and color. The eye has been much used in the past in the measurement of radiation by a visual-comparison method. The eye, of course, is worthless outside the visible region and even in this region is being supplanted by more accurate instruments.

2.04. Measurement of Radiant Power with Prism and Thermocouple.—After our survey of energy conversions and of the complete spectrum of radiant energy, we can turn advantageously to a more thorough study of the particular band of wavelengths which is of primary interest to the illuminating engineer. The remainder of the book, therefore, will emphasize the visible region and the wavelength bands immediately adjacent on both sides of this region, the total range being from approximately 0.25 to 2.5μ. Particular stress will be laid upon the band from about 0.40 to 0.70μ, but a much better perspective will be gained if we occasionally allow our gaze to stray into the neighboring fields. The subject of the present chapter is the radiant power curve and methods of calculating from it the ability of the radiation to produce photoelectric, photographic, and other effects.

Before discussing the method of measurement, we may well note some radiometric concepts. In building up such a system of concepts, we must naturally start somewhere. A convenient point is *radiant energy*, though of course we could have started farther back and have defined everything on the basis of the three fundamental concepts length, mass, and time. The cgs unit of energy is the *erg*, which is the work done by a force of one dyne acting through a distance of one centimeter.

Radiant power or *radiant flux* Φ is then defined as the time rate of change of radiant energy. The cgs unit is the erg per second, but we shall express power in *watts;*

$$1 \text{ watt} = 10^7 \text{ ergs/sec}$$

When radiant power is incident on a surface, the surface is said to be *irradiated*. The *irradiation G* (sometimes called the specific irradiation)[1] of the surface in the neighborhood of a given point is equal to the radiant power incident on the surface per unit area of surface at that point. Irradiation may be expressed

in watts per square centimeter.   Note that irradiation is not the
watts per square centimeter *absorbed* by the surface or the watts
per square centimeter *reflected* by the surface; it is the watts per
square centimeter impinging on the surface.   Thus irradiation
is entirely independent of the type of surface or of its reflecting,
transmitting, or absorbing properties.

Suppose that the surface reflects some of the incident radiant
power. It then becomes convenient to introduce another
concept dealing with the watts per square centimeter sent out
by the surface.   This concept seems to have no generally accepted
name, but we shall call it *radiosity*.   Radiosity will be expressed
in watts per square centimeter emitted by the surface.   The
emitted radiation may be due to reflection from the surface or
to transmission through the surface or may have its origin in the
surface itself (the surface of a hot tungsten filament, for example).

At the risk of repetition, the fact should be emphasized that
the *only way in which radiation can be measured is by means of an
energy transformation;* or, to put it crudely, the radiation, as
such, must be destroyed before we can discover how much there
was.   Evidently, what we are actually measuring is neither the
watts per square centimeter incident on the surface of the measuring device nor the watts per square centimeter emitted by this
surface but the power transformed in this surface to the particular
form that is used in the measurement.   However, as long as the
absorbing characteristics of the receiving surface remain constant, the transformed power is directly proportional to the
irradiation.   Thus the irradiation appears to be a more fundamental quantity than the radiosity.   All the various devices for
measuring radiation can be calibrated in watts per square
centimeter incident on the receiving surface of the measuring
device.

One way of measuring irradiation is to place the blackened
target of a radiation thermocouple or similar device at the spot
where the value of irradiation is desired.[5]   Figure 2.01 shows a
simple device of this kind[3] for measuring the radiant power per
square centimeter falling on the surface *S-S*.   Fine wires of two
metals, such as copper and constantan (a copper-nickel alloy),
are joined at *a* and *b*.   It is well-known that if the two junctions
are at the same temperature, no emf will appear; and the galvanometer *g* will not deflect.   However, if the temperature of

junction b is raised above that of a, an emf of about 40 microvolts per degree centigrade difference in temperature will be generated, and a current will flow. The heating of junction b may be accomplished by attaching to it a blackened target t which absorbs radiant energy and converts it into thermal energy. Junction a is shielded from the radiation and remains at room temperature. In this way, the galvanometer readings are directly proportional to the watts per square centimeter of radiant power falling on the surface in the neighborhood of t. It is

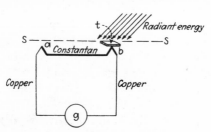

Fɪɢ. 2.01.—A radiation thermocouple.

assumed, of course, that the intensity of the radiation is essentially constant over the area of the target. A valuable feature of such an instrument is that it is *nonselective; i.e.*, the readings are independent of wavelength over a wide range. If calibrated with radiation of one wavelength, it will give accurate results with radiation of any other wavelength and, since the relation between cause and effect is linear in this case, with any combination of wavelengths.

If the radiation falling on the surface S-S is homogeneous (in a very narrow wavelength band), a complete specification is given by two numbers. These two numbers are (1) the value of the irradiation G and (2) the wavelength λ. In making such a statement, we are neglecting such factors as the polarization of the radiation, also we are not interested in the angle at which the radiation is incident on the surface (except in so far as that may influence the value of the irradiation). These factors do not concern us and will not be mentioned further.

But most radiation is not homogeneous. Mercury-vapor lamps, for instance, radiate at a number of different wavelengths. Such radiation falling on the blackened target of Fig. 2.01 will produce a galvanometer deflection proportional to the sum of the effects of each homogeneous component acting alone. The measurement thus gives the total irradiation G of the surface—the total watts per square centimeter incident on the surface from all the component radiations:

$$G = \sum_{1}^{n} G_i \qquad (2.03)$$

where G_i = irradiation due to the ith component.

n = number of component radiations.

This quantity is useful in many cases, though *it does not completely specify the radiation*, since it says nothing about how the power is distributed among the various wavelengths.

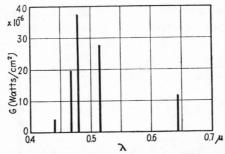

Fig. 2.02.—Irradiation of a surface due to a cadmium-vapor lamp.

Radiation from a cadmium-vapor lamp, for example (Fig. 2.02), consists of a number of homogeneous component radiations. There are also radiations in the ultraviolet and infrared, but these are omitted from the diagram. If means can be found (as by the use of filters) for cutting out all components but one, the value of G for this radiation can be measured by the use of a thermocouple. The values for the other lines of the spectrum are measured in a similar manner, giving results such as those tabulated in Fig. 2.02. If the complete radiation from 0.4 to 0.7μ falls on the target of the thermocouple, a total value of irradiation is read. In this case, $G = 100 \times 10^{-6}$ watt/sq cm.

To obtain a complete specification of the radiation, we must break up the spectrum into its components and measure the power in each narrow wavelength band. This can be done most conveniently by using a prism of glass or of quartz (Fig. 2.03) which spreads the image of the slit S_1 into a band, the short wavelengths being deflected most, and the long ones least. A second slit S_2 is introduced into this spectrum and allows a narrow wavelength band to be studied independently of all the

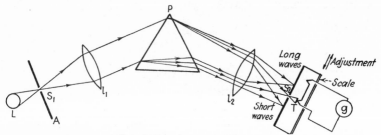

Fig. 2.03.—A spectroradiometer.

others. A thermocouple behind S_2 absorbs the radiant energy which passes through the slit, the temperature of the junction rises, and an emf is generated which produces a proportionate

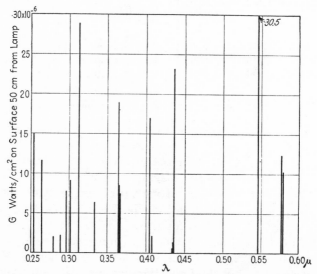

Fig. 2.04.—Irradiation of a surface due to a high-pressure mercury-vapor lamp with fused-quartz enclosure. Receiving surface 50 cm from lamp. Results are for 2.5 cm of arc length and are based on the measurements of Johnson and Burns.[31]

deflection of the galvanometer g. The receiving apparatus (S_2 and T) can be moved along a calibrated track in order to measure the power in a narrow band of wavelengths near any given λ in the visible region or in the nearby ultraviolet or infrared. Such an instrument is called a *spectroradiometer*.[3]

By the use of the arrangement of Fig. 2.03, it is possible to obtain the watts per square centimeter for any homogeneous

TABLE III.—IRRADIATION FROM HIGH-PRESSURE MERCURY-VAPOR LAMPS
Values are in microwatts per square centimeter at 2 meters from lamp
(B. T. BARNES, *J.O.S.A.*, **24**, 1934, p. 148)

λ	220-volt lamp	110-volt lamp	λ	220-volt lamp	110-volt lamp
0.2259μ	1.8	0.3	$0.3126-32\mu$	49.0	17.7
0.2302	2.5	0.5	0.3341	6.3	1.9
0.2323	1.7	0.3	0.3650-63	75.0	26.0
0.2353	2.8	0.5	0.3902-06	1.3	0.4
0.2378	4.0	0.9	0.4047-78	24.5	8.5
0.2400	4.0	1.0	0.4339-58	43.4	14.5
0.2447	1.2	0.3	0.4916	1.3	0.5
0.2464	1.5	0.4	0.5461	49.0	16.6
0.2482	9.0	2.3	0.5770-91	60.0	18.3
0.2535	25.0	8.0	0.6234	0.6	0.15
0.2576	8.0	1.0	0.6716	0.8	
0.2652	21.0	5.8	0.7082-92	1.5	0.2
0.2697	4.8	1.2	0.7605-729	0.6	
0.2753	3.4	0.9	1.014	20.6	5.4
0.2800	10.4	2.7	1.119 -1.129	7.3	2.3
0.2894	5.2	1.4	1.189 -1.213	4.1	0.9
0.2925	2.1	0.5	1.357 -96	10.8	3.2
0.2967	13.0	3.9	1.530	2.1	0.9
0.3021-27	25.5	7.8	1.690 -1.710	8.4	2.9

	220-volt lamp	110-volt lamp
Inside diameter (cm)	1.5	1.5
Arc length (cm)	16.2	8.5
Arc voltage (volts)	174	75
Current (amps)	3.75	3.75

No reflectors used.

component. If the slit is irradiated by a mercury-vapor lamp, for instance, it will be found that at certain definite wavelengths large deflections of the galvanometer g will be obtained, while at other wavelengths there is no deflection. The results of such a measurement made on a high-pressure mercury-vapor lamp

in fused quartz are shown in Fig. 2.04.   The ordinates represent
G, the watts per square centimeter received from various lines

TABLE IV.—IRRADIATION FROM LOW-PRESSURE MERCURY-VAPOR LAMPS
Values are in microwatts per square centimeter for a receiving surface
2 meters from the lamp and are referred to an arc length of 1 meter
(B. T. BARNES, *J.O.S.A.*, **24**, 1934, p. 148)

λ	Lead glass	Uviol glass	Corex D	Fused quartz
0.2259μ	0.000	0.000	0.000	0.01
0.2302	......	......	......	0.01
0.2323	......	......	......	0.005
0.2353	......	......	......	0.01
0.2378	......	......	......	0.03
0.2400	......	......	......	0.02
0.2447	......	......	......	0.01
0.2464	......	......	......	0.02
0.2482	0.000	0.000	0.000	0.08
0.2535	......	0.010	0.530	26.0
0.2576	......	0.000	0.002	0.070
0.2652	......	0.003	0.040	0.540
0.2697	......	0.000	0.003	0.023
0.2753	......	0.006	0.041	0.205
0.2800	......	0.006	0.029	0.100
0.2894	......	0.070	0.230	0.450
0.2925	0.000	0.009	0.025	0.047
0.2967	0.019	0.39	1.02	1.75
0.3021–27	0.054	0.21	0.48	0.65
0.3126–32	2.60	2.90	5.40	6.10
0.3341	0.51	0.36	0.55	0.54
0.3650–63	5.70	4.20	5.60	5.40
0.4047–78	11.5	9.9	11.2	11.0
0.4339–58	16.2	15.1	16.1	15.2
0.5461	15.9	15.1	15.8	15.0
0.5770–91	5.2	5.0	5.1	4.8
1.0140	7.0	6.3	6.0	6.0
Tube inside diameter (cm).....	2.4	2.45	2.5	2.4
Arc length (cm)...............	128	132	130	58
Arc voltage (volts)...........	71.9	73.4	72.2	39.7
Current (amps)...............	3.70	3.70	3.70	3.70

No reflectors used.   Other infrared lines too weak to be measured.

in the spectrum on a surface 50 cm from the lamp.   Some other
data on mercury-vapor lamps are given in Table III.   The value

of G for each line of the spectrum completely specifies the radiation received on a given surface from such a source.

Line spectra, such as those just considered, are characteristic of gaseous-conduction lamps. If radiation from an ordinary tungsten lamp be dispersed by a prism, however, the spectrum will be found to be *continuous,* with no gaps of zero power such as were found in the mercury spectrum. With line spectra, the width of the slit S_2 is evidently of no consequence as long as it is not so wide as to include undesired lines.* With continuous spectra, however, we must use a narrow slit, and the same width of wavelength band must be allowed to pass in all parts of the spectrum. Or, if the band is not of constant width, a correction must be applied. Evidently, the readings now obtained will depend upon the width of the slit S_2. For a given measurement, an observer using a slit that passes a wavelength band of 0.001μ will obtain readings only half as large as another observer using a band of 0.002μ. To standardize the results, therefore, it is customary to refer all values to a band of wavelengths *one micron wide.* The observer using a 0.001-μ band will multiply his results by 1000, while the observer using a 0.002-μ band will multiply his results by 500. The values will then be the same in both cases: *watts/sq cm per micron wavelength band.* We shall represent this quantity by G_λ and call it the *spectral irradiation.* With continuous spectra, G is the watts per square centimeter irradiation from the whole spectrum.

An example of a continuous spectrum is shown in Fig. 2.05 which represents the spectral irradiation of a given surface due to a black body or Planckian radiator operating at 1999°K (degrees absolute).[4] The ordinates give watts per square centimeter per micron received at a given point on a given surface at various wavelengths. Curve B is merely a magnification of the toe of curve A. Curve B is particularly important to us, since it covers the whole visible region though it includes but a small part of the total power.

The total irradiation G is represented by the area under curve A, or

$$G = \int_0^\infty G_\lambda \, d\lambda \quad \text{(watts/sq cm)} \qquad (2.04)$$

* See Fig. 2.03.

In Fig. 2.05, the area under A was measured by planimeter, and the total irradiation G was found to be 91.16×10^{-6} watt/sq cm. The watts per square centimeter due to radiation in the visible region is represented by the small crosshatched area between 0.4 and 0.7μ. Evidently, most of the radiation is in the infrared, and therefore the radiator is a very poor source of light. We shall see in Chap. V, however, that by increasing the temperature

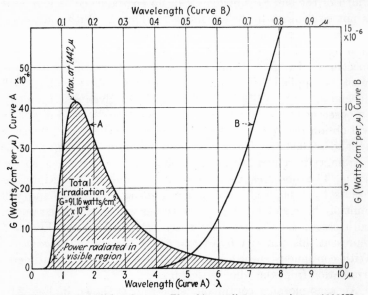

FIG. 2.05.—Irradiation due to a Planckian radiator operating at 1999°K.

of the radiator the curve can be pushed to the left, with resulting gain in visual effect.

A curve for the irradiation from the sun is shown in Fig. 2.06. The ordinates represent watts per square centimeter per micron received on a horizontal surface at sea level on a clear day with the sun at the zenith. They were obtained from Abbot's data.[9,10] The data in the ultraviolet beyond Abbot's measurements were given by Forsythe and Christison.[13] Actually, there are dark lines in the solar spectrum (Fraunhofer lines) due to incandescent gases in the sun's atmosphere, as well as large absorption bands in the infrared due to ozone and water vapor in the earth's atmosphere[12]; but these have been neglected in the curve. The corresponding data are given in Table V, while

Table VI gives the distribution of energy, with the infrared absorption bands taken into account.   The results of Table VI were obtained by using a planimeter to determine the areas under spectroradiometric curves similar to Fig. 2.06.   It will be noted that the earth is receiving 0.135 watt/sq cm from the sun, while at sea level on a clear day with the sun at the zenith, the received power is 0.120 watt/sq cm, or over a kilowatt per

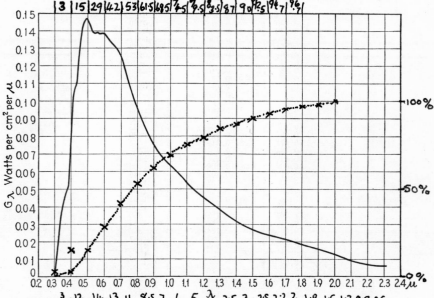

FIG. 2.06.—Solar irradiation on a horizontal surface at sea level. Clear day, sun at zenith.   Based on data from *Smithsonian Inst. Astrophys. Obs., Ann.*,[9,10] *Smithsonian Misc. Coll.*,[8] and *J.O.S.A.*[13]

square meter.   Under the latter condition, 0.0472 watt/cm, or 39.3 per cent, is in the visible region, while 55.4 per cent is in infrared, and only 1.3 per cent is in the biologically effective region at short wavelengths.   A comparison of these results with the curve of Fig. 2.05 shows that a much greater proportion of energy is radiated in the visible region in the case of sunlight than with a Planckian radiator at 1999°K.

Problem 3.   Determine the total irradiation in the visible region due to the radiator of Fig. 2.05.   What percentage of this visible radiation is capable of evoking the sensation of violet, blue, green, etc.?

Problem 4.   From the data of Table V, determine the total radiant power received by the earth (neglecting atmospheric absorption) on a square

TABLE V.—IRRADIATION FROM THE SUN

(Data from *Smithsonian Misc. Coll.*, **74**, No. 7; *Smithsonian Inst. Astrophys. Obs., Ann.*, **5**, 1932, p. 108; **2**, 1908, p. 113; *J.O.S.A.*, **20**, 1930, p. 396)

λ	$G\lambda$ (watts/square centimeter of earth's surface per micron)	
	Neglecting absorption by atmosphere	At sea level
0.290μ	......	0
0.295	......	0.0000329
0.300	......	0.000148
0.305	......	0.000987
0.310	0.0398	0.0055
0.315	0.0493	0.0110
0.320	0.0587	0.0150
0.330	0.0782	0.0240
0.34	0.0967	0.0317
0.35	0.1061	0.0376
0.36	0.1127	0.0427
0.37	0.1206	0.0467
0.38	0.1160	0.0500
0.39	0.1210	0.0537
0.40	0.1402	0.0750
0.41	0.1669	0.0960
0.42	0.1815	0.1062
0.43	0.1813	0.1093
0.44	0.1923	0.1205
0.45	0.2041	0.1308
0.46	0.2115	0.1380
0.47	0.2140	0.1435
0.48	0.2140	0.1458
0.49	0.2119	0.1471
0.50	0.2080	0.1465
0.51	0.2022	0.1442
0.52	0.1971	0.1418
0.53	0.1932	0.1393
0.54	0.1907	0.1391
0.55	0.1886	0.1393
0.56	0.1870	0.1389
0.57	0.1859	0.1385
0.58	0.1849	0.1386
0.59	0.1840	0.1387
0.60	0.1834	0.1382
0.61	0.1789	0.1373
0.62	0.1743	0.1360
0.63	0.1707	0.1345
0.64	0.1677	0.1333
0.65	0.1640	0.1322
0.66	0.1617	0.1315
0.67	0.1586	0.1301
0.68	0.1562	0.1289
0.69	0.1525	0.1270
0.70	0.1487	0.1250
0.71	0.1440	0.1222
0.72	0.1395	0.1187
0.73	0.1353	0.1153
0.74	0.1311	0.1120
0.75	0.1274	0.1090
0.76	0.1236	0.1062
0.80	0.1111	0.0960
0.85	0.0960	0.0845
0.90	0.0850	0.0752
0.95	0.0766	0.0683
1.00	0.0701	0.0635
1.10	0.0595	0.0538
1.20	0.0496	0.0451
1.30	0.0413	0.0380
1.40	0.0341	0.0315
1.50	0.0292	0.0268
1.60	0.0258	0.0236
1.70	0.02275	0.0210
1.80	0.0197	0.0181
1.90	0.0167	0.0155
2.00	0.01365	0.0124
2.10	0.01023	0.0090
2.20	0.00758	0.0068
2.30	0.00682	0.0060

centimeter of surface perpendicular to the sun's rays. (Radiant power beyond 2.3μ constitutes 2 per cent of the total.)

TABLE VI.—POWER DISTRIBUTION IN THE SOLAR SPECTRUM
(WATTS/SQ CM)
(Kimball, *Proc. Int. Ill. Cong.*, 1928, p. 501)

Conditions	Below 0.346μ	0.346 to 0.405μ	0.405 to 0.704μ	Above 0.704μ	Total
Outside atmosphere............	0.0042	0.0067	0.0542	0.0699	0.135
At high elevation (Calama, Chile), sun at zenith, clean dry air....................	0.0023	0.0047	0.0484	0.0668	0.122
Sun at zenith, moist dusty air...	0.0016	0.0043	0.0466	0.0534	0.106
At sea level, sun at zenith, clean dry air....................	0.0016	0.0042	0.0472	0.0665	0.120
Sun at zenith, moist dusty air..	0.0004	0.0030	0.0375	0.0425	0.0835
Sun 60 deg, moist dusty air.....	......	0.0014	0.0274	0.0324	0.0612
Sun 76 deg, moist dusty air.....	......	0.0003	0.0152	0.0206	0.0361

2.05. The Effectiveness of Radiation in Producing a Photoelectric Current.—The response curve of a typical caesium-oxygen-silver photocell is given in Fig. 2.07. The abscissas represent wavelengths, while the ordinates give the current produced by unit irradiation of wavelength λ. Imagine a photocell connected to a battery and galvanometer in the usual manner (Chap. VII), and allow a beam of homogeneous radiant energy of wavelength λ_1 to enter the cell. The resulting current is noted. The wavelength is now changed to some other value λ_2; and *with the same amount of radiant power entering the cell*, the current is again noted. In this way, a curve can be plotted giving *amperes per watt per square centimeter vs. wavelength.* Such a curve can be obtained with the apparatus of Fig. 2.03 by replacing the thermocouple by the photocell and applying homogeneous radiation of constant G but of various wavelengths.

Since for homogeneous radiation of any given wavelength, the current is known to be a linear function of the irradiation, the data for the response curve (Fig. 2.07) can be obtained from any convenient spectral energy distribution. The results are then corrected to a common base of 1 watt/sq cm. It should be realized, of course, that actual photocells are widely different in their characteristics,[15] so that a given curve such as that of

Fig. 2.07 applies only to the particular cell for which it was obtained. The current also depends to some extent upon the battery voltage. We are assuming that a vacuum photocell is used and that the battery voltage is sufficient to secure utilization of practically all the photoelectrons emitted by the photoelectric surface, in which case the effect of voltage is not important.

Having such a curve (Fig. 2.07), suppose we wish to determine the current that will flow owing to a given irradiation. If the incident radiation is homogeneous, we can read the value directly

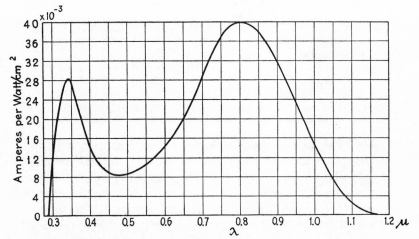

FIG. 2.07.—Spectral response curve for a typical Cs—O—Ag photocell.

from the curve. Suppose, for instance, that the irradiation is 3.0×10^{-4} watt/sq cm at wavelength 0.50μ. The ordinate of the curve at this wavelength is 8.8×10^{-3}, so the current produced will be 2.64 microamps.

If the irradiation is produced by a gaseous-conduction lamp, the linear characteristic of the cell allows us to treat each homogeneous component separately and to add the resulting currents. Thus if p_i represents the response (amps per watt/sq cm) due to irradiation of the wavelength of the ith component; and if the value of this irradiation is G_i, then the current due to the entire line spectrum is

$$i = \sum_1^n p_i G_i \qquad (2.05)$$

Example.   What current will flow if the photocell of Fig. 2.07 is placed 2 meters from the 110-volt high-pressure mercury-vapor lamp of Table III? The result can be tabulated as follows:

λ_i	G_i	p_i	p_iG_i
0.2259μ	0.3×10^{-6}	0.0	0.0
0.2302	0.5		
0.2323	0.3		
0.2353	0.5		
0.2378	0.9		
0.2400	1.0		
0.2447	0.3		
0.2464	0.4		
0.2482	2.3		
0.2535	8.0		
0.2576	1.0		
0.2652	5.8		
0.2697	1.2		
0.2753	0.9		
0.2800	2.7		
0.2894	1.4		
0.2925	0.5	0.0	0.0
0.2967	3.9	7.0×10^{-3}	27.3×10^{-9}
0.3021	7.8	12.0	93.5
0.3126	17.7	19.0	336.0
0.3341	1.9	27.0	51.3
0.3650	26.0	21.0	545.5
0.3902	0.4	15.0	6.0
0.4047	8.5	12.5	106.2
0.4339	14.5	10.0	145.0
0.4916	0.5	8.4	4.2
0.5461	16.6	10.2	169.0
0.5770	18.3	12.2	223.3
0.6234	0.1	16.8	1.7
0.7082	0.2	29.5	5.9
1.014	5.4	13.0	70.2
1.119	2.3	1.6	3.7
1.189	0.9		
1.357	3.2		
1.530	0.9		
1.690	2.9		

$$\Sigma G_i = 160.0 \times 10^{-6} \text{ watt/sq cm} \qquad \Sigma p_iG_i = 1789 \times 10^{-9} \text{ amp}$$

Thus a current of **1.79 microamps** will flow.   The total irradiation G is also seen to be **160 microwatts/sq cm.**   If this radiant power per square centimeter had been concentrated at a wavelength of 0.8μ, evidently it would have produced a much larger current. Since $p = 40 \times 10^{-3}$, the current in this hypothetical case would be $i = 40 \times 10^{-3} \times 160 \times 10^{-6}$ or **6.40 microamps.**

If the spectrum is continuous, the effect of each small wavelength band may be determined, and the resulting currents

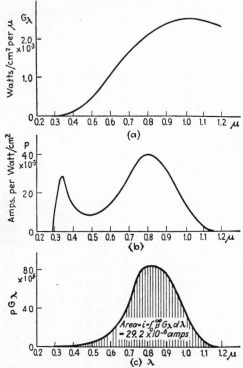

Fig. 2.08.—Photocell current due to irradiation from an incandescent lamp.

added.   Or, proceeding to the limit, the current will be

$$i = \int_0^\infty pG_\lambda \, d\lambda \tag{2.06}$$

where p = the function of λ represented by the curve of Fig. 2.07.

The kind of radiation with which photocells are most frequently used is that from incandescent lamps.   The irradiation to which a certain cell is to be exposed is indicated by the curve of G_λ shown in Fig. 2.08a.   Multiplying the ordinates of Fig. 2.08a by the corresponding values of p from (b), we obtain the curve (c). The area under this curve is found to be

$$i = \int_0^\infty p G_\lambda \, d\lambda = 29.2 \times 10^{-6} \text{ amp}$$

Problem 5. A photocell has a response curve essentially that of Fig. 7.12. What current will it give when irradiated by a cadmium-vapor lamp so that a total of 0.282×10^{-3} watt/sq cm in the visible region falls on the cell?

Problem 6. What current will be produced by the cell of Prob. 5 when irradiated by noon sunlight at sea level?

2.06. Production of Erythema.—We have considered the calculation of the photoelectric current produced by any radiation. The only data necessary are the spectral distribution curve of the radiation in question and the response curve of the photocell. Obviously, the same procedure may be applied to the calculation of other results of the radiation.

An effect that has been studied intensively in recent years by illuminating engineers is the *erythemal effect* or sunburn effect on human skin. It is believed that erythema is produced by approximately the same wavelengths as those which produce vitamin D and cure rickets. Since erythema is easy to measure while the production of vitamin D is difficult of measurement, erythema has been used as a rough basis for the biological effect of ultraviolet radiation.[2] A number of modern light sources produce a small amount of ultraviolet as well as radiation in the visible region; and the illuminating engineer is often called upon to design lighting installations in which a healthful (but not too large) amount of ultraviolet radiation is present. This requires a knowledge of erythemal efficacy of radiation.

A curve similar to the response curve of the photocell is needed. But a difficulty arises: How can we measure the effect; what kind of scale can we set up for the intensity of sunburn? It also seems likely that the effect is not a linear function of the irradiation, in which case the superposition method indicated by Eqs. (2.05) and (2.06) is inapplicable. To get around this difficulty, the investigators have agreed to use a standard result and to confine their measurements to the amount of radiant energy required to produce this standard result. The standard is arbitrarily chosen as a reddening of the skin which is just perceptible and is called *minimum perceptible erythema* (MPE).

Thus a curve similar to Fig. 2.07 is obtained for erythema by exposing for a constant time, say one second, small areas of untanned skin to various values of irradiation in a very narrow band of wavelengths at λ_1.* After a suitable time has elapsed subsequent to the exposure, the skin is observed, and the spot that shows a barely perceptible reddening is selected. The irradiation (G_1) which was used for this particular spot is noted. The wavelength of the homogeneous radiation is then changed to λ_2, and the procedure is repeated. It is found that with ultraviolet radiation of wavelength 0.297μ, a much smaller value of irradiation is needed than with radiation of any other wavelength. Using this particular wavelength as a reference, we define a new quantity which at λ_i is equal to

$$w = \frac{(G)_{\lambda\,=\,0.297\mu}}{(G)_{\lambda\,=\,\lambda_i}} \qquad (2.07)$$

and which may be regarded as the relative effectiveness of homogeneous radiation of wavelength λ_i in producing erythema. The

TABLE VII.—ERYTHEMAL EFFECT OF RADIATION ON UNTANNED HUMAN SKIN

(Values given by Coblentz, Stair, and Hogue, *Bu. Stds. J.R.*, **8**, 1932, p. 544, as the average obtained by Hausser and Vahle; Luckiesh, Holladay, and Taylor; and Coblentz, Stair, and Hogue)

λ	Relative Erythemal Effect
0.275μ	0.00
0.280	0.03
0.285	0.09
0.289	0.22
0.290	0.26
0.295	0.95
0.297	1.00
0.300	0.82
0.302	0.55
0.305	0.33
0.310	0.11
0.313	0.03
0.315	0.00

* Note that, unlike the case of the photocell, the result depends on both *irradiation* and *exposure time*. Experiments indicate that over a fairly wide range, the result depends on the product of irradiation and exposure time. Thus the experiment can be performed equally well by keeping the value of the irradiation fixed and exposing a series of spots, using different values of time.

values of G in Eq. (2.07) are, of course, referred to the same exposure time.

The results obtained with different individuals vary considerably.* Curves of w vs. λ for various subjects have been averaged, giving a curve such as that of Fig. 2.09. The part of the curve to the left of 0.28μ is a spurious one which has no connection with ordinary erythema produced by sunlight. We shall therefore

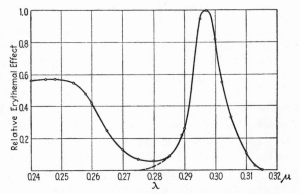

Fig. 2.09.—Erythemal effect of homogeneous radiation on untanned human skin.[22]

neglect it and shall extend the erythemal curve to zero at 0.275μ, giving the values of Table VII. These data may be considered as *standard data for a hypothetical average subject* and may be used in determining the erythemal efficacy of any given radiation.

As noted previously, the spectroradiometric curve, giving values of irradiation as a function of wavelength, constitutes a complete specification of the irradiation in the neighborhood of a given point on a given surface. Furthermore, if we are interested only in the erythemal effect of the radiation, we need specify only a small part of the complete spectrum since radiation in the visible and infrared regions has no erythemal effect. For a continuous spectrum, however, this scheme still requires the specification of 5 or 10 values, which is unnecessarily cumbersome. It would seem feasible to specify the effectiveness of a given irradiation in producing erythema *by a single number*. To do this, we use the same procedure that we used in obtaining a photoelectric

* A number of other factors, such as temperature of the skin and effect of infrared radiation, probably enter also but will not be considered here.

current, except that we substitute w in place of p.   For a line spectrum,

$$\Gamma = \sum_1^n w_i G_i \tag{2.08}$$

and for a continuous spectrum,

$$\Gamma = \int_0^\infty w G_\lambda \, d\lambda \tag{2.09}$$

Here Γ represents a new concept.   Evidently it is not radiant power or irradiation and *cannot be expressed in watts/sq cm or any other customary unit.*   It has the *dimensions* of power per unit area, but the irradiation has been evaluated by a mathematical process defined by the above equations.   We might call the new unit in which Γ is expressed (where G is in watts per square centimeter) the *erythemalwatt per square centimeter.*   Luckiesh and Moss have chosen to use a smaller unit defined as 10^{-5} of the erythemalwatt per square centimeter and called the *finsen* after the noted investigator of that name.   Thus,

$$\Gamma = \int_0^\infty w G_\lambda \, d\lambda \quad \text{(erythemalwatt/sq cm)}$$

or

$$\Gamma = 10^5 \int_0^\infty w G_\lambda \, d\lambda \quad \text{(finsens)}$$

It is found[2] that for an average individual with untanned skin, *a minimum perceptible erythema will require approximately* 0.025 *erythemalwatt/sq cm (or* 2500 *finsens) for one second.*   The reciprocity law applies over a considerable range, so that from the above datum one can determine how long an exposure will be required for MPE, using any given value of irradiation of any type whose spectroradiometric curve is known.

Example.   The ordinary tungsten lamp produces practically no erythemal effect, since the small amount of radiation produced by the filament in the region 0.28 to 0.30μ is almost completely absorbed by the glass bulb.   By using fused quartz instead of glass or by employing a special glass such as Corex D, the biologically effective wavelengths are transmitted.   Figure 2.10a shows the radiant power curve of such a special lamp.   The middle curve (b) gives the relative erythemal factor w, while (c) is the product ($w G_\lambda$)

vs. λ. The use of a planimeter allows the evaluation of the areas. From Fig. 2.10, G is 150×10^{-4} watt/sq cm, and Γ is found to be

$$\Gamma = \int_0^\infty wG_\lambda \, d\lambda = 0.105 \times 10^{-5} \text{ erythemalwatt/sq cm}$$

$$= \mathbf{0.105 \ finsen}$$

Since 2500 finsen-sec is necessary for an MPE, the time required with the

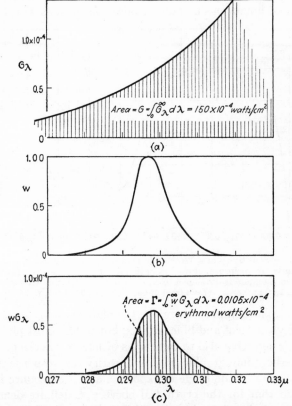

FIG. 2.10.—Erythemal effect of radiation from a special tungsten lamp.

above tungsten lamp at such a distance as to give a total irradiation of 150.8×10^{-4} watt/sq cm will be

$$\frac{2500}{0.105} = 23{,}800 \text{ sec} = \mathbf{6.6 \ hr}$$

The illuminating engineer is sometimes called upon to design dual-purpose lighting for offices or shops where the lighting may be in operation practically all day. Under these conditions, it is essential that an annoyingly large amount of ultraviolet be not introduced, and thus calculations similar to the foregoing are useful. Of course, in practice, it is often possible to simplify such calculations by using specific data furnished by the manufacturers on the particular light units used. Some such data are given in Table VIII.

2.07. Other Effects of Radiant Energy.—The curve of Fig. 2.11 gives the relative sensitivity of a panchromatic photographic plate, the ordinates representing the relative blackening effect per watt of homogeneous radiant power at various wavelengths.

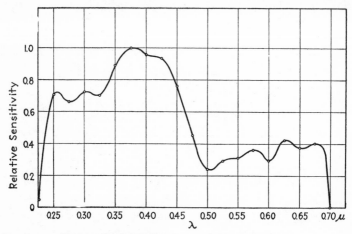

FIG. 2.11.—Sensitivity of a Wratten hypersensitive panchromatic plate. The ordinates give the reciprocal of the irradiation required to give a constant density of 0.6 when the plate is developed to a γ of $0.8\gamma \infty$. Relative values are used, referred to 1.00 at 0.38μ. (*Data from Mees, J.O.S.A.*, **21**, 1931, p. 753.)

Like most photographic materials, the plate is highly sensitive in the near ultraviolet and blue regions; but unlike most plates and films, it is sensitive also to radiations of longer wavelengths.

With the photographic plate, linearity of response is not obtained over a wide range of exposure, and a procedure is used similar to that for the erythemal curve. A definite density of silver deposit is selected arbitrarily, and an experiment is performed to find how much homogeneous radiant energy per square centimeter is required at various wavelengths to produce this particular effect. The relative sensitivity of the plate at a given wavelength is then defined by a ratio as in Eq. (2.07), the result at 0.38μ being arbitrarily taken as the standard against which the other values are compared. Since attention is confined exclusively to the *cause*, the linearity or nonlinearity of the relation between cause and effect does not enter. Thus one might define a *photographicwatt per square centimeter* by an equation similar to Eq. (2.09). Any given irradiation evaluated by this process would be expressed in photographicwatts per square centimeter which would indicate the photographic effect of this particular irradiation with this particular kind of photosensitive material. It must be realized, however, that such a procedure does not have the universality of the erythemal case, since different photographic materials differ so widely as to make the results obtained with one type meaningless with another.

TABLE VIII.—CHARACTERISTICS OF SOME ULTRAVIOLET SOURCES

Characteristic	500 W* CX	250 W* CX	S-1*	S-2*	Quartz Hg lamp	L.P. Hg in Corex
Watts input..................	500	250	440	158		
Lumens output..............	7800	...	6500	1170		
η_0 (lumens/watt)	15.7	...	14.8	7.4		
Erythemal output, in 56 cm (22 in.) circle, 76 cm (30 in.) from lamp center:						
Erythemalwatts.............	....	...	0.085	0.019		
Vitons....................	....	...	8500	1900		
Erythemal irradiation at 76 cm (30 in.) from lamp center:						
Erythemalwatts per square centimeter.................	5.0×10^{-6}	...	105×10^{-6}	15×10^{-6}		
Finsens....................	0.5	...	10.5	1.5		
Minutes exposure for MPE at 76 cm......................	83	...	4	28		

* With standard reflecting equipment.

Other effects of radiant energy may be treated in a similar manner: visual effects, all sorts of photochemical and photoelectric effects, the killing of bacteria, the treating of deep-seated human disorders by use of penetrating infrared radiation, etc. Space prohibits further consideration of the subject, except in the very important.case of visual effects which will constitute the subject matter of Chap. III.

2.08. Radiometric and Erythemal Concepts.—We have considered the radiometric concepts of radiant energy, of radiant power Φ, of irradiation G, and of radiosity J. Of these, irradiation appears to be most intimately connected with actual measurements and has consequently been used most frequently in the present chapter. The concept of radiosity, however, is found almost indispensable when dealing with incandescent filaments and other surfaces that emit radiant energy (see Chap. V).

In the consideration of biologically effective radiation, it has been convenient to introduce a new set of concepts. These new quantities are parallel to the radiometric quantities, though they are distinctly new and different and cannot be expressed in the units of energy or power. The concept corresponding to G(watts/sq cm) was represented by Γ, expressed in erythemalwatts per square centimeter or in finsens. If a surface of area S sq cm is uniformly irradiated with G watts/sq cm, the total *radiant flux*, or radiant power, is

$$\Phi = SG \quad \text{(watts)} \qquad (2.10)$$

The corresponding erythemal quantity is called *erythemal flux*:

$$\Psi = S\,\Gamma = S\int_0^\infty wG_\lambda\,d\lambda \qquad (2.11)$$

If Γ is expressed in erythemalwatts per square centimeter, erythemal flux is, of course, in *erythemalwatts*. If Γ is in finsens, erythemal flux is said to be in *vitons* or *E-vitons*.

The work of Gerstenberger and Horesh (*J. Am. Med. Assoc.*, **97**, 1931, p. 766) indicates that rickets in children can be cured by a daily dose of approximately 1.5 *erythemalwatt-sec* or 150,000 viton-sec. The important factor is evidently total erythemal flux falling on the skin rather than the value of the erythemal irradiation.

The various quantities may be summarized as shown in the table on page 43.

The reader may feel that such a multiplicity of concepts is unnecessary as well as confusing. Irrespective of what he may think on the second score, he will generally find that there can be little question regarding their necessity and usefulness. He probably thought the same thing about the concepts of mechanics when he was exposed to that subject as a freshman. To the layman, the necessity of differentiating sharply between energy and power, or force and work, is nonexistent; but for the engineer, conditions are quite different. The same applies to the various radiometric concepts as well as to the photometric concepts which we shall meet in the next chapter. These quantities are of vital importance to the illuminating engineer, and it is just as deplorable for him to confuse radiant flux and irradiation or luminous intensity and illumination as it would be for the mechanical engineer to confuse power and work. Yet there has been, and still is, a woeful amount of muddy thinking on radiometry and photometry. Whether this is the cause of the frequent confusion of concepts which can be noted in the literature, or is the result,

TABLE IX

Radiometric			Erythemal		
Name	Symbol	Unit	Name	Symbol	Unit
Radiant energy.......	U	$\begin{cases} \text{erg} \\ \text{watt-sec} \end{cases}$	Erythemal energy	..	$\begin{cases} \text{erythemalwatt-sec} \\ \text{viton-sec} \end{cases}$
Radiant flux.........	Φ	watt	Erythemal flux..	Ψ	$\begin{cases} \text{erythemalwatt} \\ \text{viton} \end{cases}$
Irradiation...........	G	watt/sq cm	Erythemal irradiation........	Γ	$\begin{cases} \text{erythemalwatt/sq} \\ \quad \text{cm} \\ \text{finsen} \end{cases}$
Radiosity............	J	watt/sq cm			

10^7 ergs = 1 watt-sec

10^5 finsens = 1 erythemalwatt/sq cm
10^5 vitons = 1 erythemalwatt
1 finsen = 1 viton/sq cm

is not apparent. In any case, it is essential that we distinguish clearly among the various concepts and that we do not use the lazy-man's trick, so common in most discussions of the subject, of lumping all the concepts into a nebulous mass known as "intensity" or "radiation" or "light."

Problem 7. If a $K2$ filter, which cuts off practically all radiant energy at wavelengths below 0.49μ, and a panchromatic plate are used in a camera, it is found that correct exposures of some black-and-white objects are obtained in sunlight with an exposure of $\frac{1}{50}$ sec. What exposure should be used if light from incandescent lamps is used instead of daylight? For sunlight, use the data of Table V. Data for a tungsten lamp are given in Table XI of Chap. III. Use the same total value of G in each case.

Problem 8. The statement is often made that a mild sunburn is experienced when untanned skin is exposed perpendicular to the sun's rays for about 19 min at noon on a clear day in summer. How does this figure check with the value of 2500 finsen-sec given in Sec. 2.06 for MPE?

Problem 9. Data given by the Eastman Kodak Company on Wratten filter F used with supersensitive panchromatic plates or films indicate that with radiation from incandescent lamps, a filter factor of 12 should be used (exposure = 12 times exposure without filter), while for sunlight a factor of 35 is necessary.   Compute the filter factors, and compare with the preceding figures.   Assume that the camera lens cuts off sharply at 0.32μ.

Problem 10.   An office is to be lighted with low-pressure mercury-vapor lamps in Corex D tubes, and the lamps may be in operation 8 hr a day. Reflectors will direct most of the ultraviolet radiation downward, so very little will be absorbed by the face; and the area of the hands (approximately 350 sq cm) is all that is exposed normal to the radiation.   What value of G is necessary on the hands to give a daily dose of 1.5 erythemalwatt-sec? What value of G will produce MPE on untanned skin in one day?   Evidently a value between these two limits should be used for the irradiation.

Problem 11.   What exposure is necessary to give an MPE at 1 meter distance from a 220-volt high-pressure mercury-vapor arc in quartz?

Problem 12.   An S-2 lamp with reflector is installed on the ceiling of a room.   How long an exposure should be used each day to prevent rickets in a baby, placed 6 ft below the lamp center, with 500 sq cm of skin exposed?

Problem 13.   Rating as 100 per cent the erythemal flux from the low-pressure mercury lamp in Corex D glass, what is the relative erythemal flux obtained from the other low-pressure lamps of Table IV?

Problem 14.   Compute and fill in the blank spaces of Table VIII.   The data on the 250-watt CX lamp are obtained from Chap. III, while the data for the 110-volt high-pressure lamp and the low-pressure lamp are found in Tables III and IV, respectively, of this chapter.

Bibliography

General

1. H. E. Ives: The Units and Nomenclature of Radiation and Illumination, *Astrophys. J.*, **45**, 1917, p. 39.
2. Luckiesh and Holladay: Fundamental Units and Terms for Biologically Effective Radiation, *J.O.S.A.*, **23**, 1933, p. 197.
3. An Outline of Atomic Physics, Physics Staff, University of Pittsburgh, John Wiley & Sons, Inc., New York, 1933.
4. W. E. Forsythe: Temperature Radiation, *J.O.S.A.*, **16**, 1928, p. 307.
5. L. Gorczyński: Recording Solar Radiation, *J.O.S.A.*, **9**, 1924, p. 455.
6. Benford and Howe: Energy Measurements in the Visible and Ultraviolet, *I.E.S. Trans.*, **26**, 1931, p. 292.
7. Ornstein, Moll, and Burger: Objektive Spektralphotometrie. Vieweg, Braunschweig, Germany, 1932.
8. Abbot, Fowle, and Aldrich: Distribution of Energy in the Spectra of the Sun and Stars, *Smithsonian Misc. Coll.*, **74**, No. 7.
9. Abbot, Aldrich, and Fowle: *Smithsonian Inst. Astrophys. Obs., Ann.*, **5**, 1932, p. 108.
10. Abbot and Fowle: *Smithsonian Inst. Astrophys. Obs., Ann.*, **2**, 1908, p. 113.

11. H. H. KIMBALL: Distribution of Energy in the Visible Spectrum of Sunlight, Skylight, and Total Daylight, *Proc. Int. Cong. Ill.*, 1928, p. 501.
12. F. E. FOWLE: Infrared Transmission of Radiation by Water-vapor, *I.E.S. Trans.*, **30**, 1935, p. 273.
13. FORSYTHE and CHRISTISON: Ultraviolet Radiation from the Sun and Heated Tungsten, *J.O.S.A.*, **20**, 1930, p. 396.
14. C. E. K. MEES: Photographic Plates for Use in Spectroscopy and Astronomy, *J.O.S.A.*, **21**, 1931, p. 753.

PHOTOCELLS

15. CAMPBELL and RITCHIE: Photoelectric Cells, Chap. II, Sir Isaac Pitman & Sons, London, 1934.
16. ZWORYKIN and WILSON: Photocells and Their Application, 2d ed., John Wiley & Sons, Inc., New York, 1932.
17. SIMON and SUHRMANN: Lichtelektrische Zellen, Julius Springer, Berlin, 1932.
18. L. R. KOLLER: Characteristics of Photo-electric Cells, *Soc. M.P.E. Trans.*, **12**, 1928, p. 921.
19. J. W. BALLARD: Infra-red Sensitivity of Caesium Oxide Photoelectric Cells, *J.O.S.A.*, **20**, 1930, p. 619.
20. PRESCOTT and KELLY: The Caesium-oxygen-silver Photoelectric Cell, *B.S.T.J.*, **11**, 1932, p. 334.
21. G. DÉJARDIN: Propriétés générales des cathodes photoélectriques, *R.G.E.*, **34**, 1933, pp. 515, 555, 591, 629.

ERYTHEMA

22. COBLENTZ, STAIR, and HOGUE: The Spectral Erythemic Reaction of Human Skin, *Bu. Stds. J.R.*, **8**, 1932, p. 541. (RP433)
23. A. H. Taylor: The Measurement of Erythemal Ultraviolet Radiation, *J.O.S.A.*, **23**, 1933, p. 60.
24. LUCKIESH, HOLLADAY, and TAYLOR: Reaction of Untanned Human Skin to U.V. Radiation, *J.O.S.A.*, **20**, 1930, p. 423.

SOURCES

25. B. T. BARNES: Spectral Distribution of Radiation from High and Low Pressure Hg Arcs, *J.O.S.A.*, **24**, 1934, p. 147.
26. B. T. BARNES: Spectral Distribution of Radiation from Three Reflector Units, *J.O.S.A.*, **25**, 1935, p. 167.
27. F. BENFORD: Radiation Characteristics of Two Mercury Arcs, *Soc. M.P.E. Trans.*, **14**, 1930, p. 404.
28. FORSYTHE, BARNES, and EASLEY: Ultraviolet Sources and their Radiation, *J.O.S.A.*, **24**, 1934, p. 178.
29. FORSYTHE and EASLEY: Radiation of the Photo-flash Lamps, *J.O.S.A.*, **24**, 1934, p. 195.

30. FORSYTHE, BARNES, and EASLEY: Characteristics of a New U.V. Lamp, *J.O.S.A.*, **21**, 1931, p. 30.

31. JOHNSON and BURNS: Line Intensity and Energy Distribution in High and Low Pressure Mercury Arcs, *J.O.S.A.*, **23**, 1933, p. 55.

32. A. H. TAYLOR: Ultraviolet Radiation from the Sunlight (Type S-1) Lamp, *J.O.S.A.*, **21**, 1931, p. 20.

CHAPTER III

LUMINOUS FLUX

In Chap. II, we have considered several of the effects of radiant energy and how the magnitudes of these effects can be calculated. The complete specification of the irradiation is given by the spectroradiometric curve, and the magnitude of any effect can be found if this curve and the response curve of the effect are known. Exactly the same procedure may be used with respect to the *visual effect* of radiant energy. The illuminating engineer will probably find the foregoing treatment of the photoelectric and photographic effects useful in the measurement of light, while the treatment of the erythemal effect will be valuable in connection with dual-purpose lighting. As a matter of fact, however, these effects have been introduced *principally* because of their similarity in method of treatment to the visual effect and to illustrate the fact that the visual effect is not unique but is merely one of many results of radiant energy, all of which may be treated in essentially the same manner. In the present chapter we shall develop from the spectroradiometric curve the visual concepts of *luminous flux, illumination, and luminosity*.

3.02. The Visibility Curve.—Let us first consider how a visibility curve similar to the response curve of Chap. II can be obtained. Since there is no way of putting an ammeter into the optic nerve, we cannot get a response curve directly as with a photocell. Even if we could measure the impulses in the optic nerve we should still be unable to say anything about the *sensation* produced by these stimuli. We are forced, therefore, to use an indirect scheme similar to that used with erythema.

Consider a screen (Fig. 3.01) made of two identical sections which will be called *half-fields*. The familiar Lummer-Brodhun screen may be used, or a simpler construction such as is shown in the figure. The left half-field is irradiated with homogeneous radiation of constant magnitude and at a fixed wavelength of 0.554μ. Homogeneous radiation is also used on the right half-field, but here both magnitude and wavelength are variable by the observer. The surroundings are dark, and the total field subtends an angle of approximately 2 deg at the eye. With radiation of any given wavelength on the right half-field, say $\lambda = 0.60\mu$, the observer sees the half-fields as two colored patches which differ from each other in both *quantity* and *quality*. By reducing the irradiation on the right half-field, however, the observer can find a place where the right half-field seems undeniably less brilliant than the left. Also, by increasing the irradiation, he finds a place where the right half-field seems undeniably more brilliant than the left. He then attempts to reduce the

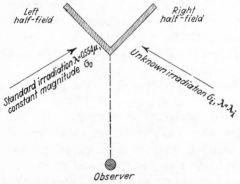

Fig. 3.01.—Schematic diagram of a photometric screen.

difference between these limits and finally arrives at a value of irradiation where the two half-fields appear equally brilliant, though by no means identical because of the difference in wavelength. Thus the quantity difference is eliminated by the adjustment of G, but the quality difference remains. The value of G_i is then noted.

If the wavelength is now changed to another value, a different adjustment of G will generally be necessary to give a brilliance match. It is found that as λ departs in either direction from approximately 0.55μ, the amount of radiant power required to give a balance against the fixed stimulus increases. In other words, the eye is most sensitive in the yellow-green and becomes less and less sensitive as the wavelength of the radiation is increased or decreased from this optimum value. This property of the eye is usually expressed by a *visibility curve* whose ordinates are called the *visibility v*:

$$v = \frac{G_0}{G_i} v_0 \qquad\qquad (3.01)$$

where v = visibility at wavelength λ_i.

v_0 = visibility at $\lambda = 0.554$ (usually considered as unity).

G_0 = value of fixed irradiation (watts/sq cm at $\lambda = 0.554\mu$).

G_i = value of variable irradiation (watts/sq cm at $\lambda = \lambda_i$).

Such a curve is shown in Fig. 3.02 and can be used like the curves for the photocell (Fig. 2.07) or for the erythemal effect (Fig. 2.09).

Such a curve applies only to the particular observer who made the measurements: each observer, in general, has his own curve which differs more or less from those of others. The statement is

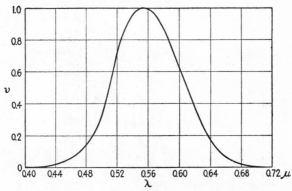

Fig. 3.02.—A visibility curve.

often made that except for a comparatively small group of color-blind people, most individuals have "normal" eyes as regards color. All such individuals would be expected to obtain the same photometric readings and would have the same visibility curve. Actual tests, however, do not support such conclusions. Figure 3.03, for instance, shows the combined visibility results obtained by Coblentz and Emerson[6] for 125 observers and by Gibson and Tyndall[7] for 52 observers. The abscissae are values of v obtained by different individuals at a fixed wavelength, while the ordinates represent the number of individuals obtaining these values of v. At 0.49μ, for instance, values ranging from 0.10 to 0.38 were obtained for v, though the greatest number of observers obtained values in the neighborhood of 0.20. Similar results were obtained at other wavelengths, as will be seen from the distributions at 0.59 and 0.64μ included in Fig. 3.03. The curves are

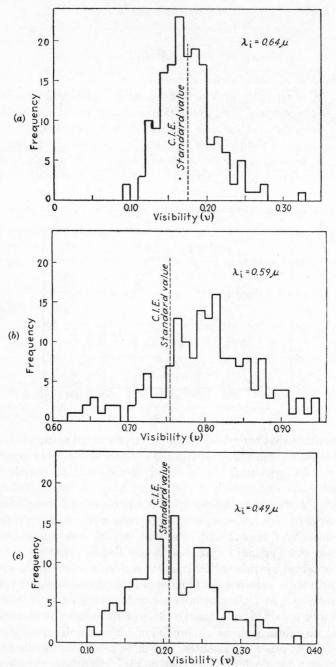

Fig. 3.03a, b, c.—Distribution of visibility data   (*From Coblentz and Emerson,*[6] *data on 125 observers; and from Gibson and Tyndall,*[7] *data on 52 observers.*)

fairly good approximations to the Gaussian form of probability curve. Evidently they show no distinct class of "red-sensitive" or "blue-sensitive" or "normal" people; at any given wavelengths, there is a wide range of v, and an observer picked at random may lie anywhere in that range, though he is more likely to be near the middle than near the ends.

Because of this wide variation of perhaps 3 to 1 in the values of visibility obtained by different observers, it is advisable to standardize on some kind of average visibility curve for use in specifying the photometric quantities. A study of the results obtained by various investigators led Gibson and Tyndall to recommend a particular set of values of v, and these were adopted by international agreement in 1924 at the Geneva meeting of the Commission Internationale de l'Éclairage. These C.I.E. values were tabulated at intervals of 0.01μ; but Judd has interpolated values at intervals of 0.001μ, results being given in Table X and plotted in Fig. 3.02.

It will be noted that the curve is simple in shape and has a maximum at about 0.555μ. Evidently, the boundaries of the visible region, as was pointed out previously, are not at all definite; the effectiveness of a watt of homogeneous radiation becomes less and less as the wavelength is changed in either direction from 0.555μ, but the use of a sufficiently great amount of radiant power even at 0.76μ or beyond may result in a slight visual sensation. The first two columns of Table X give the values for each 0.01μ, while the other columns are interpolated.

The data on which the visibility curve is based were actually obtained in two ways, neither of which is exactly like the procedure outlined above. In practice, it was found difficult to obtain sufficient precision by the direct-comparison method, owing to the psychologically confusing effect of large color differences. The difficulty was reduced by using a series of standards of different wavelengths for the left half-field or by using a flicker photometer. These details, however, need not concern us here. As pointed out in Appendix B, the curve is necessarily more or less arbitrary: no matter what is done, it is absolutely impossible to get a single curve that will represent all phases of "seeing." Thus we need worry very little about where the data came from or how well they represent the average of human eyes. The important thing is that these particular

Table X.—Standard Visibility Function
Interpolated to 0.001-μ intervals
(Judd, *Bu. Stds. J.R.*, **6**, 1931, p. 465)

λ	0	1	2	3	4	5	6	7	8	9
0.38μ	40×10^{-6}	45	49	54	59	64	71	80	90	104
0.39	120×10^{-6}	138	155	173	193	215	241	272	308	350
0.40	40×10^{-5}	45	49	54	59	64	71	80	90	104
0.41	120×10^{-5}	138	156	174	195	218	244	274	310	352
0.42	400×10^{-5}	455	515	581	651	726	806	889	976	1066
0.43	0.01160	1257	1358	1463	1571	1684	1800	1920	2043	2170
0.44	0.02300	2430	2570	2700	2840	2980	3130	3290	3450	3620
0.45	0.03800	3990	4180	4380	4590	4800	5020	5250	5490	5740
0.46	0.06000	6270	6540	6810	7090	7390	7690	8020	8360	8720
0.47	0.0910	950	992	1035	1080	1126	1175	1225	1278	1333
0.48	0.1390	1448	1507	1567	1629	1693	1761	1833	1909	1991
0.49	0.2080	2173	2270	2371	2476	2586	2701	2823	2951	3087
0.50	0.3230	3382	3544	3714	3890	4073	4259	4450	4642	4836
0.51	0.5030	5229	5436	5648	5865	6082	6299	6511	6717	6914
0.52	0.7100	7277	7449	7615	7776	7932	8082	8225	8363	8495
0.53	0.8620	8739	8851	8956	9056	9149	9238	9320	9398	9471
0.54	0.9540	9604	9661	9713	9760	9803	9840	9873	9902	9928
0.55	0.9950	9969	9983	9994	1.0000	1.0002	1.0001	9995	9984	9969
0.56	0.9950	9926	9898	9865	9828	9786	9741	9691	9638	9581
0.57	0.9520	9455	9386	9312	9235	9154	9069	8981	8890	8796
0.58	0.8700	8600	8496	8388	8277	8163	8046	7928	7809	7690
0.59	0.7570	7449	7327	7202	7076	6949	6822	6694	6565	6437
0.60	0.6310	6182	6054	5926	5797	5668	5539	5410	5282	5156
0.61	0.5030	4905	4781	4658	4535	4412	4291	4170	4049	3929
0.62	0.3810	3690	3570	3449	3329	3210	3092	2977	2864	2755
0.63	0.2650	2548	2450	2354	2261	2170	2082	1996	1912	1830
0.64	0.1750	1672	1596	1523	1452	1382	1316	1251	1188	1128
0.65	0.1070	1014	961	910	862	816	771	729	688	648
0.66	0.0610	574	539	506	475	446	418	391	366	343
0.67	0.0320	299	280	263	247	232	219	206	194	182
0.68	1700×10^{-5}	1585	1477	1376	1281	1192	1108	1030	956	886
0.69	820×10^{-5}	759	705	656	612	572	536	503	471	440
0.70	410×10^{-5}	381	355	332	310	291	273	256	241	225
0.71	2100×10^{-6}	1954	1821	1699	1587	1483	1387	1297	1212	1130
0.72	1050×10^{-6}	975	907	845	788	736	688	644	601	560
0.73	520×10^{-6}	482	447	415	387	360	335	313	291	270
0.74	250×10^{-6}	231	214	198	185	172	160	149	139	130
0.75	120×10^{-6}	111	103	96	90	84	78	74	69	64
0.76	60×10^{-6}	56	52	48	45	42	39	37	35	32
0.77	30×10^{-6}									

values have been accepted internationally and may be used to fix the photometric quantities *by definition*. We may forget, if we wish, what v represents or how it was obtained, may consider it as an arbitrary mathematical function, and may express it to any desired number of significant figures, irrespective of the inherent limitations of precision of the human eye.

3.03. Illumination Defined on the Basis of the Standard Visibility Curve.—We have seen that radiant power can be measured only by allowing it to fall on a receiving surface and transforming part of the power to another form. The concept of *irradiation* is thus very closely related to the thing that is actually being measured in all cases. With the erythemal effect, a new quantity Γ was defined on the basis of the irradiation and served to give a measure of the effectiveness of any irradiation in producing sunburn. An analogous procedure gives a photometric concept—the *illumination*. When a surface is irradiated and part or all of the radiant energy is at wavelengths in the visible region, we say that the surface is *illuminated*. For a line spectrum, the value of the *illumination* is

$$E = \sum_{1}^{n} v_i G_i \tag{3.02}$$

and for a continuous spectrum,

$$E = \int_{0}^{\infty} v G_\lambda \, d\lambda \tag{3.03}$$

The new quantity E is not power per unit area and cannot be expressed in watts per square centimeter. It is a brand-new entity and must be expressed in brand-new units. If G in the above equations is in watts per square centimeter, we may say that E is in *lightwatts per square centimeter*.

If v could be expressed as a simple mathematical function of λ, a straightforward mathematical integration of Eq. (3.03) would be possible in some cases. Various approximate formulas have been developed, but none appears to be simple enough to offer any advantage. The integral, Eq. (3.03), is usually evaluated by plotting the curve of $v G_\lambda$ and obtaining the area under it. Or ordinates may be evaluated at equal wavelength intervals and the result obtained by straight addition, as in the following example. Or the method of selected ordinates may be used, where selected values of G_λ are added, spaced in such a way that equal areas are included under the v-curve between any two consecutive selected ordinates.

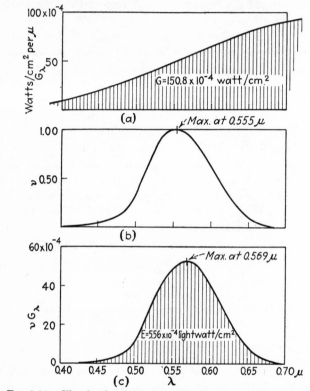

Fig. 3.04.—Illumination from a tungsten lamp operating at 2958°K.

Example. What is the illumination of a given surface the spectral irradiation of which is shown in Fig. 3.04a? The irradiation is due to a tungsten lamp with filament operating at 2958°K.

The results are shown in the figure, where the curve (a) represents the radiant power incident on the surface per square centimeter; (b) is the standard visibility curve; and (c) is the product vG_λ as a function of wavelength. The area under the final curve gives the illumination in accordance with Eq. (3.03). Its value is 5.56×10^{-4} lightwatt/sq cm.

Instead of plotting the curves and actually measuring the areas, it may be more convenient to tabulate corresponding values at each 0.01μ and to add the products. This is, of course, an approximate method, since it replaces the smooth curve by a stepped curve. If the steps are small enough, however, the results can be made as precise as desired. In practice, a width of 0.01μ is found generally to be satisfactory. The tabulation may be made as follows:

λ	G_λ watts/sq cm per micron	v	vG_λ	λ	G_λ watts/sq cm per micron	v	vG_λ
0.40μ	9.1×10^{-4}	0.0004	....	0.61μ	67.5×10^{-4}	0.503	33.9×10^{-4}
0.41	10.8	0.0012	....	0.62	70.5	0.381	26.9
0.42	12.7	0.0040	0.1×10^{-4}	0.63	73.3	0.265	19.4
0.43	14.8	0.0116	0.2	0.64	75.9	0.175	13.3
0.44	17.0	0.0230	0.4	0.65	78.6	0.107	8.4
0.45	19.4	0.0380	0.7				
0.46	21.9	0.060	1.3	0.66	81.0	0.061	4.9
0.47	24.7	0.091	2.2	0.67	83.7	0.032	2.7
0.48	27.6	0.139	3.8	0.68	86.0	0.017	1.5
0.49	30.4	0.208	6.3	0.69	88.1	0.0082	0.7
0.50	33.3	0.323	10.7	0.70	90.8	0.0041	0.4
0.51	36.3	0.503	18.2	0.71	92.8	0.0021	0.2
0.52	39.4	0.710	28.0	0.72	94.4	0.00105	0.1
0.53	42.6	0.862	36.7	0.73	96.4	0.00052	0.1
0.54	45.7	0.954	43.6	0.74	97.9	0.00025	
0.55	49.0	0.995	48.7	0.75	99.6	0.00012	
0.56	52.1	0.995	51.9	0.76	101.2	0.00006	
0.57	55.3	0.952	52.5	0.77			
0.58	58.5	0.870	50.9			Sum $= 556.1 \times 10^{-4}$	
0.59	61.5	0.757	46.6				
0.60	64.7	0.631	40.8				

Sum of all terms (including infrared) $= 15{,}080 \times 10^{-4}$

Since G_λ is in watts per square centimeter *per micron wavelength band*, while the actual width of step used in the preceding was only 0.01μ, the results are evidently too large by a factor of 100. Thus the irradiation is $G = 150.8 \times 10^{-4}$ watt/sq cm, and the illumination is $E = 5.56 \times 10^{-4}$ lightwatt/sq cm. Note that if all this radiant power had been concentrated in a homogeneous radiation of wavelength 0.554μ, the illumination would have been

$$E' = vG = 150.8 \times 10^{-4} \text{ lightwatt/sq cm}$$

Thus the radiation from this tungsten lamp is only $5.56/150.8$, or 3.7 per cent as effective in producing illumination as the particular homogeneous radiation would be.

Problem 15. A certain factory is lighted by the ordinary Cooper-Hewitt type of low-pressure mercury-vapor lamp in lead glass (Table IV, page 26). Each lamp is mounted with its center 60 in. above the work benches. What is the value of the illumination on a bench at a point directly beneath one of the lamps? The other lamps are turned off, and reflections of radiation

TABLE XI.—IRRADIATION FROM 250-WATT CX LAMP WITH REFLECTOR
On axis of reflector, 30 in. from center of lamp

λ	G_λ watts/sq cm per μ	λ	G_λ watts/sq cm per μ
0.28μ	0.059×10^{-3}	0.61μ	42.0×10^{-3}
0.29	0.133	0.62	43.9
0.30	0.244	0.63	45.6
		0.64	47.4
0.31	0.37	0.65	49.1
0.32	0.57		
0.33	0.78	0.66	50.8
0.34	1.00	0.67	52.2
0.35	1.33	0.68	
		0.69	
0.36	1.75	0.70	54.7
0.37	2.28		
0.38	2.76	0.80	67.4
0.39	3.3	0.90	76.0
0.40	3.9	1.00	83.8
		1.10	85.3
0.41	4.8	1.20	80.2
0.42	5.6		
0.43	6.5	1.30	75.6
0.44	7.8	1.40	68.2
0.45	9.1	1.50	60.3
		1.60	54.7
0.46	11.0	1.70	49.0
0.47	12.6		
0.48	14.4	1.80	44.0
0.49	16.2	1.90	39.0
0.50	18.4	2.00	34.8
		2.1	30.9
0.51	20.7	2.2	27.7
0.52	23.0		
0.53	25.3	2.3	24.8
0.54	27.6	2.4	22.4
0.55	29.8	2.5	20.2
		2.6	18.1
0.56	32.0	2.7	16.7
0.57	33.9		
0.58	36.0		
0.59	38.1		
0.60	40.8		

from the lamp reflector and from the ceiling and walls are neglected. The inverse-square law is assumed to hold at this distance; *i.e.*, the irradiation is assumed to be inversely proportional to the square of the distance from the center of the lamp.

Problem 16. Which is the better for producing erythema: a low-pressure mercury-vapor lamp or a high-pressure one? Both lamps are in fused-quartz tubes and operate on 110 volts, and they are placed such distances from the subject that the illumination is the same in both cases. What is the ratio of the erythemalwatts per square centimeter in the two cases?

3.04. Luminous Flux and Luminosity.—We can define other photometric concepts analogous to the other radiometric concepts. If the irradiation is found to be uniform over a surface of area S, the total radiant flux falling on the surface is

$$\Phi = SG \quad \text{(watts)}$$

The corresponding photometric quantity is called *luminous flux F*:

$$F = SE = S\int_0^\infty vG_\lambda \, d\lambda \quad \text{(lightwatts)} \quad (3.04)$$

Thus *luminous flux may be defined as radiant power evaluated with respect to the standard visibility function.*

Another concept is that of *luminosity*. If a surface emits radiation, some of which is at wavelengths in the visible region, the surface is said to be *luminous*. It may be self-luminous, owing to its temperature, for instance, or it may merely reflect or transmit radiation from some other source. In any case, the quantity corresponding to radiosity J is called *luminosity L*:

$$L = \int_0^\infty vJ_\lambda \, d\lambda \quad \text{(lightwatts/sq cm)} \quad (3.05)$$

The curve representing J_λ as a function of λ is plotted, giving a curve similar to that of Fig. 3.04*a*. The ordinates are multiplied by corresponding values of v, and the resulting curve of vJ_λ is obtained. The curve is generally called the *luminosity curve*. It seems reasonable, therefore, to call the area under the curve the *luminosity*, though such a name has not been standardized (see Appendix B).

The *lightwatt* is the logical unit of luminous flux, though perhaps a better name might be coined for it. However, it is not the unit generally used. As has happened in most branches of science, photometry was developed before there was any known connection between it and other branches of science. Thus the unit of luminous flux was based in an arbitrary way upon the output of a sperm candle of standard size. This unit was called the *lumen*. It would be indeed phenomenal if such a unit happened to be the same as the lightwatt. Evidently, an experiment must be performed to determine the relation between the two units, just as an experiment was performed to determine the relation between the calorie and the erg. We may use a comparison screen as before (Fig. 3.01). Keeping the same standard homogeneous radiation on the left with known values of G, we irradiate the right half-field with a standard candle or by a lamp which has been calibrated in terms of standard candles. The standard lamp is moved closer or farther from the screen until a brilliance match is obtained, and the value of the illumination (lumens/sq cm) on the right half-field is obtained from the standardization data of the lamp. We have the value of G (watts/sq cm) on the left half-field; and multiplying it by the value of visibility v, we get the illumination of the left half-field, expressed in lightwatts per square centimeter. A comparison of the two numbers obtained in such experiments[11] shows that

$$1 \text{ lightwatt} = 621 \text{ lumens} \qquad (3.06)$$

The relation is seen to be somewhat analogous to the mechanical equivalent of heat: 1 g-cal = 4.186×10^{-7} erg. But note the fundamental difference—the two quantities being compared are not energy, or power, or power per unit area; they are photometric quantities. Thus the common designation of the above relation as the "mechanical equivalent of light" is quite inexcusable.

The illuminating engineer commonly expresses luminous flux in lumens and the other photometric quantities in lumens per square centimeter or lumens per square foot. Thus,

$$E = 621 \int_0^\infty v G_\lambda \, d\lambda \quad \text{(lumens/sq cm)} \qquad (3.03a)$$

$$L = 621 \int_0^\infty v J_\lambda \, d\lambda \quad \text{(lumens/sq cm)} \qquad (3.05a)$$

The lumen is not a measure of the *sensation* (as is often mistakenly supposed) but is a measure of the *stimulus*. For our present purpose, we may consider the lumen as a definite, purely physical quantity based on Eq. (3.06) and the internationally accepted values of the function v. Turning now to the example of Fig. 3.04, we find that the area under curve (c) represents the luminous flux incident on a square centimeter of surface. Expressed in lumens per square centimeter, it is

$$5.56 \times 10^{-4} \text{ lightwatt/cm}^2 = 0.345 \text{ lumen/sq cm}$$
$$= 320 \text{ lumens/sq ft}$$

3.05. Luminous Efficacy.—Another concept which is sometimes useful is defined by the relation

$$\eta_l = \frac{\int_0^\infty v G_\lambda \, d\lambda}{\int_0^\infty G_\lambda \, d\lambda} = \frac{\int_0^\infty v J_\lambda \, d\lambda}{\int_0^\infty J_\lambda \, d\lambda} \quad \text{(lightwatts/watt)} \quad (3.07)$$

and may be called the *luminous efficacy* of the radiation. It expresses the relative effectiveness of the given radiant power in yielding luminous flux. For example, homogeneous radiation at 0.554μ has a luminous efficacy of 1.00 lightwatt/watt, while the radiation from the tungsten lamp of Fig. 3.04 has a luminous efficacy of 0.037 lightwatts/watt.

Evidently the luminous efficacy may be expressed, if desired, in lumens per watt, and such a procedure is generally used. The luminous efficacy of the above radiation is thus

$$\eta_l = \frac{0.345 \text{ lumen}}{0.01508 \text{ watt}} = 22.9 \text{ lumens/watt}$$

In this connection, it may be well to point out that the quantity *luminous efficacy* has been called generally *luminous efficiency*. It would seem preferable, however, to reserve the term efficiency for the ratio of two values of power or of energy. Evidently the luminous efficacy is not such a ratio, and thus the term "luminous efficiency" is a misnomer. The name *luminous efficacy*, on the other hand, expresses exactly what is meant by η_l: the effectiveness of one watt of radiant power in producing luminous flux. By definition, one watt of homogeneous radiation at $\lambda = 0.554\mu$ gives 621 lumens, and the luminous efficacy of this radiation is therefore 621 lumens/watt. All other forms of radiation are less effective in producing luminous flux. The radiation from the best incandescent lamps has a luminous efficacy rarely exceeding 25 lumens/watt or only 4.1 per cent of the maximum possible. For the radiation from most modern gaseous-conduction lamps, η_l is only slightly better, as we shall see in Chap. IV. A radiation of peculiarly high luminous efficacy

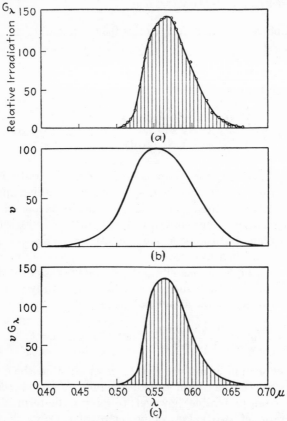

Fig. 3.05.—Irradiation from a firefly (*Photinus pyralis*).[13]

is that from the firefly. The spectral irradiation curve of Fig. 3.05a shows that nearly all the energy is concentrated in the yellow-green where the eye is most sensitive. Thus when the ordinates of (a) are multiplied by the corresponding ordinates of (b), the resulting curve (c) is almost identical with the radiation curve. A measurement of the areas shows that the firefly radiation has a luminous efficacy of approximately 560 lumens/watt, or 90 per cent of the theoretical maximum.* It is hoped that future development of light sources will allow us to approach closer to such a value than can be done at present.

Problem 17. It is found in illuminating a certain drafting room that satisfactory results are obtained when the irradiation of the drafting tables is 2.07×10^{-5} watt per square centimeter obtained from tungsten lamps having the characteristics (in the visible region) of the lamp in Table XI. It is now proposed to use sodium-vapor lamps instead of incandescent lamps. These lamps produce a strong radiation at 0.589μ and hardly any other radiation in the visible region. To obtain the same luminous effect, how many watts per square centimeter of irradiation at 0.589μ will be required?

Problem 18. How many lumens per square foot are incident on the drafting table of Prob. 17 in the two cases considered?

Problem 19. Calculate the number of lumens per square foot incident on a horizontal surface due to noon sunlight at sea level. A horizontal skylight 8 by 10 ft is used in lighting a certain room. If the effect of the glass is neglected, how much radiant energy enters the room in a minute at noon on a clear day? What is the luminous flux entering the room?

Problem 20. Compare the luminous efficacies of the radiations from the various mercury-vapor lamps of Tables III and IV.

3.06. Reflection Factor and Transmission Factor.—If homogeneous radiation (say, from a single distant source) is incident upon a surface, the irradiation may be measured and expressed in watts per square centimeter. Some of the radiant power reaching the surface is reflected. If the surface is glossy, most of the reflected power will be confined to a narrow beam; but if the surface is matt, the radiant power will be distributed in all directions. In any case, we can measure the total radiant power emanating in all directions from one square centimeter of surface, and this is equal to the *radiosity* of the surface. The ratio of the radiosity and the irradiation may be termed the *spectral reflection factor* ρ_λ for radiation of the particular wavelength λ_i used in the measurements. Thus,

$$\rho_\lambda = \frac{\text{reflected radiant power of wavelength } \lambda_i}{\text{incident radiant power of wavelength } \lambda_i} = \left(\frac{J}{G}\right)_{\lambda \,=\, \lambda_i}$$
$$\text{(numeric)} \quad (3.08)$$

---

* Note that this value is a function of the radiation alone and says nothing whatever about the over-all efficacy of the firefly as a light-producing device.

Generally, the spectral reflection factor is found to be a function of wavelength and to be vastly different for different materials. The spectral reflection factor of gold foil (Fig. 3.06b), for instance, is uniformly high in the infrared but decreases rapidly in the visible region so that little blue or violet light is reflected. This

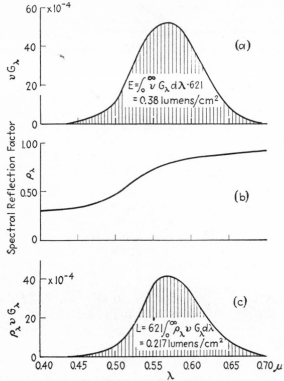

Fig. 3.06 —Reflection from gold foil. The foil is irradiated by a tungsten lamp. Operating temperature of filament is 2958°K.

gives the characteristic golden color. Knowing the spectral reflection factor curve for any surface and the spectral irradiation curve, we can easily obtain from Eq (3.08) the spectral radiosity curve showing how much radiant power is reflected in each wavelength band.

If we are working with photometric quantities, it is convenient to use a single number representing the reflecting characteristic of a surface rather than to use the whole spectral reflection factor curve. The *reflection factor* ρ is such a number, defined by the relation

$$\rho = \frac{\text{total reflected luminous flux}}{\text{total incident luminous flux}} = \frac{L}{E} \quad \text{(numeric)} \quad (3.09)$$

But

$$L = \int_0^\infty \rho_\lambda v G_\lambda \, d\lambda$$

so Eq. (3.09) may be written equally well as

$$\rho = \frac{\int_0^\infty \rho_\lambda v G_\lambda \, d\lambda}{\int_0^\infty v G_\lambda \, d\lambda} \quad \text{(numeric)} \quad (3.10)$$

The reflection factor of a surface gives a convenient way of obtaining the luminosity of the surface if the illumination is known, for, according to Eq. (3.09),

$$L = \rho E$$

One must remember, however, that *the reflection factor of a given surface is a constant only for a given type of radiation* and may be entirely different with another radiation. A red surface, for instance, may have a reflection factor of 0.40 with radiation from a certain incandescent lamp; but will generally be somewhat different when other lamps operating at different temperatures are used, while with the radiation from a mercury-vapor lamp it may appear black and have a reflection factor of perhaps 0.05.

Example. Figure 3.06*a*, for example, shows the irradiation of a gold-foil surface due to an incandescent lamp operating at 2958°K. The area under the curve gives the illumination $E = 0.38$ lumen/sq cm. Multiplying the ordinates of (*a*) by the corresponding ordinates of (*b*) gives the curve (*c*), which shows the character of the radiation *reflected from the gold foil.* The reflected radiation is somewhat redder than the incident radiation. Also the area under the $\rho_\lambda v G_\lambda$ curve is found to be less than that under the original curve. The reflection factor is equal to the ratio of the two areas, or

$$\rho = \frac{0.217}{0.38} = 0.57$$

which of course applies only to the particular kind of spectral energy distribution used.

A similar procedure may be used with transmitting surfaces. Homogeneous radiation is incident upon a piece of glass or other transparent or translucent material. Some of the incident power is reflected, some absorbed, and some transmitted. The total radiant power being transmitted divided by the radiant power incident upon the surface is called the *spectral transmission factor* for radiation of wavelength λ_i;

$$\tau_\lambda = \frac{\text{transmitted radiant power of wavelength } \lambda_i}{\text{incident radiant power of wavelength } \lambda_i} = \left(\frac{J}{G}\right)_{\lambda\,=\,\lambda_i}$$
$$\text{(numeric)} \quad (3.11)$$

Figures 3.07*a*, *b*, *c* give the spectral transmission factors of a sample of red glass, a sample of blue glass, and a sample of green glass. Figure 3.08 shows the peculiar results obtained with didymium glass.

The *transmission factor* τ may be defined as the ratio of the total luminous flux transmitted to the incident luminous flux, or

$$\tau = \frac{\text{total transmitted luminous flux}}{\text{total incident luminous flux}} = \frac{L}{E} \quad \text{(numeric)} \quad (3.12)$$

Just as with the reflection factor, the transmission factor means nothing unless the radiation with which τ was obtained is completely specified within the visible region.

The illuminating engineer has used F, L, and E (or similar quantities) in his measurements and calculations and has completely forgotten in many cases the corresponding radiation quantities which are really more fundamental. The specification of a given radiation requires, in general, not one number but the whole spectral distribution curve; and the calculation of the visual effect of the radiant power after it has been transmitted through glasses and reflected by walls and ceiling requires, in general, a consideration of the complete radiation curve at each step in this process, since each such transmission or reflection generally changes the spectral distribution of the radiant energy. In the special case where all transmitting and reflecting media are nonselective (white or neutral gray), however, it is permissible to specify the radiation by a single number which represents its luminous value and to make all calculations in terms of this quantity. This procedure effects such a great simplification

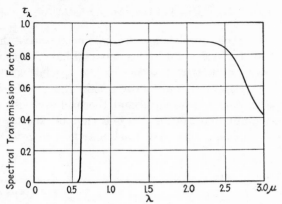

FIG. 3.07a.—Spectral transmission factor of Jena glass RG 2, 2 mm. thick. *(From Schott and Gen., Liste 4777.)*

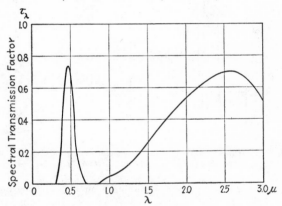

FIG. 3.07b.—Spectral transmission factor of Jena glass BG 7, 1 mm. thick. *(From Schott and Gen., Liste 4777.)*

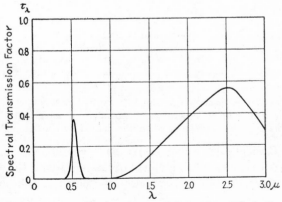

FIG. 3.07c.—Spectral transmission factor of Jena glass VG 2, 2 mm thick. *(From Schott and Gen., Liste 4777.)*

over the use of the complete spectroradiometric curve that most illuminating engineers use it exclusively and have, as a matter of fact, forgotten even that (except for the special case of non-selective materials) it is only an approximation. The ignoring of the spectroradiometric curve and the exclusive use of F, L, and E in illumination calculations is a valuable short cut which is legitimate in some cases but which may lead to gross errors in others.

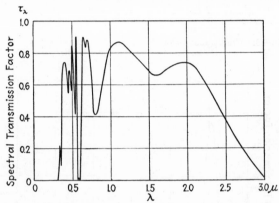

Fig. 3.08.—Spectral transmission factor of Jena glass BG 11, 8 mm thick. (*From Schott and Gen., Liste* 4777.)

Problem 21. An opaque screen having a circular opening one inch in diameter is placed some distance from a 110-volt quartz mercury-vapor lamp, and measurements show that between 0.40 and 0.70μ the radiant power passing through the opening is 0.46×10^{-3} watt. What is the illumination of the screen?

The blue glass of Fig. 3.07b is placed over the opening. How many lumens now pass through the circular aperture?

Problem 22. A cadmium-vapor lamp illuminates a room. Measurements show that at a certain spot on the table top the illumination is 23.1 lumens/sq ft. What is the irradiation (between 0.4 and 0.7μ) of the table top at that point?

Problem 23. A macadam pavement reflects 4 per cent of the radiant power which falls on it, practically independent of wavelength. What is the luminosity of the pavement when illuminated by noon sunlight?

3.07. Critical Discussion.*—We have considered the spectro-radiometric curve and a method of obtaining from it the effectiveness of the radiation in producing photoelectric, photographic,

* May be omitted in an introductory course.

erythemal, and visual effects.   All these cases have been treated
in essentially the same way.   It must be admitted, however,
that the similarity is more in the mathematical treatment than
in the phenomena themselves.   In the first place, the response
of the photocell and of the eye depends upon radiant *power*, while
the erythemal and photochemical effects depend upon radiant
energy, both power and energy being evaluated, of course, with
respect to the appropriate factors.   With the photoelectric cell,
a certain current is obtained with one watt of homogeneous
radiant power of wavelength λ_1; and since a linear relation exists
between cause and effect, 2 watts at λ_1 will produce twice the
current, and a complicated spectral distribution will produce a
current which is obtained by a summation or integration process.
If the photocell were not a linear device, however, such a method
would be inadmissible.

In the visual effect, as is well known, linearity of response is
not obtained.   Furthermore, there is no way of measuring the
sensation evoked by a given stimulus.   The measurements are
made, therefore, by a visual-comparison method which consists
essentially in comparing a fixed stimulus with a homogeneous
one of variable wavelength and variable magnitude.   A number
of values of λ are used, and at each the magnitude of the variable
homogeneous stimulus is adjusted by the observer to give
equality of magnitude of sensation with that caused by the fixed
stimulus.   The ordinates of the visibility curves are inversely
proportional to the amount of radiant power required for this
balance.   The visibility function, then, applies only to the cause;
and an integration process is assumed to be permissible as in the
other cases.   The visibility data apply under certain standard
conditions, and results computed using the v-function will not
agree with results obtained by visual comparison if the conditions
of the latter measurements are markedly different from those
used in obtaining the original visibility data.   For instance, at
very low illuminations the whole visibility curve shifts toward
the shorter wavelengths (see Chap. XII), and results obtained
by use of the standard visibility curve are not even an approximation.   At high illuminations it seems likely that the standard
data are also inapplicable, though no definite information appears
to be available.   The results are also affected by the size of the
photometric field, the illumination of the surroundings, etc.

Evidently, in using the standard visibility function we do not, in some mysterious way, evaluate the radiant energy uniquely in regard to its capacity to evoke a visual sensation. We arbitrarily select a certain standard curve (Fig. 3.02), realizing that we might have selected equally well any one of a dozen or more other curves. "Seeing" is too complex a thing to allow a single visibility curve to specify exactly all conditions.

Exactly what is the value of the mathematical process which we have outlined in this chapter? Evidently, it lies in a certain simplification of the specification of radiation and in giving us indices by which the value of a given spectral distribution of radiant power can be conveniently specified. Radiant power requires for its specification, in general, a complete spectral distribution curve or a table of perhaps 30 ordinates.* Unless all this information is available, we shall not be able to calculate the magnitude of the various effects of the radiation, nor shall we be able to determine the amount that will be transmitted or reflected by selective media.

For any given result of the radiation, however, such complete information is unnecessary. If we are interested only in the photoelectric current from a given cell, for instance, we need specify merely a single number—the amperes per watt per square centimeter for the given spectral distribution—to be able to determine the photoelectric current for any given irradiation having this type of spectral distribution. Similarly, the specifications of a single number—the luminosity, for instance—give information on the ability of the radiation to evoke a visual sensation under certain standard conditions. Since the illuminating engineer is frequently interested in the visual effect alone, his use of luminous flux rather than radiant flux eliminates in many cases the necessity of knowing and specifying the mass of information contained in the spectroradiometric curve.

To the photographic plate, "blue light" appears exactly the same as "green light" or any other type of radiant energy, except as regard the *magnitude* of its effect. Two radiations cannot be distinguished provided the integral

$$\int_0^\infty pG_\lambda \, d\lambda$$

---

* I have purposely omitted additional factors such as the angular distribution of radiant flux, the polarization of the radiation, etc.

is the same in both cases. Analogous statements can be made for the photographic effect and the erythemal effect. With the visual effect, this is no longer true, since we can distinguish not only *magnitude* differences but also differences in *quality*. A homogeneous radiation of wavelength 0.45μ evokes an entirely different sensation from one of 0.60μ, even though the "magnitudes of the sensations" are the same, *i.e.*, even though a brilliance match is obtained. It has been found that to specify a radiation with respect to its sensation-evoking ability, we must give not one number but *three*. If one number refers to magnitude, the other two may refer to *dominant wavelength* and *purity*; or other ways of specifying the quality may be used (Chap. XIII). Even such a specification by means of three numbers is much simpler than the specification of the whole spectroradiometric curve; and in many cases where a knowledge of the chromaticity of the radiation is not essential, the specification of a single number which deals with magnitude is all that is necessary. The common method of expressing all quantities in terms of luminous flux is such a simplified specification of radiation in terms of one number.

Using methods similar to those used in Chap. II, we have defined a set of photometric quantities. Corresponding to the radiometric quantity called irradiation G we have *illumination E*:

$$E = \int_0^\infty vG_\lambda \, d\lambda \tag{3.03}$$

The photometric quantity corresponding to radiosity J is *luminosity L*:

$$L = \int_0^\infty vJ_\lambda \, d\lambda \tag{3.05}$$

The photometric quantity corresponding to radiant power or radiant flux Φ is luminous flux F:

$$F = SE$$

A summary of the various concepts is given in Table XII, which also states the units used in this text. Other units in common use are noted in Appendix B.

The unit of illumination generally used in the United States is the *lumen per square foot*. It is often called by the name "foot-candle," a name that is a relic of the old days of candlelight[19]. In the nomenclature of scientific units are a number of hyphenated names such as foot-pound, watt-second, and ampere-hour. The hyphen in such names implies *multiplication:* the number of ampere-hours is equal to the number of amperes *times* the number of hours. Because of this conventional meaning of the hyphen, it seems inadvisable to use a name such as "foot-candle" where the hyphen has a quite different meaning. Also note that according to the internationally accepted definitions, the quantity E is called *illumination,* not "intensity" or "intensity of illumination." The word intensity (Appendix B) is reserved for a separate concept, and thus the term "intensity of illumination" is both redundant and ambiguous.

TABLE XII

Radiometric quantities			Photometric quantities		
Quantity	Symbol	Unit	Quantity	Symbol	Unit
Radiant energy........	U	$\begin{cases}\text{erg, watt-sec}\end{cases}$	Light	Q	$\begin{cases}\text{Lumen-sec}\\\text{Lightwatt-sec}\end{cases}$
Radiant flux.......... (radiant power)	Φ	watt	Luminous flux..	F	Lumen, lightwatt
Radiosity.............	J	$\begin{cases}\text{watt/sq cm}\\\text{watt/sq ft}\end{cases}$	Luminosity.....	L	$\begin{cases}\text{Lumen/sq cm}\\\text{Light-watt/sq cm}\\\text{Lumen/sq ft}\end{cases}$
Irradiation...........	G	$\begin{cases}\text{watt/sq cm}\\\text{watt/sq ft}\end{cases}$	Illumination....	E	$\begin{cases}\text{Lumen/sq cm}\\\text{(phot)}\\\text{Lightwatt/sq cm}\\\text{Lumen/sq ft}\end{cases}$
Spectral reflection factor	ρ_λ	Numeric	Reflection factor	ρ	Numeric
Spectral transmission factor..............	τ_λ	Numeric	Transmission factor........	τ	Numeric

Luminous efficacy $\eta_l \begin{cases}\text{lightwatts/watt}\\\text{lumens/watt}\end{cases}$ 1 lightwatt = 621 lumens

Problem 24. Criticize the following and restate in a more precise manner:

a. "It is when used with these high-powered light sources of great intrinsic brilliancy that our glassware is at its best. The construction of the glass is such that the light in passing through is broken up into an infinitesimal number of rays, producing a uniform intensity on the working plane, devoid of glare and uniform in brilliancy" (from a catalogue).

b. "That daylight may be brighter when the sun is partly hidden than when the sky is clear is shown by an automatic photographic recorder.

When the sky is covered with light clouds and the sun itself is out of view, the recorded intensity of illumination is found greater than in full sunlight in the absence of clouds" (a newspaper account).

c. "Luminous flux is visible radiation weighted according to the effectiveness of each wavelength in producing the sensation of brightness or luminosity" (*J.O.S.A.*).

d. "The Association of Railway Electrical Engineers and the American Transit Engineering Association have prescribed in their respective engineering manuals that the illumination in passenger cars shall be measured on the normal reading plane which is defined as a point on the 45-deg. plane facing the passenger 33 in. above the floor at the front middle edge of the seat. A sufficient number of measurements must be made in order to obtain a fair average of the light intensity. In the conventional railroad car where seats are transverse and arranged in pairs on each side of the aisle, it is usually sufficient to measure the lighting at half the seats on one side which constitutes one-fourth of the seating area" (*I.E.S. Trans.*).

e. "Illumination is an implicitly quantitative term referring to a supply or amount of visible radiant flux. It is here considered as synonymous with light" (*I.E.S. Trans.*).

f. "From many measurements and computations it appears that not less than 180,000 ergs of radiation of maximum erythemal effectiveness are required to produce an MPE on most untanned skins. Usually 200,000 to 300,000 ergs are required for untanned skins which have not been severely tanned for several years. At present, according to our experience and criteria, we have chosen the value of 250,000 ergs of properly weighted radiation between λ 2800 and λ 3200 as representative of the exposure necessary to produce an MPE on average untanned skin" (*J.O.S.A.*).

Bibliography

1. An Outline of Atomic Physics, Physics Staff, University of Pittsburgh, John Wiley & Sons, Inc., New York, 1933.

2. H. E. IVES: Units and Nomenclature of Radiation and Illumination, *Astrophys. J.*, **45**, 1917, p. 39.

3. H. E. IVES: The Establishment of Photometry on a Physical Basis, *Frank. Inst., J.*, **180**, 1915, p. 409.

4. E. B. ROSA: Photometric Units and Nomenclature, *I.E.S. Trans.*, **5**, 1910, p. 473.

5. HARDY and PERRIN: The Principles of Optics, McGraw-Hill Book Company, Inc., New York, 1932.

6. COBLENTZ and EMERSON: Relative Sensibility of the Average Eye to Light of Different Colors, *Bu. Stds. Bull.* **14**, 1918, p. 167.

7. GIBSON and TYNDALL: The Visibility of Radiant Energy, *Bu. Stds. Bull.*, **19**, 1923, p. 131.

8. CRITTENDEN and RICHTMYER: An "Average Eye" for Heterochromatic Photometry, *Bu. Stds Bull.*, **14**, 1918, p. 87.

9. TYNDALL and GIBSON: Visibility of Radiant Energy Equation, *J.O.S.A.*, **9**, 1924, p. 403.

10. *Proceedings* of the Commission Internationale de l'Éclairage, Geneva, 1924.

11. H. E. Ives: Note on the Least Mechanical Equivalent of Light, *J.O.S.A.*, **9**, 1924, p. 635.

12. Ives and Coblentz: The Light of the Firefly, *I.E.S. Trans.*, **4**, 1909, p. 657.

13. H. E. Ives: The Firefly as an Illuminant, *Frank. Inst., J.*, **194**, 1922, p. 212.

14. U. Dahlgren: The Production of Light by Animals, *Frank. Inst., J.*, **180**, 1915, p. 711.

15. L. T. Troland: Report on Colorimetry, *J.O.S.A.*, **6**, 1922, p. 527.

16. J. Guild: The Interpretation of Quantitative Data in Visual Problems, Discussion on Vision, 1932, Cambridge University Press, London, p. 60.

17. E. G. Boring: The Relation of the Attributes of Sensation to the Dimensions of the Stimulus, *Phil. Science*, **2**, 1935, p. 236.

18. International Photometric Units and Standards, *I.E.S. Trans.*, **27**, 1932, p. 739.

19. Illuminating Engineering Nomenclature and Photometric Standards, (Approved as Am. Std., Dec. 19, 1932) *I.E.S. Trans.*, **28**, 1933, p. 265.

20. R. A. Houstoun: Vision and Color Vision, Chap. V, Longmans, Green & Company, New York, 1932.

CHAPTER IV

RADIATION FROM GASEOUS-CONDUCTION SOURCES*

We have considered some of the characteristics of radiation of various wavelengths and how the effectiveness of radiant power in producing certain results is calculated. In this and the next two chapters, we shall turn to a study of the way in which radiation is produced and the various lamps that have been devised to emit radiation in the visible region.

Light sources are usually divided into two classes: incandescent sources and luminescent sources. By an *incandescent source* we mean one that emits light solely because of its high temperature. The tungsten lamp is an example of an incandescent radiator. The filament is heated to a temperature of from about 2400 to 3200°K, and because of the temperature it emits radiation. If the filament temperature is known, the watts radiated per square centimeter of filament surface can be accurately calculated for any band of wavelengths in the ultraviolet, visible, or infrared regions. A continuous spectrum is always produced by an incandescent source—*i.e.*, radiation is emitted at all wavelengths, as shown, for instance, in Fig. 2.05.

All sources that do not belong to the incandescent class are termed *luminescent radiators*. Thus the ordinary mercury-vapor lamp emits light whose color is a characteristic of mercury and is almost independent of the operating temperature of the lamp. Other examples of luminescent sources are the neon lamp, the sodium-vapor lamp, also the firefly, various luminous fungi, etc. Luminescent sources usually radiate only at certain definite wavelengths, though they may produce in some cases band spectra or even more or less continuous spectra. In this chapter, we shall consider the mechanism of light production from luminescent sources, and some of the lamps that use this principle, leaving the study of incandescent sources for Chap. V.

* May be omitted in an introductory course.

The treatment falls naturally into four divisions:

1. Mechanism of production of radiation in the atom.
2. Spectra.
3. Methods of excitation of spectra.
4. Gaseous-conduction lamps.

A tremendous amount of research has been done on each of the preceding topics, and in the space available here we cannot hope more than to glance at the subject. The spectroscopists and theoretical physicists have concentrated principally on (1) and (2) and have been interested in the *wavelengths* of the emitted radiation rather than in the *amount* of radiant power emitted at each wavelength. Another group has devoted a great deal of time to (3), the breakdown of gases, the nature of the discharge, and the potential distribution with various pressures, electrode spacings, etc. This group has paid very little attention to the radiation produced. A third group has worked on the development of practical lamps (4), using rule-of-thumb methods to a great extent. Only within the last few years has any attempt been made to correlate these separate fields of knowledge and to apply them to the development of new gaseous-conduction lamps. This more scientific method of attack has been remarkably successful, indicative of the still greater advances in such lamps to be expected within the next few years.

4.02. The Atom.—A knowledge of the way in which light is produced requires at least a cursory understanding of the constitution of the atom. Rutherford, as the result of his experimental work, developed a picture of the atom as a miniature solar system consisting of a very minute positively charged nucleus about which one or more electrons revolve in orbits. While it is true that the sharply defined orbits of the Rutherford-Bohr atom have been largely superseded by the methods of quantum mechanics, they remain a useful *picture* of the atom and will be used in the present treatment.

The number of electrons revolving about the nucleus is equal to the atomic number Z. It is different for each chemical element, from hydrogen $(Z = 1)$ to the heavy radioactive elements with about 90 orbital electrons. Hydrogen has a single electron and a single proton as nucleus. The second element in the periodic table is helium, with $Z = 2$.

The elements in the next group after H and He contain an inner "shell" of two orbital electrons and, in addition, from one to eight electrons in an outer shell. Two electrons form a complete inner shell, eight electrons complete the second shell, eight complete the third shell, and so on. The chemist finds that only electrons in the outermost shell take part in chemical combina-

TABLE XIII.—IONIZATION DATA FOR VARIOUS ATOMS
(DUSHMAN, *Elect. Engineering*, **53**, 1934, p. 1208)

Atom	λ_r	V_r	V_i	V_m
Li	0.6708	1.84	5.37	None
Na	$\begin{cases}0.5890\\0.5896\end{cases}$	2.10	5.12	None
K	$\begin{cases}0.7645\\0.7699\end{cases}$	1.60	4.32	None
Rb	$\begin{cases}0.7800\\0.7948\end{cases}$	1.56	4.16	None
Cs	$\begin{cases}0.8521\\0.8943\end{cases}$	1.38 1.45	3.87	None
He	$\begin{cases}0.0592\\0.0584\end{cases}$	20.91 21.12	24.47	19.77 20.55
Ne	$\begin{cases}0.0744\\0.0736\end{cases}$	16.58 16.77	21.47	16.53 16.62
A	$\begin{cases}0.1067\\0.1048\end{cases}$	11.56 11.77	15.69	11.49 11.66
Kr	$\begin{cases}0.1236\\0.1165\end{cases}$	9.98 10.59	13.94	9.86 10.51
Xe	$\begin{cases}0.1469\\0.1295\end{cases}$	8.39 9.52	12.08	8.28 9.40
Zn	$\begin{cases}0.3076\\0.2139\end{cases}$	4.01 5.77	9.36	3.99 4.06
Cd	$\begin{cases}0.3261\\0.2288\end{cases}$	3.78 5.39	8.96	3.71 3.93
Hg	$\begin{cases}0.2537\\0.1850\end{cases}$	4.87 6.67	10.38	4.64 5.44
Tl	$\begin{cases}0.3776\\0.2768\end{cases}$	3.27 4.46	6.07	0.96

λ_r = wavelength of resonance radiation (microns).
V_r = resonance potential (volts).
V_i = ionization potential (volts).
V_m = potential corresponding to metastable levels (volts).

tion.   These electrons are often called valence electrons.   Thus
one might expect atoms to be chemically inert if the outer shell
has its full quota of electrons.   Examples are the helium, neon,
and argon atoms.   Similarly, it might be expected that atoms
containing only one electron in the outer shell, such as H, Li, Na,
would lose or gain an electron easily and would be chemically
active.   Such a condition is shown by the values of ionization
potential V_i (Table XIII), which are low for atoms with few
electrons in the outermost shell and high for atoms with complete shells.   As we shall see, the valence electrons are responsible for the production of radiation in the visible region, and
thus these electrons in the outermost orbits are of particular
interest to the illuminating engineer.

4.03. Radiation from an Atom.—But how does such an atom
radiate energy?   According to the classical theory of electromagnetic radiation, each atom should act continuously as a
radiator of electromagnetic waves.   The movement of the
electrons about the nucleus should be essentially the same as the
movement of electrons in a radiotelephone antenna and should
send out waves just as the antenna does but of shorter wavelength because of the smaller dimensions.   But if an atom continuously dissipates its energy in the form of electromagnetic
radiation, it must eventually lose its original energy, and the
electron must fall into the nucleus.   According to classical
mechanics, as the energy decreases the wavelength of the emitted
radiation must change.   But such a phenomenon has not been
observed.

Evidently, this constitutes a case where it is inadmissible to
carry over our large-scale macroscopic concepts to atomic dimensions.   We must abandon our ordinary "common-sense" laws
and postulate new ones which will fit the experimental facts.
Such was the procedure of Niels Bohr in 1913.   According to
Bohr, each orbital electron in an atom normally follows a certain
definite orbit, and while in this orbit *it does not radiate*.   Besides
this stable orbit, there is a large number of other definite orbits
possible for the electron.   Each of these possible orbits is called
a stationary orbit.   The energy of the atom is constant as long
as the electron stays in a given stationary orbit, and the atom is
said to be in a *stationary state*.   Radiation is produced only when
an electron falls from an outer stationary orbit to one nearer the

nucleus.   Each time such a transition occurs, a single quantum of radiation is emitted.   Thus the radiation from an atom is not continuous, by any means, but consists of an occasional quantum which is ejected when a valence electron slips from one stationary orbit to another.   In all ordinary cases in practice, we deal with such immense numbers of atoms that the radiation seems to be continuous in time though the individual atoms emit only in discrete quanta.

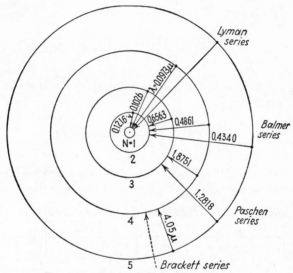

FIG. 4.01.—Origin of the hydrogen spectrum.

When the electron is in the ordinary stable orbit the atom is said to be in the *normal state*, and when the electron is in any of the other orbits the atom is said to be in an *excited state*.   To put an atom in the excited state requires that energy be added to the atom in some way, such as by collision with an electron having a reasonably high velocity or by absorption of energy from radiation.   In any case, the atom stays in the excited state a very short time (approximately 10^{-8} sec) and then reverts to the normal state with concomitant emission of radiation.

Figure 4.01 shows the simplest of all atoms.   In the normal state, the single electron of the hydrogen atom is in the circular orbit marked $n = 1$.   It may also be in the excited orbits $(n = 2, 3, \cdots)$ though it does not remain there long.

For atomic hydrogen the wavelengths of all spectral lines are given by the expression

$$\lambda = 0.0912\left[\frac{i^2 j^2}{j^2 - i^2}\right] \quad \text{(microns)} \tag{4.01}$$

where i and j are the values of n for the two orbits concerned in the transition.

If the electron falls from the second orbit to the first, for instance, a photon will be emitted, and

$$\lambda = 0.0912\left[\frac{(1)^2(2)^2}{(2)^2 - (1)^2}\right] = 0.1216\mu$$

In fact, a whole series of lines is emitted by electrons falling to the first orbit:

$$\lambda = 0.0912\left[\frac{j^2}{j^2 - 1}\right] \quad \text{(microns)} \tag{4.01a}$$

These lines constitute what is known as the *Lyman series*. The lines are all in the ultraviolet, as shown in Fig. 4.01.

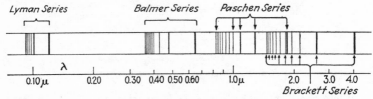

FIG. 4.02.—Spectrum of atomic hydrogen.

But it is not necessary that the electron always fall immediately to the first orbit—it may dally by the way, stopping for fleeting visits at several intermediate orbits before finally arriving home at $n = 1$. Evidently, another series of wavelengths will be produced when the electron falls from some outer orbit to the second. These lines constitute the *Balmer series* which is largely in the visible region. Other series are produced in the infrared, as shown in Fig. 4.01. The complete spectrum of atomic hydrogen is shown in Fig. 4.02, and is seen to consist of a number of separate series having intense lines far apart at the longer wavelength part and weak lines close together in the shorter-wave-

length part of each series.* The wavelengths of all of these
lines may be calculated by Eq. (4.01).

4.04. The Excitation of Atoms.—We have considered the fact
that normally the atoms are unexcited and the electrons are in
the most stable orbits. Evidently, any process that will add
energy to the valence electrons and will thus raise them to orbits
of higher energy level will allow the production of radiation.
Various chemical, thermal, and electrical processes produce such
changes and thus may act as agents for the production of light.

Perhaps the most elegant method of producing spectra is shown
schematically in Fig. 4.03. A glass tube containing a filament
F, grid G, and plate P is filled with the gas whose spectrum is

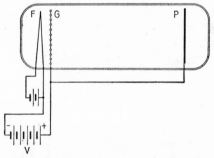

Fig. 4.03.—Three-electrode gaseous-discharge lamp.

desired. The heated filament F acts as a source of electrons
which are accelerated across the space between F and G owing to
the voltage V. Most of the electrons pass through the grid and
continue toward P with constant velocity until they collide with
atoms of the gas. The distance between F and G is made
small compared with that between G and P so that the probability
of a collision between F and G is small.

If, now, a low voltage be applied to the grid, no radiation is
produced. The electrons collide with gas molecules, it is true,
but their energy is insufficient to knock valence electrons into
outer orbits, and the collisions are elastic like the collisions of two
perfect billiard balls. If the voltage V is gradually raised, however, a critical value V_r is reached at which the atoms of the gas
suddenly begin to radiate. This value is called the *first resonance*

* In this, as in succeeding diagrams, the width of line is merely a conventional method of indicating the relative intensity.

potential of the gas, and at this voltage the electrons leaving G have energy just sufficient to knock orbital electrons from the first to the second stationary orbit. In spontaneously falling

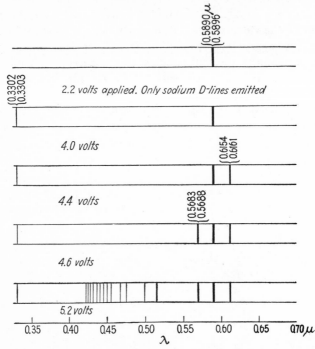

FIG. 4.04.—Controlled spectrum of sodium.[9]

back from the second to the first orbit, the absorbed energy is emitted as a photon of frequency ν:

$$\nu = \frac{1}{h}(W_2 - W_1) \tag{4.02}$$

where h = Planck's constant.

W_2, W_1 = the values of energy associated with the two orbits.

Thus radiation of a single frequency is emitted—*a single-line spectrum is produced.*

If the potential of the grid is raised still higher, other lines make their appearance, until at a potential V_i—the *ionizing potential*—the *complete arc spectrum* is produced. In the case of ionization, the bombarding electrons have sufficient energy to knock valence electrons completely out of the atom, and when these electrons are captured by other ionized atoms they are capable of producing a considerable number of spectral lines. Still higher voltages may give the *enhanced spectrum* or *spark spectrum;* but since most of the lines of the spark spectrum are in the ultraviolet, they need not concern us here.

Some results obtained experimentally with the apparatus of Fig. 4.03 using sodium vapor are shown in Fig. 4.04. No radiation is produced below about 2.2 volts. With $V = 2.2$, however, the simple spectrum shown at the top of the figure is obtained. With sodium, it happens that a doublet (the well-known sodium *D*-lines of wavelengths 0.5890 and 0.5896μ) is produced instead of a single line. As the voltage is raised, the lines next to appear are in the infrared. The photographic plate was incapable of recording these infrared lines, however, so the next lines actually obtained in the experiment were in the ultraviolet at $V = 4.0$ volts. At still higher voltages other lines appeared as shown, until at 5.2 volts the complete arc spectrum was obtained. Such results have been obtained on a number of gases and vapors and are in excellent agreement with theory.

4.05. The Energy-level Diagram.—Figure 4.01 shows the various circular orbits of the hydrogen atom and indicates graphically the wavelengths at which radiation is produced when the electron falls from one orbit to another. Evidently, it is unnecessary to use the entire circle for this purpose: a small piece would be equally advantageous. Such a diagram is given in Fig. 4.05 and shows the various orbits or energy levels as horizontal lines. The energy levels may be expressed in ergs or they may be given in volts—the potential difference through which an electron would have to fall in order to acquire this energy.

We have considered the production of radiation from the hydrogen atom and have found that the wavelengths can be represented by the simple formula of Eq. (4.01). This equation *applies only to the spectrum of atomic hydrogen.* Other atoms are more complex in structure and generally produce more complex spectra.

Figure 4.06 gives the spectrum and the energy-level diagram of lithium vapor. This diagram might have been drawn like Fig. 4.05, but evidently such a procedure would produce in this case

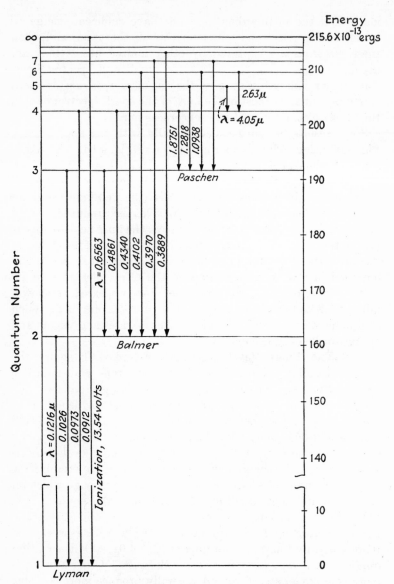

Fɪɢ. 4.05.—Energy-level diagram for atomic hydrogen.

a somewhat complicated assembly of lines.   Spectroscopists have
found that the results are clarified by dividing the energy levels
into four groups which have been arbitrarily designated as S, P,
D, and F.   A further rule, found by experiment, is that transi-

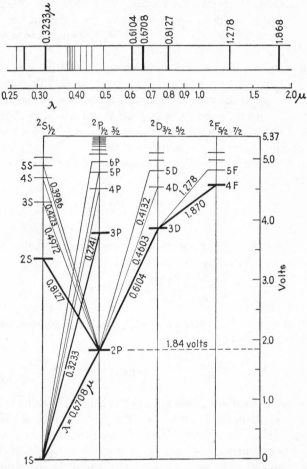

Fig. 4.06.—Spectrum and energy-level diagram for lithium.

tions occur only between adjacent columns of the diagram.   That
is, the valence electron is normally in the $1S$ level from which it
can be knocked to the $2P$, $3P$, $4P$, . . . levels but not to any of
the D or F levels.   If, however, the electron is at the $2P$ level, it
may go to the S or D levels but not to the P or F levels.   With

lithium vapor in the lamp of Fig. 4.03, evidently no radiation can be expected below 1.84 volts, at which value (according to Fig. 4.06) a single line of deep-red hue ($\lambda = 0.6708\mu$) is produced. When V is raised to about 3.4 volts, another line ($\lambda = 0.8127\mu$) in the infrared is produced. At about 3.9 volts, two other lines suddenly appear, one in the visible and the other in the ultra-violet. Ionization occurs at 5.37 volts. The complete spectrum of lithium is shown at the top of the figure. In both spectrum and energy-level diagrams, some idea of the relative intensity of the lines is given by the width of the printed lines. The strongest line in the spectrum is at 0.6708μ which shows that the lithium-vapor lamp would produce a red light and would probably be very useful and effective for that purpose, though it has not been made commercially up to the present time.

In any atomic spectrum the wavelength of any line is given by the relation*

$$\lambda = \frac{1.2336}{V_d} \quad \text{(microns)} \qquad (4.02a)$$

where V_d = the difference in the two energy levels (volts). Thus if $V_d = 1.84$ volts,

$$\lambda = \frac{1.2336}{1.84} = 0.67\mu$$

Or, for instance, the voltage required to allow the production of radiation at 0.6104μ is

$$1.84 + V_d = 1.84 + \frac{1.2336}{0.6104} = 3.86 \text{ volts}$$

Another element of the same family as lithium is sodium, whose energy-level diagram is shown in Fig. 4.07. Here we have a slight additional complexity, for this interesting material has two sets of P levels instead of one. Otherwise the diagram is similar to the one for lithium. Though the complete spectrum for sodium contains a large number of lines, the yellow doublet (0.5890μ, 0.5896μ) is so strong that the color of the light pro-

---

* Obtained very simply from Eq. (4.02). Note that the value of the constant is based on the 1929 values of Birge. In a more recent note (*Phys. Rev.*, **48**, 1935, p. 918) he gives slightly different values which may be preferable.

duced by the sodium lamp is a bright yellow.   The sodium lamp
is a recent development and is coming into use for the lighting of
highways and for other uses where its distinctive color is a
possible advantage.   Potassium gives a diagram almost identical

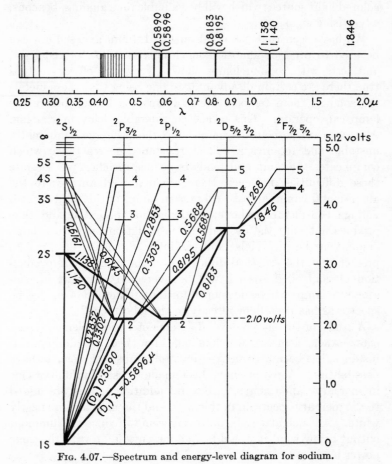

Fig. 4.07.—Spectrum and energy-level diagram for sodium.

with Fig. 4.07 except that the $1S - 2P$ lines are in the near
infrared.   The other alkali metals have similar spectra, as indicated in Table XIII.

4.06. Other Gases and Vapors.—Though great advances have
been made in recent years in the development of gaseous-conduction light sources, the commercial lamps are still confined largely

to the use of neon, mercury, and sodium. Evidently there is a tremendous field for further development, and it seems likely that the use of other gases or vapors will lead to more effective light production or will provide at least a great variety of brightly colored light sources which will be valuable for signaling, beacons, advertising signs, etc.

We have seen that the alkali metals lithium and sodium can be used to produce almost monochromatic yellow or red light, and tests with sodium lamps show a very high efficacy. It is true there are certain disadvantages, one being that these metals are solid at room temperature and must be heated before the lamp can operate. This means considerable delay in starting. Also, as in any gaseous-discharge lamp, the discharge is inherently unstable and requires a ballast resistance or reactance which complicates the lamp and tends to reduce its efficacy. Despite these difficulties, however, there are many advantages to the alkali-metal vapor lamps. All present lamps of this kind apply a voltage considerably above the ionization potential and thus produce not only the desired visible radiation but also a large amount in the ultraviolet and the infrared. Is it too much to predict that the practical difficulties of the commercial production of controlled spectra will be overcome and that in consequence lamps will be developed for the production of single-line spectra as has been done already in the laboratory?

A study of the energy-level diagrams of various elements may show other elements which should be tried. Cadmium, for instance, has been used in experimental lamps and seems to have possibilities. Attempts have been made to use cadmium or zinc in mercury-vapor lamps.[33] Several additional lines are added to the mercury spectrum in this way, and the light is more nearly white. All such attempts, however, seem to reduce the luminous output below what it would be in a mercury lamp with the same power input.

Another interesting element is thallium, whose energy-level diagram is shown in Fig. 4.08. The spectrum looks somewhat promising because of its strong green line at 0.535μ which is very near the maximum of the visibility curve for the human eye. Whether such a lamp could be made highly effective is impossible to say from existing data, since there is a large number of lines in the spectrum, including some strong ones in both infrared and ultraviolet. In any case, however, the lamp might be used (with a filter if necessary) as a source of pure green light.

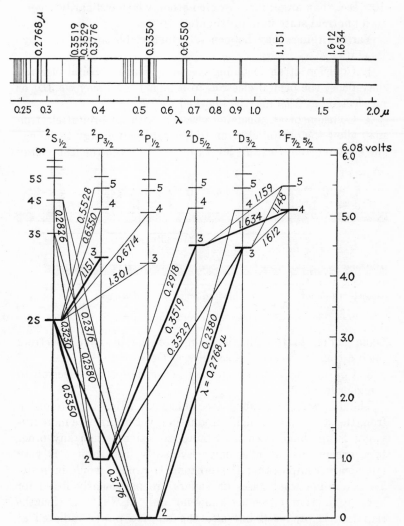

Fig. 4.08.—Spectrum and energy-level diagram for thallium.

Figure 4.09 gives the data for mercury. One of the interesting features is the absence of any apparent way of getting out of the 2^3P_2 and 2^3P_0 levels. These are called *metastable* levels, and the probability of an electron's making the transition from them to

1S is extremely small, though not zero. Experiment shows that a metastable atom remains in that state much longer (perhaps 10^{-3} sec) than an ordinary excited atom, which ordinarily reverts to its normal state in approximately 10^{-8} sec.

Various things may happen to a metastable atom to change its state:

1. Collision of an incoming electron with an orbital electron may boost the orbital electron to a higher level such as $3D$; or an electron at 2^3P_0 may be knocked to 2^3P_1.

2. Collision of an incoming electron with an orbital electron may allow the orbital electron to *lose* sufficient energy to change the electron from the 2^3P_2 level to the 2^3P_1 level, the lost energy

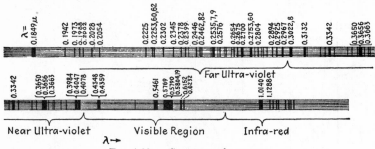

Fig. 4.09a.—Spectrum of mercury.

being added to the kinetic energy of the incoming electron. Such a collision is called a *collision of the second kind*.

3. Collision with a photon may boost the orbital electron to a higher level.

The diagram (Fig. 4.09b) does not look particularly promising from the standpoint of light production, yet in practice mercury-vapor lamps have been used more extensively than any other type except the incandescent. Evidently, the subject is very much more complex than the foregoing treatment would indicate. To determine what gases or vapors are particularly fitted for light production, one must know not only at what wavelengths radiation is produced but also the relative power radiated at each wavelength. The radiated power, for a given line, is directly proportional to the number of transitions occurring per second between the two levels considered; and this, in turn, depends upon the product of the number of bombarding electrons per second and the number of atoms present in the lower of

the two energy states. Conditions are further complicated by
the fact that an excited atom may be excited to a higher state

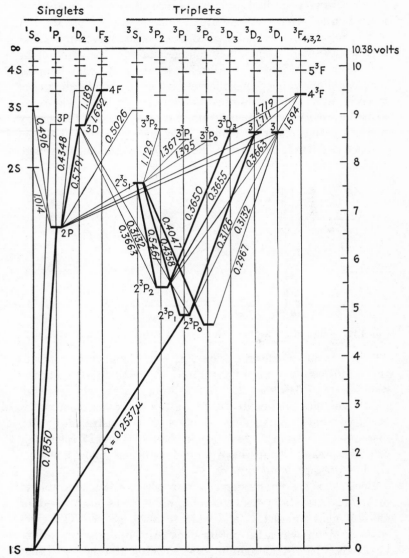

FIG. 4.09*b*.—Energy-level diagram for mercury.

by a collision with an electron or a photon of the proper energy.
Most materials, with the exception of the alkali metals, have

metastable levels which introduce additional complications. Since the life of a metastable atom is immensely longer than that of an ordinary excited atom, the probability of cumulative ionization is correspondingly greater for the metastable atom.

The relative power radiated at the various wavelengths also depends to some extent upon voltage and upon pressure of the gas or vapor. Figure 4.10, for instance, shows what happens with cadmium vapor when the velocity of the bombarding electrons is varied. Here the relative radiosity for the three prominent lines of the visible spectrum is plotted against the energy of the exciting electrons expressed in volts. With V between about 6 and 8 volts, the green line at 0.5086μ is strongly excited.

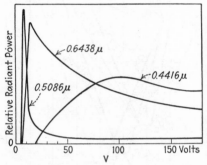

FIG. 4.10.—Effect of accelerating voltage on the visible spectrum of cadmium.[22]

This line is due to the transition $2^3S_1 - 2^3P_2$ and corresponds to the 0.5461μ line of mercury. From about 10 to 40 volts the red line ($\lambda = 0.6438\mu$, $3^1D_2 - 2^1P_1$) dominates, while at still higher voltages the line at 0.4416μ of the spark spectrum makes the color blue. The effect of pressure is illustrated by the mercury-vapor lamps. As shown in Tables III and IV (page 25), the high-pressure lamps have a much stronger yellow line than the low-pressure lamps.

Because of the complexity of the problem, it is inadvisable to make dogmatic statements regarding which gases can be used for efficient light production and which cannot. Table XIV gives some luminous efficacies obtained experimentally with various materials. Note that sodium is far ahead of all others and that the only others with reasonably high efficacies are neon and mercury. It seems not improbable, however, that further research and the development of an improved technique in the excitation of spectra will allow many other gases and vapors to be used with high efficacy.

Table XIV.—Luminous Efficacy

Obtained experimentally with various electrically excited gases and vapors.
Other experimental data may be decidedly different (both efficacy and color) owing to difference in voltage, pressure, etc.
(From H. E. Ives, Int. Crit. Tables, **5**, p. 437)

Gas or Vapor	Color	η_l, lumens per radiated watt
Argon	Red	0.24
Bromine	Blue-white	0.06
Cadmium	Blue-white	1.6
Chlorine	Blue	0.08
Caesium	Blue-white	<0.4
Hydrogen	Red	0.08
Helium	White	4.4
Mercury	Blue-green	11
	Blue-white	126
Iodine	White	1.1
Potassium	Purple	1.8
Nitrogen	Yellow-orange	1.6
Sodium	Yellow	214
Neon	Red-orange	23
Oxygen	Blue-white	0.05
Rubidium	Red	0.24
Sulphur	Blue-white	0.89
Thallium	Green-white	0.08

We have considered the production of radiation from atoms such as neon, atomic hydrogen, etc. But we need not confine ourselves to atomic gases. Hydrogen, for instance, under ordinary conditions occurs in the molecular form H_2 and gives not only the spectrum previously noted but also an additional spectrum which may be thought of as due to the motion of the two atoms in the molecule. The spectra of polyatomic molecules consist of bands of great numbers of lines very close together and may even be continuous over a limited range. A curve of the relative energy emitted in various wavelength bands from a carbon dioxide lamp is shown in Fig. 4.11, which gives some idea of the complexity of such a spectrum. Because of the almost continuous nature of its spectrum, the CO_2 lamp has been used commercially as a substitute for daylight in color matching. TiCl₄ and ZrCl₄ have also been used to some extent for the same purpose.[26]

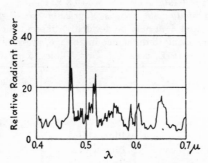

Fig. 4.11.—Spectroradiometric curve for the CO_2 lamp.[26]

4.07. Discharge in a Gas at Low Pressure.—When an electric current flows between two electrodes in a gas at approximately 1 mm pressure, the phenomena of Fig. 4.12 are often obtained.

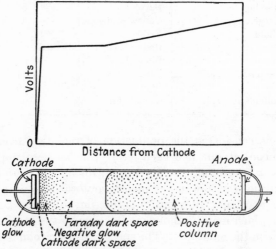

Fig. 4.12.—Electrical discharge in a gas at low pressure.

Very close to the cathode is the *cathode glow*, followed by the *cathode dark space* and a bright region of some extent called the *negative glow*. Beyond this are the *Faraday dark space* and the luminous *positive column*. Electrons from the cathode are accelerated in a short distance, which explains the high potential gradient in the space near the cathode. A much lower but constant potential gradient is found in the positive column.

The boundaries of Fig. 4.12 can be moved about by changing the pressure. A decrease in pressure causes the cathode dark space to expand until it can be made to fill the whole tube. An increase in pressure causes the positive column to expand. In many of the commercial lamps, the positive column fills almost the whole tube.

If the cathode is heated so that it gives an adequate supply of electrons, the voltage drop at the cathode is low—approximately equal to V_i. Owing to cumulative ionization, results may be obtained even with the cathode drop less than V_i but greater than V_r. Thus hot-cathode lamps, such as the sodium lamp and the mercury-vapor lamp using a mercury pool, are essentially low-voltage devices. They may be grouped, according to the relative dimensions of the tube, as

1. Cathodic lamps.
2. Positive-column lamps.

Cathodic lamps are so short that the positive column is practically absent. An example is the 4000-lumen sodium lamp. Positive-column lamps have tubes that are long compared with their diameter (6000 and 10,000-lumen sodium lamps, hot-cathode neon lamp, etc.)

It might be expected that any hot-cathode lamp would start immediately upon the application of a voltage somewhat above V_i, assuming that the cathode is emitting electrons. With short spacing (cathodic type), starting does occur under these conditions, but this is not true with the positive-column type. Charges on the glass walls of the tube generally prevent starting at low voltage. A high-voltage kick may be employed to initiate ionization, or some form of starting electrode may be used.

Cold-cathode lamps are still used extensively in the familiar advertising signs. In such lamps, the voltage drop at the cathode must be greatly increased, to perhaps ten times V_i. This high drop accelerates the positive ions toward the cathode and gives them sufficient kinetic energy so that when they bombard the cathode they liberate electrons. To minimize the effect of the large power loss at the cathode, a long lamp is necessary, and in consequence high voltage is required. The bombardment of the cathode also causes its gradual disintegration, with consequent blackening of the tube; and there is a tendency for "cleanup" of the gas and resulting reduction in the life of the lamp.

4.08. Hot-cathode Lamps.—We have considered how controlled spectra may be produced in a three-electrode tube owing to the bombardment of neutral gas molecules by electrons emitted by a heated filament. Such lamps have been used in the laboratory in the study of spectra but have not entered the commercial lighting field. The two-electrode hot-cathode lamp is coming into extensive use, however. Figure 4.13 gives a schematic diagram of such a lamp for use on direct current. A filament F emits electrons which are accelerated toward the plate P by the electric field. The speed of such electrons continues to increase until they reach P or collide with an atom of the gas which fills the tube. Evidently, conditions are not so accurately controlled as in Fig. 4.03, since here instead of an ordered array of electrons going at the same speed we have collisions occurring at all velocities. A sufficiently high voltage is used so that most of the collisions will ionize the atom, and the spectrum will consist of a large number of lines. A series resistance must be used to limit the current through the lamp.

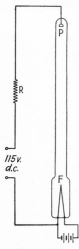

FIG. 4.13.—Schematic diagram of a hot-cathode lamp.

The lamp could be started by merely closing the line switch if the distance between P and F were small enough. As shown, however, charges on the glass tube prevent starting and require the momentary application of a high voltage.

A hot-cathode neon lamp for use on alternating current is similar to the lamp of Fig. 4.13. The cathode consists of an oxide-coated cylinder heated to a dull red by an internal filament. Since current can flow in only one direction, two anodes are used, connected to the two ends of the transformer secondary. Starting is accomplished by the momentary application of a high voltage obtained by the sudden break of an inductive circuit. The tube is filled with neon gas at low pressure, which produces light of a characteristic orange-red color. The distribution of energy in the spectrum of one of these lamps is shown in Fig. 4.14 where only the most important lines have been measured. It will be noted that a slight amount of power is radiated in the green but that by far the greatest part is in the orange and red regions. Test data on the lamp are given in Table XV.

Hot-cathode lamps are not limited to the use of neon. Other gases, such as helium and argon, may be used, and very successful lamps of this type have been made using mercury vapor. Other

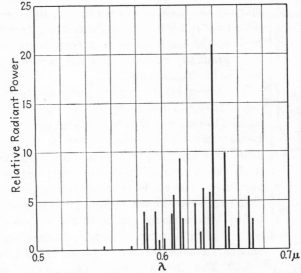

Fig. 4.14.—Relative radiant power in 22 of the strongest lines in the visible spectrum of a hot-cathode neon lamp.[36]

metallic vapors may also be used, though some provision must be made for melting the metal before the lamp will operate. One scheme is to fill the lamp with argon or other inert gas. The discharge starts in this gas, and the temperature of the lamp gradually rises until sufficient metallic vapor is present to conduct the current. Because of the low ionization potential of the vapors used, the metallic vapors will carry nearly all the current, and the spectrum of the inert gas will practically disappear. A sodium-vapor lamp is shown in Fig. 4.15. An inner bulb of special glass contains the sodium and the inert gas and is fitted with two filaments. This is inclosed in a larger bulb which is evacuated to prevent the escape of heat as much as possible.

Since the radiation is mostly in the yellow sodium lines, which are near the maximum of the visibility curve, the efficacy is high.

The 6000- and 10,000-lumen a-c sodium lamps produced in this country are similar to the lamp in Fig. 4.15, but the vacuum flask is a separate unit which slips over the lamp proper instead of being incorporated in it.[42] The normal operation is at about 220°C. The 10,000-lumen lamp has two filaments. The arc current is 6.6 amps, and the arc drop is approximately 25 volts. A separate starting electrode allows starting at 40 to 60 volts. The bulb is filled with neon at a pressure of 1.5 mm, so the lamp starts as a neon lamp, and the light gradually changes from red to yellow as the lamp temperature rises.

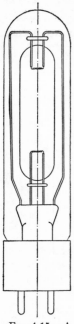

The lamps can be used in series for street lighting. They can also be operated in parallel on the usual 115-volt a-c circuits, using a special reactive transformer. The over-all power factor is 65 per cent. A relay must be used to short-circuit the arc until the filaments have reached operating temperature. The a-c lamp is highly stroboscopic.

A small 4000-lumen sodium lamp is made also in the United States. It is of the cathodic type with a bulbular form, a central filament, and two anodes. It operates on 5 amps and about 15 volts.

FIG. 4.15.—A small sodium-vapor lamp.

4.09. The Mercury-vapor Lamp.—One of the best-known lamps of the metallic-vapor type is the mercury lamp developed by Peter Cooper Hewitt. The lamp (Fig. 4.16) is made in the form of a tube of glass one inch in diameter and about 50 in. long which is exhausted of air and contains a pool of mercury at one end. It may be used on either direct or alternating current, the a-c circuit being shown in the diagram. The autotransformer T supplies the two anodes. When the lamp is connected to the line, direct current flows through the small copper-oxide rectifier r, through inductance L and the contacts of the shifter s. The magnetic field from L moves the shifter, suddenly breaking the circuit at s and applying a high voltage between the cathode and a tinfoil coating S' on the outside of the bulb. A spark passes to the mercury, vaporizes a small amount of it, and forms the cathode spot which is the source of electrons. In normal operation, the current through the lamp is a pulsating direct current sufficiently smoothed by the inductance in the circuit so that

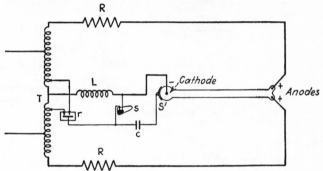

FIG. 4.16.—Circuit for a-c low-pressure mercury-vapor lamp.

the light is practically free from flicker. Table IV (page 26) gives the characteristics of the radiation, while Table XV indicates the electrical characteristics.

TABLE XV.—CHARACTERISTICS OF SEVERAL COMMERCIAL LAMPS
(BUTTOLPH, *I.E.S. Trans.*, **30**, 1935, p. 176)

Source	Auxiliary	Power factor	Watts in auxiliary	Arc current (amp)	Arc voltage	Arc length (cm)	F* lumens	Lumens per watt
Neon, cold cathode.....	Transformer	0.55	4	0.03	2050	250	5,800	14.5
Mercury, cold cathode..	Transformer	0.55	5	0.03	2300	250	1,600	3.2
Mercury............ {	Resistor	Dc	135	3.5	71	125	6,000	16.0
	Resistor, reactor	0.90	175	3.7	74	125	6,750	15.0
	Resistor, reactor	0.90	100	3.7	40	56	6,750	12.0
Neon, hot cathode.....	Resistor, reactor	0.90	200	3.5	70	46	4,950	10.0
H.P. mercury, quartz...	Resistor	Dc	250	4.0	160	15	21,600	24.0
glass................	Reactor	0.65	25	2.9	160	15	13,500	32.0
Sodium, 4,000.........	....	....	...	5.0	13	...	4,000	
6,000..............	Transformer	0.65	15	5.0	20	18	6,000	36.0
10,000.............	Transformer	0.65	25	6.6	25	23	10,000	45.0

* Without reflector.

Another form of mercury-vapor lamp operates at higher vapor pressure and higher temperature, and the tube is made of fused silica which transmits the ultraviolet (Table III, page 25). This lamp also uses a pool of mercury as the source of electrons, but the elaborate starting arrangement of Fig. 4.16 is usually omitted, and the starting is accomplished by tipping the lamp so that the mercury bridges the electrodes momentarily.

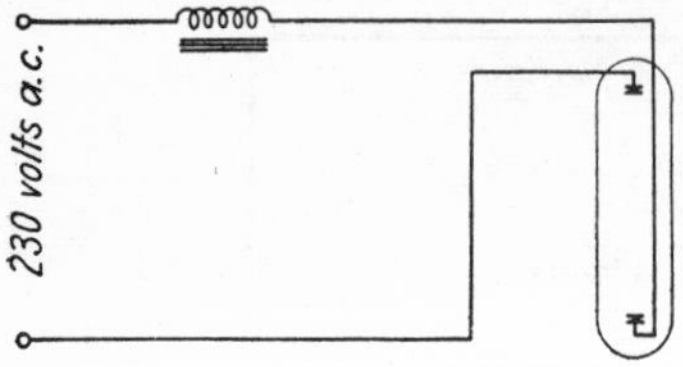

FIG. 4.17.—Circuit for the high-pressure mercury-vapor lamp.

A more recent development is a high-pressure mercury lamp in a double-glass bulb. Metal electrodes are used; the pool of mercury is dispensed with; and only a small, carefully measured drop of mercury is introduced into the lamp. In operation, the vapor pressure rises until all the mercury is vaporized, which is the normal operating condition. The over-all efficacy is high—approximately 35 lumens/watt—and the lamp is extremely simple. It screws into the ordinary mogul socket, requires no filament supply, and operates from the 230-volt a-c circuit with merely a small reactor in series (Fig. 4.17). The power factor is 65 per cent. A disadvantage is the stroboscopic effect. A still more recent development in mercury lamps is an ultra-pressure lamp operating at about 40 atm pressure and having an efficacy comparable with that of the sodium lamp.

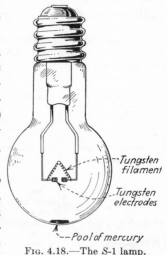

Tungsten filament

Tungsten electrodes

Pool of mercury

FIG. 4.18.—The S-1 lamp.

The S-1 and S-2 lamps may also be classed as mercury-vapor lamps, though some of the light is produced by the incandescent tungsten electrodes. As shown in Fig. 4.18, the S-1 lamp consists of tungsten electrodes in an evacuated bulb containing a little mercury. A filament bridges the electrodes. A voltage of about 40 applied to the lamp results in heating the filament, and in a few seconds an arc forms in the mercury vapor between the electrodes. The characteristic of the transformer supplying the lamp must be such that the voltage will then fall to about

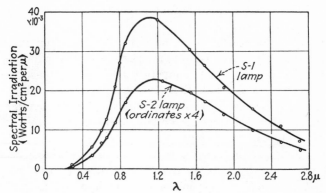

FIG. 4.19.—Spectral irradiation from *S*-1 and *S*-2 lamps. Measurements made on the axis of the reflector at a distance of 30 in. from lamp center. Only continuous portion of spectrum is shown. A line spectrum is also produced.[48]

TABLE XVI.—IRRADIATION FROM SUN LAMPS

Values are in microwatts per sq cm at 76.2 cm from the lamp on the axis of the reflector. All units use the commercial applicator-type reflectors. The total radiation from the *S*-1 and *S*-2 lamps also contains continuous radiation (Fig. 4.19).

(FORSYTHE, BARNES, and EASLEY, *J.O.S.A.*, **24**, 1934, p. 178; B. T. BARNES, *J.O.S.A.*, **25**, 1935, p. 168)

λ	*S*-1 unit	*S*-2 unit	*G*-5 unit
0.2537	0.2	0.1	
0.2652	0.6	0.4	0.1
0.2804	2.6	0.8	0.2
0.2894	4.0	1.2	0.9
0.2967	19.9	5.0	3.6
0.3022	49.0	10.2	2.2
0.3129	180	36.4	21.4
0.3341	23.0	4.5	
0.3650–0.3663	424	67	
0.4047	169	28	
0.4358	285	48	
0.5461	280	52	
0.5770–0.5791	261	42	
1.014	67.5	12	
1.357–1.367	73.7	14	
Volts..................	12.2	11.4	15.8
Amps..................	28.7	9.1	5.0

10 volts, at which approximately 30 amps will flow through the lamp. By use of Corex glass for the bulb, radiation is obtained in the ultraviolet, and thus the lamp may be used for dual-purpose lighting. The continuous portion of the radiation, due principally to the high temperature of the tungsten electrodes, produces an irradiation given by the curves of Fig. 4.19. The mercury arc adds to this continuous spectrum a number of lines in the ultraviolet, visible, and infrared regions (Table XVI).

4.10. Cold-cathode Lamps.—We have now considered various types of lamps for exciting spectra, from the three-electrode type where conditions are carefully controlled to the mercury-vapor type where the motion of the ions and electrons is complicated and not too well understood. We now turn to a type

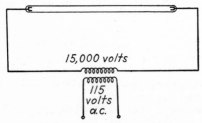

Fig. 4.20.—A cold-cathode lamp.

of lamp where the production of spectra is left almost entirely in the hands of the gods—the cold-cathode lamp. About 1850, Geissler found that beautiful lights could be produced by filling a glass tube with gas at low pressure and passing a high-tension discharge through the gas by means of an induction coil connected to two cold electrodes sealed in the ends of the tube. Such lamps are being used today very extensively in the neon and mercury-vapor signs which form such a prominent part of our modern night advertising. As shown in Fig. 4.20, the lamp consists of a long piece of glass tubing which may be formed in any shape and which must be exhausted and then filled with gas at a pressure of a few tenths of a millimeter. It is equipped with two metal electrodes which are connected to the terminals of a small high-voltage transformer. It should be noted that the cold-cathode lamp requires a voltage of the order of 10,000 volts for its operation, while all the lamps described previously operate on voltages of 200 or less.

Since practically no electrons are furnished by the electrodes, the question might arise as to how ionization is started. However, a continuous but slow process of ionization goes on at all times, principally because of the action of cosmic rays. Thus several ions will be present normally in each cubic centimeter of gas; and if a sufficiently high voltage is applied, these ions or the few free electrons which may also be present will be accelerated sufficiently to ionize other atoms, thus causing breakdown of

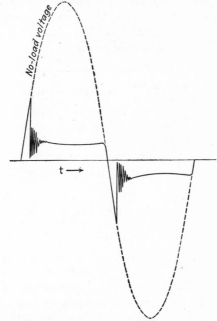

Fig. 4.21.—Voltage across cold-cathode neon lamp.[50]

the gas. Immediately upon breakdown, the gas becomes a good conductor, and the applied voltage must be reduced to a few hundred volts in order to limit the current to a reasonable value. Such a result might be accomplished by the use of a large series resistance, but actually it is usually obtained by using a special transformer having a high leakage reactance. In each half cycle of the a-c wave the voltage rises until breakdown occurs. After breakdown, the lamp has a very low impedance, and the transformer-secondary voltage falls to a low value. The alternating voltage passes through zero, and the lamp is extinguished. The voltage then rises on the other half of the wave until breakdown again occurs, and the process is repeated. An oscillogram of the secondary voltage of a transformer supplying a neon sign is shown in Fig. 4.21.

Certainly this method of producing light is simple, as regards both the construction of the tubes and the absence of complicated starting and regulating equipment. It is, however, a very haphazard method of producing the result and will probably be superseded in time by the hot-cathode method. One of the disadvantages of this method is the very low power factor due to the high leakage reactance of the transformer. A survey of neon signs gave the following results:[49,51]

Diameter of tubing, millimeters	Av. watts/ft	Av. p.f.
12	8.37	0.410
15	6.06	0.476

Another factor which limits the use of such neon lamps for general illumination is the fact that the light is not constant but goes out twice per cycle. This gives a stroboscopic effect which may be annoying.

Most of the present cold-cathode lamps used as signs use either neon or mercury vapor, which in conjunction with colored glass tubing gives a variety of possible colors. A great many other gases have been used at various times, however. D. McFarlane Moore did a large amount of research on the cold-cathode lamp and developed a variety of practical forms. Since a large part of the loss occurred at the electrodes, he was able to increase the over-all efficacy somewhat by using a great length of tubing. Tests on a Moore nitrogen lamp 176 ft long and $1\frac{7}{8}$ in. in diameter showed an input of 3450 watts and an output of 17,400 lumens, or an efficacy of 5.5 lumens/watt.[54] The light was of a pleasing yellow color. Another Moore light using CO_2 gave perhaps the best light for color matching yet developed. Its efficacy, however, was only about 2 lumens/watt. Practical difficulties connected with the great size as well as the low output of these Moore cold-cathode lamps caused them to be superseded.

One reason for the use of neon in cold-cathode lamps is that, being an inert gas, it does not "clean up" so rapidly as do many gases. In cold-cathode lamps there is a marked tendency for the gas gradually to disappear owing to absorption by the electrodes and by the glass walls. Thus the gas pressure gradually falls until the tube will no longer operate. Moore had great difficulty in this respect with CO_2 and found it necessary to provide each tube with a CO_2 generator and automatic valve mechanism to keep the gas pressure constant in the tube.[52]

4.11. Other Gaseous-conduction Sources.—We have considered several types of gaseous-discharge lamps, all of which have electrodes sealed through the glass. It has been found possible, however, to make lamps with no electrodes, the discharge being produced by induction. A sphere of glass or of fused silica is filled with neon or other gas. This simple device is all that there is to the lamp itself. A few turns of copper strap around the sphere are connected to a vacuum-tube oscillator or other source of high frequency. The gas acts as a single-turn transformer secondary; and if the voltage per turn of the exciting coil is sufficiently high, the gas is ionized. The efficacy of the lamp itself is high, though the losses in the auxiliary equipment and its complexity limit the use of such sources.[55]

Mention should also be made of the ordinary arc lamp using electrodes operating in air. With pure carbon electrodes most of the light is emitted by incandescence of the hot crater, but with impregnated carbons the arc itself emits a large part of the light whose color is determined largely by the impregnating material. In the past, such lamps were used extensively for street lighting and even for interior illumination, but they are being rapidly replaced by better lamps except where a very intense source of very small dimensions is necessary, as in searchlights.

Problem 25. Calculate the illumination on the axis of the *S*-1 and *S*-2 lamps with reflectors, 76 cm from the arc.

Problem 26. For some purposes such as advertising signs, it is desirable to obtain yellow, green, and blue light from mercury-vapor lamps. Examine the data on filters (Table XXVII, page 172) and determine which filters would be suitable for this purpose.

If the luminous flux from the low-pressure quartz lamp is called 100 per cent (Table IV, page 26), what luminous flux will be obtained when the above filters are used to obtain blue, green, and yellow light?

Problem 27. Which lamp has the lowest total operating cost per lumen output—the high-pressure mercury-vapor lamp in glass, the 10,000-lumen sodium lamp, or the 500-watt incandescent lamp (Chap. VI)?

Assume a cost of $10 each and a life of 1500 hr for the metal-vapor lamps. Power costs 5 cts per kilowatt-hour.

Bibliography

SPECTRA

1. F. K. RICHTMYER: Introduction to Modern Physics, McGraw-Hill Book Company, Inc., New York, 1934.

2. An Outline of Atomic Physics, Physics Staff, University of Pittsburgh, John Wiley & Sons, Inc., New York, 1933.

3. H. E. WHITE: Introduction to Atomic Spectra, McGraw-Hill Book Company, Inc., New York, 1934.

4. RUARK and UREY: Atoms, Molecules, and Quanta, p. 11 and Chap. III, McGraw-Hill Book Company, Inc., New York, 1930.

5. S. DUSHMAN: Quantum Theory and Atomic Structure (H. S. Taylor, *Physical Chemistry*), Vol. II, p. 1119, D. Van Nostrand Company, Inc., New York, 1931.

6. FOOTE and MOHLER: The Origin of Spectra, Chemical Catalog Company, Inc., New York, 1922.

7. FOOTE, MEGGERS, and MOHLER: Excitation of the Enhanced Spectrum of Sodium and Potassium in a Low-voltage Arc, *Astrophys. J.*, **55**, 1922, p. 145.

8. WELLS and BALINKIN: The Spectra of Potassium and Sodium in the Mercury Arc, *J.O.S.A.*, **23**, 1933, p. 105.

9. F. H. NEWMAN: The Spectrum of Sodium at Low Voltages, *Phil. Mag.*, **50**, 1925, pp. 165, 796, 1276.

10. PASCHEN and GÖTZE: Seriengesetze der Linienspektren, Julius Springer, Berlin, 1922.

11. W. GROTRIAN: Graphische Darstellung der Spektren von Atomen, Julius Springer, Berlin, 1928.

ELECTRICAL DISCHARGES

12. S. DUSHMAN: Low Pressure Gaseous Discharge Lamps, *Elect. Engineering*, **53**, 1934, pp. 1204, 1283.

13. S. DUSHMAN: Production of Light from Discharges in Gases, *G.E. Rev.*, **37**, 1934, p. 260.

14. LANGMUIR and COMPTON: Electrical Discharges in Gases. *Rev. Modern Physics*, **3**, 1931, p. 191.

15. R. SEELIGER: Einführung in die Physik der Gasentladungen, J. A. Barth, Leipzig, 1934 (2d ed.).

15a. ENGEL and STEENBECK: Elektrische Gasentladungen, Julius Springer, Berlin, 1934.

16. KOHLER and ROMPE: Die elektrischen Leuchtröhren. Vieweg, Braunschweig, Germany, 1933.

17. W. FUCKS: Zur Erklärung von Lichterscheinungen beim elektrischen Gasdurchschlag, *Zeits. f. techn. Physik*, **14**, 1933, p. 59.

18. FONDA and YOUNG: The Characteristics of the Sodium Lamp as Influenced by Vapor Pressure, *J.O.S.A.*, **24**, 1934, p. 31.

19. C. G. FOUND: Fundamental Phenomena in Sodium-vapor Lamps, *G.E. Rev.*, **37**, 1934, p. 269.

20. JOHNSON and BURNS: Line Intensity and Energy Distribution in High- and Low-pressure Mercury Arcs, *J.O.S.A.*, **23**, 1933, p. 55.

21. FORBES and LEIGHTON: Relations in Mercury-vapor Lamps, *J.O.S.A.*, **12**, 1926, p. 53.

22. K. LARCHÉ: Die Leuchtausbeute in Abhängigkeit von der Voltgeschwindigkeit, *Zeits. f. Physik*, **67**, 1931, p. 440.

LAMPS

23. L. J. BUTTOLPH: A Review of Gaseous-conduction Lamps, *I.E.S. Trans.*, **28**, 1933, p. 153.

24. L. J. BUTTOLPH: Gaseous-conduction Lamps and Light, *I.E.S. Trans.*, **30**, 1935, p. 147.

25. VON GÖLER and PIRANI: Über die Anwendung von Leuchtröhren, *C.I.E. Proc.*, 1931, p. 301.

26. LAX and PIRANI: Künstliches Tages- und Sonnenlicht, *C.I.E. Proc.*, **1**, 1932, p. 324.

27. F. BENFORD: Visible Radiation from the Low-pressure Mercury Arc, *M.P.E. Trans.*, **11**, 1927, p. 365.

28. F. BENFORD: Radiation Characteristics of Two Mercury Arcs, *M.P.E. Trans.*, **14**, 1930, p. 404.

29. JOHNSON and BURNS: Line Intensity and Energy Distribution in High and Low Pressure Mercury Arcs, *J.O.S.A.*, **23**, 1933, p. 55.

30. HARRISON and FORBES: Spectral Energy Characteristics of the Mercury Vapor Lamp, *J.O.S.A.*, **10**, 1925, p. 1.

31. B. T. BARNES: Spectral Distribution of Radiation from High and Low Pressure Hg Arcs, *J.O.S.A.*, **24**, 1934, p. 147.

32. L. J. BUTTOLPH: Incandescent Lamps as Mercury-arc Ballast, *G. E. Rev.*, **36**, 1933, p. 482.

33. H. J. SPANNER: The High-pressure Mercury-cadmium Vapor Lamp, *I.E.S. Trans.*, **30**, 1935, p. 178.

34. F. BATES: A New Cadmium-vapor Arc Lamp, *Bu. Stds. Sci. Paper*, No. 371, 1920, p. 45.

35. FOUND and FORNEY: Hot Cathode Neon Arcs, *A.I.E.E. Trans.*, **47**, 1928, p. 747.

36. BENFORD and BUTTOLPH: Visible Radiation from the Neon Hot Cathode Arc, *M.P.E. Trans.*, **13**, 1928, p. 1011.

37. W. F. WESTENDORP: Dimming of Hot-cathode Gaseous-discharge Lamps, *G. E. Rev.*, **36**, 1933, p. 488.

38. T. E. FOULKE: Transmission of Visible Radiation through the Atmosphere, *I.E.S. Trans.*, **24**, 1929, p. 384.

39. F. C. BRECKENRIDGE: Transmission of Light through Fog, *I.E.S. Trans.*, **27**, 1932, p. 215.

40. G. A. EDDY: Sodium-vapor Highway Lighting, *G. E. Rev.*, **37**, 1934, p. 372.

41. W. F. WESTENDORP: Circuits for Sodium-vapor Lamps, *G. E. Rev.*, **37**, 1934, p. 368.

42. FONDA and YOUNG: The A-c. Sodium-vapor Lamp, *G. E. Rev.*, **37**, 1934, p. 331.

43. W. HARRISON: Applications of the New Gaseous-conductor Lamps, *I. E. S. Trans.*, **30**, 1935, p. 190.

44. N. T. GORDON: Operating Characteristics of Sodium-vapor Lamps, *G. E. Rev.*, **37**, 1934, p. 338.

45. A. H. TAYLOR: Ultraviolet Radiation from the Sunlight Lamp (Type *S*-1), *J.O.S.A.*, **21**, 1931, p. 20.

46. FORSYTHE, BARNES, and EASLEY: Characteristics of a New U.V. Lamp, *J.O.S.A.*, **21**, 1931, p. 30.

47. FORSYTHE, BARNES, and EASLEY: Ultraviolet Sources and their Radiation, *J.O.S.A.*, **24**, 1934, p. 178.

48. B. T. BARNES: Spectral Distribution of Radiation from Three Reflector Units, *J.O.S.A.*, **25**, 1935, p. 167.

49. Power-factor Correction for Neon Signs, *El. World*, **96**, 1930, p. 728.

50. McMILLAN and STARR: High-voltage Gaseous-conductor Lamps, *A.I.E.E. Trans.*, **48**, 1929, p. 11.

51. H. A. COOK: Survey of Neon Signs, *I.E.S. Trans.*, **24**, 1929, p. 133.

52. D. M. MOORE: A Standard for Color Values—The White Moore Light, *I.E.S. Trans.*, **5**, 1910, 209.

53. D. M. MOORE: Gaseous Conduction Light from Low-voltage Circuits, *G. E. Rev.*, **23**, 1920, p. 577.

54. SHARP and MILLAR: Tests of a Moore Tube, *I.E.S. Trans.*, **4**, 1909, p. 885.

55. T. E. FOULKE: The Induction Lamp, *A.I.E.E. Trans.*, **45**, 1926, p. 1242.

56. U. DAHLGREN: The Production of Light by Animals, *Frank. Inst., J.*, **180**, 1915, p. 711.

57. H. E. IVES: The Fire-fly as an Illuminant, *Frank. Inst., J.*, **194**, 1922, p. 212.

CHAPTER V

RADIATION FROM INCANDESCENT SOURCES

In Chap. IV we have considered the production of light by luminescent sources, the various gaseous-conduction lamps used today, and the possibility of future developments in lamps of this type. While it is true that the gaseous-conduction lamp offers great possibilities for the production of a variety of colors, as well as possibilities for improvement in efficacy, it seems doubtful if the gaseous-conduction lamp will ever supplant entirely the incandescent lamp because of the simplicity, convenience, and cheapness of the latter. Certainly today the incandescent lamp holds such an important position that electric lighting may be considered almost as incandescent-lamp lighting. Thus it becomes necessary for the illuminating engineer to be acquainted with the properties of incandescent lamps and the laws of radiation from incandescent filaments. These laws of radiation constitute the subject matter of the present chapter.

We have seen that the production of light by an atom of a gas is generally caused by the valence electron's falling from one stationary orbit to another orbit nearer the nucleus. A line spectrum is produced, with radiation only at certain definite wavelengths. With a diatomic molecule, there is also a possibility of periodic variations in the distance between atomic centers and rotation of the molecule as a whole, and band spectra are produced as well as line spectra. With polyatomic molecules containing more than two atoms, the number of degrees of freedom is further increased, with a corresponding increase in the complexity of spectra (*e.g.*, see Fig. 4.11). In matter at high temperatures, all the molecules are in violent agitation. One might expect the resulting radiation to contain many frequencies. In fact, experiment shows that incandescent bodies radiate at all wavelengths in a wide range, producing continuous spectra.

5.02. The Black-body Radiator.—We begin our study by a consideration of the radiation from what is known as a *black* *body.* A black body is defined as a body that absorbs all the radiation that falls on it. It can be shown that such a body also radiates more power in any band of wavelengths and more total power than any other incandescent radiator operating at the same temperature. It is this property of the black body that interests us. Black-body radiation, then, represents an upper limit which can be approached very closely but which can never be exceeded by any incandescent light source. The ordinary tungsten lamp, for instance, radiates less than half as much power per square centimeter of filament surface as that emitted by a black-body radiator at the same temperature.

The black-body radiator* can be realized almost perfectly, however, by using any uniformly heated inclosure with a small

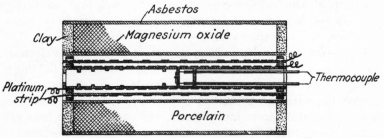

FIG. 5.01.—An experimental black-body radiator.[10]

opening. Owing to multiple reflections within the inclosure, the radiation from the opening is greatly strengthened and is found to obey certain definite laws. Thus the radiation from a small opening in an ordinary furnace or muffle whose walls are at reasonably constant temperature is found to follow the laws of the black body very closely, and, in practice, furnace temperatures are often obtained by measuring the radiation with some form of optical pyrometer. An experimental form of black body designed for use in precision radiation measurements is shown in Fig. 5.01. A tube of porcelain, or other material that will stand a fairly high temperature without oxidizing, is heated electrically by a coil of platinum wire wound around it. The temperature within the tube is kept uniform by the use of heavy thermal insulation. The actual temperature of the interior is measured by a thermocouple or by some form of thermometer.

---

* Sometimes called also a "complete radiator."

By the use of such an experimental radiator, the spectral distribution of black-body radiation can be studied.

In order to extend the measurements to higher temperatures than can be obtained with this form of complete radiator, some experimenters have used tungsten cylinders in a vacuum or in an inert gas. Müller, Theissing, and Esmarch,[13] for instance, have used a tungsten cylinder 30 mm long operated in nitrogen at low pressure and heated by induction. Another ingenious

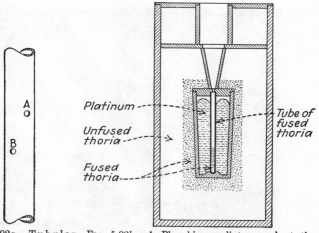

FIG. 5.02a.—Tubular tungsten filament.[19,23] Radiation from the openings A and B is practically Planckian.

FIG. 5.02b.—A Planckian radiator used at the Bureau of Standards.[14]

method has been used by Worthing.[19] An incandescent lamp is built with a filament of tungsten tubing about 1.3 mm outside diameter and 0.8 mm inside diameter. This is heated in the usual manner by passing a heavy current through it, and the inside of the tungsten tube acts as a complete radiator whose radiation can be observed through tiny holes drilled through the tube walls (Fig. 5.02a).

Another form of complete radiator is shown in Fig. 5.02b. A tube of fused thorium oxide, 2.5 mm inside diameter and about 45 mm high, is the black body proper. It is held at constant temperature by being immersed in molten platinum, and readings are taken at the melting point. Heating is accomplished by electromagnetic induction.

An interesting example of black-body effect is found in the coiled tungsten filaments now used in nearly all incandescent lamps. Formerly, all filaments were of straight wire which was looped back and forth over the supports. When the wire is coiled into a tight helix, however, multiple reflections of radiation within the helix give an increased brightness to the inside of the turns (as shown in Fig. 5.03) and change somewhat the character of the radiation. The radiation is still not that of a black-body

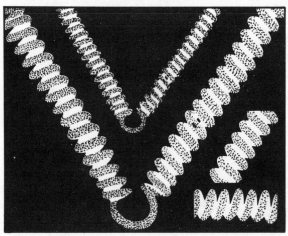

Fig. 5.03.—An incandescent helical filament of tungsten in a gas-filled lamp, showing the increased brightness of the inside of the helix due to multiple reflections. (*Courtesy of the Bureau of Standards.*)

radiator, but it does approach it more closely than when a straight filament is used.

5.03. Planck's Equation.—Using an experimental source somewhat like the one shown in Fig. 5.01, Lummer and Pringsheim[9] made a thorough study (1897-1900) of the radiation from a complete radiator. It will be noted from Fig. 5.04 that the spectrum is continuous and that the curves have a characteristic shape. Planck found that these curves could be represented accurately by the equation that bears his name. The equation is

$$J_\lambda = \frac{C_1}{\lambda^5} \frac{1}{e^{\frac{C_2}{\lambda T}} - 1} \tag{5.01}$$

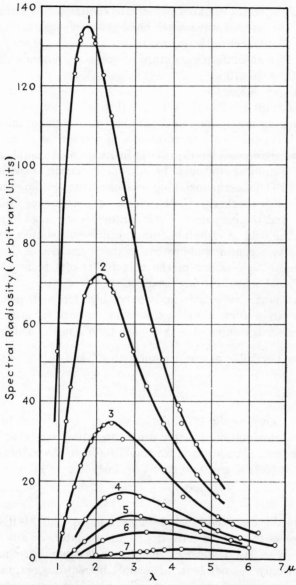

Fig. 5.04.—Experimental radiation curves for a black body.[9]

1—1646°K	5—998°K
2—1449	6—904
3—1259	7—723
4—1095	

where J_λ = watts radiated per square centimeter of surface per micron wavelength band at wavelength λ.

λ = wavelength (microns).

T = absolute temperature (degrees centigrade + 273).

$C_1 = 36{,}970$.

$C_2 = 14{,}320$.

An attempt by Planck to give a theoretical derivation of the preceding formula was the beginning of the quantum theory which plays such an important role in modern physics. However, we shall consider Eq. (5.01) in its original complexion—a purely empirical formula based upon certain experimental results. The most painstaking measurements of a large number of physicists check Eq. (5.01) over a very wide range of wavelengths and temperatures. This formula is the most important one in the field of radiation from incandescent sources and will be used to a considerable extent in the remainder of this book.

Special Cases.—Some of the valuable results to be obtained from Planck's law will now be given.

1. At short wavelengths and not too high temperatures, (5.01) reduces to a form that is somewhat simpler for calculation. If λT is small compared with C_2, the term 1 in the denominator becomes negligible in comparison with $e^{\frac{C_2}{\lambda T}}$ and

$$J_\lambda = \frac{C_1}{\lambda^5} e^{\frac{-C_2}{\lambda T}} \tag{5.02}$$

This is known as the *Wien radiation law*. It happens to give a good approximation at the usual operating temperatures of incandescent filaments and for wavelengths in the visible region. For $T = 3000°\text{K}$ and $\lambda = 0.70\mu$, for instance,

$$e^{\frac{C_2}{\lambda T}} = e^{6.819} = 910$$

Even in this case, the exponential term in Eq. (5.01) is 910 times as large as the second term in the denominator. Thus the use of the Wien law instead of the Planck law here introduces an error of only $\frac{1}{10}$ per cent. It should be remembered, however, that in the infrared region or at sufficiently high temperatures the use of Eq. (5.02) may lead to large errors.

2. It is common experience that as the temperature of a body is raised, the color of the emitted light changes. At 500°C

the body emits a barely perceptible deep-red glow.   At higher
temperatures it passes successively through the stages of bright
red, orange, and yellow and approaches white.   The phenomenon
is explained on the basis of the Planck law by the shift of the
spectral radiosity curve to shorter wavelengths as the temperature is raised.   In Eq. (5.01), let $C_2/\lambda T = x$ for convenience.
Then for a Planckian radiator,

$$J_\lambda = \frac{C_1 T^5 x^5}{C_2{}^5} \frac{1}{e^x - 1} \tag{5.01a}$$

The peak occurs where

$$\frac{dJ_\lambda}{d\lambda} = 0$$

But

$$\frac{dJ_\lambda}{d\lambda} = \frac{dJ_\lambda}{dx}\frac{dx}{d\lambda} = -\frac{C_2}{T\lambda^2}\frac{dJ_\lambda{}'}{dx} \tag{5.02a}$$

Thus the maximum occurs when

$$\frac{dJ_\lambda}{d\lambda} = 0 = -\frac{C_2}{T\lambda^2}\frac{C_1 T^5 x^4}{C_2{}^5(e^x-1)}\left(5 - \frac{xe^x}{e^x - 1}\right) \tag{5.03}$$

or

$$e^x(x - 5) + 5 = 0 \tag{5.04}$$

This equation is satisfied by

$$x = 4.9651 = \frac{C_2}{\lambda_{\max}T} \tag{5.05}$$

where $\lambda_{\max}$ signifies the wavelength at which the curve has its
maximum ordinate.   Thus we obtain the expression

$$\lambda_{\max}T = \frac{14320}{4.9651} = 2883.6 \text{ micron-degrees} \tag{5.06}$$

which is often called the *Wien displacement law*.*

* Equations (5.06) and (5.07) are merely consequences of Wien's general
displacement law, which may be written

$$J_\lambda = \frac{1}{\lambda^5} \cdot f(\lambda T) \tag{5.06a}$$

or

$$\lambda^5 J_\lambda = f(\lambda T) \tag{5.06b}$$

Evidently, as T is increased the peak of the radiation curve shifts to shorter wavelengths.

Figure 5.05 shows a graph of this phenomenon. Note that for the ordinary temperatures of incandescent lamps (2500 to 3000°K), the peak of the curve is in the infrared. To move λ_{max} to the center of the visible region requires a temperature of 5200°K, while to place it in the biologically effective region at 0.28μ requires a temperature of approximately 10000°K.

The maximum ordinate of the radiosity curve for a Planckian radiator may also be of interest. Equation (5.01a)

$$J_\lambda = \frac{C_1 T^5 x^5}{C_2{}^5} \frac{1}{e^x - 1},\tag{5.01a}$$

becomes, for $x = 4.9651$,

$$\begin{aligned}
J_{\lambda max} &= \frac{36{,}970}{(14{,}320)^5} \frac{(4.9651)^5}{e^{4.9651} - 1} T^5 \\
&= 1.3017 \times 10^{-15} T^5
\end{aligned}\tag{5.07}$$

Thus the maximum ordinate of the curve varies as the fifth power of the absolute temperature. Values can be obtained from Fig. 5.05.

3. Another important relation is the total energy radiated per square centimeter per second from a Planckian radiator. Evidently, this can be obtained by integrating under a J_λ curve (Fig. 5.04) from zero to infinity. The total radiant power per square centimeter of radiator surface is thus

$$J = \int_0^\infty J_\lambda \, d\lambda = C_1 \int_0^\infty \frac{\lambda^{-5}}{e^{\frac{C_2}{\lambda T}} - 1} d\lambda \quad \text{(watts/sq cm)}\tag{5.08}$$

Again, it is convenient to introduce the variable $x = C_2/\lambda T$, and Eq. (5.08) reduces to

---

where $f(\lambda T)$ is a function of the independent variable (λT). Equation (5.06b) states that if a single curve of $\lambda^5 J_\lambda$ be plotted against λT, *this curve will represent the radiation from black bodies at all temperatures.* As a special case, the peak of this curve is determined by a fixed value of λT, or

$$\lambda_{max} T = \text{const}$$

The general displacement law was derived by Wien (*Wied. Ann.*, **52**, 1894, p. 132) a number of years before the development of the Planck equation.

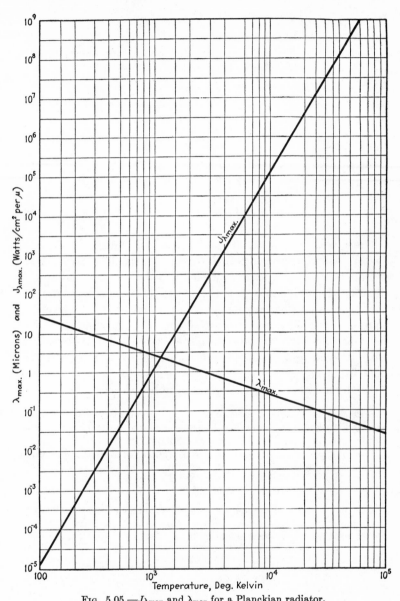

Fig. 5.05.—$J\lambda_{max}$ and λ_{max} for a Planckian radiator.

$$J = C_1\left(\frac{T}{C_2}\right)^4 \int_0^\infty \frac{x^3\, dx}{e^x - 1}$$

$$= C_1\left(\frac{T}{C_2}\right)^4 \int_0^\infty (e^{-x} + e^{-2x} + e^{-3x} + \cdots)x^3\, dx$$

As

$$\int_0^\infty x^n e^{-ax}\, dx = \frac{n!}{a^{n+1}}$$

then

$$J = 6C_1\left(\frac{T}{C_2}\right)^4\left[\frac{1}{1} + \frac{1}{2^4} + \frac{1}{3^4} + \cdots\right]$$

$$= 6C_1\left(\frac{T}{C_2}\right)^4\frac{\pi^4}{90} = \sigma T^4 \quad \text{(watts/sq cm)} \qquad (5.09)$$

where $\sigma = $ a const $= 5.709 \times 10^{-12}$ watt cm^{-2} deg^{-4}. Equation (5.09) expresses the *Stefan-Boltzmann law:* The total power radiated from a square centimeter of Planckian radiator is directly proportional to the fourth power of the absolute temperature. It should be noted that J is the *total* radiant power per square centimeter and that the Stefan-Boltzmann law says nothing about how the power radiated in the visible region varies with temperature. To conclude, as some have done, that the *light* from an incandescent lamp varies as the fourth power of the temperature is, of course, quite erroneous.

Example. A Planckian radiator having an opening of 0.1 sq cm area is operated at 1999°K. Determine the power radiated (watts), the luminous output, and the luminous efficacy of the radiation.

The total power radiated per square centimeter of surface is, according to the Stefan-Boltzmann law,

$$J = 5.709 \times 10^{-12}(1999)^4 = 91.16 \text{ watts/sq cm}$$

and the power radiated through an opening of 0.1 sq cm area is **9.116 watts.**

To find the luminous output, it is necessary to plot the curve of J_λ vs. λ for the visible region. From Planck's law,

$$J_\lambda = \frac{36,970}{\lambda^5}\frac{1}{e^{\frac{14,320}{\lambda T}} - 1}$$

$$= \frac{36,970}{\lambda^5}\frac{1}{10^{\frac{6219.10}{\lambda T}} - 1} \quad \text{(watts/sq cm per micron wavelength band)}$$

$$(5.10)$$

Various values of λ are selected, and corresponding values of J_λ are computed. The resulting curve is shown in Fig. 2.05.

The luminosity is found by obtaining the area under the curve whose ordinates are the products of the visibility factor and J_λ. The area may be determined by the use of a planimeter or by other methods of mechanical integration, the result being 151 lumens/sq cm. The luminous output of this complete radiator is **15.1 lumens.** The luminous efficacy is therefore **1.65 lumens/watt.**

Problem 28. Repeat the preceding for a temperature of 1800°K.

Problem 29. It has been suggested that one way of greatly increasing the sensitivity of vacuum thermocouples and bolometers is to immerse the vacuum bulb in liquid air. This will reduce the radiation from the target, which will thus reach a higher temperature due to irradiation. If it is assumed that the blackened target acts essentially like a Planckian radiator (not a bad assumption), that its temperature is −180°C, and that the sensitivity of the device is inversely proportional to the power radiated from the target,

1. What percentage increase in sensitivity will result from the use of liquid air?

2. Calculate to four significant figures λ_{max} and $J_{\lambda\ max}$.

Problem 30. The roof of a house is heated by the radiation from the summer sun and reaches a temperature of 100°F.

1. Plot the curve of J_λ vs. λ.

2. Obtain, to four significant figures, the watts radiated per square foot of roof surface.

Problem 31. The value of C_1 given by Birge is

$$C_1 = 3.697 \times 10^{-5} \text{ erg cm}^2 \text{ sec}^{-1}$$

Prove that this is in agreement with the value used in this chapter.

5.04. Calculation of Radiation from a Planckian Radiator.*—It is evident from Fig. 5.04 that the ordinary way of plotting the data for radiation from a Planckian radiator is not particularly satisfactory. Both J_λ and λ cover such a great range that usually if the whole curve is plotted, nothing whatever can be determined from the curve about the ordinates in the ultraviolet. A plot on log-log paper, as in Fig. 5.08, is much more useful.

The log-log curve is found to have another useful property:†
Having plotted one curve of J_λ vs. λ by use of Eq. (5.01), we may easily obtain the curve for any other temperature by merely shifting the scales by a suitable amount. Let us consider the method. Taking the logarithm of both sides of Eq. (5.01),

---

* May be omitted in an introductory course.

† Which may be considered as another consequence of Wien's general displacement law, Eq. (5.06a).

$$\log J_\lambda = \log \left(\frac{C_1}{e^{\frac{C_2}{\lambda T}} - 1} \right) - 5 \log \lambda \qquad (5.11)$$

For all values of λ and T such that $\lambda T = a_1$, a constant, the first term on the right is a constant. Thus if we plot $(\log J_\lambda)$ against $(\log \lambda)$, we obtain a straight line:

$$y = A - 5x$$

of slope -5. Thus every straight line of this slope represents a line of constant λT.

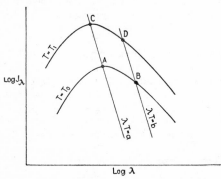

Fig. 5.06.—Spectral radiation curves for a Planckian radiator at two temperatures, T_0 and T_1.

Consider two curves, one at constant temperature T_0 and the other at an arbitrary temperature T_1 (Fig. 5.06). Two straight lines of slope -5 represent two constant values of λT, say $\lambda T = a$ and $\lambda T = b$.

Then *for point A,*

$$\log J_A = \log \left(\frac{C_1}{e^{\frac{C_2}{a}} - 1} \right) - 5 \log \lambda_A$$

and

$$T = T_0 \qquad \text{and} \qquad \lambda_A = a/T_0$$

For point B,

$$\log J_B = \log \left(\frac{C_1}{e^{\frac{C_2}{b}} - 1} \right) - 5 \log \lambda_B$$

and

$$T = T_0 \quad \text{and} \quad \lambda_B = b/T_0$$

For point C,

$$\log J_C = \log \left(\frac{C_1}{e^{\frac{C_2}{a}} - 1} \right) - 5 \log \lambda_C$$

and

$$T = T_1 \quad \text{and} \quad \lambda_C = \frac{a}{T_1}$$

For point D,

$$\log J_D = \log \left(\frac{C_1}{e^{\frac{C_2}{b}} - 1} \right) - 5 \log \lambda_D$$

and

$$T = T_1 \quad \text{and} \quad \lambda_D = \frac{b}{T.}$$

The difference in the ordinates of C and A is

$$
\begin{aligned}
y_{CA} = \log J_C - \log J_A &= 5 \left(\log \lambda_A - \log \lambda_C \right) \\
&= 5 \left(\log \frac{a}{T_0} - \log \frac{a}{T_1} \right) \\
&= 5 \log \left(\frac{T_1}{T_0} \right).
\end{aligned}
\tag{5.12}
$$

The difference in the ordinates of D and B is

$$
\begin{aligned}
y_{DB} = \log J_D - \log J_B &= 5 \left(\log \frac{b}{T_0} - \log \frac{b}{T_1} \right) \\
&= 5 \log \left(\frac{T_1}{T_0} \right) = y_{CA}
\end{aligned}
\tag{5.13}
$$

The difference in the abscissas of C and A is the same as the difference in the abscissas of D and B, or $x_{DB} = x_{CA}$.

Thus the curve for any temperature may be obtained by merely shifting the curve for any other temperature along the line AC. Or instead of shifting the curve, we may use a stationary curve as in Fig. 5.07a and shift the coordinate axes (Fig. 5.07b). In this way, the single curve of Fig. 5.07a can be made to serve for

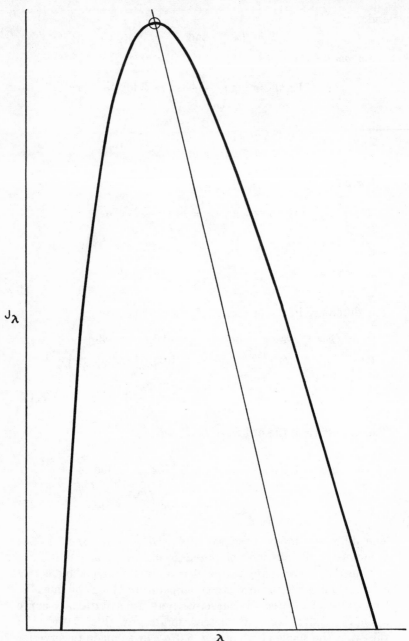

J_λ

λ

Fig. 5.07a.—Spectral radiation curve for a Planckian radiator operating at any temperature.   To be used with Fig. 5.07b.

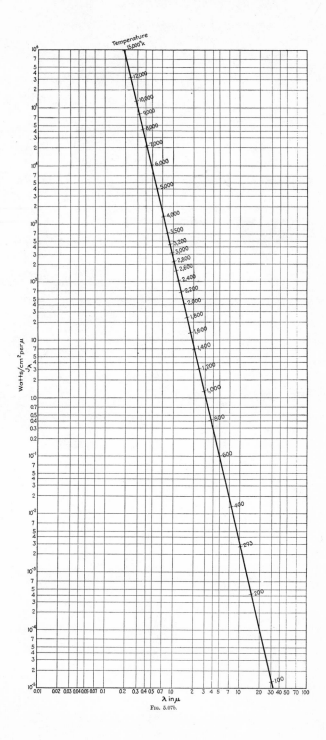

Fig. 5.07b.

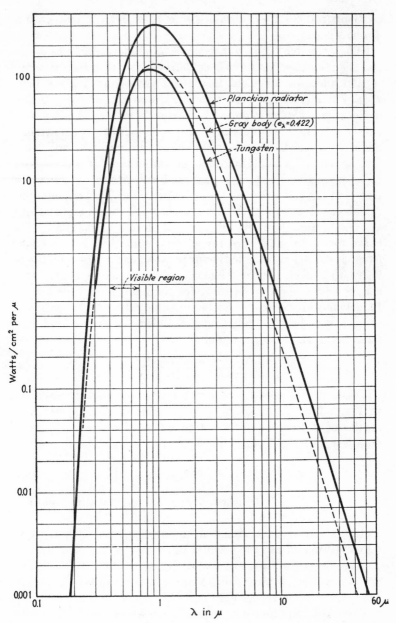

Fig. 5.08.—Spectral radiation curves for various radiators operating at 3000°K.

all temperatures from absolute zero to as high a temperature as one wishes.

5.05. Selective and Nonselective Radiators.—Planck's law and the relations that have been derived from it in the preceding section allow us to calculate the radiation from a black body at any temperature. As previously stated, however, actual incandescent filaments do not radiate as does a black body. Evidently, either of two procedures might be followed. An attempt might be made to obtain an empirical formula like the Planck law for each filament material, or the curve for a Planckian radiator might be used as a standard with everything else referred to it. In practice, the latter procedure has been adopted. A filament of known material is operated at a known temperature, say 3000°, and the radiation curve is plotted (Fig. 5.08). The curve for a Plankian radiator at 3000° can then be calculated from Eq. (5.01) and the curve for the filament will be found to be below the curve for the Planckian radiator throughout. It is convenient to specify the curve for the filament in terms of the Planckian-radiator curve by giving the ratio of the ordinates at each wavelength. This ratio is called the *spectral radiation factor* e_λ of the filament material:

$$e_\lambda = \frac{(J_\lambda) \text{ filament}}{(J_\lambda) \text{ Planckian radiator}} \tag{5.14}$$

Values for the spectral radiation factor for tungsten are given in Fig. 5.09. The curves are plotted from the experimental results of a number of investigators, with values beyond 2μ obtained from the Drude equation

$$e_\lambda = 36.50 \sqrt{\frac{\Re}{\lambda}} \tag{5.15}$$

where $\Re$ = electrical resistivity of the emitting material (ohm-cm).

Note that the spectral radiation factor depends somewhat upon temperature and has the peculiar property of decreasing with an increase of temperature at short wavelengths and increasing with an increase of temperature at long wavelengths. Evidently these data allow us to calculate the actual number of watts radiated by a square centimeter of tungsten filament surface per micron wavelength band for any value of λ.

* Often called "spectral emissivity" (see Appendix B).

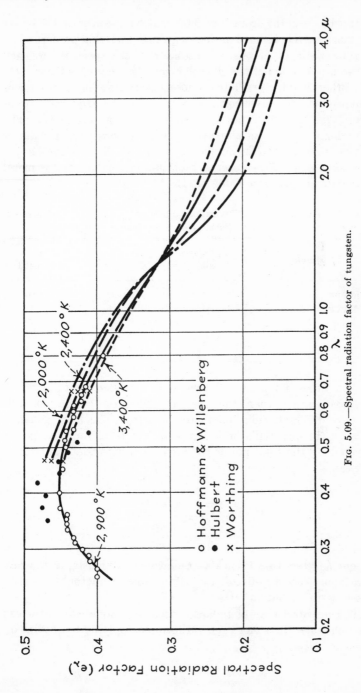

Fig. 5.09.—Spectral radiation factor of tungsten.

It will be noted from Fig. 5.09 that tungsten radiates better at short wavelengths than at long ones, and this property is a characteristic of metals. A radiator whose spectral radiation factor is a function of wavelength is called a *selective radiator*. On the other hand, a radiator whose spectral radiation factor is independent of wavelength is called a *nonselective radiator* or *gray body*. A carbon filament approximates a gray body. The Planckian radiator is a special case of a nonselective radiator having a spectral radiation factor of 1.00 at all wavelengths.

Some values of the spectral radiation factor for various metal filaments are given in Table XVII.

TABLE XVII.—VALUES OF SPECTRAL RADIATION FACTOR FOR SOME METALS
(WORTHING, *Physical Rev.*, **28**, 1926, p. 174)

Metals	T, degrees abs.	e_λ ($\lambda = 0.665$)	e_λ ($\lambda = 0.463$)
Tantalum.............	2400	0.404	0.450
Platinum.............	1800	0.310	0.386
Nickel...............	1400	0.375	0.450
Gold.................	1275	0.14	0.632
Molybdenum..........	2400	0.341	0.371

Sometimes it is more convenient to consider the total power radiated rather than the spectroradiometric curve. In this case, a different radiation factor is used. The *total radiation factor* e_t of any radiator is equal to the total radiated power divided by the total power radiated by a Planckian radiator at the same temperature:

$$e_t = \frac{\int_0^\infty e_\lambda J_\lambda \, d\lambda}{\int_0^\infty J_\lambda \, d\lambda} \tag{5.16}$$

where J_λ refers to a Planckian radiator. Obviously, in the case of a nonselective radiator, the total radiation factor is equal to the spectral radiation factor.

The previous laws of radiation from a complete radiator can now be stated in a more general form as applying to any incandescent body.

Planck's law:

$$J_\lambda = e_\lambda \frac{36,970}{\lambda^5} \frac{1}{e^{\frac{14,320}{\lambda T}} - 1} = e_\lambda \frac{36,970}{\lambda^5} \frac{1}{10^{\frac{6219.10}{\lambda T}} - 1} \qquad (5.17)$$

Wien radiation law:

$$J_\lambda = e_\lambda \frac{36,970}{\lambda^5} 10^{-\frac{6219.10}{\lambda T}} \quad \text{(applies only where } \lambda T \text{ is small)} \quad (5.18)$$

Wien displacement law:

$$\lambda_m = \frac{2883.6}{T} \quad \text{(applies only to nonselective radiators)} \qquad (5.19)$$

Stefan-Boltzmann law:

$$J = e_t 5.709 \times 10^{-12}(T)^4 \qquad (5.20)$$

For a Planckian radiator, $e_t = e_\lambda = 1.00$; for all other incandescent sources, e_t and e_λ are less than unity.

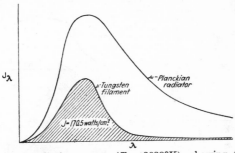

Fig. 5.10.—Spectral radiation curves ($T = 3038°\text{K}$), showing the change of shape caused by the selective radiation from tungsten.

Example. A tungsten lamp has a filament 0.030 cm in diameter and 100 cm long which is operated at 3038°K. Determine the luminous flux emitted and the luminous efficacy.

Calculations of J_λ for a complete radiator can be used by multiplying each value of J_λ by the value of e_λ for the same wavelength. Using the data from Fig. 5.09, we obtain the solid curve of Fig. 5.10. The area under the complete curve from $\lambda = 0$ to $\lambda = \infty$ is obtained by mechanical integration, giving

$$J = 170.5 \text{ watts/sq cm}$$

The values in the visible region are multiplied by the visibility factor v, and mechanical integration is again used to obtain

$$L = 4230 \text{ lumens/sq cm}$$

The surface area of the filament is

$$\pi(0.030)100 = 9.42 \text{ sq cm}$$

so the total luminous flux emitted by the filament is

$$F = 4230 \times 9.42 = \textbf{39,800 lumens}$$

The luminous efficacy of the radiation from the filament is

$$\eta_l = \frac{4230}{170.5} = \textbf{24.8 lumens/watt.}$$

Problem 32. Repeat the foregoing for the same filament operated at 1800°K.

Problem 33. In the house of Prob. 30, it is decided to use a sheet of aluminum foil beneath the roof to reduce the heating of the house. If it is assumed that the foil is at the same temperature as the roof, how many watts does it radiate into the house per square foot of foil surface? Neglect interreflections and use the Drude formula for spectral radiation factor.

5.06. Radiation Factor and Reflection Factor.*—It has long been known that bodies that are good absorbers are also good

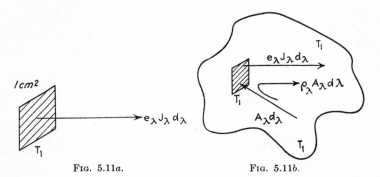

FIG. 5.11a.   FIG. 5.11b.

radiators—a soot-covered surface absorbs most of the radiant power that falls on it and also radiates well; a clean metal surface absorbs little and has a low radiation factor. Thus one might expect a relation to exist between radiation factor and reflection factor. We shall consider such a universal relation.

One square centimeter of radiating surface (Fig. 5.11a) at a given temperature T_1 is imagined to be isolated in space. The power radiated in the wavelength band λ to $(\lambda + d\lambda)$ is

$$d\Phi = e_\lambda J_\lambda \, d\lambda \tag{5.21}$$

---

* May be omitted in an introductory course.

where J_λ refers to the radiation from a Planckian radiator and e_λ is the spectral radiation factor of the square centimeter of surface. Since the surface receives no radiation, it must be supplied continuously with energy at the rate $d\Phi$.

Now place the surface in an opaque inclosure whose walls are at constant temperature T_1 (Fig. 5.11b). The square centimeter of surface is now part of a black body, and consequently the radiant power sent out by the surface element is $J_\lambda \, d\lambda$. The surface also receives radiant power from the walls, say

$$A_\lambda \, d\lambda$$

Naturally, part of this power is absorbed, and the remainder is reflected. If the spectral reflection factor is ρ_λ, the power reflected by the surface element is

$$\rho_\lambda A_\lambda \, d\lambda$$

and the amount radiated by the surface element due to the temperature T_1 is, as before, Eq. (5.21),

$$e_\lambda J_\lambda \, d\lambda$$

Thus the total power emitted between the wavelengths λ and $(\lambda + d\lambda)$ is

$$J_\lambda \, d\lambda = \rho_\lambda A_\lambda \, d\lambda + e_\lambda J_\lambda \, d\lambda \qquad (5.22)$$

Consider the power absorbed by the square centimeter of surface. Since the reflected power is $\rho_\lambda A_\lambda \, d\lambda$, the absorbed power must be

$$(1 - \rho_\lambda)A_\lambda \, d\lambda$$

But thermal equilibrium has been postulated, so the radiated power must be equal to the absorbed power, or

$$(1 - \rho_\lambda)A_\lambda \, d\lambda = e_\lambda J_\lambda \, d\lambda \qquad (5.23)$$

From Eqs. (5.22) and 5.23),

$$\begin{cases} (1 - e_\lambda)J_\lambda = \rho_\lambda A_\lambda \\ \quad\ e_\lambda J_\lambda = (1 - \rho_\lambda)A_\lambda \end{cases}$$

or

$$e_\lambda = 1 - \rho_\lambda \qquad (5.24)$$

Thus there is a definite relation between the radiation factor and the reflection factor of any surface. The derivation also brings out clearly the reason that the complete radiator radiates more power in any wavelength band than any other body— it is sending out not only its own radiant power ($e_\lambda J_\lambda \, d\lambda$) which depends upon the kind of material of which it is composed, but it is also sending out the reflected radiant power ($\rho_\lambda J_\lambda \, d\lambda$) which it receives from the rest of the black body. The complete radiation is entirely independent of the shape, size, and material of the enclosing walls, the only requirements being uniform temperature and a small opening for the issuing radiant power.

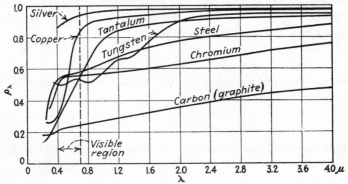

FIG. 5.12.—Spectral reflection factor for various materials.

Figure 5.12 shows the spectral reflection factor of a number of metals. The measurements were made at room temperature and for a wide range of wavelengths. It will be noted that the best reflector is silver with a spectral reflection factor of over 90 per cent in the visible region; while polished steel, tungsten, and chromium have in the visible region an almost constant spectral reflection factor of about 0.55. The red color of copper is accounted for by its high reflection factor in the red end of the spectrum. A characteristic of most metals is the very high reflection in the infrared region, a characteristic of great importance in incandescent lamps, as will be seen later.

Figure 5.13 gives the corresponding values of spectral radiation factor obtained by the use of Eq. (5.24). The high spectral reflection factor in the infrared accounts for the very low value of e_λ for Ta, W, and Ag at wavelengths beyond 1 or 2μ. This means that a smaller proportion of the energy is radiated from these metals in the infrared. They are *selective radiators* and because of the comparatively low radiation in the infrared will tend to produce more luminous flux per watt than if they were nonselective radiators. Notice the curve for graphite which more nearly approaches the properties of a gray body. The spectral radiation factor is high, but the amount of power radiated in the infrared region will be very large because of the somewhat nonselective character of the radiation. A comparison of Figs. 5.13 and 5.09 shows slight discrepancies between the values for tungsten. This is caused by the fact that e_λ varies somewhat with temperature and that the data in one case are

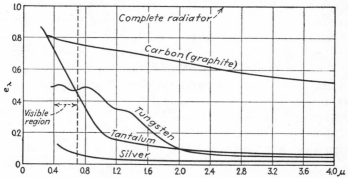

Fig. 5.13.—Spectral radiation factor for various materials at room temperature.

for room temperature while in the other they are for high temperatures.

Problem 34. Using the curves of Fig. 5.13, determine the luminous efficacy that is obtained from a tantalum filament operating at 1800°K and compare this value with that obtained for a tungsten filament (Prob. 32).

5.07. Color Temperature.*—We have seen that the irradiation of any surface due to a Planckian radiator may be specified by two numbers, one giving the magnitude of the spectral irradiation at an arbitrary wavelength, and the other giving the temperature of the radiator. The temperature of the radiator specifies the *quality* of the irradiation, since when the temperature is known the whole spectroradiometric curve can be plotted.

A similar specification is often used when the source is not a Planckian radiator but an incandescent lamp. Here the specifi-

* May be omitted in an introductory course.

cation of the true temperature of the filament does not determine the spectroradiometric curve in a precise manner, since the spectral radiation factor of tungsten is not very accurately known, and the coiling of the filament introduces another indefinite factor. Also, there is no satisfactory way of measuring the actual temperature of the filament. To overcome these difficulties and to give a convenient specification of the quality of radiation, the concept of *color temperature* was introduced.

A photometric comparison screen is used, one side being illuminated by the unknown source. By moving the screen, a place will be found where the two sides appear equally brilliant though somewhat different in color. The temperature of the Planckian radiator can then be changed until the difference is minimized. In the *ideal* case, simultaneous adjustments of the Planckian-radiator temperature and of the distances to the screen result in a perfect match, with the two half-fields identical in appearance. The temperature of the Planckian radiator is then determined, and *this temperature is the value of the color temperature T_c of the incandescent lamp.*

The foregoing description of the method of measuring color temperature is in agreement with the usual definition. According to Priest,[33] "The color temperature of a radiator [source, lamp] is the [absolute] temperature at which a complete radiator must be operated in order to emit energy competent to evoke a color of the same chromaticity as the color evoked by the radiant energy from the source in question."

Color temperature has been very useful in engineering work and is employed extensively at present. Tables XVIII and XIX give data on some common sources. One cannot deny, however, that the whole concept of color temperature is on a very insecure foundation. First, the preceding definition assumes tacitly that an exact match can be obtained. It is well-known that such is rarely the case. Radiation from a Planckian radiator will match the radiation from another Planckian radiator or from a gray body at the same temperature, but that is of no help, since color temperature then becomes the same as true temperature. Radiation from tungsten lamps can be matched, approximately but not exactly, with radiation from a Planckian radiator. The conditions are shown in Fig. 5.14. A Planckian radiator operating at 2800°K gives the dotted spectroradiometric curve, while a tungsten filament also operating at 2800° gives the experimental points, shown by circles. The radiation from the filament is comparatively high at the shorter wavelengths because of the shape of the curve of spectral radiation factor (Fig. 5.09). Thus the light from the filament will appear distinctly less yellow than that from the Planckian radiator at the same temperature.

By varying the temperature of the Planckian radiator, an approximate match can be obtained, giving the solid curve of Fig. 5.14. The temperature of the Planckian radiator is now found to be higher than before—approximately 2850 instead of 2800°. But *an exact match can never be obtained;* no matter

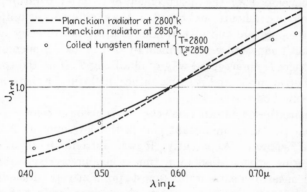

FIG. 5.14.—Radiation from a tungsten filament and from a Planckian radiator.

how the temperature of the Planckian radiator is adjusted, its spectroradiometric curve will never agree exactly with the points representing the radiation from the tungsten filament. The curves of Fig. 5.14 have been exaggerated purposely to show more clearly the differences. Actual departures of the points from the solid curve rarely exceed one or two per cent, but this does not alter the fact that Priest's definition cannot be used. It must be modified by the substitution of some phrase such as "nearest possible approximation to" for "same."

Color temperature has been applied to many other kinds of radiation; to sunlight, to skylight, and even to radiation from gaseous-conduction lamps. With some types of radiation, the concept of color temperature does not apply, since there is no possibility of getting even the roughest approximation to a match.

With other sources the approximation is very good.   But a very bothersome question is introduced: How good an approximation allows a color temperature to be assigned to a given radiation?

Secondly, with or without modification, the concept of color temperature remains quite out of the modern picture of a physical basis of photometric quantities.   What we are trying to do is to specify the *quality* of the radiation—a purely physical thing. But instead of specifying it physically, we place it on a physiological basis.   This basis brings in all the usual troubles, such as differences among "normal" observers, and places a limit of approximately $\pm 5°$ on the precision that we can ever hope to attain.[32]   It is true that several photoelectric instruments have been developed for the measurement of color temperature,[34] but all such instruments are based upon a different definition of color temperature and give results that are not directly related to color temperature as defined by Priest (see Appendix B). Also, there is no accepted way of obtaining T_c from the spectroradiometric curve, and it seems rather doubtful if a rigorous and simple method can be devised.

Despite these and other defects, the concept of color temperature has played an important part in the development of incandescent sources.   Apparently, it was introduced as a rough engineering specification at a time when precise spectroradiometric measurements were almost prohibitively difficult.   It still serves as a convenient rough engineering specification. However, one may expect it to decline gradually, to be replaced by the much more satisfactory spectroradiometric curve and by the colorimetric methods of Chap. XIII.

5.08. Relative Values of J_λ in the Visible Region.*—In the foregoing sections, the experimental value of $C_1 = 36{,}970$ has been used in calculating the actual watts radiated per square centimeter of surface per micron.   Often, however, it is more convenient to deal with *relative values* rather than absolute values. For such a purpose, it is common practice arbitrarily to make the ordinate of the J_λ curve at 0.59μ equal to unity.   In this way, all the radiation curves are easily plotted on one sheet, as shown in Fig. 5.15.   To facilitate numerical work, the values for these curves have been computed by the Planck formula and are tabulated for each 0.01μ in Appendix C.   The use of the table

* May be omitted in an introductory course.

allows the easy determination of $J_{\lambda_{rel}}$ for any temperature and for any wavelength in the visible region. Absolute values for a Planckian radiator can also be obtained, if desired, by the use of the values of $J_{0.59}$ given at the bottom of each page of the table. Appendix C gives the relative value of J_λ at temperatures from 2000 to 23,950°K and from 0.32 to 0.76μ. In most cases, the values of temperature are taken in steps of such magnitude that linear interpolation may be used without serious error.

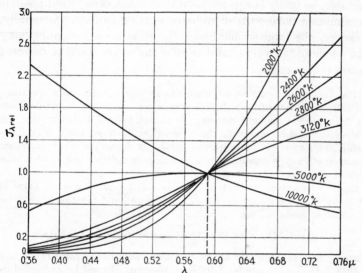

Fig. 5.15.—Spectral radiosity curves (computed) for a Planckian radiator.

The table of Appendix D is also useful in many cases. It was obtained from Appendix C by multiplying the values of $J_{\lambda_{rel}}$ by the visibility factor v. Since all values are relative, it has been found convenient to readjust the ordinates so that the maximum for each curve is 1.00.

Because the tables are calculated from Planck's law, they are strictly applicable only to nonselective radiators. The values of $J_{\lambda_{rel}}$, however, may be used* directly for filaments of tungsten or of any other material provided the temperature used is the *color temperature*, not the true temperature.

5.09. Maximum Luminous Efficacy.—It is an unfortunate fact that most of the energy radiated by incandescent lamps is not

*Subject to the limitations discussed in Sec. 5.07.

in the visible region where it would be useful but is in the infrared where it is usually worse than useless. The ordinary incandescent lamp is a very efficient heater—*i.e.*, from about 85 to 95 per cent of the input is radiated in the infrared region, and this radiation is absorbed by the surroundings with a resulting increase in their temperature. It is true that in some cases this fact has been utilized to provide some or all the heating for a room. In the ballroom of the St.George Hotel, Brooklyn, N. Y., for example, so many lamps are used that it has been found possible to eliminate 2500 sq ft of radiator heating surface. Generally, however, the large amount of infrared is a distinct annoyance and we should be very glad if more of the power could be radiated in the visible region.

The fact that incandescent filaments radiate a continuous spectrum, with all wavelengths (theoretically) from zero to ∞, makes them inherently far from perfect as light sources. It is well-known, however, that the efficacy is raised by increasing the filament temperature; and it is an interesting application of the appendix tables to determine what maximum luminous efficacy is possible from a nonselective radiator and at what temperature this maximum efficacy is obtained.

Select a temperature, such as 2798°K. Appendix C gives a value of 88.39 watts/sq cm per micron for $J_{0.59}$. The visibility function has a value of 0.7570 at 0.59μ. Thus

$$vJ_{0.59} = 0.7570 \times 88.39 = 66.91 \text{ lightwatts/sq cm per micron}$$

Turning now to Appendix D, we find that the relative value of $vJ_{0.59}$ is 0.9073. Thus all values for 2798°K in Appendix D must be multiplied by

$$\frac{66.91}{0.9073} = 73.75$$

This ratio applies also to the area under the luminosity curve. But the sum of all the luminosity values is 10.5719; and since the unit step is 0.01μ, the foregoing corresponds to an area of 0.1057. Multiplying by 73.75,

$$\int vJ_\lambda \, d\lambda = L = 0.1057 \times 73.75$$
$$= 7.795 \text{ lightwatts/sq cm}$$
$$= 4840 \text{ lumens/sq cm}$$

According to the Stefan-Boltzmann law,

$$J = 5.709(10^{-12})(2,798)^4 = 349.91 \text{ watts/sq cm}$$

Thus the luminous efficacy is

$$\eta_l = \frac{4840}{349.91} = \textbf{13.8 lumens/watt}$$

Other values are computed in a similar manner. A complete curve from the lowest temperatures to 10000°K is given in Fig. 5.16. It is interesting to note that below 2000°K the efficacy is very low but that at higher temperatures it rises rapidly and reaches a broad peak at about 6500°K. At still higher temperatures the luminous efficacy declines again, since the peak of the (J_λ vs. λ) curve has now passed into the ultraviolet.

The curve was calculated for a Planckian radiator but is equally applicable to any other nonselective radiator. For a selective radiator, however, the energy radiated in the infrared tends to be less, and thus the luminous efficacy is generally higher.

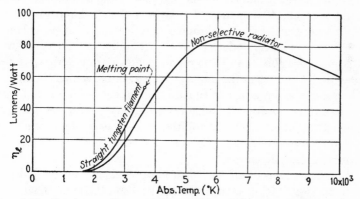

Fig. 5.16.—Luminous efficacy of the radiation from a nonselective radiator and from a tungsten filament.

This is shown by the curve for a tungsten filament which is plotted in Fig. 5.16 from data given in Chap. VI. It will be noted that at all temperatures up to the melting point of tungsten (3655°K), the luminous efficacies are considerably higher than for a nonselective radiator. If a nonselective radiator could be found, however, which would operate at over 4000°K, it would have a higher luminous efficacy than tungsten.

Problem 35. The maximum luminous efficacy of a nonselective radiator occurs around 6500°K. Determine the luminous efficacy to four significant figures by the use of the table for 6486°K in Appendix C.

Problem 36. According to the Eastman Kodak Company, the No. 15 Wratten filter transmits 67.0 per cent of the luminous flux incident on it normal to the surface. This value was obtained experimentally using "white" light. Plot a curve of percentage luminous flux transmitted by this filter for Planckian sources operating at 2000 to 3200°K. Use filter data from Table XXVII (page 172).

5.10. Possibility of Increasing the Efficacy of Incandescent Lamps.—Most energy conversions connected with electrical engineering are highly efficient, generators having 90 to 95 per cent efficiency being common, while transformers have been built with efficiencies up to 99 per cent. It is with a distinct sense of shock, therefore, that an electrical engineer realizes that his best lamps are able to produce only a few per cent of the luminous flux which is theoretically possible. The ordinary 100-watt, 115-volt tungsten lamp, for instance, produces 1520 lumens, while 100 watts of radiant power in a small band about $\lambda = 0.55\mu$ would give 62,100 lumens. Thus the 100-watt lamp produces only 2.4 per cent of the maximum theoretical visual effect. Here is a field, evidently, offering great possibility of development. It is inconceivable that the present conditions should continue indefinitely, and when the inevitable great improvement in lamps does occur it will produce in the life of mankind a change that can be classed as hardly less than revolutionary. Chapter IV has touched on some of the possibilities of increasing the efficacy of gaseous-condition lamps. Let us now turn to the possibilities with incandescent lamps.

While the over-all efficacy of a lamp (lumens output divided by watts input) is affected by all the losses in the lamp itself and in its auxiliary equipment, it is obvious that one cannot hope to obtain a high over-all efficacy if the source radiates a large amount in the ultraviolet or in the infrared and thus has a low luminous efficacy. The over-all efficacy of a nonselective incandescent radiator can never exceed about 85 lumens/watt (Fig. 5.16), and this value can be approached only at the temperature of about 6500°K. At present, there is no metal capable of standing such a temperature. The highest melting point of an element, with the possible exception of carbon, appears to be that of tungsten (3655°K). But even if an incandescent lamp could be operated at 6500°, the efficacy would still be far below the theoretical value of 621 lumens/watt because of the large amount of power radiated outside the visible spectrum.

The luminous output of tungsten lamps is gradually raised almost yearly owing to small improvements made in the method of manufacture. Evidently, anything that will make the filament more uniform* or will reduce the evaporation of the tungsten will tend to increase the life of the lamps or will allow a slightly higher temperature to be used for the same life. Undoubtedly, we can expect further small increases in efficacy. The value is definitely limited, however, by the melting point of the material, and Fig. 5.16 shows that there is no possibility of increasing the efficacy of the tungsten lamp above about 50 lumens/watt.

Another possibility is in the use of highly selective radiators which will radiate less energy in the infrared. That such highly selective materials are more than figments of the imagination is

TABLE XVIII.—COLOR TEMPERATURE OF STRAIGHT FILAMENTS OF VARIOUS
MATERIALS
(FORSYTHE, Int. Crit. Tables, V, p. 246)

True Temperature, T, °K	Color temperature, T_c					
	C	Ni	Pt	Ta	W	Nernst glower
1000	....	1020	1011	....	1006	
1100	....	1125	1116	....	1108	
1200	....	1231	1222	....	1210	
1300	1300	1336	1328	....	1312	
1400	1396	1442	1435	....	1414	
1500	1492	1546	1542	1532	1517	1517
1600	1590	....	1649	1642	1619	1631
1700	1687	....	1757	1751	1722	1744
1800	1785	....	1865	1859	1825	1857
1900	1884	....	1974	1967	1929	1968
2000	1984	....	2083	2075	2033	2074
2100	2086	....	....	2182	2137	2173
2200	2187	....	....	2288	2242	2265
2300	2288	....	....	2393	2347	2345
2400	....	....	....	2497	2452	2426
2500	....	....	....	2601	2557	2502
2600	....	....	....	2705	2663	
2800	....	....	....	2911	2878	
3000	....	....	....	....	3094	

* Considerable research has been done on filaments made of a *single* tungsten crystal instead of many crystals.

Table XIX.—Color Temperature of Various Light Sources
Lamps
(Forsythe, Int. Crit. Tables, V, 1929, p. 245)

Gas-filled tungsten lamps	Operating at lumens per watt	T	T_c
50 watts.............................	10.0	2685	2670
75 watts.............................	11.8	2735	2705
100 watts............................	12.9	2760	2740
200 watts............................	15.2	2840	2810
900 watts (movie)...................	27.3	3290	3220
1000 watts..........................	20.0	2990	2980
10 kw...............................	31.0	3350	3300
30 kw...............................	31.0	3350	3300
50-watt untreated carbon..............	2.5	2095	2080
50-watt GEM carbon..................	4.0	2130	2195
Osmium lamp........................	6.3	....	2185
50-watt tantalum lamp.................	6.3	2180	2260
10-watt tungsten vacuum lamp..........	7.7	2355	2390
25-watt tungsten vacuum lamp..........	9.8	2450	2493
40-watt tungsten vacuum lamp..........	10.0	2460	2504
60-watt tungsten vacuum lamp..........	10.1	2465	2509

Tungsten lamps (average values obtained by Sharp)

50-watt A-21 Mazda C....................	11.0	2656
60-watt A-21 Mazda C....................	11.7	2710
75-watt PS-22 Mazda C...................	12.7	2731
75-watt A-23 Mazda C....................	12.9	2744
100-watt A-23 Mazda C...................	13.5	2746
150 PS-25 Mazda C.......................	15.1	2753
200 PS-30 Mazda C.......................	16.3	2842
15-watt A-17 Mazda B....................	9.1	2441
25-watt A-19 Mazda B....................	10.0	2478
40-watt A-21 Mazda B....................	10.0	2503

Other sources

Solid carbon arc............................	3,780
Sperm candle...............................	1,930
Kerosene lamp..............................	2,055
Hefner lamp................................	1,880
Gas flame, batswing.........................	2,160
Clear sky on Mount Wilson...................	50,000
Clear sky at Davos-Platz, Switzerland..........	14,000
Clear sky before sunrise......................	24,150
Whole sky, clear, in June.....................	8080–9280
Overcast sky................................	6300–7175
Noon sunlight at Washington, D.C..............	5000–6500

shown by Table XX, which gives the spectral radiation factor
of a Welsbach gas mantle composed of thorium oxide and cerium
oxide.   An electric lamp based on the use of selective materials
was the Nernst glower, consisting of a small rod of rare-earth
oxides heated to incandescence in air by the passage of current
through it.   Actually, the over-all efficacy of the Nernst lamp
was low, and it could not compete with the tungsten lamp.   The
redevelopment of the Nernst lamp on more modern lines,
however, might result in something of value.

TABLE XX.—e_λ OF WELSBACH GAS MANTLE
0.993 Th O_2, 0.007 Ce_2O_3. $T = 1800°K$
(H. RUBENS, *Ann. d. Physik*, **18**, 1905, p. 725)

λ	e_λ
0.45	0.86
0.50	0.72
0.55	0.49
0.60	0.24
0.70	0.062
1.00	0.019
1.2	0.012
1.5	0.009
2.0	0.007

A question frequently asked is why some frequency-changing
substance cannot be used that will transform the undesirable
infrared radiation into radiation in the visible region.   If the
excess energy were in the ultraviolet instead of in the infrared,
such a scheme might be fruitful, since there are a number of
fluorescent materials which emit visible radiation when excited
by ultraviolet.   Stokes's law, however, states that the emitted
radiation is always of *lower* frequency than the exciting radiation; and though some cases have been found where this law does
not apply, the idea of frequency-changing substances does not
seem particularly fruitful.

Problem 37.   What would be the luminous efficacy of an ideal source which
would radiate equally from 0.40 to 0.76μ (J_λ = const) with no radiation
in the infrared and ultraviolet regions?

Problem 38.   Plot a curve of luminous efficacy *vs.* temperature for a
selective filament emitting according to Table XX, assuming that the
spectral radiation factors are independent of temperature.

Problem 39.   We wish to obtain a filter that can be used in front of an
incandescent lamp (T_C = 2798°K) to give a *relative* spectroradiometric
distribution equivalent to T_C = 5000°K.   Plot the spectral transmission

factor of the proposed filter for wavelengths from 0.4 to 0.7μ. The filter is to have the highest possible transmission consistent with the correct spectral distribution between these limits.

Problem 40. A spectral response curve for a Photronic cell is shown in Fig. 7.26. Calculate the sensitivity of the cell (microamperes per lumen per square foot) for radiation from a source at $T_C = 2998°K$.

Bibliography

GENERAL

1. F. REICHE: The Quantum Theory, Chap. I, E. P. Dutton & Company, Inc., New York, 1922.
2. S. DUSHMAN: Quantum Theory and Atomic Structure, (Physical Chemistry, H. S. Taylor), Vol. II, p. 1119, D. Van Nostrand Company, Inc., New York, 1931.
3. RUARK and UREY: Atoms, Molecules and Quanta, p. 11 and Chap. III, McGraw-Hill Book Company, Inc., New York, 1930.
4. CADY and DATES: Illuminating Engineering, Chap. II, John Wiley & Sons, Inc., New York, 1928.
5. J. W. T. WALSH: Photometry, pp. 31, 132, Archibald Constable & Company, Ltd., London, 1926.
6. M. PLANCK: Wärmestrahlung, J. A. Barth, Leipzig, 1923.
7. W. E. FORSYTHE: Temperature Radiation, *J.O.S.A.*, **16**, 1928, p. 307.
8. R. T. BIRGE: Probable Values of the General Physical Constants, *Phys. Rev. Supp.*, **1**, 1929, p. 1.

BLACK-BODY RADIATION

9. LUMMER and PRINGSHEIM: Die Verteilung der Energie im Spektrum des schwarzen Körpers, *Verh. d. D. phys. Ges.*, **1**, 1899, pp. 23, 215; **2**, 1900, p. 163.
10. W. W. COBLENTZ: Constants of Spectral Radiation of a Uniformly Heated Inclosure, *Bu. Stds. Bull.*, **10**, 1914, p. 1; **13**, 1916, p. 459.
11. HYDE, CADY, and FORSYTHE: Optical Pyrometry, *Astrophys. J.*, **42**, 1915, p. 294.
12. W. E. FORSYTHE: Optical Pyrometers, *J.O.S.A.*, **10**, 1925, p. 19.
13. MÜLLER, THEISSING, and ESMARCH: Über einen induktiv-geheizten Hohlraumstrahler, *Zeits. f. tech. Physik*, **14**, 1933, p. 107.
14. WENSEL, ROESER, BARBROW, and CALDWELL: The Waidner-Burgess Standard of Light, *Bu. Stds. J.R.*, **6**, 1931, p. 1103. (RP 325).
15. CUNNOLD and MILFORD: Blackness of a Black Body Radiator, *Phil. Mag.*, **18**, 1934, p. 561.
16. H. BUCKLEY: Radiation from the Inside of a Circular Cylinder, III, *Phil. Mag.*, **17**, 1934, p. 576.

SELECTIVE RADIATORS

17. L. L. HOLLADAY: Proportion of Energy Radiated by Incandescent Solids in Various Spectral Regions, *J.O.S.A.*, **17**, 1928, p. 329.

18. FORSYTHE and CHRISTISON: Ultraviolet Radiation from the Sun and Heated Tungsten, *J.O.S.A.*, **20**, 1930, p. 396.
19. A. G. WORTHING: Spectral Emissivities, *Phys. Rev.*, **28**, 1926, p. 174.
20. BECKER and EWEST: Die physikalischen und strahlungstechnischen Eigenschaften des Tantalkarbids, *Zeits. f. techn. Physik*, **11**, 1930, p. 148.
21. H. RUBENS: Über das Emissionsspectrum des Auerbrenners, *Ann. d. Physik*, **18**, 1905, p. 725.
22. FORSYTHE and WORTHING: The Properties of Tungsten, *Astrophys. J.*, **61**, 1925, p. 146.
23. A. G. WORTHING: Das spektrale Emissionsvermögen des Wolframs, *Zeits. f. Physik*, **22**, 1924, p. 9.
24. HYDE, CADY and MIDDLEKAUFF: Selective Emission of Incandescent Lamps, *I.E.S. Trans.*, 4, 1909, p. 334.
25. HOFFMANN and WILLENBERG: Das Emissionsvermögen des Wolframs, *Phys. Zeits.*, **35**, 1934, p. 713.
26. LAX and PIRANI: Künstliches Tages und Sonnenlicht, *C.I.E. Proc.*, **1**, 1932, p. 324.

COLOR TEMPERATURE

27. PATTERSON and DUDDING: The Estimation of High Temperature by the Method of Color Identity, *Phys. Soc., Proc.*, **27**, 1915, p. 230.
28. HYDE and FORSYTHE: The Quality of Light from an Illuminant as Indicated by its Color Temperature, *Frank. Inst. J.*, **183**, 1917, p. 353.
29. HYDE and FORSYTHE: Color Temperature & Brightness of Various Illuminants, *I.E.S. Trans.*, **16**, 1921, p. 419.
30. W. E. FORSYTHE: Color Match & Spectral Distribution, *J.O.S.A.*, **7**, 1923, p. 1115.
31. I. G. PRIEST: Measurement of the Color Temperature of the More Efficient Artificial Light Sources, *J.O.S.A.*, **6**, 1922, p. 27.
32. I. G. PRIEST: Colorimetry and Photometry of Daylight and Incandescent Illuminants, *J.O.S.A.*, **7**, 1923, p. 1175.
33. I. G. PRIEST: A Proposed Scale for Use in Specifying the Chromaticity of Incandescent Illuminants, *J.O.S.A.*, **23**, 1933, p. 41.
34. C. H. SHARP: An Apparatus to Measure Color Temperature of Incandescent Lamp Filaments, *J.O.S.A.*, **20**, 1930, p. 62.
35. W. F. ROESER: Thermoelectric Temperature Scales, *Bu. Stds. J.R.*, **3**, 1929, p. 343.   (RP 99)
36. ROESER, SCHOFIELD, and MOSER: An International Comparison of Temperature Scales between 660° and 1063°C., *Bu. Stds. J.R.*, **11**, 1933, p. 1.   (RP 573)
37. WENSEL, ROESER, BARBROW, and CALDWELL: The Waidner-Burgess Standard of Light, *Bu. Stds. J.R.*, **6**, 1931, p. 1103.   (RP 325)
38. ROESER, CALDWELL, and WENSEL: Freezing Point of Platinum, *Bu. Stds. J.R.*, **6**, 1931, p. 1119.   (RP 326).
39. HENNING and WENSEL: Freezing Point of Iridium, *Bu. Stds. J.R.*, **10**, 1933, p. 809.   (RP 568)

40. ROESER and WENSEL: Freezing Point of Rhodium, *Bu. Stds. J.R.*, **12**, 1934, p. 519. (RP 676)
41. WENSEL, JUDD and ROESER: Establishment of a Scale of Color Temperature, *Bu. Stds. J.R.*, **12**, 1934, p. 527. (RP 677)
42. G. K. BURGESS: The International Temperature Scale, *Bu. Stds. J.R.*, **1**, 1928, p. 635. (RP 22)
43. W. E. FORSYTHE: Color Temperature Scale of the Nela Laboratories, *Phys. Rev.*, **47**, 1935, p. 789.
44. R. DAVIS: A Correlated Color Temperature for Illuminants, *Bu. Stds. Res. Paper* 365, 1931.

TABLES

45. FREHAFER and SNOW: Tables and Graphs for Facilitating Computations of Spectral Energy Distribution, *Bu. Stds. Misc. Pub.*, 56, 1925.
46. J. F. SKOGLAND: Tables of Spectral Energy Distribution, *Bu. Stds. Misc. Pub.*, 86, 1929.
47. R. L. GOUCHOE: Computation of Spectral Energy Distribution for Incandescent Sources, M.I.T. thesis, Electrical Engineering Dept., 1934.
48. L. F. CLEVELAND: Computation of Spectral Energy Distributions. M.I.T. thesis, Electrical Engineering Dept., 1935.

CHAPTER VI

INCANDESCENT LAMPS

The incandescent-lamp industry, since its origin in 1879, has grown to be one of the big industries of the country.[1] In a typical year (1931), 347,000,000 large incandescent lamps were sold in the United States alone, 344,000,000 of them having tungsten filaments. In the same year, 217,678,000 miniature tungsten lamps and 1,163,000 miniature carbon lamps were sold for flashlights, motor-vehicle headlights, etc. Thus over 560,-000,000 tungsten lamps were sold, a number that is almost constant from year to year irrespective of business conditions and that represents a sale of well over $100,000,000 a year.

6.02. History.—This industry had its beginning in 1879 when Edison produced the first successful incandescent lamp.[2] Many previous attempts to develop an incandescent lamp had been made in the nineteenth century by various investigators, but none of the lamps had proved practicable. Edison's first successful lamp had a filament of sewing thread carbonized by heating in an airtight crucible. The filament was mounted in a glass bulb, and the filament ends were clamped to platinum lead-in wires sealed through the bulb which was then evacuated.

In later lamps, various materials were carbonized and used for filaments: paper, bamboo, etc. The first commercial lamps had filaments of carbonized paper in a "hairpin" form, but carbonized bamboo was found to be somewhat stronger and was used for the next 10 years.

Since the invention of the incandescent lamp, continual effort has been made by lamp manufacturers to improve their product, resulting in a gradual upward trend in luminous output per watt input. The approximate over-all efficacies are given in Table XXI. At an early date, it was found that the luminous output could be raised somewhat by "treating" the carbonized filament, which was done by heating the filament in an atmosphere of gasoline vapor. This formed a coating of graphite on the fila-

143

ment surface and resulted in a smoother and more uniform filament. In 1894, bamboo was abandoned in favor of a filament of cellulose which was squirted through a die, dried, and then carbonized. An efficacy of 3.3 lumens/watt was obtained, as indicated in Table XXI.

Table XXI.—The Development of the Incandescent Lamp

Lamp	Date	Approximate watts	Approximate lumens per watt
Edison's first incandescent lamp........	1879	. . . .	1.4
Carbonized-bamboo filament...........	1880–1884	. . . .	1.6
Squirted-cellulose filament, carbonized and treated........................	1894	. . . .	3.3
GEM lamp..........................	1905	60	4.2
Osmium lamp.......................	. . . .	60	5.9
Tantalum lamp.....................	1906	60	5
Pressed-tungsten filament in vacuum....	1907	60	7.8
Drawn-tungsten filament in vacuum....	1911	60	10
Drawn-tungsten filament in gas*.......	1913	1000	20

* Note that the large improvement in efficacy made in 1913, due to the use of an inert gas, was obtainable only with lamps of high wattage.

In 1905, a new process was developed of heating the carbonized filament at a very high temperature in an electric furnace to burn out some of the impurities. The resulting filament was said to be "metallized," since its temperature coefficient of resistance was positive like a metal instead of negative as in the previous lamps. The lamp was called a GEM lamp (General Electric Metallized) and operated at about 4.2 lumens/watt.

Now we come to the introduction of metal-filament lamps. Platinum had been tried by Edison and others but had not been used because of its comparatively low melting point and its high cost. An incandescent lamp whose filament was of a very rare metal, osmium, was developed in Europe by Welsbach. Despite the fact that its melting point (2500°K) was below that of carbon, it could be operated at a higher temperature than carbon because of its lower evaporation. The radiation was selective, which also tended to give greater luminous output than a carbon lamp. The osmium lamp did not come into extensive use, however, principally because of the difficulty of obtaining the metal. Tantalum filaments were introduced into the United States in 1906 but were soon superseded by tungsten. The first tungsten lamps used filaments made from powdered tungsten which produced a fairly efficacious but very fragile lamp. Later, a method of drawing tungsten into wire was developed, resulting in much greater ruggedness.

All the foregoing lamps were made with as good a vacuum as could be obtained commercially. It was realized that the useful life of a lamp was governed largely by the blackening of the bulb, this blackening being due to the evaporation of the filament material as well as to certain chemical effects. To determine if an increase in the useful life of tungsten lamps could be obtained by a further improvement in the vacuum, Langmuir made a thorough study of the effect of small traces of various gases. A trace of water vapor was found to play havoc with the filament. Apparently, the heat of the filament dissociated the water, the oxygen attacked the tungsten, and the tungsten oxide deposited on the bulb. The hydrogen then reacted with this oxide, leaving a metallic deposit of tungsten on the lamp bulb, and again formed water which proceeded to attack the filament as before. Thus a slight trace of water vapor led to a short life. Langmuir found however, that the vacuum then used in commercial lamps was so good that further improvements in it did not materially lengthen the life. Apparently, then, the blackening of the bulb of a tungsten lamp was due almost entirely to a true evaporation and not to the effect of chemical impurities. The problem was to reduce this evaporation.

A filament evaporates gradually at high temperatures much as water in a dish evaporates at room temperature. Owing to the temperature of the water, the molecules are in constant vibration, as can be shown by the Brownian motion of small particles which may be suspended in it. The velocity of all molecules is not the same, however, so occasionally a molecule acquires an unusually high velocity and shoots completely out of the liquid. In this way, the liquid evaporates. In a vacuum, there is nothing external to keep the molecules from leaving the water, and the evaporation is rapid. This corresponds to the conditions in a vacuum tungsten lamp. If the dish of water is in air or other gas, however, the gas molecules bombard the liquid surface owing to their thermal motion and tend to keep the water molecules from emerging. It might be expected that the same thing could be done with incandescent lamps—*i.e.*, filling the bulb with a gas at fairly high pressure would be expected to reduce the evaporation of the filament.

This scheme, as a matter of fact, was not a new one. Edison patented the idea in 1883 and experimented with carbon lamps filled with nitrogen. The results were disappointing, however, since so much heat was lost from the filament by convection that

TABLE XXII.—PROPERTIES OF TUNGSTEN
(JONES and LANGMUIR, *G. E. Rev.*, 1927)

T (°K)	$\mathfrak{R}$		e_l	J		η_l		ζ		T, (°K)
	microhm-cm	α		watts/ sq cm	α	lumens/ watt	α	g cm^{-2} sec^{-1}	α	
1000	24.93	1.200	0.105	0.602	5.65	0.000693	17.3	5.32×10^{-34}	94.8	1000
1100	27.94	1.195	0.124	1.027	5.57	0.00344	15.6	2.17×10^{-30}	87.5	1100
1200	30.98	1.189	0.141	1.66	5.49	0.0126	14.2	3.21×10^{-27}	80.6	1200
1300	34.08	1.185	0.158	2.57	5.41	0.0355	13.1	1.35×10^{-24}	74.0	1300
1400	37.19	1.182	0.175	3.83	5.34	0.0899	12.0	2.51×10^{-22}	68.3	1400
1500	40.36	1.179	0.192	5.52	5.27	0.199	11.1	2.37×10^{-20}	63.5	1500
1600	43.55	1.179	0.207	7.74	5.20	0.395	10.3	1.25×10^{-18}	59.3	1600
1700	46.78	1.180	0.222	10.62	5.12	0.724	9.5	4.17×10^{-17}	55.7	1700
1800	50.05	1.182	0.237	14.19	5.06	1.19	8.8	8.81×10^{-16}	52.5	1800
1900	53.35	1.184	0.250	18.64	4.99	1.94	8.2	1.41×10^{-14}	49.8	1900
2000	56.67	1.186	0.263	24.04	4.93	2.84	7.6	1.76×10^{-13}	47.2	2000
2100	60.06	1.188	0.274	30.5	4.87	4.08	7.1	1.66×10^{-12}	44.9	2100
2200	63.48	1.190	0.285	38.2	4.81	5.52	6.7	1.25×10^{-11}	42.9	2200
2300	66.91	1.192	0.295	47.2	4.76	7.24	6.2	8.00×10^{-11}	40.9	2300
2400	70.39	1.195	0.304	57.7	4.71	9.39	5.8	4.26×10^{-10}	39.0	2400
2500	73.91	1.197	0.312	69.8	4.66	11.72	5.5	2.03×10^{-9}	37.3	2500
2600	77.49	1.200	0.320	83.8	4.61	14.34	5.1	8.41×10^{-9}	35.8	2600
2700	81.04	1.202	0.327	99.6	4.58	17.60	4.8	3.19×10^{-8}	34.3	2700
2800	84.70	1.205	0.334	117.6	4.54	20.53	4.5	1.10×10^{-7}	32.9	2800
2900	88.33	1.207	0.340	137.8	4.51	23.64	4.2	3.30×10^{-7}	31.6	2900
3000	92.04	1.210	0.346	160.5	4.48	27.25	4.0	9.95×10^{-7}	30.4	3000
3100	95.76	1.213	0.352	185.8	4.46	30.95	3.7	2.60×10^{-6}	29.2	3100
3200	99.54	1.216	0.357	214.0	4.43	34.70	3.5	6.38×10^{-6}	28.2	3200
3300	103.3	1.218	0.362	245.4	4.42	38.90	3.3	1.56×10^{-5}	27.3	3300
3400	107.2	1.221	0.366	280.0	4.41	43.20	3.1	3.47×10^{-5}	26.4	3400
3500	111.1	1.224	0.370	318.0	4.40	47.15	2.9	7.54×10^{-5}	25.6	3500
3600	115.0	1.227	0.374	360.0	4.39	50.70	2.8	1.51×10^{-4}	24.8	3600
3655	117.1	1.229	0.376	382.6	4.38	53.10	2.7	2.28×10^{-4}	24.4	3655

very little light could be obtained. The problem before Langmuir in 1913 was to see if this loss of heat by convection could be more than counterbalanced by the effect of reduced evaporation which for the same life would allow the filament to be operated at a higher temperature. After numerous failures, a successful 1000-watt gas-filled tungsten lamp was put on the market in 1913. The gas was nitrogen at approximately atmospheric pressure, and a tightly coiled tungsten filament was used, instead of the old straight filament, in order to reduce convection loss as much as possible.[5,6] Later experience led to the development of gas-filled lamps of lower wattage. The effectiveness of the gas in increasing the luminous output is found to be less marked with the smaller wattage lamps; so even today, the smallest lamps (115-volt lamps of 6, 10, 15, and 25 watts) are of the vacuum type (Mazda B), while the 40-watt and larger sizes are made gas filled (Mazda C).

Table XIX (page 138) gives the properties of a number of vacuum and gas-filled lamps. The much higher filament temperatures of the gas-filled lamps should be noted, also the higher luminous efficacies.

6.03. Properties of Tungsten.—The design of tungsten filaments is based upon the properties of tungsten given in Table XXII.* The results are for straight filaments of pure tungsten in a good vacuum. The first column gives the temperature of the filament; the second is the resistivity of tungsten in microhm-centimeters; while the third column is the exponent of the temperature in the equation

$$\frac{\Re}{\Re'} = \left(\frac{T}{T'}\right)^{\alpha} \tag{6.01}$$

where $\Re$ and $\Re'$ = two values of resistivity at the respective temperatures T and T'.

Figure 6.01 shows that this equation holds with considerable accuracy over the usual range of operating temperatures even if α = constant. If greater accuracy is desired, the variation of α with temperature given in Table XXII may be used.

The fourth column gives the total radiation factor e_t at various temperatures. The fifth column deals with J, the watts per

---

* See also the recent results of Forsythe and Watson.[21]

square centimeter radiated by the filament. J for tungsten was obtained by multiplying the value of J for a Planckian radiator by the total radiation factor e_t. For a tungsten filament at 3000°K,

$$J = e_t \sigma T^4 = 0.346(5.709)(3)^4 = 160 \text{ watts/sq cm}$$

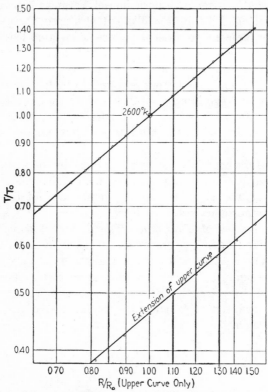

Fig. 6.01.—Variation of resistance with temperature for tungsten filaments. Based on the data of Jones and Langmuir.[8]

The remaining part of Table XXII gives the luminous efficacy (lumens per radiated watt) and the rate of evaporation ζ of the filament in grams vaporized per square centimeter of surface per second.

The values of α refer in each case to the exponents of the temperature and are included as an aid in interpolation. Values of $\mathfrak{R}$ at temperatures between those given in the table can generally be obtained by ordinary linear interpolation. However, with some of the other quantities, particularly with vaporization, linear interpolation leads to grave errors which are greatly reduced by using a power-function formula. Suppose, for instance, that the values of J are given at 1800 and at 2000°, and we wish to obtain the value for 1900° by interpolation. Linear interpolation gives

$\frac{1}{2}(14.19 + 24.04) = 19.12$ watts/sq cm, while the true value is 18.64. Now use the formula

$$\frac{J}{J'} = \left(\frac{T}{T'}\right)^{\alpha} \qquad (6.02)$$

and if J is the value at 1900° and J' refers to the value at 1800°,

$$\frac{J}{14.19} = \left(\frac{1900}{1800}\right)^{5.06}$$

or $J = 18.65$, which is in excellent agreement with 18.64, the correct value given in the table.

6.04. Design of Lamps.—It is not the purpose of this section to provide a detailed account of the methods used in the design of lamps but rather to give a rough idea of the principles involved. By actually working with numerical cases, the student will obtain a grasp of the characteristics and possibilities of incandescent lamps such as can be obtained in no other way.

Given the watts P and the voltage rating V of the proposed lamp, the resistance of the filament is fixed by

$$R = \frac{V^2}{P} \qquad (6.03)$$

The resistivity of tungsten is known, so the diameter and length of a filament that will have the resistance R is easily found. It will be noted, however, that the filament is not uniquely determined. There is an infinite number of possible filaments having the same resistance, ranging from short ones of small diameter to very long ones of large diameter. To proceed further, we must make use of the radiation from the filament. P watts are being supplied to the lamp. By the law of conservation of energy, P watts must therefore be dissipated by the filament when thermal equilibrium has been reached. Part (P_r) of the power is dissipated by radiation, and part is dissipated by the conduction of heat through the filament leads and supports and by convection loss if the bulb is filled with gas. Thus,

$$P = P_r + \text{losses} \tag{6.04}$$

Tests show that in the average vacuum lamp having a straight filament, about 7 per cent of the input is lost by conduction of heat through the leads and filament supports. For a gas-filled lamp using a coiled filament, about 3 per cent is lost in this way,

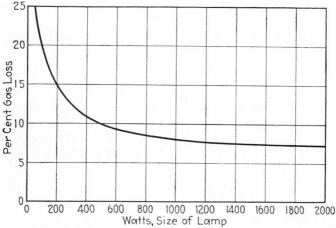

Fig. 6.02.—Convection loss in lamps filled with a mixture of nitrogen and Argon. Loss is expressed in per cent of lamp input. (*From Forsythe and Worthing.*[7])

a smaller number of supports being used in this case. The filament of a gas-filled lamp also loses heat by convection, the magnitude of this loss for average lamps being given in Fig. 6.02.*

If the operating temperature of the proposed filament is known, the watts J radiated per square centimeter of filament surface can be obtained from Table **XXII**, and the necessary filament surface is

$$S = \frac{P_r}{J} \tag{6.05}$$

* See also Forsythe and Watson, *Frank. Inst., J.*, **213**, 1932, p. 630.

Equation (6.05), in conjunction with Eqs. (6.03) and (6.04), gives all the necessary information for fixing the size of the filament.

The filament surface is

$$S = \pi \delta l$$

and

$$R = \Re \frac{4l}{\pi \delta^2}$$

Thus,

$$\begin{cases} \delta = \sqrt[3]{0.405 \dfrac{\Re P_r}{JR}} & \text{(6.06)} \\[2ex] l = \dfrac{S}{\pi \delta} = \dfrac{P_r}{\pi \delta J} & \text{(6.07)} \end{cases}$$

which determine uniquely the diameter and length of the filament. Here J = watts/sq cm radiated by the filament.

   $\Re$ = resistivity of filament (ohm-cm).

   S = surface of filament (sq cm).

   δ = diameter of filament (cm).

   l = length of filament (cm).

The density of tungsten is 19.3, so the mass of the filament is $19.3 \dfrac{\pi l \delta^2}{4}$ grams. The mass of tungsten evaporated from the filament in 1000 hr is

$$1000(3600)\pi \delta l \zeta = 1.13 \times 10^7 \delta l \zeta \text{ grams} \tag{6.08}$$

Evidently, the useful life of a filament may be taken as the number of hours required for the evaporation of a certain percentage of the original mass of the filament, the exact percentage depending upon the uniformity of the filament wire and other factors. In this work, it will be convenient arbitrarily to define the useful life of a lamp as the number of hours required for the evaporation of 25 per cent of the original filament mass, the calculation being based upon Eq. (6.08) with the original filament diameter δ.

Example, Vacuum Lamp.   Consider a 40-watt, 115-volt vacuum tungsten lamp operating at 2460°K, with a filament 51.0 cm long and 0.038 mm in diameter.   What are the approximate life and lumens per watt?

The filament surface is

$$S = \pi \delta l = 0.609 \text{ sq cm}$$

and the filament mass is

$$m = \frac{19.3 \pi \delta^2 l}{4} = 11.2 \times 10^{-3} \text{ gram}$$

Also,

$$\zeta = 4.26 \times 10^{-10} \left(\frac{2460}{2400} \right)^{39.0} = 1.12 \times 10^{-9} \text{ gram cm}^{-2} \text{ sec}^{-1}$$

and the total amount of tungsten vaporized in 1000 hr is

$$1.13 \times 10^7 (0.0038)(51.0)(1.13)10^{-9} = 2.44 \times 10^{-3} \text{ gram}$$
$$= 22 \text{ per cent of the original filament mass}$$

Thus we conclude that the *life will be approximately* 1000 *hr.*

The luminous efficacy of the lamp is found from Table XXII:

$$\eta_l = 9.39 + 0.6(11.72 - 9.39) = 10.7 \text{ lumens/watt}$$

The over-all efficacy is less than the foregoing, owing to the loss of heat through the leads and supports, so

$$\eta_0 = 10.7(1.00 - 0.07) = \textbf{10.0 lumens/watt}$$

Example, Gas-filled Lamp. With a gas-filled lamp, the same kind of calculations can be carried out, but the additional convection loss must be taken into account in calculating the over-all efficacy (Fig. 6.02). Also, the values of ζ given in Table XXII are for a straight filament in a good vacuum. The coiled filament is found to reduce the tabulated values to about 50 per cent, while with a coiled filament in a gas (Mazda-C lamp) the vaporization is reduced, apparently to from 1 to 5 per cent of the tabulated values.

In the design of a lamp of given watts and voltage, the resistance is determined by Eq. (6.03). A temperature is then assumed, and l and δ are calculated by use of Eqs. (6.06) and (6.07). The approximate life is determined from Eq. (6.08). If life is decidedly different from the desired life, another temperature must be assumed, and the process repeated. Usually, after two or three trials the result is sufficiently close to the result desired. There is no need of great refinement in these calculations, since they are based upon simplifying assumptions which may cause error, and the criterion for useful life is only a rough approximation.

Determine the approximate diameter and length of filament for a 1000-watt 115-volt gas-filled lamp to have a 1000-hr life,

$$\text{where } P = 1000 \text{ watts;}$$
$$V = 115 \text{ volts;}$$
$$R = 13.2 \text{ ohms.}$$

A temperature of 2950°K is assumed.   Then

$$\mathcal{R} = 90.2 \times 10^{-6} \text{ ohm-cm.}$$
$$J = 149 \text{ watts/sq cm.}$$
$$\eta = 25.40 \text{ lumens/watt.}$$
$$\zeta = 5.66 \times 10^{-7}$$
$$P_r = 1000(1.00 - 0.08 - 0.03)$$
$$= 890 \text{ watts}$$

Thus

$$\delta = \sqrt[3]{0.405 \frac{90.2 \times 10^{-6}(890)}{149(13.2)}}$$
$$= 0.025 \text{ cm}$$
$$l = \frac{890}{\pi(.025)(149)} = 76.2 \text{ cm}$$

The over-all efficacy will be approximately

$$\eta_0 = 25.44 \times 0.89 = 22.6 \text{ lumens/watt}$$

and the vaporization in 1000 hr (assuming that 2 per cent as much tungsten is vaporized as in a vacuum lamp with straight filament) is

$$5.66 \times 10^{-7}(0.02)1.13 \times 10^7(0.025)(76.2) = 0.243 \text{ gram}$$

The initial mass of the filament is

$$m = 19.3\pi \frac{(0.025)^2}{4}(76.2) = 0.723 \text{ gram}$$

so that about 34 per cent of the mass is vaporized.   It is probable that this design will give as close to a 1000-hr life as can be calculated from our data, though a slight reduction in filament temperature might be advisable.

Assumptions.—Since it is not the purpose of this chapter to give a detailed and accurate treatment of filament design, the foregoing has purposely been made free of refinements.   The principal assumption is that the entire filament is at the temperature T.   Actually, the temperature near the ends of the filament gradually decreases so that for a few centimeters near each end the properties are distinctly different from those calculated. An example of the actual temperature distribution is shown in Fig. 6.03.   The assumption of uniform temperature of the filament does not introduce very large errors in lamps designed for 115 volts, where the filament is usually 50 to 100 cm long, but may introduce serious errors with a 2.5-volt filament for a triode. The subject has been studied extensively by Langmuir[12] and others, to whose papers the reader is referred for further information.[13,14]

Table XXII is based on the assumption of a straight filament. The present practice of coiling the filament[15] introduces different conditions as regards both vaporization and spectral radiation factor. The characteristics of the lamp are affected also by traces of impurities in the tungsten or in the gas, the condition of the filament surface, and many other factors. Nevertheless, the present elementary treatment is believed to fulfill its primary purpose of giving an insight into the characteristics of incandes-

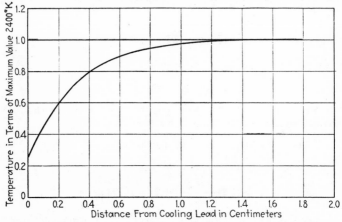

FIG. 6.03.—Temperature distribution along a tungsten filament.[13]

cent lamps. Also, the method can be used without great error in the actual design of experimental lamps for voltages of 100 or higher.

Problem 41. Design a vacuum lamp and a gas-filled lamp for the rating of 500 watts, 220 volts, and 1000-hr life and determine which will give the more luminous flux.

6.05. Modern Incandescent Lamps.—A great variety of incandescent lamps is constructed today, the data for some of them being given in Table XXIII. The fourth column shows that all the 115-volt lamps except the smallest sizes are now made gas filled (Mazda C). The second column gives the bulb sizes. The letter refers to the shape of the bulb (Fig. 6.04), G being spherical, P pear-shaped, S straight-sided, T tubular, etc. The number following the letter is the largest diameter of the bulb in eighths of an inch. Thus, a G-30 bulb is a spherical one having a diameter of 3% or $3\frac{3}{4}$ in. The bulbs marked *cl* are made of clear glass, while those marked *day* are of a light-blue glass to filter out some of the red rays and thus produce a light whose

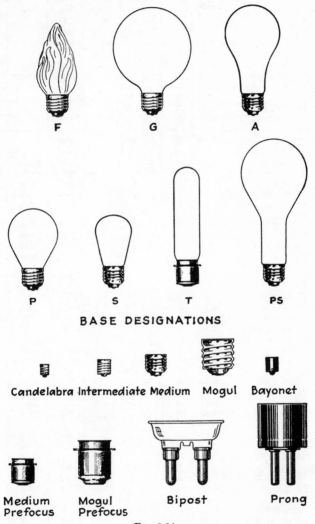

BULB DESIGNATIONS

F   G   A

P   S   T   PS

BASE DESIGNATIONS

Candelabra Intermediate Medium Mogul Bayonet

Medium   Mogul   Bipost   Prong
Prefocus Prefocus

FIG. 6.04.

color approaches that of daylight. Formerly, some lamps were produced with diffusing globes obtained by sandblasting or acid etching the outside of the globe. With such lamps the glare was

Table XXIII.—Mazda Lamps for 110-, 115-, and 120-volt Circuits
(From Standard Price Schedule, Large Lamps, Westinghouse, Apr. 1, 1935)

Watts	Bulb	List price	Mazda B or Mazda C lamp	Approx. value, rated initial lumens	Rated initial lumens per watt	Rated ave. lab. life (hr.)	Base	Max. over-all length (in.)
6	S-6 clear.........	$0.20	B	38	6.4	1,500	Cand.	$1\frac{7}{8}$
6	S-14 clear........	0.15	B	38	6.3	1,500	Med.	$3\frac{1}{2}$
6	S-14 colored......	0.20	B	......	....	1,500	Med.	$3\frac{1}{2}$
10	S-11.............	0.20	B	76	7.6	1,500	Inter.	$2\frac{5}{16}$
10	S-14 clear........	0.15	B	77	7.7	1,500	Med.	$3\frac{1}{2}$
10	S-14 colored......	0.20	B	......	....	1,500	Med.	$3\frac{1}{2}$
15	A-17 I. F.........	0.15	B	138	9.2	1,000	Med.	$3\frac{5}{8}$
15	F-10 F. T., white ivory...........	0.35	B	......	....	750	Cand.	$3\frac{1}{16}$
25	A-19 A. F........	0.15	B	252	10.1	1,000	Med.	$3\frac{15}{16}$
25	A-19 colored......	0.20	B	......	....	1,000	Med.	$3\frac{15}{16}$
25	A-19 day. clear...	0.30	B	......	....	1,000	Med.	$3\frac{15}{16}$
25	G-18½ white.....	0.30	B	......	....	750	Med.	$3\frac{9}{16}$
25	G-18½ F. T......	0.35	B	......	....	750	Med.	$3\frac{9}{16}$
25	G-25 white.......	0.35	B	......	....	750	Med.	$4\frac{7}{16}$
25	G-25 F. T........	0.40	B	......	....	750	Med.	$4\frac{7}{16}$
25	F-15 F. T., white, ivory...........	0.20	B	......	....	750	Med.	$4\frac{1}{2}$
25	T-6½ clear.......	0.45	B	232	9.3	1,000	Inter.	$5\frac{1}{2}$
25	T-10 clear........	0.35	B	240	9.6	1,000	Med.	$5\frac{5}{8}$
30	T-8 clear Lumiline	0.95	B	......	....	1,500	Disk	$17\frac{3}{4}$
30	T-8 col. Lumiline.............	1.05	B	......	....	1,500	Disk	$17\frac{3}{4}$
40	A-19 I. F........	0.15	C	432	10.8	1,000	Med.	$4\frac{1}{4}$
40	G-25 white.......	0.35	B	......	....	750	Med.	$4\frac{7}{16}$
40	G-25 F. T........	0.40	B	......	....	750	Med.	$4\frac{7}{16}$
40	T-8 cl.............	0.90	B	392	9.8	1,000	Med.	$11\frac{7}{8}$
40	T-8 clear Lumiline	0.85	B	......	....	1,500	Disk	$11\frac{3}{4}$
40	T-8 col. Lumiline.............	0.95	B	......	....	1,500	Disk	$11\frac{3}{4}$
50	A-19 I. F. Rough Serv.............	0.37	B	445	8.9	1,000	Med.	$3\frac{15}{16}$
50	A-19 day. clear....	0.35	B	......	....	1,000	Med.	$3\frac{15}{16}$
50	P-19 vibration....	0.25	B	550	11.0	1,000	Med.	$3\frac{15}{16}$
60	A-21 I. F.........	0.15	C	750	12.5	1,000	Med.	$4\frac{15}{16}$
60	A-21 day. I. F....	0.30	C	490	....	1,000	Med.	$4\frac{15}{16}$
60	A-21 cl. traffic signal.............	0.30	C	678	11.3	1,500	Med.	$4\frac{7}{16}$
60	T-8 clear Lumiline	0.95	B	......	....	1,500	Disk	$17\frac{3}{4}$
60	T-8 col. Lumiline.............	1.05	B	......	....	1,500	Disk	$17\frac{3}{4}$

Table XXIII.—Mazda Lamps for 110-, 115-, and 120-volt Circuits.—
(*Continued*)

Watts	Bulb	List price	Mazda B or Mazda C lamp	Approx. value, rated initial lumens	Rated initial lumens per watt	Rated ave. lab. life (hr.)	Base	Max. over-all length (in.)
75	A-21 I. F.........	$0.20	C	1,035	13.8	750	Med.	5$\frac{5}{16}$
100	A-23 I. F.........	0.20	C	1,520	15.2	750	Med.	6$\frac{1}{16}$
100	A-23 day. I. F....	0.35	C	*988	....	750	Med.	6$\frac{1}{16}$
150	A-25 I. F.........	0.35	C	2,505	16.7	750	Med.	6$\frac{15}{16}$
150	PS-25 clear.......	0.40	C	2,415	16.1	1,000	Med.	6$\frac{15}{16}$
150	PS-25 W. B......	0.45	C	2,340	....	1,000	Med.	6$\frac{15}{16}$
150	PS-25 day. clear..	0.65	C	1,570	....	1,000	Med.	6$\frac{15}{16}$
150	PS-25 day. I. F...	0.70	C	1,570	....	1,000	Med.	6$\frac{15}{16}$
200	PS-30 clear.......	0.55	C	3,400	17.0	1,000	Med.	8$\frac{1}{8}$
200	PS-30 I. F........	0.60	C	3,400	17.0	1,000	Med.	8$\frac{1}{8}$
200	PS-30 W. B......	0.60	C	3,300	....	1,000	Med.	8$\frac{1}{8}$
200	PS-30 day. clear..	0.90	C	2,210	....	1,000	Med.	8$\frac{1}{8}$
200	PS-30 day. I. F...	0.95	C	2,210	....	1,000	Med.	8$\frac{1}{8}$
300	PS-35 clear.......	0.90	C	5,520	18.4	1,000	Mog.	9$\frac{7}{16}$
300	PS-35 I. F........	0.95	C	5,520	18.4	1,000	Mog.	9$\frac{7}{16}$
300	PS-35 W. B......	0.95	C	5,350	....	1,000	Mog.	9$\frac{7}{16}$
100 200 300 }	G-30 I. F. indirect three-lite........	1.00	C	{ 1,310 3,480 4,790 }	13.1 17.4 16.0 }	1,000 }	Three Contact Mogul }	6$\frac{3}{4}$ }
300	PS-35 day. clear..	1.35	C	3,590	....	1,000	Mog.	9$\frac{7}{16}$
300	PS-35 day. I. F...	1.45	C	3,590	....	1,000	Mog.	9$\frac{7}{16}$
500	PS-40 clear.......	1.55	C	9,800	19.6	1,000	Mog.	9$\frac{13}{16}$
500	PS-40 I. F........	1.65	C	9,800	19.6	1,000	Mog.	9$\frac{13}{16}$
500	PS-40 W. B......	1.65	C	9,510	....	1,000	Mog.	9$\frac{13}{16}$
500	PS-40 day. clear..	2.30	C	6,370	....	1,000	Mog.	9$\frac{13}{16}$
500	PS-40 day. I. F...	2.45	C	6,370	....	1,000	Mog.	9$\frac{13}{16}$
750	PS-52 clear.......	3.75	C	14,550	19.4	1,000	Mog.	13$\frac{1}{8}$
750	PS-52 W. B......	3.95	C	14,100	....	1,000	Mog.	13$\frac{1}{8}$
1,000	PS-52 clear.......	4.00	C	20,500	20.5	1,000	Mog.	13$\frac{1}{8}$
1,000	PS-52 W. B......	4.20	C	19,900	....	1,000	Mog.	13$\frac{1}{8}$
1,500	PS-52 clear.......	5.75	C	33,000	22.0	1,000	Mog.	13$\frac{1}{8}$
1,500	PS-52 W. B......	5.95	C	32,000	....	1,000	Mog.	13$\frac{1}{8}$

Type-D Lamps (Not Mazda)

Watts	Bulb	List price		Approx. value, rated initial lumens	Rated initial lumens per watt	Rated ave. lab. life (hr.)	Base	Max. over-all length (in.)
7$\frac{1}{2}$	G-11 outside wh. & red............	0.10	Vac.	......	......	1400	Med.	2$\frac{1}{4}$
15	A-15 I. F.........	0.10	Vac.	142	9.5	750	Med.	3$\frac{1}{2}$
30	G-19............	0.10	Vac.	330 I.F.	11.0 I.F.	500	Med.	3$\frac{9}{16}$
60	A-19 I. F.........	0.10	Gas F.	822	13.7	500	Med.	4$\frac{5}{8}$

Table XXIII.—Mazda Lamps for 110-, 115-, and 120-volt Circuits.—
(Continued)

Watts	Bulb	List price	Mazda B or Mazda C lamp	Rated initial lumens	Rated initial lumens per watt	Rated ave. lab. life, (hr.)	Base	Max. over-all length (inches)
Mazda Lamps for Motion-picture Production Service								
1,000	PS-52 clear.......	$ 4.00	C	24,000	22.2	500	Mog.	13⅛
1,500	PS-52 clear.......	5.75	C	38,000	23.7	500	Mog.	13⅛
2,000	PS-52 clear.......	5.25	C	65,000	....	15	Mog.	13⅛
2,000	G-48 clear........	13.00	C	49,000	24.5	200	Bipost	9⅜
5,000	G-64 clear........	40.00	C	145,000	29.0	100	Bipost	11⅞
10,000	G-96 clear........	100.00	C	295,000	29.5	100	Prong	20
Mazda Lamps for Projection and Stereopticon Service								
50	T-8 clear.........	1.10	C	790	15.8	50	S. C. Bay.	3⅛
100	T-8 clear.........	1.50	C	1,870	18.7	50	S. C. Bay.	3⅛
200	T-8 clear.........	2.20	C	4,500	22.5	25	S. C. Bay.	3⅝
200	T-10 clear........	2.20	C	4,080	20.4	50	Md. Pf.	5¾
200	T-10 clear........	2.20	C	4,080	20.4	50	Med.	5½
300	T-10 clear........	3.10	C	7,050	23.5	25	Md. Pf.	5¾
500	T-10 clear........	5.50	C	12,500	25.0	25	Md. Pf.	5¾
500	T-20 clear........	3.00	C	13,150	26.3	50	Md. Pf.	5¾
500	T-20 clear........	3.00	C	13,150	26.3	50	Med.	5½
750	T-12 clear........	6.75	C	19,500	26.0	25	Md. Pf.	5¾
1,000	T-20 clear........	6.50	C	27,000	27.0	50	Mg. Pf.	9½
1,000	T-20 clear........	6.50	C	27,000	27.0	50	Mog.	9¹⁄₁₆
1,000	T-20 clear........	8.75	C	27,600	27.6	25	Md. Pf.	5¾
Mazda Lamps for Spotlight and Floodlight Service								
100	P-25 clear spot....	1.15	C	1,360	13.6	200	Md. pf.	5
100	P-25 clear spot....	1.00	C	1,360	13.6	200	Med.	4¾
250	G-30 clear spot...	1.90	C	4,425	17.7	200	Md. pf.	5⅜
250	G-30 clear spot...	1.75	C	4,425	17.7	200	Med.	5⅛
250	G-30 clear flood...	1.75	C	3,700	14.8	800	Med.	5⅛
400	G-30 clear spot...	3.15	C	7,840	19.6	200	Md. pf.	5⅜
400	G-30 clear spot...	3.00	C	7,840	19.6	200	Med.	5⅛
500	G-40 clear flood...	3.25	C	8,650	17.3	800	Mog.	7¹⁄₁₆
1,000	G-40 clear spot...	7.15	C	22,000	22.0	200	Mg. pf.	8⁷⁄₁₆
1,000	G-40 clear spot...	6.75	C	22,000	22.0	200	Mog.	7¹⁄₁₆
1,000	G-40 clear spot...	6.75	C	22,000	22.0	200	Mog.	8
1,000	G-40 clear flood...	6.75	C	19,300	19.3	800	Mog.	8

Table XXIII.—Mazda Lamps for 110-, 115-, and 120-volt Circuits.— (*Continued*)

Mazda Lamps for Street-series Service

Amperes	Rated initial lumens	Bulb	List price	Average volts	Average watts	Rated initial lumens per watt	Mean lumens % of aver. initial lumens	Max. over-all length (inches)
6.6	1,000	S-24½............	$0.65	9.8	64.5	15.5	100	7⅛
6.6	2,500	PS-35............	1.30	22.2	146.2	17.1	100	9⁷⁄₁₆
6.6	4,000	PS-35............	1.55	33.9	223.5	17.9	100	9⁷⁄₁₆
15	4,000	PS-35............	1.55	14.2	212.8	18.8	98	9⁷⁄₁₆
6.6	6,000	PS-40............	2.10	51.1	337.1	17.8	98	9¹³⁄₁₆
20	6,000	PS-40............	2.10	15.3	306.1	19.6	95	9¹³⁄₁₆
20	10,000	PS-40............	2.60	25.0	500.0	20.0	92	9¹³⁄₁₆
20	15,000	PS-40............	3.70	37.9	757.6	19.8	88	9¹³⁄₁₆
20	25,000	PS-52............	6.60	60.7	1213.6	20.6	84	13⅛

reduced, since the filament could not be seen and the bulb luminosity was much less than the filament luminosity. But such lamps were hard to keep clean because of the rough outer surface. An improvement is the inside-frosted bulb which is perfectly smooth on the outside yet diffuses the light in an effective manner. The lamps for general use are now made regularly with this type of bulb except in the largest sizes.

The fifth column gives the initial lumens. After the lamp has been burned at constant voltage for some time, its filament resistance is increased owing to evaporation, and thus the power input and the luminous output are reduced somewhat. The blackening of the bulb also reduces the light so that generally the average lumens during life are 85 to 95 per cent of the initial lumens. Lamps burned in series, as in street-lighting circuits, show less reduction in luminous output during life.

The glass used in the ordinary incandescent lamps cuts out the ultraviolet at wavelengths less than approximately 0.30μ. A desire for sources that radiate a slight amount of beneficial ultraviolet in addition to the usual visible radiation has led to the development of the CX lamp with a globe of special glass transmitting to a wavelength of about 0.28μ. An ordinary tungsten filament is used, but it is operated at a somewhat higher temperature than in the usual lamps in order to give as large an ultraviolet output as is consistent with a life of 500 hr. Many other special lamps are produced, as well as lamps for various voltages. For information the reader is referred to the Manufacturers' Schedules of Lamps.

6.06. Effect of Voltage.—It is well-known that for best results the variation of voltage applied to incandescent lamps must be controlled within narrow limits. If the voltage is only a few volts low, the light will be cut down materially; while if it is a volt or two high, the life will be considerably reduced. For a filament of known dimensions operating at known temperature, the effect of voltage variation can be calculated by the method of the preceding paragraphs. However, in most cases the calculations can be performed more easily by using one of the empirical formulas obtained from numerous tests on actual lamps. The latest information from the Bureau of Standards is summarized in the following formulas:[17]

$$\log (F/F_0) = A_2[\log (V/V_0)]^2 + B_2 \log (V/V_0) \quad (6.09)$$
$$\log (P/P_0) = A_3[\log (V/V_0)]^2 + B_3 \log (V/V_0) \quad (6.10)$$
$$\log (i/i_0) = A_4[\log (V/V_0)]^2 + B_4 \log (V/V_0) \quad (6.11)$$

TABLE XXIV.—CONSTANTS FOR USE IN EQS. (6.09), (6.10), (6.11)

nbol	Vacuum lamps	Gas-filled lamps		
	15–60 watts	40–50 watts	60–150 watts	200–500 watts
Normal lumens per watt.........	10.0	12.5	12.5	16.0
A_2..............................	−0.946	−1.425	−1.669	−1.607
B_2..............................	3.513	3.685	3.613	3.384
A_3..........	−0.028	0.057	0.057	0.083
B_3..............................	1.5805	1.523	1.523	1.543
A_4..............................	−0.028	0.057	0.057	0.083
B_4..............................	0.5805	0.523	0.523	0.543

where the A's and B's are constants whose values are given in Table XXIV, and

F = luminous output (lumens) at the voltage V.

P = watts input at voltage V.

i = current (amps) at voltage V.

F_0, P_0, V_0, and i_0 are the corresponding quantities at an over-all efficacy of 10.0 lumens/watt for vacuum lamps, 12.5 lumens/watt for gas-filled lamps of 40 to 150 watts, and 16.0 lumens/watt for lamps of 200 to 500 watts.

Example. A certain 500-watt Mazda-C lamp is found to give 16.0 lumens/watt at a voltage of 105, the luminous output being 7520 lumens. What is the luminous output at 115.5 volts?

By Eq. (6.09) and Table XXIV,

$$\log\left(\frac{F}{F_0}\right) = -1.607\left[\log\left(\frac{V}{V_0}\right)\right]^2 + 3.384\log\left(\frac{V}{V_0}\right)$$

and since $V = 115.5$ and $V_0 = 105.0$, $V/V_0 = 1.100$, and

$$\log\left(\frac{F}{F_0}\right) = -1.607[0.0415]^2 + 3.384(0.0414)$$
$$= -0.00275 + 0.1401 = 0.1372$$

Thus

$$\frac{F}{F_0} = 1.372$$

and

$$F = 1.372(7520) = \textbf{10,317 lumens}$$

Problem 42. Plot curves of *lumens vs. volts* and *watts vs. volts* for the above lamp from $V = 80$ to $V = 130$. In case (V/V_0) is less than one, use the reciprocal (V_0/V) and call the logarithm negative, since

$$\log (V/V_0) = -\log (V_0/V)$$

It has been found that the constants for the 40- to 50-watt column apply also to 3-cp, 6- to 8-volt lamps; that the 60- to 150-watt column applies to the 21-cp automobile-headlight lamp; while the 200- to 500-watt column applies to the 32-cp headlight lamp. Tests at the Bureau of Standards show that with voltages ranging from 80 to 130 per cent of normal, the formulas are remarkably accurate. They are not very convenient for calculation, however, since the voltage V_0 corresponding to the normal lumens per watt (Table XXIV) must be known before any computations can be made.

For most purposes, the preceding formulas can be approximated by equations of a simpler form. Equation (6.09), for instance, may be written in the form

$$F/F_0 = 10^x (V/V_0)^{B_2} \tag{6.12}$$

where $x = A_2[\log (V/V_0)]^2$.

Since 10^x is approximately equal to unity if (V/V_0) is near one, Eq. (6.09) reduces to

$$F/F_0 = (V/V_0)^{B_2} \qquad (6.13)$$

To determine how large an error is introduced by using Eq. (6.13) instead of Eq. (6.09), 10^x is calculated for voltage ratios up to twice normal, as shown in Table XXV. This table is for the constants $A_2 = -1.669$ and $B_2 = 3.613$, given for the 60- to 150-watt gas-filled lamps. It will be noted that for a voltage between 77 and 130 per cent normal, the value of 10^x does not exceed 1.051, which corresponds to an error of 5.1 per cent. With lamps of other sizes and in the computation of other quantities than luminous flux, the errors will in most cases be somewhat less than this.

TABLE XXV.—VALUES OF 10^x IN EQ. (6.12)

V/V_0	x	10^x	V/V_0	x	10^x
0.50	0.1507	1.415	1.00	0.00	1.000
0.67	0.0517	1.126	1.05	0.00075	1.002
0.72	0.0356	1.085	1.10	0.00286	1.006
0.77	0.0217	1.051	1.15	0.00615	1.014
0.80	0.0157	1.037	1.20	0.01045	1.024
0.83	0.01045	1.024	1.25	0.0157	1.037
0.87	0.00615	1.014	1.30	0.0217	1.051
0.91	0.00286	1.006	1.40	0.0356	1.085
0.95	0.00075	1.002	1.50	0.0517	1.126
1.00	0.00	1.000	2.00	0.1507	1.415

Evidently, then, a simplified formula is justified provided too great accuracy is not required. In case greater accuracy is desired, the reader is referred to *Bureau of Standards Research Paper* 502 for further details and for tables.

We may write:

$$F/F_0 = (V/V_0)^{B_2} \quad \text{luminous flux} \qquad (6.14)$$
$$P/P_0 = (V/V_0)^{B_3} \quad \text{power} \qquad (6.15)$$
$$i/i_0 = (V/V_0)^{B_4} \quad \text{current} \qquad (6.16)$$
$$\eta_l/\eta_{l0} = (V/V_0)^{B_1} \quad \text{over-all efficacy} \qquad (6.17)$$
$$\mathcal{L}/\mathcal{L}_0 = (V/V_0)^{-B_5} \quad \text{life} \qquad (6.18)$$
$$T/T_0 = (V/V_0)^{B_6} \quad \text{temperature} \qquad (6.19)$$

where V_0 may be taken without large error as the rated voltage of the lamp, and F_0, P_0, etc., are the values at rated voltage. The constants (Table XXVI) are obtained from Table XXIV, with some data from Table XXII used in the cases of B_5 and B_6.

TABLE XXVI.—CONSTANTS FOR USE IN EQS. (6.14) TO (6.19)

Symbol	Vacuum lamps 15–60 watts	Gas-filled lamps		
		40–50 watts	60–150 watts	$\geqq 200$ watts
B_2	3.513	3.685	3.613	3.384
B_3	1.5805	1.523	1.523	1.543
B_4	0.5805	0.523	0.523	0.543
B_1	1.932	2.162	2.090	1.841
B_5	13.5	13.5	13.5	13.1
B_6	0.350	0.398	0.398	0.382

Example. What is the life of a 25-watt, 110-volt Mazda lamp when operating on 125 volts?

According to Table XXIII, the regular 25-watt lamp is a vacuum lamp and has a life of 1000 hr at rated voltage. At 125 volts, the life is

$$\mathcal{L} = 1000\left(\frac{125}{110}\right)^{-13.5} = \mathbf{177\ hr}$$

Problem 43. Check one value of B_6 given in Table XXVI by using data from Table XXII.

Problem 44. A 200-watt 120-volt gas-filled lamp is operated on a 115-volt circuit. Calculate F, P, i, η_l, $\mathcal{L}$ for 115 volts.

Problem 45. The 100-watt 115-volt gas-filled lamp has a life of 750 hr at rated voltage. At what voltage must it be operated to give a life of 1000 hr? 500 hr? What are the over-all efficacies when the lamp is operated at these two voltages?

6.07. Voltage Control Necessary for Photometric Work.—As an application of Eq. (6.14), consider what voltage variation is allowable in the photometry of incandescent lamps. It is desired to measure, to a certain precision, the luminous flux F_0 from a lamp operating at the voltage V_0. What is the allowable voltage variation?

At any voltage V, the luminous flux will be (for gas-filled lamp, 60 to 150 watts)

$$F = F_0\left(\frac{V}{V_0}\right)^{3.613}$$

Suppose that the flux is desired to a precision represented by $F_0(1 + \beta)$ and let this variation be caused by a small variation in voltage $\pm \gamma V_0$. Then if the voltage rises slightly to a value $V = V_0(1 + \gamma)$, the flux will change to

$$F = F_0(1 + \beta) = F_0 \left[\frac{V_0(1 + \gamma)}{V_0} \right]^{3.613}$$

or

$$1 + \beta = (1 + \gamma)^{3.613}$$

To find the allowable voltage variation, we must solve for γ.

$$\gamma = (1 + \beta)^{\frac{1}{3.613}} - 1 = (1 + \beta)^{0.277} - 1$$

Expanding according to the binomial theorem:

$$\gamma = 0.277\beta - 0.100\beta^2 + \cdots \tag{6.20}$$

For instance, if F is desired to a precision of 1 per cent, $\beta = 0.01$ and

$$\gamma = 0.277(0.01) - 0.100(10^{-4}) = 0.00276$$

Thus the voltage must not vary more than ± 0.276 per cent. In the most accurate visual comparison methods, a precision of about 0.3 per cent is obtained. Evidently, under these conditions the voltage must be controlled to $\pm 0.276(0.3) = \pm 0.083$ per cent. This simple calculation indicates the need for accurate control and measurement of the voltage and shows why in photometric work of the highest precision the voltage is determined by means of a potentiometer.

6.08. Most Economical Voltage.—As another application of the equations for the effect of voltage on the characteristics of incandescent lamps, let us find the most economical voltage for operation. If the voltage is very low, cost of lamp renewals is almost eliminated, but the cost of electric power per lumen is high. On the other hand, too high a voltage will give a high luminous efficacy but will be uneconomical because of short life. Evidently, for any given lamp and with electric power costing a given amount per kilowatt-hour, a certain voltage must exist at which the total cost of a given amount of light will be a minimum. Our purpose is to determine this optimum condition.

Let c = cost of one lamp + installation charge (cts).

b = cost of energy (cts/kw-hr).

V = actual operating voltage.

V_0 = rated voltage of lamp.

At rated voltage, the cost of energy for 1000 hr operation is

$$b\frac{P_0}{1000}1000 = bP_0$$

The total cost of operating the lamp for 1000 hr (using lamps with 1000-hr life at V_0) is

$$\text{Total cost} = c + bP_0 \tag{6.21}$$

Similarly, at the voltage V the cost for 1000 hr of operation is

$$c\left(\frac{\mathcal{L}_0}{\mathcal{L}}\right) + bP = c\left(\frac{V}{V_0}\right)^{B_5} + bP_0\left(\frac{V}{V_0}\right)^{B_3} \tag{6.22}$$

and the luminous output is

$$F = F_0\left(\frac{V}{V_0}\right)^{B_2}$$

Thus the cost per lumen for 1000 hr is

$$y = \frac{c}{F_0}\left(\frac{V}{V_0}\right)^{B_5-B_2} + \frac{bP_0}{F_0}\left(\frac{V}{V_0}\right)^{B_3-B_2}$$

or

$$y = \frac{c}{F_0}x^{B_5-B_2} + \frac{bP_0}{F_0}x^{B_3-B_2}$$

where $x = (V/V_0)$ is the only independent variable.

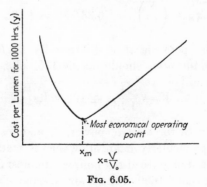

Fig. 6.05.

From a qualitative consideration of the problem one would expect a curve something like Fig. 6.05 with a minimum total cost per lumen at some voltage ratio x_m. To find x_m, differentiate and equate to zero in the usual manner.

$$\frac{dy}{dx} = 0 = \frac{c}{F_0}(B_5 - B_2)x^{B_5-B_2-1} + \frac{bP_0}{F_0}(B_3 - B_2)x^{B_3-B_2-1}$$

or

$$x_m = \left[\frac{bP_0}{c}\frac{B_2 - B_3}{B_5 - B_2}\right]^{\frac{1}{B_5-B_3}} \tag{6.23}$$

Equation (6.23) is a general formula which may be used for any size of lamp.

For Mazda-C lamps from 60 to 150 watts,

$$B_2 = 3.613$$
$$B_3 = 1.523$$
$$B_5 = 13.5$$

and Eq. (6.23) reduces to

$$x_m = \left[\frac{2.090}{9.9}\frac{bP_0}{c}\right]^{\frac{1}{12.0}} = \left[0.211\frac{bP_0}{c}\right]^{0.083} \tag{6.23a}$$

For example, consider a residence where $b = 6$ cts/kw-hr, $P_0 = 100$ watts, and $c = 20$ cts. Then the voltage ratio for most economical operation is

$$x_m = \left(\frac{V}{V_0}\right)_m = (6.33)^{0.083} = 1.165$$

If the circuit is operating at $V = 115$ volts, *the lamp rating for most economical operation* should not be 115 volts, but

$$V_0 = \frac{V}{1.165} \cong 100 \text{ volts}$$

With a lower rate for electric power, V and V_0 become more nearly equal, particularly if an allowance is made in c for the annoyance caused by burned-out lamps. In most cases, however, it will be found that a 1000-hr life is not so economical as a shorter one and that it is better to operate incandescent lamps *above* rather than *below* their rated voltage. The public in general does not realize this fact, however, and one point where the illuminating engineer can easily make himself useful is in recommending the best rated voltage for lamps to be used in large buildings.

Problem 46. The principal rooms of a factory are lighted by 300-watt Mazda lamps which are operated at 115 volts. The list price of the lamps is 90 cts, and a discount of 31 per cent is obtained by contract with the lamp manufacturer. The power costs 1.9 cts per kilowatt-hour, and the labor cost of replacing a lamp is estimated at 3 cts. The factory has purchased all lamps rated at 120 volts and has paid the lamp manufacturer an average of $8620 a year for the 300-watt lamps. What should be the rated voltage of these lamps for most economical operation, and how much would be saved per year by such a change, for the same total lumens?

Problem 47. With a residence lighting rate of 7.5 cts/kw-hr and zero labor cost for lamp replacements, is it more economical to buy 60-watt 115-volt A-21 Mazda lamps or 60-watt, 115-volt, A-19 "D" lamps?

Problem 48. A student uses an I.E.S. study lamp for an average of 5 hr a day 300 days in the year. What is his total cost per lumen-year if he uses

    1. 100-watt, 115-volt, A-23 lamp?

    2. 100-watt, 115-volt, P-25 spotlight lamp?

    3. 100-watt, 115-volt, T-8 projection lamp?

    4. 100-watt, 32-volt, A-23 lamp costing 40 cts, having a life of 1000 hr and giving 17.2 lumens/watt?

In 4, the student has to buy a 115–32-volt transformer costing $5 and having an efficiency of 90 per cent at rated load. He assumes that the transformer will last him four years. He pays 8 cts per kilowatt-hour, and the voltage at the lamp socket is 115 volts.

6.09. Modification of Radiation by Filters.—In most cases, unmodified radiation from the ordinary incandescent lamps considered in the previous sections is of satisfactory quality. Sometimes, however, it is imperative or at least desirable to modify the radiation by means of filters—to eliminate the infrared or the ultraviolet radiation, to obtain a closer approximation to daylight quality, to produce a warmer tone for decorative lighting, or to eliminate all but a portion of the spectrum as in colored floodlighting. The use of filters is inherently a wasteful method, since the energy in those parts of the spectrum cut off by the filter is wasted. Nevertheless, filters are very useful, very versatile, and the illuminating engineer has need of information on their characteristics.

As mentioned previously, the infrared radiation from incandescent lamps is often troublesome; and thus a filter that eliminates the infrared while transmitting the visible radiation is sometimes useful. Perhaps the most effective filter of this type is water. Figure 6.06 shows the spectral transmission factor (τ_λ) of pure water, curves being given for thicknesses of 1 cm, 1 meter, and 10 meters. With a thickness of a few centimeters, the visible region is transmitted almost perfectly, but little radiant power is transmitted beyond approximately 1.2μ. For a thickness of a meter of more, the extremes of the visible spec-

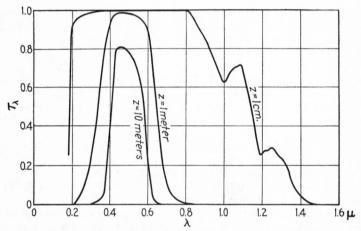

Fig. 6.06.—Spectral transmission factor of pure water (neglecting surface reflections).

trum (particularly the long wavelengths) are not transmitted, so the water takes on a blue-green appearance.

The family of curves (Fig. 6.06) illustrates the fact that the spectral transmission factor changes greatly with the thickness. According to Bouguer's law, the ratio of the transmitted radiant power to the incident radiant power for homogeneous radiation is an *exponential function of the thickness z*, or

$$\frac{J_\lambda}{G_\lambda} = e^{-az} \tag{6.24}$$

Equation (6.24) neglects the small loss by reflections at the filter surfaces (Chap. IX). Because of the exponential variation, the apparent cutoff and the entire appearance of the transmission curves are changed by a change in thickness.   The same phenomena occur also in glass filters.

Figure 6.07 shows the results obtained with a filter cell consisting of two plates of polished optical glass separated by 21 mm,

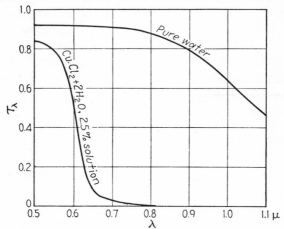

Fig. 6.07.—Spectral transmission factor of two filters which transmit the visible region but not the infrared.   Thickness of liquid = 21 mm.   (*W. W. Coblentz, Bu. Stds. Sci. Paper* 168.)

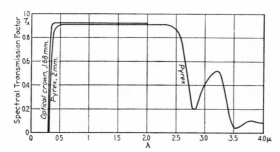

Fig. 6.08.—Spectral transmission factor of glass.

the cell being filled with either distilled water or a 2.5 per cent solution of cupric chloride.   The cupric chloride gives a sharper cutoff and is useful where a reduction in the longer-wavelength portions of the visible spectrum is of less importance than a fairly complete elimination of the infrared.   Figure 6.08 shows that ordinary clear glasses cause considerable diminution in the infrared beyond about 3.5μ.   The infrared portion of the curve is characteristic not only of clear glasses but also of most yellow, orange, and red glasses.

Table XXVII gives some additional data on filters that transmit well at the shorter wavelengths but have very low spectral transmission factors at the longer wavelengths (sometimes called filters of Class 2). Several glasses, such as *Aklo*, are in this class and give results similar to the cupric chloride solution. Glasses of this kind are sometimes used in the windows of air-conditioned buildings to reduce the heating effect of summer sunlight.

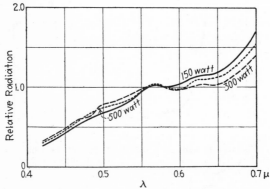

Fig. 6.09.—Spectral irradiation from Mazda "Daylight" lamps. (*A. H. Taylor, G. E. Rev.,* **37**, 1934, *p.* 413.)

Much more numerous and satisfactory are the filters of Class 1, which have a high spectral transmission factor at long wavelengths and a fairly sharp cutoff at almost any desired wavelength. Filters of Class 3 transmit a band of wavelengths. Table XXVII shows that none of these filters has a sharp cutoff. Other filters give a gradual change in spectral transmission factor throughout the visible region and are useful in changing the apparent color temperature of the source. Figure 6.09 shows the results obtained by using blue-glass bulbs on incandescent lamps. The aim has been to reduce some of the superfluity of red and yellow in the light from the incandescent lamp without too great an absorption of radiant power. Evidently, the result is far from daylight quality. Filters are produced, however, which give a very good approximation to the quality of daylight when used with ordinary incandescent lamps*.

* See H. P. Gage, *J.O.S.A.*, **23**, 1933, p. 46.

Filters can be obtained of color glass, of colored gelatin, or of gelatin cemented between colorless glass plates. Since in most cases a considerable proportion of the incident radiant power is absorbed by the filter, a considerable temperature rise of the filter can be expected unless the quantity of radiant power is very small. Glass of low thermal expansion is often desirable. Gelatin filters cannot be expected to give satisfaction when used for long periods near incandescent lamps, since the gelatin deteriorates owing to the heat.

The data of Table XXVII are results obtained on certain filters, and these data can be used to get an approximate idea of what such filters can do. It must be realized, however, that unavoidable variations in manufacture cause fairly large differences among filters of the same kind. Thus if accurate results are desired, the curve of the spectral transmission factor must first be obtained by measurement on the particular filter used.

Problem 49. What is the transmission factor τ of Wratten filter 40 with 2778°K Planckian radiation?

Problem 50. An office has a glass area of 300 sq ft in the windows. If the daytime illumination of the window glass is 500 lumens/sq ft, how much luminous flux and how much radiant power are entering the office, if a Planckian distribution at 5000°K is assumed for the irradiation of the window glass, and the glass is

1. Ordinary window glass (use data on 2-mm Pyrex).

2. Five-millimeter Aklo glass.

Problem 51. Repeat Prob. 49 for a 20000°K Planckian distribution.

Problem 52. 1. The preceding office is lighted by ten 300-watt, PS-35 115-volt lamps operating at rated voltage. Ordinary opal-glass luminaires are used, hung 4 ft 0 in. below the ceiling. How much heat enters the room from the luminaires? How much luminous flux enters the room, if it is assumed that the luminaire absorbs 18 per cent of the lamp lumens?

2. It is decided to replace the old lighting system by luminous panels built into the ceiling. The same lamps are used, and the same luminous flux would enter the room were it not for the absorption of 5 mm of Aklo glass which covers the light boxes. By how many per cent is the luminous flux reduced due to the Aklo glass? By how many per cent is the radiant energy reduced because of the glass? Assume that sufficient cool air is circulated through the light box so that the glass is kept cool and does not radiate appreciably.

Problem 53. How long will it take to get an MPE with noon sunlight shining through

1. Two millimeters of Corex A?

2. Two millimeters of Corex D?

3. Two millimeters of Pyrex?

TABLE XXVII.—FILTERS OF CLASS 1
Spectral Transmission Factor

No. Thickness λ	Corex A 2.00mm	Corex D 2.00	Pyrex 2.00	GG 2 1.00	GG 5 1.00	6 (K1)	8 (K2)	15 (G)	G 11 1.00	OG 2 1.00	28	25	29	RG 1 1.00	RG 5 1.00	RG 8 1.00
	(3)	(3)	(3)	(2)	(2)	(1)	(1)	(1)	(2)	(2)	(1)	(1)	(1)	(2)	(2)	(2)
0.27μ	0.78	0.14														
0.28	0.82	0.32	0.00		0											
0.29	0.86	0.55	0.00		0.01											
0.30	0.89	0.72	0.01		0.02											
0.31	0.90	0.81														
0.32	0.91	0.85	0.09		0.02											
0.33	0.92	0.88	0.22		0.03											
0.34		0.89	0.48	0	0.04											
0.35		0.90	0.60	0.33	0.05											
0.36		0.92	0.69		0.07											
0.37			0.74	0.71	0.09	0.0891										
0.38			0.80	0.90	0.10	0.0982										
0.39			0.83	0.94	0.12											
0.40			0.85	0.97	0.14											
0.41			0.86	0.97	0.20											
0.42			0.87	0.98	0.25	0.123										
0.43			0.88	0.98	0.32	0.158			0							
0.44			0.88	0.99	0.40	0.209			0.01							
0.45			0.88	0.99	0.88	0.276			0.02							
0.46			0.89	0.99	0.97	0.380	0.0158		0.05							
0.47			0.89	1.00	0.98	0.500	0.100		0.12	0.00						
0.48			0.90	1.00	0.99	0.630	0.251		0.24	0.05						
0.49			0.90		0.99	0.742	0.438		0.39	0.14						
0.50			0.90		0.99	0.815	0.588		0.96	0.79						
0.51			0.90		1.00	0.832	0.725	0.0260	0.97							
0.52			0.91			0.850	0.790	0.290	0.97		0.0010					
0.53						0.864	0.824	0.576	0.98		0.0017					
0.54						0.874	0.845	0.760	0.98		0.0038			0.00		
0.55						0.878	0.854	0.815	0.99							
0.56						0.882	0.860	0.840	0.99							
0.57						0.886	0.866	0.855	0.99	0.90	0.0240	0.0016				
0.58						0.889	0.872	0.865	0.99	0.94	0.109	0.102				
0.59						0.892	0.877	0.875	0.99	0.97	0.315					

λ (μ)	1	2	3	4	5	6	7	8	9	10	11	12	13	14	15	16
0.60						0.894	0.882	0.882		0.98	0.548	0.501	0.0039	0.10	0.00	0.00
0.61						0.896	0.886	0.887		0.98	0.705	0.700	0.0645	0.89	0.02	0.01
0.62						0.897	0.889	0.892		0.98	0.800	0.805	0.316	0.92	0.04	0.02
0.63						0.898	0.892	0.895		0.98	0.835	0.840	0.530	0.94	0.31	0.03
0.64						0.899	0.895	0.898		0.99	0.855	0.855	0.710	0.96		
0.65						0.900	0.897	0.900			0.867	0.870	0.780	0.96		
0.66					0.99		0.898		0.98		0.875	0.870	0.820	0.96		
0.67					0.98		0.899		0.97		0.878		0.835	0.97	0.53	0.10
0.68					0.98		0.900		0.96		0.880		0.845	0.97	0.90	0.15
0.69					0.97				0.97				0.849	0.98	0.95	0.39
0.70				0.99	0.98				0.93				0.850		0.96	0.71
0.71			0.91		0.95										0.96	0.94
0.72															0.96	0.98
0.73															0.97	0.99
0.74															0.97	0.99
0.75															0.97	0.99
0.80															0.98	0.99
0.90		0.92													0.98	0.99
1.0			0.87	0.98											0.98	0.99
1.5	0.92														0.99	0.99
2.0										0.96				0.96	0.99	0.95
2.5															0.95	
3.0			0.40	0.70	0.62				0.66	0.60				0.65	0.58	0.58

Columns 6 (K) and 13 (D): Good transmission in the infrared.

FILTERS OF CLASS 3

No. Thickness λ	586A 3.20 mm (3)	585 4.62 (3)	BG 12 1.00 (2)	50 (1)	47 (1)	44 (1)	75 (1)	40 (1)	61 (1)	62 (1)	401 1.66 (3)	VG 2 1.00 (2)	BG 11 4.00 (2)	VG 3 1.00 (2)
0.27μ	0.00	0.00	0.00										0.00	
0.28	0.00	0.00	0.00										0.02	
0.29	0.00	0.00	0.00										0.05	
0.30	0.00	0.00	0.00										0.08	
0.31	0.00	0.04	0.02										0.10	
0.32	0.06	0.25	0.05										0.30	0.00
0.33	0.25	0.55	0.30										0.39	0.01
0.34	0.60	0.75	0.39										0.50	0.10
0.35	0.75	0.83	0.62										0.30	0.20
0.36	0.85	0.85	0.69										0.32	0.38
0.37	0.87	0.86	0.77										0.78	0.49
0.38	0.84	0.85	0.81										0.89	0.53
0.39	0.73	0.83	0.84	0.00									0.90	0.41
0.40	0.45	0.78	0.86	0.0046	0.251	0.0500							0.90	0.27
0.41	0.16	0.70	0.86	0.0037	0.354	0.0456							0.90	0.20
0.42	0.02	0.61	0.86	0.0077	0.490	0.0605					0.00		0.90	0.11
0.43	0.00	0.50	0.85	0.0400	0.495	0.158			0.00		0.01	0.00	0.90	0.08
0.44		0.40	0.84	0.0871	0.480	0.273			0.0250		0.04	0.05	0.89	0.06
0.45		0.28	0.81	0.138	0.478	0.366	0.00	0.00	0.178	0.00	0.08	0.12	0.78	0.10
0.46		0.16	0.67	0.144	0.437	0.425	0.0080	0.0524	0.338	0.0026	0.12	0.20	0.93	0.11
0.47		0.09	0.55	0.0675	0.374	0.476	0.0630	0.276	0.479	0.0800	0.20	0.28	0.90	0.10
0.48		0.01	0.48	0.0197	0.303	0.524	0.173	0.549	0.524	0.147	0.27	0.37	0.78	0.02
0.49		0.00	0.32	0.0012	0.218	0.556	0.191	0.660	0.479	0.109	0.35	0.45	0.99	0.03
0.50			0.15	0.00	0.125	0.564	0.141	0.725	0.381	0.0500	0.41	0.54	0.95	0.08
0.51			0.12		0.0542	0.534	0.0500	0.730	0.257	0.0146	0.47	0.59	0.81	0.38
0.52			0.06		0.0130	0.469	0.0126	0.718	0.144	0.0016	0.50	0.62	0.86	0.68
0.53			0.04		0.0015	0.378	0.0031	0.660	0.0630	0.000	0.50	0.64	0.67	0.45
0.54			0.03		0.00	0.268	0.00	0.600	0.0218		0.46	0.63	0.89	0.20
0.55			0.02			0.170		0.506	0.0051		0.40	0.61	0.99	0.06
0.56			0.02			0.0932		0.361			0.35	0.50	0.98	0.75
0.57			0.02			0.0317		0.229			0.27	0.46	0.62	0.70
0.58			0.01			0.0027		0.118			0.20	0.44	0.02	0.50
0.59			0.01			0.00		0.0500			0.16	0.35	0.21	0.40
0.60			0.00					0.0195			0.11	0.30	0.01	0.32

FILTERS OF CLASS 3.—(*Continued*)

No. Thickness λ	586A 3.20 mm (3)	585 4.62 (3)	BG 12 1.00 (2)	50 (1)	47 (1)	44 (1)	75 (1)	40 (1)	61 (1)	62 (1)	401 1.66 (3)	VG 2 1.00 (2)	BG 11 4.00 (2)	VG 3 1.00 (2)
0.61								0.0071			0.08	0.27	0.92	0.15
0.62								0.0028			0.05	0.23	0.97	0.02
0.63								0.0010			0.03	0.14	0.98	0.00
0.64								0.00			0.03	0.10	1.00	0.00
0.65								0.00			0.02	0.10	1.00	0.02
0.66	→ 0.05							0.00			0.01	0.09	0.98	0.00
0.67	0.11							0.00			0.01	0.09	0.97	0.00
0.68		→ 0.11	→ 0.04					0.0197			0.00	0.08	0.95	0.03
0.69							→ 0.0010	0.0795				0.08	0.94	0.15
0.70				→	→	→	0.0024	0.157	→	→		0.08	0.99	0.85
0.71	0.21	0.35	0.04		0.00							0.08	0.94	0.88
0.72	0.30	0.55	0.04		0.02							0.08	0.88	0.87
0.73			0.05		0.06							0.07	0.80	0.86
0.74			0.06		0.10							0.07	0.78	0.84
0.75			0.06		0.20							0.07	0.73	0.80
0.80			0.08		0.50	Good transmission in infrared						0.06	0.67	0.45
0.90			0.10		0.92							0.08	0.83	0.34
1.0			0.15		0.92							0.11	0.95	0.29
1.5			0.20		0.92							0.40	0.87	0.32
2.0			0.53									0.65	0.90	0.47
2.5			0.80		0.92							0.75	0.64	0.30
3.0			0.55		0.92							0.54	0.08	0.12

(1) Wratten gelatin filter, Eastman Kodak Company. .... Transmission data from *Wratten Light Filters*, 1932 ed.
(2) Jena glass filter, Fish-Schurman Corporation. .... Transmission data from *Jenaer Farb- und Filtergläser*, Liste 4777.
(3) Corning glass filter, Corning Glass Works. .... (Data do not include reflection losses at surfaces.)
NOTE.—These data can be regarded as approximate only.

FILTERS OF CLASS 2

Filter Thickness λ	H₂O 21 mm	CuCl₂ 21 mm	BG 17 1.00 (2)	UG 1 1.00 (2)	Aklo 2.00 (3)	Aklo 5.0 (3)
0.27μ			0.00	0.00		
0.28			0.00	0.00		
0.29			0.02	0.06		
0.30	0.88		0.03	0.17		
0.31	0.89		0.11	0.37		
0.32	0.89		0.25	0.55		
0.33	0.89		0.40	0.65		
0.34	0.90		0.62	0.81		
0.35	0.90		0.74	0.84	0.44	0.24
0.36	0.90		0.85	0.85		
0.37	0.91		0.90	0.85		
0.38	0.91		0.91	0.75		
0.39	0.91	Good transmission	0.82	0.50		
0.40	0.92		0.97	0.08	0.73	0.54
0.41			0.97	0.00	0.75	0.56
0.42			0.97		0.77	0.58
0.43			0.97		0.78	0.60
0.44			0.98		0.79	0.63
0.45					0.80	0.65
0.46					0.81	0.67
0.47					0.81	0.69
0.48					0.82	0.70
0.49					0.82	0.70
0.50	0.92	0.84	0.98	0.00	0.82	0.70
0.51		0.83			0.82	0.70
0.52		0.83			0.82	0.70
0.53		0.82			0.81	0.68
0.54		0.81			0.81	0.66
0.55		0.79			0.80	0.64
0.56		0.77			0.79	0.62
0.57		0.73			0.78	0.59
0.58		0.69			0.76	0.56
0.59		0.62			0.74	0.53
0.60	0.92	0.50	0.98	0.00	0.72	0.49
0.61					0.70	0.45
0.62					0.67	0.41
0.63					0.64	0.37
0.64			0.97		0.61	0.32
0.65		0.08	0.96		0.58	0.28
0.66			0.96		0.55	0.25
0.67			0.95		0.53	0.22
0.68			0.95		0.50	0.19
0.69			0.94		0.47	0.16
0.70	0.91	0.03	0.93	0.01	0.43	0.14
0.71			0.91	0.05	0.40	0.12
0.72			0.89	0.14	0.37	0.10
0.73			0.88	0.28	0.35	0.10
0.74			0.86	0.30	0.33	0.09
0.75	0.90	0.01	0.85	0.32	0.30	0.08
0.80	0.87	0.00	0.70	0.32		
0.90	0.79	0.00	0.50	0.16		
1.00	0.64	0.0025	0.35	0.08	0.07	0.005
1.5		0.00	0.36	0.04	0.18	0.010
2.0	0.00	0.00	0.42	0.04	0.29	0.050
2.5	0.00	0.00	0.38	0.13	0.37	0.095
3.0	0.00	0.00	0.27	0.17	0.30	0.070

Column 2 gives τ for a filter using 21 mm of pure water.

Column 3 gives τ for the same filter cell filled with a 2.5 per cent solution of CuCl₂ + 2H₂O in water (data from W. W. COBLENTZ, *Bu. Stds. Sci. Paper*, 168).

Problem 54. You wish to take some long-distance photographs from a mountain top, using supersensitive panchromatic plates and an RG5 filter. On the assumption that the radiation reflected from the distant landscape is equivalent to 6500°K Planckian radiation and that with a K2 filter an exposure of $\frac{1}{100}$ sec would be satisfactory at $f/8$, what exposure should be used with the RG5 filter?

Bibliography

1. National Electric Light Association: Report of the Lamp Committee. June, 1932 (also other years).
2. HOWELL and SCHROEDER: History of the Incandescent Lamp, The Maqua Company, Schenectady, N. Y., 1927.
3. Edison Lamp Works: Theory and Characteristics of Mazda Lamps, *Bull.* LD-114D.
4. H. E. IVES: The Luminous Properties of the Black Body, *J.O.S.A.*, **12**, 1926, p. 75.
5. I. LANGMUIR: Tungsten Lamps of High Efficiency, *A.I.E.E. Trans.*, **32**, 1913, p. 1913.
6. LANGMUIR and ORANGE: Tungsten Lamps of High Efficiency, *A.I.E.E. Trans.*, **32**, 1913, p. 1935.
7. FORSYTHE and WORTHING: Properties of Tungsten, *Astrophys. J.*, **61**, 1925, p. 146.
8. JONES and LANGMUIR: The Characteristics of Tungsten Filaments as Functions of Temperature, *G. E. Res. Lab. Reprints*, No. 419, 1927. *G.E. Rev.*, **30**, 1927, pp. 310, 354, 408.
9. P. G. NUTTING: The Design of Large Incandescent Lamps, *J.O.S.A.*, **7**, 1923, p. 399.
10. HYDE, CADY, and FORSYTHE: Color Temperature Scales for Tungsten and Carbon, *Phys. Rev.*, **10**, 1917, p. 397.
11. G. STEAD: The Short Tungsten Filament as a Source of Light and Electrons, *I.E.E., J.*, **58**, 1920, p. 107.
12. LANGMUIR, MACLANE and BLODGETT: The Effect of End Losses on the Characteristics of Filaments, *Phys. Rev.*, **35**, 1930, p. 478.
13. A. G. WORTHING: Theory of End-loss Corrections, *Frank. Inst., J.*, **194**, 1922, p. 597.
14. BUSH and GOULD: Temperature Distribution along a Filament, *Phys. Rev.*, **29**, 1927, p. 337.
15. FONDA and VERNON: Characteristics of Coiled Filaments in Incandescent Lamps, *J.O.S.A.*, **22**, 1932, p. 223.
16 H. A. JONES: The Theory and Design of Ballast Resistors, *G. E. Rev.*, **28**, 1925, p. 650.
17. BARBROW and MEYER: Characteristic Equations of Vacuum and Gasfilled Tungsten Filament Lamps, *Bu. Stds. J.R.*, **9**, 1932, p. 721.
18. P. S. MILLAR: Safeguarding the Quality of Incandescent Lamps, *I.E.S. Trans.*, **26**, 1931, p. 948.
19. N. T. GORDON: Water Cooling of Incandescent Lamps, *M.P.E. Trans.*, **14**, 1930, p. 332.

20. W. E. FORSYTHE: Tungsten Lamp Characteristics as Functions of Applied Voltage, *G.E. Rev.*, **37**, 1934, p. 191.

21. FORSYTHE and WATSON: Resistance and Radiation of Tungsten as a Function of Temperature, *J.O.S.A.*, **24**, 1934, p. 114.

22. FORSYTHE and WATSON: Some Lamps Intended for Special Services, *G.E. Rev.*, **37**, 1934, p. 251.

23. FORSYTHE and EASLEY: Radiation of the Photo-flash Lamps, *J.O.S.A.*, **24**, 1934, p. 195.

24. J. D. WHITTAKER: Silver-processed Incandescent Lamps, *I.E.S. Trans.*, **28**, 1933, p. 418.

FILTERS

25. E. O. HULBURT: The Transparency of Ocean Water, *J.O.S.A.*, **13**, 1926, p. 553.

26. OSTER and CLARKE: Penetration of Daylight into Atlantic Waters, *J.O.S.A.*, **25**, 1935, p. 85.

27. W. W. COBLENTZ: Light Filters which Absorb All the Infrared, *Bu. Stds. Bull.* **9**, 1913, p. 110.

28. H. P. GAGE: Methods of Measuring Visible and Total Energy Transmissions of Heat-absorbing Glasses, *I.E.S. Trans.*, **30**, 1935, p. 411.

29. W. W. COBLENTZ: Recent Progress in the Manufacture of Glasses for Protecting the Eye, *Frank. Inst., J.*, **188**, 1919, p. 255.

30. Eastman Kodak Co.: Wratten Light Filters, 1932.

31. H. P. GAGE: Glass Color Filters, *J.O.S.A.*, **17**, 1928.

32. L. A. JONES: Light Filters for the Isolation of Narrow Spectral Regions, *J.O.S.A.*, **16**, 1928, p. 259.

33. K. S. GIBSON: Spectral Filters, *J.O.S.A.*, **13**, 1926, p. 267.

34. DAVIS and GIBSON: Filters for the Reproduction of Sunlight, *Bu. Stds., Misc. Pub.*, 114, 1931.

35. A. H. TAYLOR: Spectral Distribution of Energy in Common Illuminants, *G.E. Rev.*, **37**, 1934, p. 410.

36. M. G. V. POTAPENKO: The Theory and Technique of Light Filters, *Russ. Phys. Chem. Soc., Journal*, **48**, 1916, p. 790, trans. C.E.K. Mees, *Brit. J. Phot.*, **68**, 1921, pp. 507, 522, 534.

37. W. W. COBLENTZ: Tests of Stellar Radiometers, *Bu. Stds., Sci. Paper* 438, **17**, 1922, p. 725.

38. W. W. COBLENTZ: Spectroradiometric Investigation of the Transmission of Various Substances, *Bu. Stds. Sci. Paper* 418, **16**, 1921, p. 267.

39. GIBSON, TYNDALL, and McNICHOLAS: The Transmission of Various Colored Glasses, *Bu. Stds. Tech. Paper* 148, 1920.

40. COBLENTZ and EMERSON: Glasses for Protecting the Eyes, *Bu. Stds. Tech. Paper* 93, 1919.

41. GIBSON and McNICHOLAS: The Transmission of Eye-protective Glasses, *Bu. Stds. Tech. Paper* 119, 1919.

42. E. J. BRADY: The Development of Daylight Glass, *I.E.S. Trans.*, **9**, 1914, p. 937.

43. H. P. GAGE: Color Filters for Altering Color Temperature, *J.O.S.A.*, **23**, 1933, p. 46.

44. E. H. HOBBIE: Glass for Protection from Infrared Radiation, *I.E.S. Trans.*, **28**, 1933, p. 658.

45. K. S. GIBSON: A Filter for Obtaining Light at Wavelength 560mμ, *J.O.S.A.*, **25**, 1935, p. 131; *Bu. Stds. J. R.*, **14**, 1935, p. 545. (RP 785.)

46. F. BENFORD: Coördinated System of Optical Filters for Color-temperature Determinations, *J.O.S.A.*, **25**, 1935, p. 136.

CHAPTER VII

MEASUREMENT OF LIGHT

PHOTOMETRIC CONCEPTS

The preceding three chapters have discussed the production of radiation by incandescent sources and by gaseous-conduction sources. We shall now consider the measurement of this radiation and in particular the measurement of this radiation evaluated with respect to the standard visibility function. A restatement of the definitions of photometric quantities follows:

Radiant power or radiant flux (Φ) is power in the form of electromagnetic radiation. It is expressed in watts.

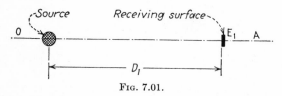

Fig. 7.01.

Luminous flux (F) is radiant power evaluated with respect to the standard visibility function. It is expressed in lumens.

Illumination (E) of a surface is equal to the luminous flux falling on the surface per unit area. The lumen per square foot is a common unit.

Luminosity (L) of a source is equal to the luminous flux emitted by source per unit area. The lumen per square foot is a practical unit.

Another concept will be found useful in many cases, the concept of *luminous intensity*. We wish to develop a convenient way of specifying the strength of a source with respect to its ability to produce illumination. Instead of using the old-fashioned definition dealing with nonexistent solid angles or with sperm candles, let us consider how intensity is measured by measuring its effect —the illumination (see Appendix B). A source of any size or shape is fixed at O (Fig. 7.01), and its intensity is desired in the direction OA. A receiving surface, such as the target of a radiation thermocouple, is placed at any convenient distance D_1 and is oriented so that it is normal to the direction of flow of radiant power at that point. The illumination E_1 is measured by obtaining the spectroradiometric curve and evaluating it mathematically with respect to the standard visibility curve or by simpler methods to be described in this chapter. The distance D_1 from the emitting surface to the receiving surface is then measured. If the measurements of illumination and distance are repeated at several points on the straight line OA drawn from the center of the source, it will be found that the illumination E will decrease rapidly as the distance D is increased. The values of ED^2, however, are found to approach a constant as D increases.

Figure 7.02, for example, shows the results obtained with sources in the form of diffusing cylinders. Such sources, formed by cylinders of opal glass inclosing tubular lamps, are often used for lighting mirrors and in other applications. It will be noted that near the source the values of ED^2 vary in a marked manner but that as D increases the values all approach a constant. The use of cylinders of different proportions changes the shape of the curve. The use of other kinds of sources also changes the shape but does not alter the fact that sooner or later the value of ED^2 becomes essentially independent of D.

This limiting value of ED^2 is used as a measure of the strength of the source and is called the *luminous intensity* or *candlepower* I:

$$I = \lim_{D \to \infty} (ED^2) \tag{7.01}$$

The unit of intensity is called the *candle*, and Eq. (7.01) is in candles if E is expressed in lumens per unit area. Evidently, intensity or candlepower is a property of the source. For a particular source and a particular direction it is a constant, independent of the distance. A uniform sphere might be expected to have the same candlepower in all directions. Practical light sources, however, are found to have different values of candlepower in different directions, so that in specifying the intensity of a source it is necessary to state the direction in which the intensity is measured.

7.02 Laws of Illumination.—The concept of intensity is introduced merely because of its convenience in the calculation of illumination. The illuminating engineer decides to use a certain size of lamp, say a 200-watt lamp, in lighting a room and wishes to know the illumination that will be produced at various parts of the room. Knowing the candlepower of the lamp, he can then use Eq. (7.01) in calculating E. In fact, unless he is very close

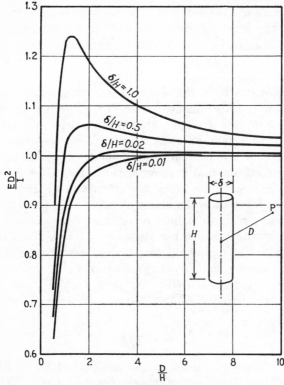

Fig. 7.02.—Variation of ED^2 for circular-cylinder source with perfectly diffusing walls. (*From Yamauti, Electrot. Lab. Tokyo, Researches, 148, 1924.*)

to the lamp, he can forget all about the "limit as D approaches infinity" in the preceding equation and can use the inverse-square law,

$$E = \frac{I}{D^2} \tag{7.02}$$

If the engineer had decided to use a large luminous panel or artificial window to illuminate his room, he could still talk about the intensity of this source, but he could not use this intensity in calculating the illumination by Eq. (7.02) unless the room was very large.   The distance from the source at which the inverse-square law begins to be applicable depends upon the size of the source, the shape of the source, and the precision demanded.   It is evident from Fig. 7.02 that if absolute accuracy were necessary, we could, theoretically, never use the inverse-square law.   For any given accuracy, however, we can pick a place where the curve is sufficiently close to its asymptote so that calculations with the inverse-square law will be satisfactory. A rough rule is that if the error of Eq. (7.02) is to be less than 1 per cent, the distance from the surface source must generally be at least five times the greatest dimension of the source.   If illumination is to be calculated at distances less than this value, integration methods must be used (Chap. IX), and the concept of intensity is less useful.   In a great many practical cases, however, the concept of intensity is found very helpful because of the simplicity of Eq. (7.02).   Intensity could have been omitted entirely from our list of photometric concepts, which would simplify the set of concepts but would cause a

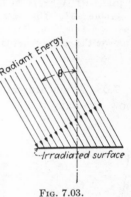

Fig. 7.03.

little inconvenience in the calculation of illumination.   On the whole, it seems advisable to retain this least important of the photometric concepts.

Besides the inverse-square law, another fundamental law is the *cosine law of illumination*.   If the illuminated surface is tilted, the luminous flux falling on unit area is reduced in proportion to the cosine of the angle θ between the incoming ray and the normal to the surface (Fig. 7.03).   Combining the two laws, we obtain for the illumination of any surface by any source that is not too close to the surface

$$E = \frac{I}{D^2} \cos \theta \qquad (7.03)$$

This equation will be found very useful.

Problem 55. Measurements on the radiation from an ordinary diffusing globe luminaire attached to the ceiling of a room show that at a distance of 5 ft directly beneath the center of the globe the irradiation is 0.00370 watt/sq cm, while at a distance of 8 ft the irradiation is 0.00146 watt/sq cm.

Is it permissible to use the inverse-square law beyond 5 ft if we do not need greater accuracy than 2 per cent? Than 0.5 per cent?

A diffusing-glass panel 2 by 4 ft and of uniform luminosity ($L = 200$ lumens/sq ft) lights a staircase in a modern building. Is it permissible to use the inverse-square law in calculating the illumination at 6 ft from the panel?

Problem 56. The head lamps of an automobile illuminate a detour sign 100 ft in front of the car. The sign is white and has a reflection factor of 0.82. The center of the head lamps is 30 in. above the pavement, and the total intensity of the two head lamps is 25,000 candles in the direction considered. What is the luminosity of the sign?

Problem 57. The same car is on a macadam pavement whose reflection factor is 4 per cent. What is the illumination of the pavement 172 ft in front of the car? What is its luminosity?

SPECTRORADIOMETRY

7.03. Monochromators.—In Chap. II, we considered briefly how irradiation could be measured and how the spectroradiometric curve could be obtained by means of a prism and a thermocouple. The complete instrument is called a *spectroradiometer;* and the optical part, exclusive of the thermocouple or other radiometer, is often called a *monochromator.*

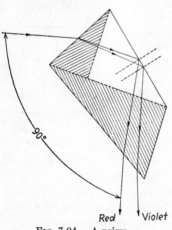

Fig. 7.04.—A prism.

Besides the common 60-deg prism, a number of modified prisms have been used. Figure 7.04, for instance, shows one form of constant-deviation prism which acts like a combination of two 30-deg prisms and a 45-deg reflecting prism. Actually, the prism is generally made of one piece of glass. The advantage of such an arrangement is that both slits of the spectroradiometer may be fixed, and the prism turned to vary the wavelength of the radiation emitted by the second slit. The axes of the two lenses of the instrument are 90 deg apart. Another arrangement[13] uses two 30-deg prisms as shown in Fig. 7.05.   In this case, the axes of telescope and collimator make an angle of 129 deg, and manipulation of the wavelength dial turns both prisms.

One of the difficulties encountered in precise spectroradiometry is caused by stray light.   A number of glass-air surfaces are necessary, and at each such surface there is some light reflected. Multiple reflections at the various surfaces* generally result in a small amount of radiation at various wavelengths mixed with the homogeneous component to be measured.   Stray light can be reduced by the use of blackened shields at various places within

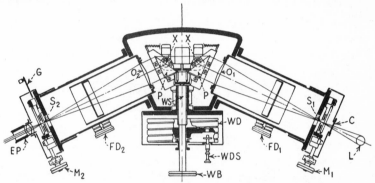

FIG. 7.05.—Quartz monochromator using two 30° prisms, *P-P*, turned about axes *X-X*.   (*Bausch and Lomb.*)

the instrument.   Another method for reducing stray light is to use two prisms in a *double monochromator*.   A large instrument of this type[15] is shown in Fig. 7.06.   The homogeneous component selected by the first monochromator passes through the second instrument with little change, but most of the stray light passed by the first prism will be weeded out by the second prism and exit slit.

Prisms and lenses are generally made of glass.   If measurements are to be extended into the ultraviolet or far into the infrared, however, materials other than glass are necessary. For the ultraviolet, quartz is generally used, giving a range of approximately 0.2 to 3μ.   The lenses and prisms of the instrument of Fig. 7.06, for instance, are cut from large quartz crystals. If measurements in the ultraviolet can be dispensed with, glass is found to be very satisfactory and much cheaper than quartz.

* Also scattering of light by dust particles, air bubbles in the glass, etc.

For longer waves than approximately 3μ, rock salt may be used.[9]

The target of the thermocouple (Fig. 2.03) can be so blackened that it absorbs nearly all the radiant energy that falls on it, practically independent of wavelength over the range in which the illuminating engineer is interested. The characteristics of such a nonselective receiver might lead one to expect that the spectroradiometric curve could be obtained directly from the galvanometer deflections. Unfortunately, however, the monochromator is selective:

1. The absorption and reflections in the optical system vary with wavelength.

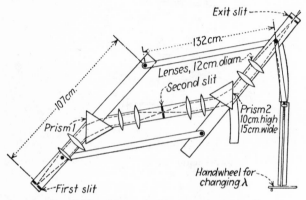

FIG. 7.06.—A large double monochromator.[15]

2. The second slit passes a wider wavelength band in some parts of the spectrum than in others.

Both factors 1 and 2 can be evaluated and the proper correction applied to the readings. The transmission characteristics of the instrument of Fig. 7.06 are shown in Fig. 7.07. Each glass-air surface reflects about 4 per cent or more of the radiant power incident on it, and these reflections reduce the irradiation of the exit slit. Figure 7.07 shows that in the middle of the visible region the reflections reduce the irradiation to 36 per cent of the value that it would have if reflections were absent. Absorption in the quartz elements of this instrument reduce the irradiation still further.

Instead of attempting to correct for the losses in the monochromator, it may be more convenient to consider the complete spectroradiometer as a unit and calibrate it by means of a standard source of radiation. An experimental Planckian radiator may be used to irradiate the entrance slit, or an incandescent lamp having a known spectral energy distribution. The experimental spectroradiometric curve is then compared with the known spectral distribution curve for the irradiation, and a spectral calibration curve is obtained. Such a curve takes into account all factors, including reflections and selective absorption, slit-width correction, and any selective characteristics that may exist in the absorption of the target surface.

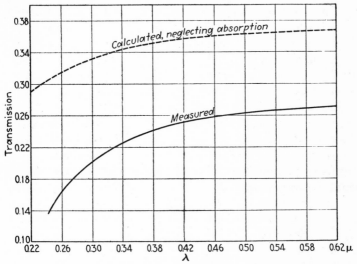

Fig. 7.07.—Transmission of a double monochromator.[15]

7.04. Thermocouples and Bolometers.—The early radiation thermocouples were essentially as shown in Fig. 2.03. They were insensitive, owing to the cooling of the junction by convection, and the results were somewhat erratic because of air currents. By inclosing the junctions in an evacuated bulb, convection losses were eliminated; and by using very fine wires or strips, heat conduction was reduced to a minimum. In thus reducing the heat losses, the temperature rise of the thermojunction was increased, and the instrument was made very much more sensitive. The work of Moll and Burger[11] and of others revolutionized the radiation thermocouple.

Another instrument for the measurement of radiation is the *bolometer*. Instead of being attached to thermojunctions, the targets are fastened to thin wires; or flat strips are used, blackened on one side. The irradiated wire or strip becomes hotter than its neighbor which is shielded from the radiation. The resistance of the irradiated strip rises, and the Wheatstone bridge, in which the two wires are connected, is thrown out of balance. The deflection of the galvanometer is a measure of the irradiation.

With either the thermocouple or the bolometer, the voltages obtained are extremely small. It is generally necessary to be able to detect a voltage of 10^{-7} or 10^{-8} volt. A d-c amplifier for such voltages is out of the question, so a low-resistance, high-sensitivity galvanometer must be used. Obviously, as long as we are handicapped by the difficulties inherent in the use of delicate galvanometers, we cannot expect to put radiation measurements on the usual commercial basis. The measurement of light is still dominated by the spirit of the eighteenth century rather than by the spirit of the twentieth century. There is still a preoccupation with standard candles and visual-comparison methods which have little or no place in the modern scheme of photometry. *The placing of photometry upon a firm physical basis requires accurate and rapid methods of obtaining the spectroradiometric curve.* This is the crux of the whole matter. Unless the delicate laboratory methods can be supplanted, we cannot hope to get either accuracy or speed.

Two recent improvements eliminate the galvanometer completely. D-c amplification is impossible with these low voltages of 10^{-7} volt, but a-c amplifiers can be made to detect a voltage of 10^{-7} volt or even less. Thus the problem is to obtain an alternating instead of a direct voltage. Harris[18] uses a motor-driven shutter which causes a periodic fluctuation in the irradiation of a thermojunction. By using a junction of extremely low heat capacity and a low frequency of fluctuation, the generated emf will tend to follow the variations in the irradiation. The junctions are made of extremely thin films of metal, tellurium and bismuth giving the highest voltages. The voltage applied to the amplifier is pulsating instead of alternating, but the sharply tuned amplifier selects the fundamental a-c component of this pulsating voltage. It can be shown that the greatest single-frequency rms voltage that can be obtained at the amplifier input is 35 per cent of the d-c voltage that would be obtained if the shutter were eliminated.

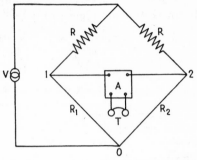

FIG. 7.08.—Schematic diagram of the alternating-current bolometer bridge.[24]

Another scheme uses a bolometer but operates it from an a-c source[23,24] rather than from the customary d-c source. The arrangement is shown in Fig. 7.08, where a source of alternating voltage V supplies the bolom- eter bridge. The bridge con- sists of two equal noninductive resistors R, R and two identical bolometer wires R_1 and R_2, one of which receives radiant power. A tuned amplifier A is connected between points 1 and 2 and operates an a-c milliammeter or a pair of head phones T. The type of bolometer cell constructed at Massachusetts Institute of Technology[24] is shown in Fig. 7.09, where the numbers refer to corresponding points in Fig. 7.08. The a-c bolometer has

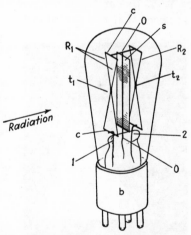

FIG. 7.09.—Bolometer cell for use in alternating-current bolometer bridge.[24]

no moving parts, is compact and portable, and is not affected by ordinary vibration or by spurious thermal emfs.

Both a-c bolometer and the a-c thermocouple are so new that they will require considerable further development. That such development will be worth while is evidenced by the many advantages, including ruggedness, ease of operation, and high sensitivity. The minimum detectable irradiation for various vacuum thermocouples and for the a-c bolometer is given in Table XXVIII. The table is based on the assumption that either the galvanometer or the a-c amplifier can detect 10^{-8} volt.

Problem 58. Check the statement that with an a-c thermojunction the rms voltage cannot exceed 35 per cent of the direct voltage obtained with the same irradiation.

TABLE XXVIII.—MINIMUM DETECTABLE IRRADIATION[23]

	G_{min} (watts/sq cm)
With galvanometer:	
Constantan-manganin thermocouple	29×10^{-8}
Bismuth-alloy thermocouple	9
Burt thermocouple	14
With a-c amplifier:	
Bismuth-alloy thermocouple	24
Tellurium-bismuth thermocouple	7
A-c bolometer (easily obtainable value)	5

MEASUREMENT OF ILLUMINATION

7.05. Use of Templates and Filters.—As we have seen, it often happens that the wealth of information afforded by the spectro-radiometric curve is unnecessary and that quicker and simpler methods are desirable. If the value of illumination is wanted, why not perform the evaluation of the spectral irradiation curve experimentally instead of mathematically? This has been done in a very neat manner by Ives.[33] The second slit of the monochromator is replaced by a fixed template which cuts down the radiant power according to the ordinates of the standard visibility curve. The entire spectrum is then focused upon a blackened target by means of a lens.

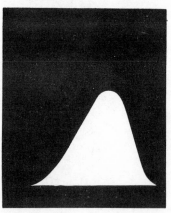

FIG. 7.10.—Template.

Here we have an experimental counterpart of the mathematical procedure of Chap. III. The multiplication of the values of spectral irradiation by v is performed by the template (Fig. 7.10) the height of whose opening is proportional to v (corrected for slit width, selective absorption, etc.).   The subsequent integration of Chap. III is performed by the lens, which combines all the vG_λ components and focuses them on the target.   The reading of the radiometer gives E directly.

Another scheme is to eliminate the monochromator and use a filter in front of the thermojunction or the bolometer target. The spectral transmission curve of the filter must be the same as the standard visibility curve.   Therein lies the difficulty, since to obtain even an approximation to the visibility curve is no simple matter.   Ives has used a liquid filter 10.0 mm thick with the following solution contained in a glass cell.[32,33]

Cupric chloride	60	grams
Cobalt ammonium sulphate	14	grams
Potassium chromate	1.9	grams
Nitric acid (sp. gr., 1.05)	18	cc
Water to	1000	cc

It must be used with a water cell at least 4 cm thick to eliminate the infrared and when used with a nonselective radiometer will give a fairly good approximation to the standard visibility function.

7.06. Characteristics of Photocells.—If spectroradiometric measurements are not needed beyond about 1.2μ, the thermocouple of Fig. 2.03 may be replaced by a photoelectric cell. There are several advantages to such a step: a greater response, and the possibility of using d-c vacuum-tube amplifiers, for which the vacuum photocell is ideally suited.   The disadvantages are obvious.   The response varies with wavelength in a decided and somewhat erratic manner, and the characteristics of the best cells obtainable today are none too constant; so unless special methods are used, one is never certain that the cell has not changed since it was last calibrated.   Besides its use in spectroradiometry, however, the photocell is applicable to measurements of illumination and is finding considerable use in such measurements.

Before considering the characteristics of commercial photocells, let us review very briefly the theory.   When a *photon* or *energy quantum* of $h\nu$ ergs strikes a metal surface, the energy may be absorbed by an electron near the surface of the metal.   If, however, the energy absorbed by the electron is below a certain value W_p, the electron will be unable to free itself from the surface.

If the absorbed energy is greater than the critical value W_p, the electron will leave the surface with a kinetic energy

$$\tfrac{1}{2}mv^2 = h\nu - W_p$$

W_p is called the *work function* of the surface. Its value for the alkali metals (according to Zworykin and Wilson)[37] is given below.

WORK FUNCTION OF THE ALKALI METALS

Alkali metal	Electron volts	W_p
Lithium	2.36	3.75×10^{-12} erg
Sodium	1.82	2.90
Potassium	1.55	2.46
Rubidium	1.45	2.31
Caesium	1.36	2.16

For sodium, for instance, an electron must acquire energy equal to at least $W_p = 2.90 \times 10^{-12}$ erg in order to leave the

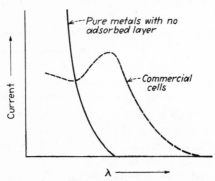

FIG. 7.11.—Photoelectric-response curves.

surface of the metal. The energy value below which there is no emission is determined by $h\nu = 2.90 \times 10^{-12}$ erg. Hence the critical frequency is $\nu = 0.44 \times 10^{15}$ cycles/sec, corresponding to a wavelength of $\lambda = 0.68\mu$. With sodium, wavelengths longer than 0.68μ will produce no photoelectric effect.

The values just given are for pure metals carefully freed from all adsorbed gas. To one who has studied the theory of the photoelectric effect, the transition from the theoretical to the actual cell comes as a distinct shock. There seems to be little

relation between them, either in the values or in the shapes
of the curves obtained.   Actual cells respond to much longer
wavelengths than the theory would indicate.   Even for caesium,
the table indicates that wavelengths beyond 0.9μ would produce
no photoelectric effect, while we have seen in Chap. II that
commercial cells using caesium operate at wavelengths up to
1.2μ.   The theoretical and the commercial curves are sketched
in Fig. 7.11.   The difference between them is due to the fact that
commercial cells do not use pure metals carefully freed from

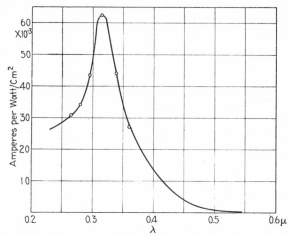

FIG. 7.12.—Response curve for a photocell using pure sodium.[35]

adsorbed layers but purposely contaminate the surface of the
metal in various ways in order to shift the response curve to
longer wavelengths.   Figure 7.12 shows a typical curve for a
sodium cell.   Maximum response is obtained at 0.32μ.   Considerable study has also been made of cells that have a sharp
peak in the ultraviolet and that can be used in measuring the
biological effectiveness of radiant power.   Figure 7.13 shows
results for a number of cells that have been sensitized by treating
the metal surface with oxygen, hydrogen, sulphur fumes, etc.
Figure 7.14 gives some results on the latest types of cells.   Figure
7.15 illustrates a type of cell using a fairly heavy coating of
caesium.   The PJ-14 cell, which is often used in photometry,*
has a characteristic similar to that of the cell of Fig. 7.15.   With

* See Fig. 7.19.

all these cells the curves are believed to be fairly representative, though it must be realized that no two cells of the same type will, in general, have the same response curves.   The slightest differ-

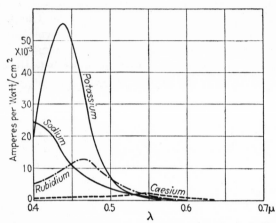

Fig. 7.13.—Response curves for photocells using sensitized alkali metals.[35]

ence in treatment during manufacture entirely alters the shape of the curves.   Results of some minute differences in surface treatment of a cell are shown in Fig. 7.16.

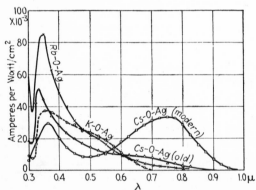

Fig. 7.14.—Response curves for photocells using thin films of alkali metals on oxides.[35]

Other characteristics of photocells are shown in Figs. 7.17 and 7.18.   Photoelectric theory predicts that the number of electrons emitted per second should be directly proportional to the illumination, provided the *shape* of the spectral irradiation curve

remains fixed.   This prediction can be checked experimentally
with all well-constructed cells* (Fig. 7.17), except perhaps at very

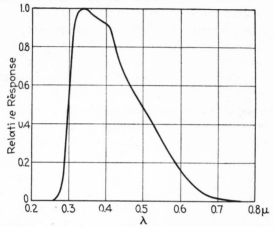

FIG. 7.15.—Relative response at various wavelengths, Westinghouse caesium
photocell.

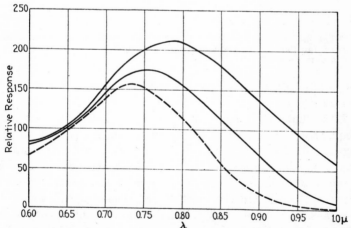

FIG. 7.16.—Photocell response; three Cs-O-Ag cells with different surface
treatments.[44]

low values of illumination where leakage current may affect the
results.

* Of the vacuum type. Gas-filled cells usually give a current which
increases more rapidly than the first power of the illumination.

If the irradiation is held constant and the voltage V applied to the photocell circuit is varied, a curve like Fig. 7.18 is obtained. With $V = 0$, there is little tendency for electrons to reach the anode of the cell; but a few do so, and a small current flows. As V is increased, greater numbers of electrons emitted by the metal surface of the cathode are pulled to the anode, and the curve of current rises, a saturation effect also taking place at high values of V. By filling the cell with a gas, ionization takes place at sufficiently high voltage, and the current curve rises rapidly, as shown by the dotted line. Such gas-filled cells are not used generally for photometry, since in the flat portion of their characteristic they are no more sensitive than the vacuum

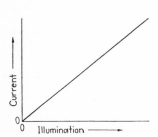

Fig. 7.17.—Photocell current as a function of illumination (vacuum photocell).

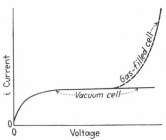

Fig. 7.18.—Photocell current as a function of applied voltage.

cell, while on the dotted portion of the curve they are not sufficiently stable.

7.07. Photocell Sensitivity.—Since photocells are used most frequently with radiation from incandescent lamps, it is advantageous to have data on the current produced per unit illumination from incandescent-lamp sources. Such indices can be obtained by the methods of Chap. II, using the spectral-response curve of the cell and the spectral irradiation curve. The same results can be obtained by a simple measurement of current for a known irradiation. Note, however, that in general each source will entail a separate determination of amperes per lumen per square foot, while a single determination of the spectral-response curve allows the calculation of photoelectric current for any conceivable kind of radiation.

Representative values of sensitivity are given in Table XXIX.*
The illumination is produced by incandescent lamps operating

* Page 213.

at two temperatures. It is interesting to note that a reduction in filament temperature causes a decided *diminution* in sensitivity for cells that have their greatest response at short wavelengths but *increases* the sensitivity for some of the modern cells (such as the PJ-22 and the 5A) which have a large response in the near infrared. With the latter cells, one can get unbelievably high values of sensitivity by merely reducing the voltage on the lamp to a sufficient extent. Even with two sources producing exactly the same illumination and operating at exactly the same color temperature, the sensitivity may be widely different because of differences in the two spectra in the infrared. Evidently, the sensitivity expressed in amperes per lumen per square foot is not a particularly precise concept and means absolutely nothing unless the kind of radiation is specified exactly.

If a photocell could be obtained with a response curve like the visibility curve (Fig. 3.02), the measurement of illumination would be a simple matter. A glance at Figs. 7.12, 7.13, and 7.14, however, shows that the actual curves are not at all what we want. We could, of course, use the cell behind a monochromator with template (Fig. 7.10), as has been done at Massachusetts Institute of Technology,[14] shaping the template to compensate for the variations in spectral response of the cell as well as for the selective properties of the monochromator. Or we could use a filter in front of the cell and eliminate the monochromator.

Gray and Eckweiler[47] have used filters with a PJ-14 caesium cell, as shown in Fig. 7.19. They say:

> The progress which has been made since 1925 in the production of photoelectric cells, notably increases in sensitivity and in the distribution of the sensitivity throughout the spectrum, has rendered it possible to obtain photoelectric cells of such characteristics that by the use of selectively absorbing filters their response at all wavelengths is rendered proportional to the selective visibility of the light at those wavelengths. Evidently, a cell so corrected will give true photometric values irrespective of the color of the light.

After considerable experimenting, they finally obtained a filter consisting of a piece of amber glass, 8 mm of 2.76 per cent solution of copper chloride, and a Wratten No. 12 gelatin filter so punched with holes that only 55 per cent of the original area remained. The result (Fig. 7.19) is a remarkably good approximation to the standard visibility curve.

One disquieting thought in regard to the use of either templates or filters with photocells is that after spending several weeks obtaining the desired result, one has obtained it only for a particular cell. The same filter cannot be used with any other photocell, nor has one any assurance that this photocell will not change its characteristics with temperature or with time. It is interesting to note that those experts who have had most experience with photocells are apparently most skeptical about their constancy and dependability. Little definite information seems to be available, if we except the results of Peters and

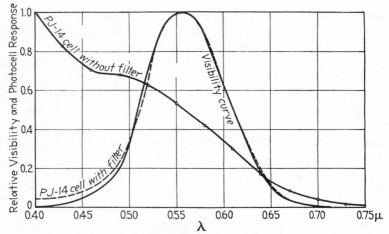

Fig. 7.19.—Effect of using special filter with PJ-14 photocell.[47]   (Ordinates are adjusted to give a maximum of 1.00 in all cases.)

Woodford.[41] They found with all gas-filled cells tremendous variations in the current under apparently the same external conditions. The vacuum cells were much more stable, though erratic fluctuations of as much as 4 per cent were obtained with the PJ-14, 25 per cent for the PJ-22 and 30 per cent for the VB.

Problem 59. Plot a curve of photocell sensitivity (amperes per watt per square centimeter) vs. T for Planckian radiators operating between 2000 and 3000°K. Use any cell whose response curve is given in this chapter or in Chap. II.

Problem 60. A tungsten-filament lamp and a carbon-filament lamp are both operated at 2000°K. A photocell, whose response curve is given in Fig. 2.07, is placed so that the illumination from either lamp is 35 lumens/sq ft. What current is obtained in the two cases? Consider the carbon filament as a gray body.

7.08. Photocell Circuits.—An ordinary photocell circuit can hardly be expected to yield precision results, though the results may be sufficiently good for some purposes. Figure 7.20 shows the simplest circuit using a galvanometer or a microammeter. Fortunately, the resistance of the photocell is so high that the current is practically independent of the resistance of the measuring instrument, so multirange microammeters may be used without correction for the change in resistance when the scale is changed.

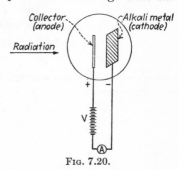

FIG. 7.20.

In most cases, the current is too small to be read on a microammeter. The high resistance of the photocell, however, makes it peculiarly well adapted for use with a vacuum-tube amplifier. The various circuits may be classified as follows:

1. Those which require that both photocell and amplifier remain constant during the measurements.

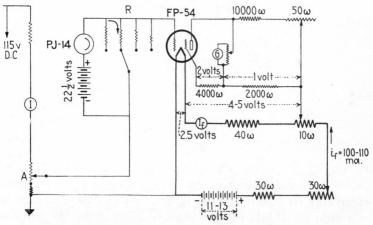

FIG. 7.21.—A circuit used in measuring small amounts of luminous flux.

2. Those which require that the photocell remain constant.

3. Those which depend upon the constancy of neither.

Of these, (1) is obviously of little value. A highly developed form of (2), due to DuBridge,[53] is indicated in Fig. 7.21. In the form used at Massachusetts Institute of Technology, the cell is a PJ-14, and the resistors R range from 10^7 to 10^{11} ohms. An FP-54 tube is connected as shown, and a shunted portable galvanometer is used at G. With the cell dark, the circuit is adjusted to give zero deflection of the galvanometer. If properly adjusted (see paper by DuBridge and Brown), the circuit is remarkably stable, and the zero remains fixed for long periods. If the photocell is illuminated, the galvanometer deflects but is brought back to zero by changing the grid bias a known amount

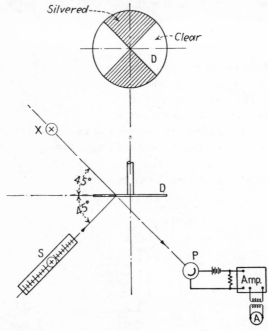

Fig. 7.22.

by use of the calibrated voltage divider A. Evidently, the characteristics of the amplifier do not enter into the measurements, the IR drop in R being compensated by the introduction of a known emf into the grid circuit. Numerous other circuits have been used, which (like that of Fig. 7.21) are subject to error due to changes in the photocell and in R but not to changes in the amplifier.

To eliminate errors due to variations in the photocell, some form (3) of rapid intercomparison of two sources is used. Figure 7.22 shows a scheme developed by Sharp and Kinsley[48] and

used by the Electrical Testing Laboratories.   The photocell P
is illuminated by the unknown source X or by the standard S.
A glass disk D is divided into a number of sectors, half of which
are silvered, with alternate ones clear.   The disk is driven by
a motor.   The photocell current due to X is shown as a function
of time in the top diagram of Fig. 7.23a.   The current due to S
is similar in shape but displaced in time and generally of different
amplitude.   By sliding S along the calibrated track, however, a
place can be found where a practically constant photocell current
is obtained (Fig. 7.23b).   If such a constant current can be
realized, the output instrument A will read zero.   To use the

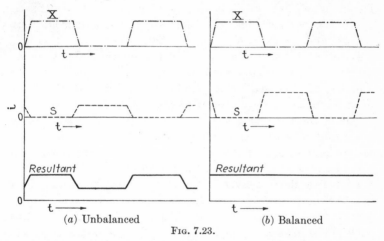

(a) Unbalanced   (b) Balanced

Fig. 7.23.

instrument, therefore, one merely moves S until A reads zero.
The illumination of the photocell due to X is then equal to the
known illumination due to S, if it is assumed that the spectral
distribution of the two sources is the same.   If the two sources
are incandescent lamps but are not operating at the same temperature, a simple yellow filter in front of P often allows sufficiently accurate results to be obtained.   To eliminate *completely*
errors due to changes in the photocell, a monochromator may be
introduced between D and P, and the instrument can be used to
obtain the spectroradiometric curve of X.

7.09. Methods of Balancing.—In the use of a null method
such as that of Fig. 7.22, a quick and continuous variation of
the illumination due to S is required on balancing.   Such a
variation cannot be obtained by adjusting the voltage applied

to S, since that alters the quality of the radiation.   Permissible methods are

1. Use of the inverse-square law, as in Fig. 7.22.

2. Use of neutral filters or wedges.   By introducing a gray absorbing filter between S and D, it is possible to reduce the illumination by known amounts.   This eliminates the inconvenience of a movable lamp but is hardly ideal, particularly because of the difficulty of obtaining filters that are truly nonselective.

3. A uniformly luminous surface, such as a piece of opal glass between S and D, may be altered in area with an opaque shutter. The illumination at P will be directly proportional to the exposed area of the glass, provided the luminosity of the surface is strictly uniform and the surface is not too large.

4. Use of a flicker disk to cut off part of the radiant energy. Often used in visual photometry.

5. Use of polarized light.   An elegant scheme, though somewhat complicated and expensive.

One of the best examples of (5) is the Hardy instrument for measuring reflection and transmission factors.[57]   A device for the rapid measurement of spectral irradiation curves could be obtained by a modification of the Hardy device.

7.10. The Barrier-layer Cell.—It has been known for some time that an oxidized copper plate has the property of conducting current better in one direction than in the opposite direction. Such plates have been used extensively in the familiar dry-disk rectifiers.[58]   About 1927, Grondahl noticed peculiarities in the operation of these rectifiers and attributed the inconsistencies to the effect of illumination.[67]   Light-sensitive cells were produced, consisting of a copper disk oxidized by heating in air to 1040°C and annealing at 600°C.   The copper plate (Fig. 7.24a) formed one electrode, while a spiral of wire (pressed against the Cu_2O) constituted the other electrode.   When radiant power is transmitted through the cuprous oxide layer, electrons are liberated at or near the boundary of the oxide and the mother copper.   The electrons flow through the external circuit and operate the microammeter A.

Most of the radiant energy was absorbed in passing through the oxide layer, so an improvement was effected by moving the active layer to the *top* of the oxide (Fig. 7.24b).   This was accomplished by sputtering a very thin, semitransparent film of gold, silver, or platinum on the oxide layer. Most of the photoelectric effect now occurs at the top of the oxide layer, and the current flows in the direction opposite from that in Fig. 7.24*a*.

Physicists have recently studied this peculiar photoelectric and rectifying action which takes place at the boundary of a conductor and a semiconductor and have evolved some interesting theories.[59,60]   It might be expected that other semiconductors besides Cu_2O would work, and one of this class of substances—selenium—has been found to be very effective.   The familiar

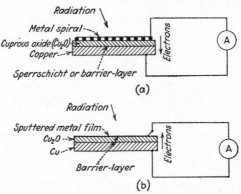

FIG. 7.24.—Barrier-layer photocells.

Weston Photronic cell,[68] for example, uses selenium as the semiconductor.   A detailed description of the production and test of selenium-sulphur barrier-layer cells is given by Barnard.[69]

The spectral response of a typical Weston cell[68] is shown in Fig. 7.25.   Notice the much greater response than that of the photocells of Figs. 7.14, also the much better approximation to the visibility curve of the eye.   Still closer approximation to the *v*-function is obtainable by the addition of a green filter. These advantages are so important that the barrier-layer cell has practically revolutionized the commercial measurement of illumination. · A large number of manufacturers, both here and abroad, are now producing such cells, some with selenium and others with copper oxide.

The variation of current with illumination is shown in Fig. 7.26. Unlike the photocell, the barrier-layer cell is a low-resistance device and will give a linear response only when the external resistance approaches zero. The low voltage also prohibits the use of vacuum-tube amplifiers, while the high capacitance of the barrier layer eliminates the possibility of using periodically varying light and an a-c amplifier, except at low frequencies.

Figure 7.27 shows another characteristic of the barrier-layer cell. Let such a cell be illuminated by a small source at some distance, so that the radiation is incident at practically the same angle at all points on the sensitive surface. We record the cur-

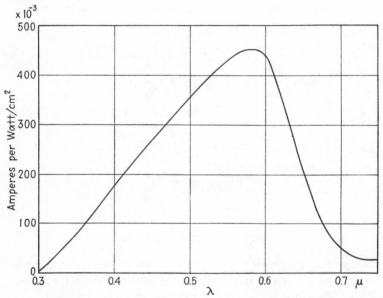

FIG. 7.25.—Spectral-response curve of a Weston Photronic cell.

rent at normal incidence and then turn the cell through various angles θ_i and note the values of current, keeping all other factors fixed. The resulting curve is shown by the heavy line of Fig. 7.27. If the instrument is to read the values of illumination correctly at all angles, the curve must be a cosine curve. The actual curve is much too low, which shows that gross errors may be introduced in illumination measurements if the angle of incidence is large. If illumination is to be measured, on a desk for instance, using a single light source, the best method is to orient the cell so that the radiation strikes the sensitive surface normally. The angle of incidence on the desk surface is then measured, and the desk illumination is computed by use of the cosine law. If the illumination is due to several sources or is

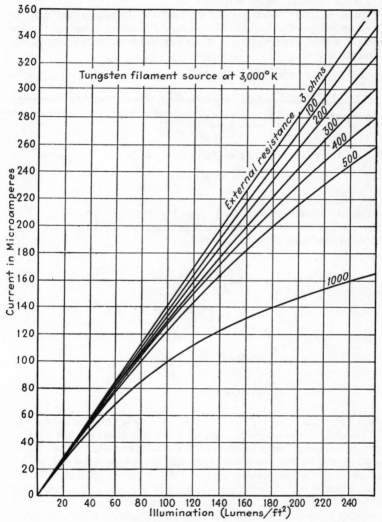

FIG. 7.26.—Characteristics of Photronic cell. (*Technical Data, Weston Electrical Instrument Corporation.*)

partly caused by reflections from walls and ceiling, the values given by the barrier-layer cell will generally be in error.

Example. A barrier-layer cell is placed horizontally on the ground at P (Fig. 7.28) and is illuminated by a uniform layer of dense clouds at distance D. What error is introduced in the illumination reading due to the failure of the cosine law in the cell response?

We assume that the clouds constitute a perfectly diffusing layer of uniform luminosity L (see Chap. IX). We divide the luminous surface into circular rings of radius ξ and width $d\xi$. Each ring will have an intensity in the direction of P of

$$dI = 2L\xi \, d\xi \cdot \cos\theta$$

and will produce an illumination (using the inverse-square law)

$$dE = \frac{2L\xi d\xi \cos^2\theta}{r^2}$$

The relative current due to this illumination will be

$$di = \frac{2L\xi d\xi \cos\theta}{r^2} \cdot f(\theta)$$

where $f(\theta)$ = the function obtained from Fig. 7.27.

The effect of the entire luminous surface is obtained by integration of the above expressions. The ratio will be

$$\frac{2L \int_0^{\frac{\pi}{2}} \frac{\xi d\xi \cos\theta}{r^2} \cdot f(\theta)}{2L \int_0^{\frac{\pi}{2}} \frac{\xi d\xi \cos^2\theta}{r^2}}$$

$$= \frac{\int_0^{\frac{\pi}{2}} \sin\theta \cdot f(\theta) \, d\theta}{\int_0^{\frac{\pi}{2}} \sin\theta \cos\theta \, d\theta} = 2 \int_0^{\frac{\pi}{2}} \sin\theta \cdot f(\theta) \, d\theta$$

since $\xi = D \tan\theta$, $d\xi = D \sec^2\theta \, d\theta$, and $r = D \sec\theta$. The integral can be evaluated mechanically, giving a ratio of 0.70. If the cell had followed the cosine law, the ratio would have had a value of unity. *Thus an error of 30 per cent is introduced because of the cell characteristic shown in Fig.* 7.27. It can be shown that this error applies in the case of a room of any shape or size, indirectly lighted, with perfectly diffusing walls and ceiling, both being of uniform luminosity. If some direct overhead light is used, the error will probably be reduced, though it may still be appreciable; and if the sources are distributed along the walls, the error may be even greater.

7.11. Elimination of Errors in the Measurement of Illumination.

—We have considered the measurement of illumination by thermocouples and bolometers, photoelectric cells, and barrier-

layer cells.   None of these devices is ideal.   The principal errors
may be classified as follows:

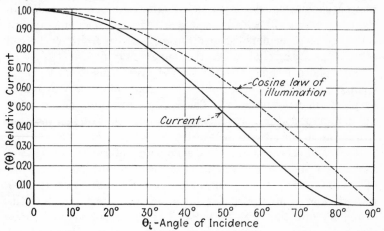

FIG. 7.27.—Effect of angle of incidence on the current obtained from a typical
barrier-layer photocell.

1. Errors due to differences between the spectral response
curve and the standard visibility curve.

2. Errors due to deviations from the cosine law of illumination.

3. Errors due to temperature and fatigue effects.

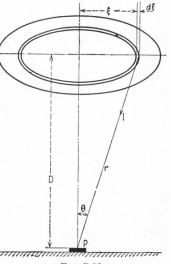

FIG. 7.28.

As regards (1), the barrier-layer cells are much better than the other instruments. Some cells of this type, even without a filter, give a fairly good approximation to the standard visibility curve. The photoelectric cells appear to be the worst offenders, since they do not even provide a standard fixed response curve on which to base the determination of the required filters or templates. It is essential that the illuminating engineer realizes the seriousness of the errors (1), especially when gaseous-conduction sources are used.

Blackened targets follow the cosine law rather closely, but apparently large departures are obtained with all commercial photocells and barrier-layer cells. Barnard has succeeded in reducing errors (2) with specially constructed selenium-sulphur cells. A piece of depolished diffusing glass in front of the cell often helps, or a small integrating sphere may be used.

Both photoelectric cells and barrier-layer cells exhibit erratic changes in current which are very troublesome in any attempts at precision measurement. The reasons for these changes are not understood at present, though it is hoped that further research will improve the situation.

Radiation thermocouples and bolometers of modern design are very stable and are free from most of the annoying characteristics of photoelectric devices. It would seem that the a-c bolometer is particularly promising for precision measurements, but the simplicity and the large response of the barrier-layer cell make this device invaluable for ordinary commercial measurements.

METHODS OF MEASURING OTHER PHOTOMETRIC QUANTITIES

7.12. Measurement of Intensity.—We have seen that all photometric quantities may be based upon the measurement of illumination, which accounts for the large space devoted in this chapter to the measurement of this particular quantity. According to Sec. 7.01, the *intensity* or *candlepower* is always calculated from measurements of illumination:

$$I = \lim_{D \to \infty} (ED^2) \qquad (7.01)$$

In setting up a photometer for the measurement of candlepower, one merely decides upon the physical dimensions of the largest source that he expects to measure and, knowing the desired precision of the measurements, estimates the distance D_1 which must be used with this largest source. This distance may be used in all measurements, and the intensity is simply

$$I = ED_1{}^2 \qquad (7.01a)$$

Since candlepower is generally a function of direction, measurements in various directions are often required (Chap. VIII). A distribution photometer is used. One can be made very easily by fastening a barrier-layer cell at the end of a long arm which can be rotated in a plane about the luminaire to be measured. The long arm and the resulting large space required for such a photometer have led to a number of modifications using mirrors. Figure 7.29 secures a long distance between luminaire and measur-

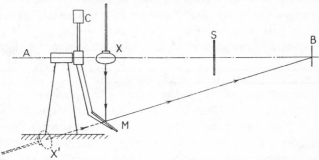

FIG. 7.29.—A candlepower-distribution photometer.

ing device yet requires only a short rotating arm. The luminaire X is placed with its center on the axis AB of the photometer. A large mirror M is counterweighted at C and moves in an arc about the axis AB. To an observer at B, the image of X is seen in M and appears to be at X'. The photoelectric cell or other measuring device is at B and is shielded by an opaque plate S. The arm may be driven electrically, and the candlepower-distribution curve plotted automatically[72] by the device at B.

7.13. Measurement of Luminous Flux.—The total luminous flux emitted by a source is often desired. Knowing the candlepower distribution, one can calculate the total flux by methods that will be discussed in

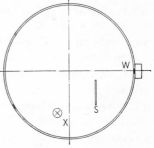

FIG. 7.30.—Integrating-sphere photometer.

Chap. VIII. A simpler way is to obtain the flux by a single measurement using an integrating-sphere photometer.[74]

The source X is placed in a sphere (Fig. 7.30) which is large compared with the dimensions of the source to be measured. The sphere is painted inside with a special flat white paint which is as nonselective as possible. A window W is shielded from the direct light from X by the shield S. At W may be placed any type of measuring device, such as a photoelectric cell. If the sphere walls are uniform, perfectly diffusing, and nonselective, and if the lamp socket and the shield have negligible effect, it can be proved (Chap. X) that *the illumination at every point on the sphere wall* (due to reflected light) *is the same and is directly proportional to the total flux F emitted by the lamp.* Under these conditions, the reading of the photometric device at W depends only upon F, irrespective of how the flux from the lamp is distributed.

Thus F is obtained by a single measurement, supplemented by the standardization of the entire instrument by use of a standard lamp calibrated in lumens. The standard lamp should be preferably of approximately the same size and spectral distribution as the lamp to be measured. This minimizes the errors due to the fact that no paint satisfies the ideal conditions of perfect diffusion and of constant spectral reflection factor.

7.14. Measurement of Reflection Factor.—Another use of the integrating sphere is in the measurement of reflection factor,

$$\rho = \frac{\text{total reflected flux}}{\text{total incident flux}}$$

The original sphere for this purpose was devised by Taylor.[75] Many modified forms have been developed, and a great deal of research has been done recently on the reduction of errors in the measurement[77,78] of reflection factor.

One type of reflectometer is shown in Figs. 7.31a and b. A small integrating sphere, having a diameter of perhaps 15 cm, has an opening W for the measuring device, an opening 1 for the incoming beam of light, an opening 2 for the sample to be measured, and an opening 3 for a sample of magnesium carbonate or a surface smoked with magnesium oxide. The reflection factors for the carbonate and oxide of magnesium are well-established and are almost 1.00. The sphere is placed upon the surface 2 whose reflection factor is to be measured. A narrow beam of light produced by a small incandescent lamp enters the sphere at 1, being focused upon 2 by means of a lens system. If the luminous flux in this beam is denoted by F_1, the flux reflected by sample 2 is

$$F_2 = \rho_2 F_1 \tag{7.04}$$

This flux F_2 enters the sphere and causes an illumination E_2 at W. This illumination is directly proportional to F_2, according to the theory of the integrating sphere.

$$E_2 = KF_2 = K\rho_2 F_1 \qquad (7.05)$$

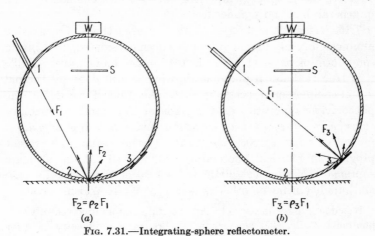

$$F_2 = \rho_2 F_1 \qquad\qquad F_3 = \rho_3 F_1$$
$$(a) \qquad\qquad\qquad (b)$$

Fig. 7.31.—Integrating-sphere reflectometer.

We now shift the beam to 3, keeping everything else the same. The flux entering the sphere after reflection is now

$$F_3 = \rho_3 F_1 \qquad (7.06)$$

and the illumination of W is

$$E_3 = K\rho_3 F_1 \qquad (7.07)$$

Thus the ratio of the two readings gives

$$\frac{E_2}{E_1} = \frac{K\rho_2 F_1}{K\rho_3 F_1}$$

or the reflection factor of the unknown is given by

$$\rho_2 = \rho_3 \left(\frac{E_2}{E_3}\right) \qquad (7.08)$$

The reflection factor depends upon the angle of incidence and upon the spectral distribution of the source. Thus in specifying reflection factors, both of these variables should be stated. If incandescent lamps are to be used, it is generally satisfactory in commercial work to use an incandescent lamp (with T_c equal to 2700 or 2800°K) in the test apparatus and an angle of incidence of 40 to 50 deg. If the surfaces are to be lighted by gaseous-conduction lamps, such values of reflection factor obtained with an integrating sphere employing an incandescent source will, in general, have no significance.

7.15. Visual Photometry.—A number of methods of measuring luminous flux and illumination have been considered, all utilizing some form of physical "eye" instead of the human eye. While it is true that much photometric work is still done by the old visual-comparison process, it is evident that if we define the photometric quantities on the basis of the standard visibility curve, *we must regard visual methods as giving mere approximations to the true values obtained by physical measurements.* The recent progress in physical photometry augurs well for the ultimate supremacy of physical methods because of their superior ease and rapidity if for no other reasons. J. W. T. Walsh[82] says:

It is due in large measure to the uncertain factors involved in visual photometry . . . that workers in this branch of radiometry have for many years sought for some physical instrument which may be used instead of the eye for the measurement of light, and which is not subject to the limitations inseparable from the employment of any physiological organ of special sense.

In the first place, it should be realized that the eye is inherently incapable of measuring anything, and thus all visual photometers are necessarily *comparison devices.* In a visual photometer, the observer compares the sensations produced by the two half-fields; and an adjustment is made in the illumination of these half-fields until the observer considers the two half-fields to be equally brilliant.

In practically every other branch of physical measurement, man has progressed beyond this naïve appeal to the senses. In measuring temperature, for instance, we have advanced far beyond the original physiological concept and no longer rely on a comparison by touch. We use some form of thermometer and read temperature directly. It is only in photometry that we still cling to the inaccurate and tiresome method of direct appeal to the senses.

Of the various types of comparison screens that have been developed, those using the Lummer-Brodhun cube are undoubtedly the best. The reduction in the illumination of one of the comparison faces is accomplished by any of the methods considered in Sec. 7.09. Evidently, a great variety of photometers can be produced by the use of these various methods, and visual comparison can be applied to the integrating sphere, reflectometer, etc. The details will not be treated here because of lack of space and because they are fully covered in almost every one of the several hundred texts on illumination written during the past hundred years.

Problem 61. Criticize the following and restate in a more precise manner:

1. "The term *lumen* has been coined to express that which radiation produces, as appraised by the visual sense" (*J.O.S.A.*).

2. "In arriving at a measure of the quantity of light represented by either I_h [total daylight illumination on an unobstructed horizontal surface] or L [average direct sky illumination within the building being investigated], the basic assumption is that:

"The intensity of skylight upon, or the amount of skylight transmitted through, a given point in space is directly proportional to the extent or solid angle of sky to which it is exposed. . . . The verity of the above assumption is conditioned upon the sky being of uniform brightness" (*I.E.S. Trans.*).

TABLE XXIX.—SENSITIVITY OF VARIOUS PHOTOELECTRIC CELLS
(Based on data of CAMPBELL and RITCHIE, *Photoelectric Cells*, p. 47, and a cathode area of 1.0 sq cm)

Cathode	Amperes per lumen/sq ft	
	$T_c = 2848°K$	$T_c = 2400°K$
Na	4×10^{-9}	2×10^{-9}
K − H	11	9
K − S	19	14
Na − S	29	24
Na − (O + S)	81	82
Cs − Mg	23	20
K − O − Ag	48	43
K − Ag − O − Ag	300	400
Rb − O − Ag	58	65
Rb − Ag − O − Ag	130	160
Cs − O − Ag	250	380
Cs − Ag − O − Ag	500	790

3. "Quantity of light (foot-candles):

"Eventually visual tasks must be rated according to a scale of difficulty, and eventually lighting recommendation must be made in accordance with such a scale. Such a procedure requires adequate knowledge of the effectiveness of quantity of light as a factor in seeing. The foot-candle as a unit of quantity is merely a means to an end. It is meaningless, excepting as a physical unit, until interpreted into seeing. . . . The purpose of the foot-candle is to produce brightness. Therefore, foot-candles are meaningless unless reflection factors are specified" (*I.E.S. Trans.*).

Bibliography

PHOTOMETRIC CONCEPTS

1. International Photometric Units and Standards, *I.E.S. Trans.*, **27**, 1932, p. 738.
2. Illuminating Engineering Nomenclature and Photometric Standards, *I.E.S. Trans.*, **28**, 1933, p. 265.
3. H. E. IVES: The Units and Nomenclature of Radiation and Illumination, *Astrophys. J.*, **45**, 1917, p. 39.

SPECTRORADIOMETRY

4. Spectrophotometry: O.S.A. Committee Report, *J.O.S.A.*, **10**, 1925, p. 169.
5. W. W. COBLENTZ: Methods and Apparatus in Spectroradiometry, *J.O.S.A.*, **7**, 1923, p. 439.
6. L. TAYLOR: A Comparison of Three Spectrophotometric Methods, *J.O.S.A.*, **14**, 1927, p. 332.
7. C. W. KEUFFEL: A Direct-reading Spectrophotometer, *J.O.S.A.*, **11**, 1925, p. 403.
8. K. E. GOULD: Integration of a Functional Product by Measurement of Infrared Radiation, M.I.T., Sc. D. thesis, 1927.
9. SCHAEFER and MATOSSI: Das Ultrarote Spektrum, Vol. X, Struktur der Materie, Julius Springer, Berlin, 1930.
10. An Outline of Atomic Physics, Physics Staff, University of Pittsburgh, John Wiley & Sons, Inc., New York, 1933.
11. ORNSTEIN, MOLL, and BURGER: Objektive Spektralphotometrie, Vieweg, Braunschweig, Germany, 1932.
12. H. J. McNICHOLAS: Equipment for Spectral Measurements, *Bu. Stds. J.R.*, **1**, 1928, p. 793.
13. H. F. KURTZ, A New Quartz Ultraviolet Monochromator, *J.O.S.A.*, **13**, 1926, p. 495.
14. L. G. EATON: Development of a Photoelectric Spectroradiometer, M.I.T. thesis, Electrical Engineering Dept., 1933.
15. FORSYTHE and BARNES: A Large Crystalline-quartz Double Monochromator, *R.S.I.*, **4**, 1933, p. 289.
16. MOLL and BURGER: Un nouveau thermo-élément dans le vide, *Revue d'Optique*, **4**, 1925, p. 562.
17. MOLL and BURGER: Ein neues vakuum Thermoelement, *Zeits. f. Phys.*, **32**, 1925, p. 575.

18. L. HARRIS: Thermocouples for the Measurement of Radiation, *Phys. Rev.*, **45**, 1934, p. 635.

19. C. H. CARTWRIGHT: Radiation Thermopiles for Use of Liquid Air Temperatures, *R.S.I.*, **4**, 1933, p. 382.

20. S. P. LANGLEY: The Bolometer and Radiant Energy, *Am. Acad. Sci., Proc.*, **16**, 1880, p. 342.

21. ABBOT, FOWLE, and ALDRICH: *Smithsonian Inst. Astrophys. Obs., Ann.*, IV, 1922. The Vacuum Bolometer, p. 45.

22. ABBOT, ALDRICH, and FOWLE: *Smithsonian Inst. Astrophys. Obs., Ann.*, V. 1932, p. 75.

23. P. MOON: Theory of the Alternating-current Bolometer, *Frank. Inst., J.*, **219**, 1935, p. 17.

24. MOON and MILLS: Construction and Test of an A-c Bolometer, *R.S.I.*, **6**, 1935, p. 8.

25. W. R. MILLS, JR.: Development of an A-c Bolometer, M.I.T. thesis, Electrical Engineering Dept., 1934.

26. W. H. ESDORN: Theoretical Design of an Alternating-current Bolometer, M.I.T. thesis, Electrical Engineering Dept., 1934.

27. E. P. HYDE: Pyrometer Symposium, *Am. Inst. Mining Met. Eng.*, 1920, p. 288.

28. COBLENTZ and STAIR: A Portable U.V. Intensity Meter, *Bu. Stds. J.R.*, **12**, 1934, p. 231.

29. ORNSTEIN, VERMEULEN, and VAN DER HELD: Calibration of Standard Lamps for Relative and Absolute Measurement, *J.O.S.A.*, **20**, 1930, p. 573.

30. COBLENTZ and STAIR: Present Status of the Standards of Thermal Radiation Maintained by the Bureau of Standards, *Bu. Stds. J.R.*, **11**, 1933, p. 79.

MEASUREMENT OF ILLUMINATION

31. A. BLONDEL: Sur une solution de la photométrie hétérochrome permettant une mesure physique de l'intensité lumineuse, *Comptes Rendus*, **169**, 1919, p. 830.

32. W. W. COBLENTZ: The Physical Photometer in Theory and Practice, *Frank. Inst., J.*, **180**, 1915, p. 335.

33. H. E. IVES: A Precision Artificial Eye, *Phys. Rev.*, **6**, 1915, p. 334.

34. IVES and KINGSBURY: Physical Photometry with Thermopile Artificial Eye, *Phys. Rev.*, **6**, 1915, p. 319.

35. CAMPBELL and RITCHIE: Photoelectric Cells, Chap. II, Sir Isaac Pitman & Sons Ltd., London, 1934.

36. HUGHES and DuBRIDGE: Photoelectric Phenomena, McGraw-Hill Book Company, Inc., New York, 1932.

37. ZWORYKIN and WILSON: Photocells and their Applications, John Wiley & Sons, Inc., New York, 1932.

38. SIMON and SUHRMANN: Lichtelektrische Zellen, Julius Springer, Berlin, 1932.

39. G. DÉJARDIN: Propriétés générales des cathodes photoélectriques. *R.G.E.*, **34**, 1933, pp. 515, 555, 591, 629.

40. A. H. TAYLOR: The Measurement of Erythemal U.V. Radiation, *J.O.S.A.*, **23**, 1933, p. 60.

41. PETERS and WOODFORD: Characteristics of Certain Caesium-oxide Photoelectric Cells, *Physics*, **3**, 1932, p. 172.

42. IVES and OLPIN: Optical Factors in Caesium-silver-oxide Photoelectric Cells, *J.O.S.A.*, **24**, 1934, p. 198.

43. YOUNG and ·PIERCE: Wave-length Sensitivity Curve of a Caesium-oxide Photocell, *J.O.S.A.*, **21**, 1931, p. 497.

44. PRESCOTT and KELLY: The Caesium-oxygen-silver Photoelectric Cell. *B.S.T.J.*, **11**, 1932, p. 334.

45. J. W. BALLARD: Infra-red Sensitivity of Caesium-Oxide Photoelectric Cells, *J.O.S.A.*, **20**, 1930, p. 619.

46. L. R. KOLLER: Characteristics of Photoelectric Cells, *M.P.E. Trans.*, **12**, 1928, p. 921.

47. SHARP, GRAY, LITTLE, and ECKWEILER: The Photometry of Solar Eclipse Phenomena, *J.O.S.A.*, **23**, 1933, p. 234.

48. SHARP and KINSLEY: Practical Photometry with Photoelectric Cells, *I.E.S. Trans.*, **21**, 1926, p. 117.

49. SHARP and SMITH: Further Developments in Photoelectric Photometry, *I.E.S. Trans.*, **23**, 1928, p. 428.

50. DESHLER and SCHROEDER: Photoelectric Cell Photometry, *I.E.S. Trans.*, **23**, 1928, p. 391.

51. K. S. GIBSON: Spectrophotometry at the Bureau of Standards, *J.O.S.A.*, **21**, 1931, p. 564.

52. IVES and KINGSBURY: Applicability of Photoelectric Cells to Colorimetry, *J.O.S.A.*, **21**, 1931, p. 541.

53. DU BRIDGE and BROWN: An Improved D-c Amplifying Circuit, *R.S.I.*, **4**, 1933, p. 532.

54. JOHNSON and NEITZERT: The Measurement of Small Alternating Voltages at Audiofrequencies, *R.S.I.*, **5**, 1934, p. 196.

55. G. A. LOWN: Alternating-current Amplification in Photoelectric Measurements, M.I.T. thesis, Electrical Engineering Dept., 1932.

56. E. B. MOSS: An Automatic Photoelectric Photometer, *Phys. Soc. Proc.*, **46**, 1934, p. 205.

57. A. C. HARDY: A New Photoelectric Spectrophotometer, *J.O.S.A.*, **25**, 1935, p. 305.

58. GRONDAHL and GEIGER: Electronic Rectifier, *A.I.E.E. Trans.*, **46**, 1927, p. 357.

59. A. H. ·WILSON: The Theory of Electronic Semi-conductors. *Proc. Roy. Soc.*, **133**, 1931, p. 458; **134**, 1931, p. 277.

60. R. H. FOWLER: Report on the Theory of Semi-conductors, *Phys. Zeits. d. Sowjetunion*, **3**, 1933, p. 507.

61. L. BERGMANN: Über eine neue Selen-Sperrschicht-Photozelle, *Phys. Zeits.*, **32**, 1931, p. 286.

62. GOLDMANN and LUKASIEWITCH: Über die Abhängigkeit der elektromotorischen Kraft von Kupferoxydulphotozellen, *Phys. Zeits.*, **34**, 1933, p. 66.

63. H. TEICHMANN: Der Temperaturabhängigkeit des Sperrschichtphotoeffekts, *Zeits. f. Physik*, **67**, 1931, p. 192.
64. W. SCHOTTKY: Leitungs- und Photoeffekte an Sperrschichten, *Phys. Zeits.*, **32**, 1931, p. 833.
65. B. LANGE: Über die Temperaturabhängigkeit des Sperrschicht-Photoeffekts, *Phys. Zeits.*, **32**, 1931, p. 850; *Naturwiss.*, **19**, 1931, p. 527.
66. WAIBEL and SCHOTTKY: Einige neue Feststellungen über den Sperrschicht-Photoeffekt, *Phys. Zeits.*, **33**, 1932, p. 583.
67. L. O. GRONDAHL: The Copper-cuprous-oxide Rectifier and Photoelectric Cell, *Rev. Modern Physics*, **5**, 1933, p. 141.
68. W. N. GOODWIN, JR.: The Photronic Illumination Meter, *I.E.S. Trans.*, **27**, 1932, p. 828.
69. G. P. BARNARD: A New Selenium-Sulphur Rectifier Photoelectric Cell, *Proc. Phys. Soc.*, **47**, 1935, p. 477.
70. FINK and ALPERN: Chrom-Selenium Photovoltaic Cells, *Am. Electrochem. Soc., Trans.*, **62**, 1932, p. 369.
71. B. P. ROMAIN: Notes on the Weston Photronic Cell, *R.S.I.*, **4**, 1933, p. 83.

MEASUREMENT OF OTHER PHOTOMETRIC QUANTITIES

72. LITTLE and ECKWEILER: An Automatic Recording Photoelectric Distribution Photometer, *I.E.S. Trans.*, **26**, 1931, p. 810.
73. PARKS and POEHLER: Design of an Automatic Distribution Photometer, M.I.T. thesis, Electrical Engineering Dept. 1934.
74. ROSA and TAYLOR: The Integrating Photometric Sphere, *I.E.S. Trans.*, **11**, 1916, p. 453.
75. A. H. TAYLOR: A Simple Portable Instrument for the Absolute Measurement of Reflection and Transmission Factors, *Bu. Stds. Sci. Papers*, **17**, 1922, No. 405, p. 1; **16**, 1920, p. 421, No. 391.
76. E. KARRER: Use of the Ulbricht Sphere in Measuring Reflection and Transmission Factors, *Bu. Stds. Sci. Papers*, **17**, 1922, p. 203.
77. H. J. McNICHOLAS: Absolute Methods in Reflectometry, *Bu. Stds. J.R.*, **1**, 1928, p. 29.
78. A. H. TAYLOR: Errors in Reflectometry, *J.O.S.A.*, **25**, 1935, p. 51.
79. F. BENFORD: Reflectometer for all Types of Surfaces, *J.O.S.A.*, **24**, 1934, p. 165.
80. F. BENFORD: A Reflectometer for all Types of Reflecting Surfaces, *G.E. Rev.*, **37**, 1934, p. 457.
81. HARDY and PINEO: Errors Due to Finite Size of Holes and Sample in Integrating Spheres, *J.O.S.A.*, **21**, 1931, p. 502.
82. J. W. T. WALSH: Photometry, Archibald Constable & Company, Ltd., London, 1926.
83. J. W. T. WALSH: Primary Standard of Light, *World Power*, **20**, 1933, p. 68; **21**, 1934, p. 19.
84. C. MÜLLER: Über die Realisierung einer rationalle Lichteinheit mit Hilfe absoluter Messung der Gesamtstrahlung, *Zeits. f. Phys.*, **47**, 1928, p. 751.

85. L. S. Ornstein: Unité de lumière ou méthode standardisée, *Rev. d'Optique*, **12**, 1933, p. 385; *K. Akad. Amsterdam, Proc.*, **36**, 1933, p. 764.

86. Ornstein, Eymers, and Vermeulen: Une méthode simple et exacte pour la standardisation d'étalons secondaires, *Rev. d'Optique* 12, 1933, p. 390.

87. Richtmyer and Crittenden: The Precision of Photometric Measurements, *J.O.S.A.*, **4**, 1920, p. 371.

88. Eymers and Vermeulen: Méthode visuelle pour la mesure absolue de l'intensité, *Rev. d'Optique*, **12**, 1933, p. 392.

CHAPTER VIII

ILLUMINATION FROM POINT SOURCES

This chapter and the two succeeding chapters treat of the calculation of illumination—a subject that is peculiarly the province of the illuminating engineer. In Chap. VIII are considered sources sufficiently distant from the illuminated surface so that the inverse-square law can be used with inappreciable error. The illumination of streets, highways, and airports is calculated accurately by the use of the inverse-square law. This law applies also in some cases to interior illumination, though here the use of windows, skylights, and luminous panels and particularly the reflection of luminous flux from walls and ceiling usually make further refinements necessary. Thus Chaps. IX and X will be devoted to the illumination from surface sources and the problem of interreflection between surfaces.

8.02. Candlepower-distribution Curves (with Axial Symmetry).—The direct illumination at any point can be calculated from the fundamental formula:

$$E = \frac{I}{r^2} \cos \theta \tag{8.01}$$

provided the dimensions of the source are sufficiently small compared with r (Chap. VII). But the intensity I is not a constant. For all commercial sources it is found to vary with the direction from the source. Thus to calculate the illumination at any point, we must know the candlepower as a function of direction. Such data are commonly found by use of a distribution photometer.

The luminaire to be measured is placed at A, Fig. 8.01, and the candlepower is measured for various values of the vertical angle θ and the horizontal angle φ. In each direction, a radius vector can be imagined, whose length is equal, on a suitable scale, to the candlepower in that direction. The result is a candlepower-distribution *solid* which gives a complete representation of

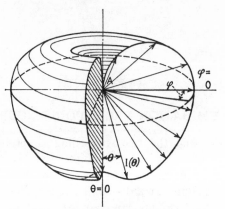

Fig. 8.01.—Candlepower-distribution solid.

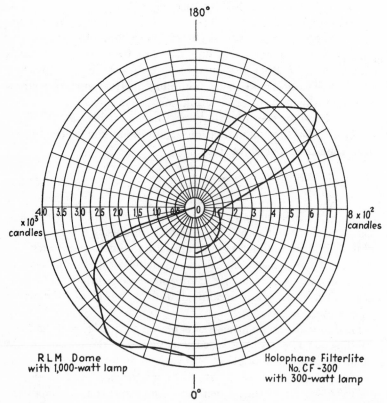

Fig. 8.02.—Polar-distribution curves.

$I(\theta, \varphi)$, the intensity of the source in all directions.   Convention places the zero of θ directly downward.   The zero of φ may be taken at any convenient place.

The distribution of Fig. 8.01 is symmetrical about a vertical axis, a condition obtaining at least approximately with most commercial luminaires.   This greatly simplifies both the measurements and the diagram.   With axial symmetry the three-dimensional representation is unnecessary, and $I(\theta)$ can be

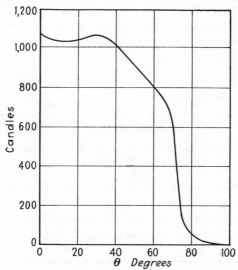

FIG. 8.03.—Candlepower distribution.   RLM reflector, 300-watt lamp, 5400 lumens.

plotted on an ordinary sheet of polar-graph paper.   In fact, only the range 0 to 180 deg need be considered, since the other 180 deg is the same.   Figure 8.02 gives two such polar diagrams, one for an RLM (Reflector and Lamp Manufacturers' Standard) reflector of porcelain-enameled steel, and the other for a prismatic-glass, semi-indirect luminaire.

Obvious disadvantages of the polar diagram, such as poor accuracy at low values of candlepower, are overcome by the use of rectangular coordinates.*   Such a diagram for an RLM reflector is shown in Fig. 8.03.   Test results on a Glassteel diffuser are given in Fig. 8.04.   The construction of this unit is

* See, for instance, the results of an international questionnaire, *Compte Rendu, C.I.E.*, 1931, p. 684.

similar to that of the RLM, but a diffusing glass globe fits over the lamp to reduce glare. Holes in the steel shade allow some

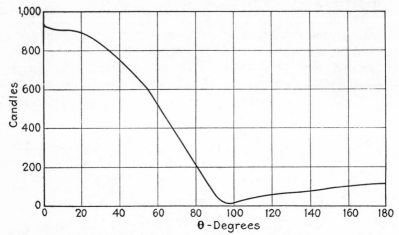

Fig. 8.04.—Candlepower distribution. Glassteel diffuser, 300-watt lamp, 5400 lumens.

flux to be sent upward, as shown by the portion of the curve beyond 90 deg.

Figures 8.05 and 8.06 give experimental results on two common shapes of opal-glass diffusing globes. Note that the candle-

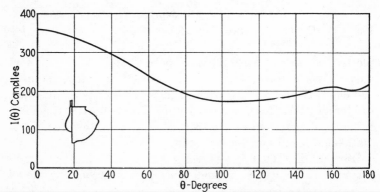

Fig. 8.05.—Candlepower distribution. Opal-glass diffusing globe, 200-watt lamp, 3237 lumens.

power is fairly uniform in all directions for both; but the luminaire of Fig. 8.05, because of its larger projected area for $\theta = 0$, gives the greatest intensity downward ($\theta = 0°$), while the luminaire of Fig. 8.06 has its greatest candlepower at $\theta = 55°$. Figure 8.07 shows a different type of luminaire with an open

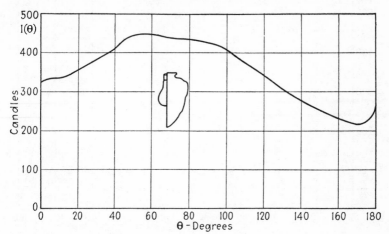

Fig. 8.06.—Candlepower distribution. Opal-glass diffusing globe, 300-watt lamp, 5340 lumens.

diffusing globe shielding the lamp from view.   However, there is a considerable amount of flux reflected directly from a diffusing plate, which is generally fastened to the ceiling.   A semi-indirect

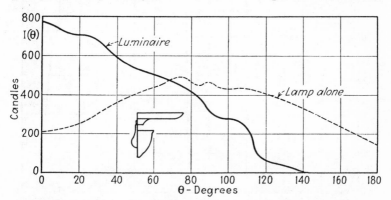

Fig. 8.07.—Candlepower distribution. Planetlite luminaire, 300-watt lamp, 4893 lumens.

luminaire is shown in Fig. 8.08.   Note the high candlepower for θ greater than 90 deg.   Another type of unit, using a Silvray lamp, silver plated on the bottom, is shown in Fig. 8.09.

Figure 8.10 gives data for a common form of symmetrical silvered-glass reflector used when it is desirable to concentrate

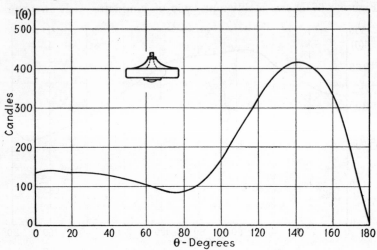

Fig. 8.08.—Candlepower distribution. Keldon semi-indirect luminaire, 200-watt lamp, 3300 lumens.

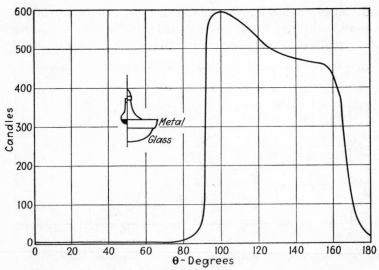

Fig. 8.09.—Candlepower distribution. Indirect luminaire with Silvray lamp, 200-watt lamp, 3303 lumens.

the luminous flux upon a particular object or area. Such reflectors are often used to supplement the general lighting in obtaining high levels of illumination on work benches, lathes, etc.   Similar units, though usually asymmetric, are used in lighting store windows.

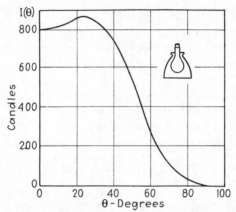

Fig. 8.10.—Candlepower distribution.   Silvered-glass reflector, 200-watt lamp.

Another way of obtaining concentrated illumination is by means of a lens.   Figure 8.11 shows experimental results obtained

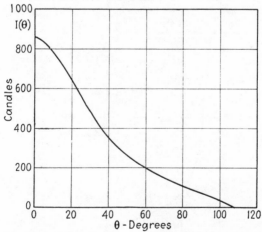

Fig. 8.11.—Candlepower distribution.   RLM reflector with 16-in. Corning lens, sandblasted inside.   200-watt lamp, 3398 lumens.

with a large Pyrex lens, sandblasted on the inside and mounted in the ceiling.   Data on Holophane lens plates are given in Fig. 8.12.   The diagram shows that a variety of distributions can be

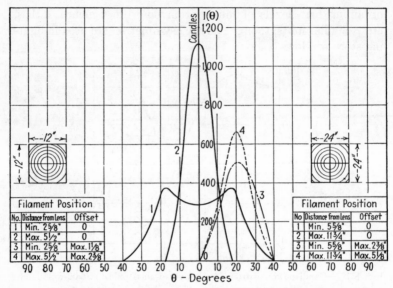

Fig. 8.12.—Candlepower distribution curves. Holophane lens plates without reflectors. Lamp lumens = 1000. (*From Holophane Data Sheets.*)

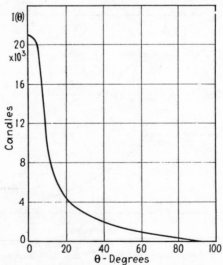

Fig. 8.13.—Candlepower distribution. Four hundred twenty-five-watt high-pressure mercury-vapor lamp in 45-deg right cone reflector, chromium plated. (*L. J. Buttolph, I.E.S. Trans.*, **30**, 1935, p. 172.)

obtained by moving the lamp.   That an intense beam can be obtained even with some gaseous-conduction lamps is shown by Fig. 8.13, which gives data on a high-pressure mercury-vapor lamp with conical reflector.   The ultraviolet distribution of dual-purpose lamps is generally somewhat different from the candlepower distribution because of the difference in spectral reflection factor of the reflector in the visible and ultraviolet regions.   The U.V. distribution can be obtained if desired and gives a curve such as that of Fig. 8.14.

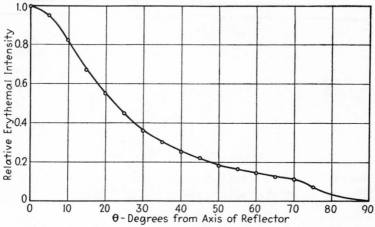

Fig. 8.14.—Distribution of erythemal radiation from a standard S-1 unit. (*Data from Forsythe, Barns, and Easley, J.O.S.A.,* **24**, 1934, *p.* 180.)

The candlepower-distribution curves of Sec. 8.02 were obtained by laboratory measurements on particular luminaires.   Other luminaires of the same type may exhibit small differences in candlepower, but the general forms of the curves are believed to be representative.   We shall want to use the curves with lamps of various wattages.   Generally, the manufacturers make complete lines of luminaires of each type, with candlepower-distribution curves of essentially the same shape.   To find the distribution for a different wattage unit using a lamp of F_2 lumens, having given the distribution for a lamp of F_1 lumens, we multiply all the given values of candlepower by the ratio of lamp lumens, F_2/F_1 (*not by the ratio of lamp watts*).

8.03. Calculation of Total Flux (for Axial Symmetry).—The use of an integrating sphere for measuring the total luminous output of a source was mentioned in Chap. VII. For various reasons, however, it is often necessary to obtain luminous flux from the candlepower diagram.

Consider a source at A (Fig. 8.15) and imagine it to be surrounded by a large sphere of radius R. The intensity of the source in any direction is $I(\theta)$, which is a function of θ. It is

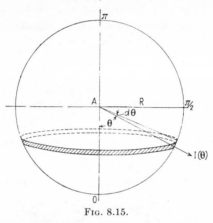

FIG. 8.15.

independent of the azimuthal angle φ because of axial symmetry. The area of the shaded band shown in Fig. 8.15 is

$$2\pi R^2 \sin \theta \, d\theta$$

The illumination on this area is

$$E = \frac{I(\theta)}{R^2}$$

and the total flux incident on this area is

$$dF = \frac{I(\theta)}{R^2} \cdot 2\pi R^2 \sin \theta \, d\theta = 2\pi I(\theta) \sin \theta \, d\theta$$

Thus the total luminous flux from the source is

$$F = 2\pi \int_0^\pi I(\theta) \sin \theta \, d\theta \qquad (8.02)$$

which is a general formula applicable to any source that has an axially symmetrical distribution of intensity. Consider, for example, the two distributions shown by the polar diagrams of Fig. 8.16. At first glance, one might be tempted to say that the two had equal total fluxes. But it is necessary to remember that these are merely cross sections of three-dimensional diagrams which are symmetrical about the vertical axis. Thus (a) is a doughnut-shaped distribution, while (b) is two spheres, one resting on the other. The two-dimensional plot in either polar or rectangular form gives little idea of total flux.

To obtain F in Fig. 8.16a, we use Eq. (8.02) and substitute the relation

$$I(\theta) = I_{max} \sin \theta$$

where I_{max} = the value of intensity at $\theta = \pi/2$.

Then

$$F = 2\pi I_{max} \int_0^\pi \sin^2 \theta \, d\theta$$

$$= 2\pi I_{max} \left[\theta - \tfrac{1}{2} \sin 2\theta \right]_0^\pi = \pi^2 I_{max}$$

In Fig. 8.16b,

$$I(\theta) = I_0 \cos \theta$$

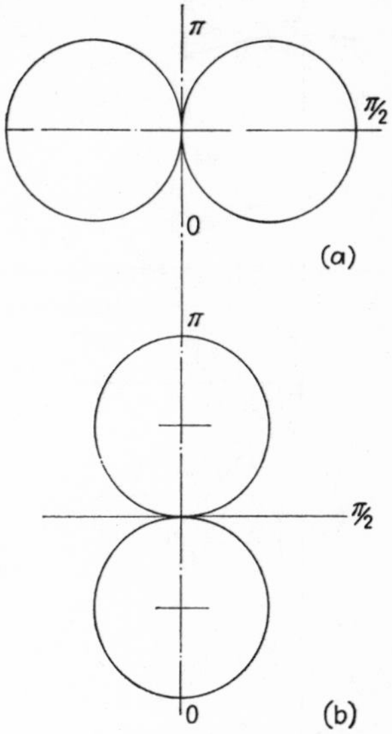

and

$$F = 2\pi I_0 \int_0^\pi \cos \theta \sin \theta \, d\theta$$

$$= 2\pi I_0 \left[\sin^2 \theta \right]_0^{\frac{\pi}{2}} = 2\pi I_0.$$

FIG. 8.16.

Therefore for equal maximum candlepower in the two cases, the flux in (b) is only about two-thirds that in (a).

We have seen how Eq. (8.02) is used when $I(\theta)$ is expressible as a simple mathematical function. Generally, however, $I(\theta)$ is an experimentally determined relation represented by a curve, and Eq. (8.02) cannot be evaluated by direct integration. A variety of methods have been developed for performing the integration, and most books on photometry devote considerable space to an explanation of these mysteries. Actually, however, all these methods are obvious variations on a single theme. Thus we may evaluate Eq. (8.02) by

1. Direct graphical integration. Plot $[I(\theta) \sin \theta]$ against θ and use a planimeter.

2. Use of a new variable x, so that $dx = \sin \theta \, d\theta$. This is accomplished most easily by employing rectangular cross-section paper with a θ scale spaced sinusoidally. The experimental values are plotted directly, and the integration is performed by use of a planimeter. This is called the *Rousseau method*.

3. The selected-ordinate method, an approximation that replaces the integral by a summation

$$F = \frac{4\pi}{m} \sum_{i=1}^{m} I(\theta)_i$$

where the values of $I(\theta)$ are taken at certain selected angles.* Data for the selected-ordinate method are given in Table XXX (page 244).

4. Another approximate scheme, the zonal method, takes the values of $I(\theta)$ at even steps in θ but multiplies each by a factor before summing. The zonal method is probably used more often than any other. Consider $I(\theta)$ to be constant over a zone of β deg. (Fig. 8.17). The flux in the first zone is

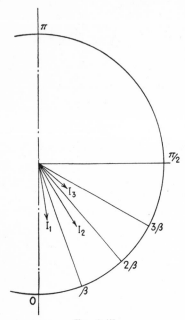

Fig. 8.17.

$$F_1 = 2\pi I_1 \int_0^\beta \sin \theta \, d\theta = 2\pi I_1(1 - \cos \beta)$$

where $I_1 =$ the candlepower in the middle of the zone ($\theta = \beta/2$), I_1 being assumed constant from $\theta = 0$ to $\theta = \beta$.

Similarly, the flux in the second, third, and succeeding zones is

$$F_2 = 2\pi I_2 \int_\beta^{2\beta} \sin \theta \, d\theta = 2\pi I_2(\cos \beta - \cos 2\beta)$$

$$F_3 = 2\pi I_3 \int_{2\beta}^{3\beta} \sin \theta \, d\theta = 2\pi I_3(\cos 2\beta - \cos 3\beta)$$

. . . .

* The selected-ordinate method is also used in evaluating the area under the luminosity curve and in obtaining the specification of color (see Hardy and Pineo, *J.O.S.A.*, **22**, 1932, p. 430; D. Nickerson, *J.O.S.A.*, **25**, 1935, p. 255).

$$F_n = 2\pi I_n \int_{(n-1)\beta}^{n\beta} \sin\theta \, d\theta = 2\pi I_n [\cos(n-1)\beta - \cos n\beta]$$

$$\cdot \quad \cdot \quad \cdot \quad \cdot \quad \cdot \quad \cdot \quad \cdot \quad \cdot \quad \cdot$$

As the flux in the nth zone is

$$F_n = 2\pi I_n [\cos(n-1)\beta - \cos n\beta]$$

we have

$$\frac{F_n}{I_n} = 2\pi[\cos(n-1)\beta - \cos n\beta] \tag{8.03}$$

where $n = 1, 2, \cdots \pi/\beta$

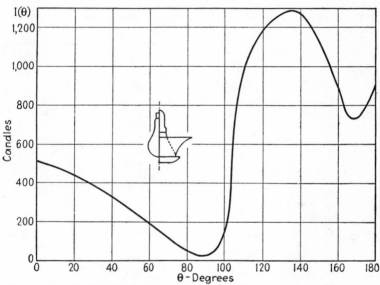

Fig. 8.18.—Candlepower distribution.   Duplexalite semi-indirect luminaire, 500-watt lamp, 9850 lumens.

Equation (8.03) may be used to evaluate a set of factors F_n/I_n for any desired value of β.   For 10-deg. zones and $n = 1$, for example,

$$\frac{F_1}{I_1} = 2\pi[1.00000 - 0.98481]$$

$$= 0.09547$$

For $n = 2$,

$$\frac{F_2}{I_2} = 2\pi[0.98481 - 0.93969] = 0.2835$$

Results calculated in this way are given in Table XXXI (page 244.)
Similar data for $\beta = 5$ deg are tabulated in Table XXXII.

To use the tables in computing total flux, we obtain $I(\theta)$ at
the angles specified, multiply each by the factor F_n/I_n, and find
the sum of these products

$$F = \sum_{n=1}^{n=\frac{\pi}{\beta}} \left(\frac{F_n}{I_n}\right) I_n \qquad (8.04)$$

Example. What is the total luminous output of the semi-indirect luminaire of Fig. 8.18, using a 500-watt, 115-volt, PS-40 lamp emitting 9850
lumens?

The measured values of intensity are tabulated at 10-deg intervals and
are multiplied by the factors of Table XXXI.

θ	I_n	F_n/I_n	$(F_n/I_n) \cdot I_n$
5°	496	0.095	47
15	458	0.284	130
25	420	0.463	194
35	368	0.628	231
45	306	0.774	237
55	234	0.897	210
65	158	0.993	157
75	83	1.058	88
85	32.6	1.091	36
95	56	1.091	61
105	610	1.058	645
115	1110	0.993	1102
125	1230	0.897	1103
135	1290	0.774	998
145	1220	0.628	766
155	1030	0.463	477
165	750	0.284	213
175	790	0.095	75

$$F = 6770 \text{ lumens}$$

The total luminous output is 6770 lumens, which is 69 per cent of the
output of the lamp alone. It is often desirable to calculate also the flux
in the zones 0 to 60 and 0 to 90 deg, which in this case is 1049 and 1330
lumens, respectively.

Problem 62. A circular opal-glass disk mounted in the ceiling illuminates
a room by flux from a lamp housed above it. The candlepower distribution
is found to be

$$I(\theta) = 100 \cos \theta \quad \text{(candles)}$$

Determine F to four significant figures by
1. Direct integration.
2. Selected-ordinate method.
3. Zonal method, 10-deg zones.
4. Zonal method, 5-deg zones.
Compare the results.

Problem 63. Diffusing globes (either Fig. 8.05 or 8.06) with standard 300-watt general-service lamps are to be used in illuminating an office with desk level 60 in. beneath the center of the luminaires.

Calculate values of illumination due to one luminaire (Fig. 8.05) at a point on the desk directly beneath the luminaire and at a point on the same plane 5 ft away. Repeat for Fig. 8.06.

Problem 64. Determine the total luminous flux emitted by an I.E.S. luminaire (study lamp) whose test data are given in Fig. 8.19. What percentage of the lamp lumens are absorbed by the luminaire? What percentage of the luminous output of the luminaire is thrown upward?

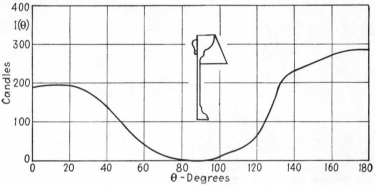

Fig. 8.19.—Candlepower distribution. I.E.S. study lamp, 100-watt lamp, 1490 lumens.

Problem 65. Plot the illumination of the desk as a function of the distance from the lamp axis for the luminaire of Fig. 8.19. The lamp filament is approximately 24 in. above the desk top. Assume that the inverse-square law holds (not a very good assumption at these distances) and that there is no reflection from walls and ceiling.

8.04. Asymmetric Sources.—The preceding paragraphs have dealt with distributions which are symmetrical about an axis. Some luminaires do not have this property. Many street luminaires, for instance, are asymmetric, as well as a great variety of reflectors for lighting store windows, etc. In such cases, the usual curve of $I(\theta)$ vs. θ is not sufficient, and curves of candlepower distribution must be obtained for various values of azimuth φ, say for each 10 deg. A thoroughly asymmetric source would require 36 curves of $I(\theta)$ vs. θ, but in most cases there is a plane of symmetry so that 19 suffice. Occasionally nine curves suffice. Naturally, the collection of such a mass of data and its representation are time consuming, but considerable research has been done to reduce the labor as much as possible.

The representation of $I(\theta, \varphi)$ as a family of curves in rectangular coordinates is not without merit, though it is hard to visualize. As Benford[9] says:

The results of any photometric exploration for intensities of radiation might well be left in the form of tabulated figures if it were not for the desire to present the data in the simplest and most comprehensible

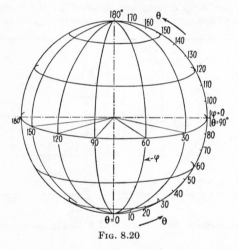

Fig. 8.20

form. Thus, an 18-curve unit might be represented by 308 values of candles found at the crossing points of azimuth and altitude lines 10 deg. apart, but it is readily seen that a complete comprehension of this tabulation would be out of the question. Therefore, recourse is had to plotting the data in the form of curves, but this does not entirely solve the difficulty; for even if the data can be plotted in the form of nine curves, it is no simple task to fix these curves in the memory sufficiently well to visualize the true nature of the distribution. As for a mental comparison between different units, it may be classed as a practical impossibility.

To obtain a better picture of the distribution, we may use contour lines of equal candlepower, called *isocandle lines*. Imagine the source A to be enclosed in a large sphere (Fig. 8.20). The altitude θ and the azimuth φ are measured as before. The surface of the sphere may be covered with a coordinate web, as shown. The candlepower distribution is now obtained, and points of equal candlepower are connected by smooth curves on the surface of the sphere, giving perhaps some such set of iso-candle curves as shown in Fig. 8.21a. Here is a method of giving the complete candlepower specification for an asymmetric source. Such diagrams drawn on cardboard spheres or on large rubber balls might actually be used. But the spherical form has obvious disadvantages, and a representation on a sheet of paper would be much more convenient.

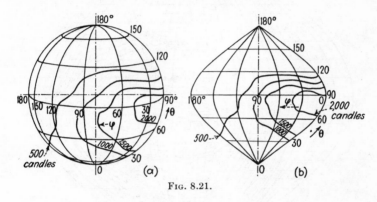

Fig. 8.21.

This is exactly the problem studied by cartographers in connection with maps of the world. It is found that any such map must distort either the shape or the area or both. In the iso-candle diagram, the shapes of the curves are relatively unimportant, but the areas should be preserved if possible in order to allow the determination of luminous flux. Mercator's projection, for instance, would not be satisfactory for the purpose; on it Greenland looks as large as the whole of South America. One solution has been given by Benford[9] who has proposed a sinusoidal-coordinate system which is extensively used. The web on the surface of the hemisphere (Fig. 8.21a) becomes the plane web of Fig. 8.21b. The lines $\theta =$ const are straight horizontal lines equally spaced, while the lines $\varphi =$ const are sinusoids of various amplitudes. The isocandle curves of (a) become the plane curves of (b), with their shapes distorted but with relative areas unaltered. Thus a planimeter can be used to evaluate the areas between curves, and the multiplication of each area by the corresponding average intensity allows the luminous flux to be obtained. Figure 8.22 shows an isocandle diagram for a sodium luminaire for street lighting.

Naturally, the Benford diagram is only one of many methods for representing the candlepower distribution from an asymmetric luminaire. A slight modification in the coordinate

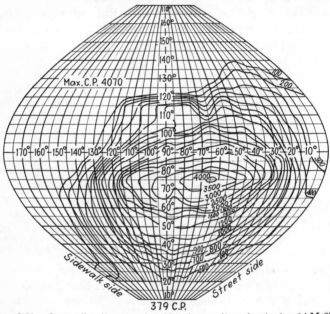

Fig. 8.22.—Isocandle diagram for Novalux sodium luminaire 2AM-2TA1 with 10,000-lumen, 6.6-amp, sodium-vapor lamp. (*Courtesy General Electric Company.*)

system gives Fig. 8.26 where all the coordinate lines are straight and where the sinusoidal effect is incorporated in the θ scale instead of in the shape of the web. The areas are still true, just as in Fig. 8.22.

If values of illumination are needed on only one or two planes, a contour map of illumination may be more advantageous than a diagram of candlepower. Such maps are being used extensively in specifying the distributions for street-lighting units, the results being applicable to any horizontal plane. Another system divides the plane into squares and gives the illumination at the center of each square.   Such a method is used for store-window reflectors.*

Problem 66.   Prove that the area of the curvilinear element formed by two lines of constant θ and two lines of constant φ in Fig. 8.22 is equal to k times the corresponding area on the sphere and that k is a constant for a given diagram, irrespective of θ and φ.   What condition must hold for k to be equal to unity?

Problem 67.   Determine the total luminous output of the street-lighting unit of Fig. 8.22.

Problem 68.   Draw an isocandle diagram similar to 8.22 for the luminaire of Fig. 8.07.   Calculate the total flux by the methods of Sec. 8.04.   Calculate total flux by one of the methods of Sec. 8.03.

Problem 69.   Repeat Prob. 68, using the coordinate system of Fig. 8.26 but the luminaire of Fig. 8.07.

8.05. Calculation of Illumination.—Consider the calculation of illumination where the sources are so small compared with the distance that the inverse-square law is applicable and where there is negligible flux reflected from surroundings.   The fundamental law, Eq. (8.01), can always be used; but if many calculations are to be made for points on the same plane, a simplification allows some saving of time.   Suppose that values of illumination are to be calculated at a number of points on the horizontal plane BC (Fig. 8.23), the plane representing the desk level in a room, for instance.   A single luminaire A is used, and the candlepower distribution is symmetrical about the vertical axis.   The illumination at any point on the plane BC is

$$E = \frac{I(\theta)}{r^2} \cos \theta \qquad (8.01a)$$

But $r = u/\cos \theta$, so

$$E = \frac{I(\theta)}{u^2} \cos^3 \theta \qquad (8.05)$$

Equation (8.05) eliminates all measurement or calculation of r. A tabulation is made of θ, $I(\theta)$, and $\cos^3 \theta$ for all points at which the illumination is desired.   A single multiplication and a division by the constant u^2 give the illumination at each point.

* For further details, the reader is referred to Testing Specifications for Lighting Equipment, *I.E.S. Trans.*, **28**, 1933, p. 512; and to a paper by S. McK. Gray, *I.E.S. Trans.*, **29**, 1934, p. 463.

Similarly, if values of illumination are desired on a vertical plane at distance D from the luminaire axis (Fig. 8.23),

$$D = r \sin \theta$$

and

$$E = \frac{I(\theta)}{D^2} \sin^3 \theta \qquad (8.06)$$

This is for the special case of a vertical plane which is perpendicular to the plane of the paper. If the normal of the illumi-

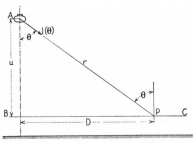

Fig. 8.23.

nated vertical plane makes an angle ψ with the plane of Fig. 8.23, Eq. (8.06) must be multiplied by $\cos \psi$.

When illumination is to be calculated at a large number of points, it is usually easiest to select the values of θ such as 0, 5, 10 . . . deg. The corresponding values of $I(\theta)$ can be read from a table or graph for the luminaire in question, while values of $\cos^3 \theta$ or $\sin^3 \theta$ are obtained from Table XXXIII. Values of distance corresponding to the chosen values of θ are obtainable with sufficient accuracy by measurement from a scale drawing, though they can be computed if desired. The results are usually plotted as in Fig. 8.24 with illumination as a function of distance from the luminaire axis.

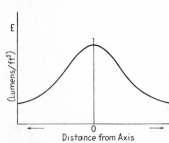

Fig. 8.24.—Illumination from a single luminaire having axial symmetry.

With a number of identical sources, time is generally saved by the use of a plan drawing which is made to scale and on which

are located the axes of the luminaires.   The illumination from a
single unit is then computed by Eq. (8.05), and a graph
similar to Fig. 8.24 is made, using the same distance scale as was
used in the floor plan.   The graph of illumination *vs.* distance can
now be laid on the floor plan, and values of illumination due to
each luminaire can be read directly.   Or instead of using a graph,
we can merely make a scale *AB* (Fig. 8.25) with values of
illumination on it instead of distances.   To find the illumination
at *P*, for instance, due to the source at *A*, the scale is laid between
A and *P*, and the value of *E* is read directly.   The procedure is
repeated for each of the other luminaires in turn, and the actual
illumination at *P* is the sum of all these components.   For any
other point, the procedure is repeated.

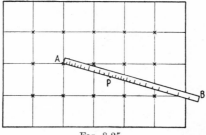

F<small>IG</small>. 8.25.

The foregoing method is applicable to any interior where the
luminous flux reflected from walls and ceiling is negligible.   Thus
it applies to many factories where the roof is so high, so filled with
skylights, or so dark that it reflects little flux and where the
walls are mostly of glass.   The method is also useful in street
lighting, floodlighting, etc.   If asymmetric distributions are
used, the procedure is essentially the same except that both θ
and φ must be taken into account.   With a single symmetrical
luminaire, a diagram like Fig. 8.24 is all that is necessary, since
the illumination is symmetrical about the luminaire axis.   In
the case of more than one luminaire or an asymmetric luminaire, it is customary to plot contour lines of constant illumination.   Such lines (Fig. 8.27) are called *isolux lines*, and the set
of curves is called an *isolux diagram*.

Example.   A street is illuminated by asymmetric lighting units whose
isocandle diagram is shown in Fig. 8.26.   The mounting height is 15 ft,
directly over the curb; the pavement width is 38 ft; and the spacing is

100 ft, staggered.* Figure 8.26 shows that maximum candlepower is about 1200 and occurs at θ = 75 deg, φ = 20 deg, approximately. The unit has symmetry about a plane, so a strong beam is sent down the street in both directions. Very little flux is emitted upward, and the upper half of the diagram has been omitted for this reason.

In plotting pavement illumination, it is convenient to consider values along lines parallel to the curb. Such lines can be drawn in the isocandle diagram, since for any straight line there is a definite relation between θ and φ.† Three lines have been included in Fig. 8.26. Illumination from

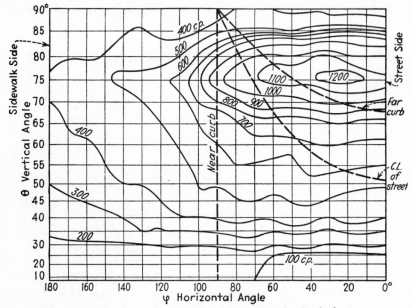

Fig. 8.26.—Isocandle diagram for a street-lighting luminaire.[9]

a single unit is now computed along several such lines by the use of Eq. (8.05), the candlepower values being taken from the isocandle diagram. The curves for all the lamps are superposed to give the actual illumination of the street, and an isolux diagram is plotted (Fig. 8.27).

This diagram gives complete information on the illumination of the pavement. In many cases, however, the *average* illumination is sufficient‡ and can be obtained very easily from the isocandle diagram. The two

* From *I.E.S. Trans.*, **21**, 1926, p. 152.

† See *I.E.S. Trans.*, **21**, 1926, p. 142.

‡ With street lighting, in particular, the peculiarly large angle from the normal at which the street is viewed emphasizes specular reflection, so that illumination alone means less than in most applications (*e.g.*, see papers by P. S. Millar).[21,22]

boundary lines for the pavement are indicated in Fig. 8.26.   Thus we need
to obtain only the total flux falling on the area from one luminaire.   Dividing the flux by the pavement area per luminaire gives the average pavement
illumination.

The flux falling on the pavement is obtained by measuring the areas
between contour lines in the isocandle diagram, multiplying each area by
average candlepower.   Between 1100- and 1200-candlepower contours, for
instance, there is a small area included between the two lines representing

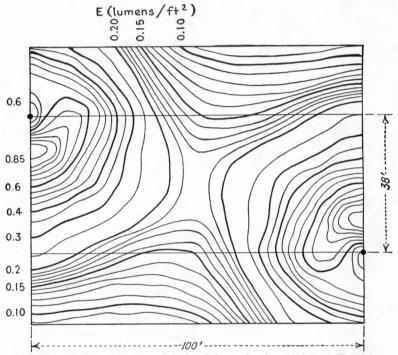

Fig. 8.27.—Isolux diagram.[9]   Calculated from the distribution of Fig. 8.26.

the curbs.   The area of this portion (φ from 45 to 68 deg, θ from 74 to 78 deg)
was measured with a planimeter and found to be 0.40 sq in. on a diagram
7 by 9 in.   The average candlepower in the area is assumed to be 1150.   The
product is thus 460.   If the intensity were constant at this value over the
hemisphere (which would be represented by a diagram 14 by 9 in.), we
should have a product of $1150 \times 14 \times 9 = 1150 \times 126$.   But we know
that the actual flux from such a source would be

$$F = 2\pi I = 6.28 \times 1150$$

Thus the actual flux in the above is

$$F = 460 \times \frac{6.28}{126} = 23 \text{ lumens}$$

The same procedure is used for the areas between the other contour lines, giving the following:

I (candlepower)	Area (square inch)	Product
50	2.25	110
150	1.60	240
250	1.63	410
350	1.47	510
450	3.08	1,390
550	3.99	2,200
650	3.44	2,240
750	2.39	1,800
850	1.34	1,140
950	1.32	1,250
1050	1.31	1,380
1150	0.40	460
		13,130

$$F = \frac{13,130}{20} = .656 \text{ lumens}$$

Thus each half of the luminaire sends 656 lumens to the pavement. But each half is responsible for an area of 38 by 50 ft, so the average pavement luminosity must be

$$E_{av} = \frac{656}{38 \times 50} = 0.346 \text{ lumen/sq ft}$$

Benford obtained 0.340 from the isolux curves (Fig. 8.27).

Problem 70. Check the values of the angles for the 10-ordinate method (Table XXX).

Problem 71. Two buildings of a small manufacturing plant are shown in Fig. 8.28. Some complaints have been received as to the illumination in the factory building (which is used for armature winding and motor assembly). The present lighting system is as shown.

Plot a curve of illumination on the bench level (30 in. above the floor) along the line AB and along the line CD. Discuss the adequacy of the lighting system from the standpoint of quantity and uniformity of illumination.

Problem 72. S-1 Sun lamps (Fig. 8.14) are used in lighting a portion of the surroundings of an indoor swimming pool. The axes of the reflectors are vertical, and the distance from lamp center to floor is 10 ft. Plot the erythemal irradiation on the floor as a function of distance from the lamp axis. For a person reclining on the floor directly beneath a lamp, what exposure is required for MPE?

Problem 73.   Four luminaires (Fig. 8.05) are to be used in lighting a classroom, with the lamp center h ft above the table level.   What spacing S between units will be required so that the variation in illumination will

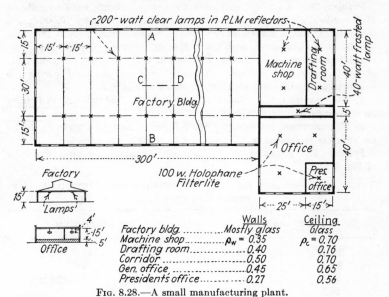

FIG. 8.28.—A small manufacturing plant.

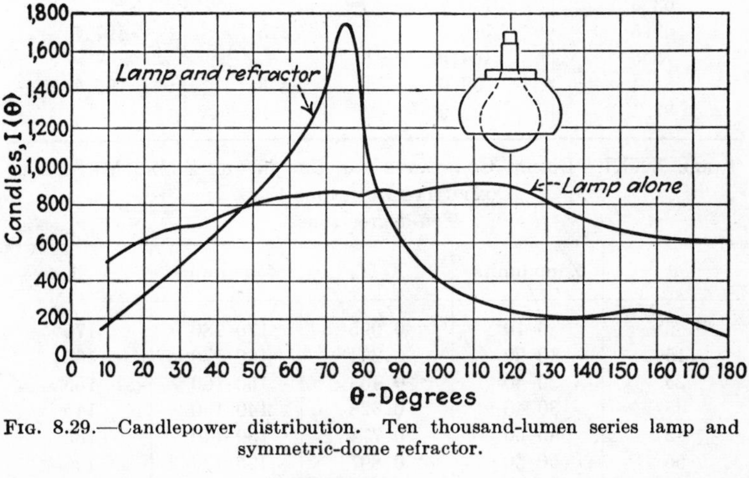

FIG. 8.29.—Candlepower distribution.   Ten thousand-lumen series lamp and symmetric-dome refractor.

not exceed 10 per cent?   The walls are $S/2$ ft from the luminaires.   Neglect reflections from walls and ceiling.

Problem 74.   Repeat Prob. 73 for a different type of direct luminaire.

Problem 75. For the semi-indirect luminaire of Fig. 8.18, hung h ft below the ceiling, what spacing s between units would be required in the room of Prob. 71 to reduce variations in ceiling illumination to 10 per cent?

Problem 76. A straight portion of a two-way highway, consisting of two 30-ft roadways separated by a 10-ft grassplot, is lighted by 10,000-lumen incandescent lamps suspended over the pavements from posts at the curb. The lamps are staggered, with 150-ft spacing (between projections of adjacent lamps on centerline of street). They are 12 ft from the curb and 30 ft above the pavement surface. Prismatic refractors are used, giving the symmetrical candlepower distribution shown in Fig. 8.29

1. Plot pavement illumination along a line AB (300 ft long), 12 ft from an outside curb.

2. Plot pavement luminosity along AB, assuming that a perfectly diffusing concrete pavement can be obtained ($\rho = 0.35$).

Problem 77. Repeat Prob. 76 for the 10,000-lumen sodium-vapor units of Fig. 8.22.

TABLE XXX.—ANGLES FOR THE SELECTED-ORDINATE METHOD OF COMPUTING LUMINOUS FLUX

For 20 ordinates		For 10 ordinates	
18.2°	161.8°	25.8°	154.2°
31.8	148.2		
41.4	138.6	45.6	134.4
49.5	130.5		
56.6	123.4	60.0	120.0
63.3	116.7		
69.5	110.5	72.5	107.5
75.5	104.5		
81.4	98.6	84.3	95.7
87.1	92.9		

TABLE XXXI.—LUMEN CONSTANTS FOR USE IN THE ZONAL METHOD OF COMPUTING LUMINOUS FLUX
Ten-degree zones

θ	Zone limits	F_n/I_n	Zone limits	θ
5°	0–10°	0.095	170–180°	175°
15	10–20	0.284	160–170	165
25	20–30	0.463	150–160	155
35	30–40	0.628	140–150	145
45	40–50	0.774	130–140	135
55	50–60	0.897	120–130	125
65	60–70	0.993	110–120	115
75	70–80	1.058	100–110	105
85	80–90	1.091	90–100	95

TABLE XXXII.—LUMEN CONSTANTS
Five-degree zones

0	Zone limits	F_n/I_n	Zone limits	θ
2.5°	0–5°	0.0239	175–180°	177.5°
7.5	5–10	0.0715	170–175	172.5
12.5	10–15	0.1186	165–170	167.5
17.5	15–20	0.1648	160–165	162.5
22.5	20–25	0.2098	155–160	157.5
27.5	25–30	0.2531	150–155	152.5
32.5	30–35	0.2945	145–150	147.5
37.5	35–40	0.3337	140–145	142.5
42.5	40–45	0.3703	135–140	137.5
47.5	45–50	0.4041	130–135	132.5
52.5	50–55	0.4349	125–130	127.5
57.5	55–60	0.4623	120–125	122.5
62.5	60–65	0.4862	115–120	117.5
67.5	65–70	0.5064	110–115	112.5
72.5	70–75	0.5228	105–110	107.5
77.5	75–80	0.5352	100–105	102.5
82.5	80–85	0.5435	95–100	97.5
87.5	85–90	0.5476	90–95	92.5

TABLE XXXIII.—VALUES FOR USE IN EQS. (8.05) AND (8.06)

θ	$\cos^3 \theta$	$\sin^3 \theta$	θ	$\cos^3 \theta$	$\sin^3 \theta$
0°	1.0000	0.0000	45	0.3536	0.3536
1	0.9996	⁵5316	46	0.3352	0.3722
2	0.9982	⁴4254	47	0.3172	0.3912
3	0.9959	³1434	48	0.2996	0.4104
4	0.9927	3394	49	0.2824	0.4299
5	0.9886	³6620	50	0.2656	0.4495
6	0.9836	²1142	51	0.2492	0.4694
7	0.9778	1810	52	0.2334	0.4893
8	0.9711	2695	53	0.2180	0.5094
9	0.9635	3828	54	0.2031	0.5295
10	0.9551	²5236	55	0.1887	0.5497
11	0.9459	6947	56	0.1749	0.5698
12	0.9359	8987	57	0.1616	0.5899
13	0.9251	¹1138	58	0.1488	0.6099
14	0.9135	1416	59	0.1366	0.6298
15	0.9012	¹1734	60	0.1250	0.6495
16	0.8882	2094	61	0.1140	0.6690
17	0.8745	2499	62	0.1035	0.6883
18	0.8602	2951	63	¹9357	0.7074
19	0.8453	3451	64	8424	0.7261
20	0.8298	¹4001	65	¹7548	0.7444
21	0.8137	4603	66	6729	0.7624
22	0.7971	5257	67	5965	0.7800
23	0.7800	5964	68	5257	0.7971
24	0.7624	6729	69	4603	0.8137
25	0.7444	¹7548	70	¹4001	0.8298
26	0.7261	8424	71	3451	0.8453
27	0.7074	9357	72	2951	0.8602
28	0.6883	0.1035	73	2499	0.8745
29	0.6690	0.1140	74	2094	0.8882
30	0.6495	0.1250	75	¹1734	0.9012
31	0.6298	0.1366	76	1416	0.9135
32	0.6099	0.1488	77	1138	0.9251
33	0.5899	0.1616	78	²8987	0.9359
34	0.5698	0.1749	79	6947	0.9459
35	0.5497	0.1887	80	²5236	0.9551
36	0.5295	0.2031	81	3828	0.9635
37	0.5094	0.2180	82	2695	0.9711
38	0.4893	0.2334	83	1810	0.9778
39	0.4694	0.2492	84	1142	0.9836
40	0.4495	0.2656	85	³6620	0.9886
41	0.4299	0.2824	86	3394	0.9927
42	0.4104	0.2996	87	1434	0.9959
43	0.3912	0.3172	88	⁴4254	0.9982
44	0.3722	0.3352	89	⁵5316	0.9996
			90	0000	1.0000

NOTE.—Superscripts refer to number of zeros after decimal point. Thus, ³6620 = 0.0006620.

Bibliography
GENERAL

1. J. W. T. WALSH: Photometry, Chap. IV.
2. H. H. HIGBIE: Lighting Calculations, pp. 71–106, John Wiley & Sons, Inc., New York, 1934.
3. C. P. STEINMETZ: Radiation, Light and Illumination, McGraw-Hill Book Company, Inc., New York, 1918.
4. UPPENBORN-MONASCH: Lehrbuch der Photometrie, R. Oldenbourg, Berlin, 1912.
5. S. G. HIBBEN: New Methods of Showing Photometric Data, *I.E.S. Trans.*, **21**, 1926, p. 169.
6. L. SCHNEIDER: Ein Beitrag zur Kennzeichnung der Lichtverteilung, *C.I.E., Proc.*, **1**, 1931, p. 494.

ASYMMETRIC LUMINAIRES

7. CLOSE and CLARKE: Map, Encyclopaedia Britannica (11th ed.), **17**, p. 658.
8. R. K. MELLUISH: Mathematics of Map Projections, Cambridge University Press, London, 1931.
9. F. BENFORD: Isocandles, *I.E.S. Trans.*, **21**, 1926, p. 129.
10. F. BENFORD: Isocandles and the Asymmetric Lighting Unit, *G.E. Rev.*, **28**, 1925, p. 271.
11. A. A. WOHLAUER: Efficiency of Asymmetrical Light Sources, *I.E.S. Trans.*, **23**, 1928, p. 551.
12. Testing Specifications for Lighting Equipment, *I.E.S. Trans.*, **28**, 1933, p. 512.
13. S. McK. GRAY: A New and Simpler Method for the Presentation of Photometric Data of Street Luminaires, *I.E.S. Trans.*, **29**, 1934, p. 463.

APPLICATIONS

14. HARRISON, HAAS, and REID: Street Lighting Practice, McGraw-Hill Book Company, Inc., New York, 1930.
15. C. J. STAHL: Electric Street Lighting, John Wiley & Sons, Inc., New York, 1929.
16. I.E.S. Code of Street Lighting, *I.E.S. Trans.*, **30**, 1935, p. 96.
17. P. H. GOODELL: Street Lighting and the Science of Seeing, *I.E.S. Trans.*, **30**, 1935, p. 49.
18. REID and CHANON: Studies in Fundamentals of Highway Lighting, *I.E.S. Trans.*, **31**, 1936, p. 119.
19. A. K. TAYLOR: Reflection Characteristics of Road Surfaces, *C.I.E. Proc.*, 1928, p. 49.
20. A. K. TAYLOR: Reflection from Road Surfaces, *Dept. of Sci. & Ind. Res. Tech. Paper* 9, 1930.
21. P. S. MILLAR: An Unrecognized Aspect of Street Illumination, *I.E.S. Trans.*, **5**, 1910, p. 546.
22. P. S. MILLAR: Brightness of Street Surface as an Element of Effectiveness in Street Lighting, *I.E.S. Trans.*, **23**, 1928, p. 1051.

CHAPTER IX

ILLUMINATION FROM SURFACE SOURCES

Thus far, we have considered the calculation of illumination from light sources of dimensions sufficiently small compared with r that the sources can be considered as point sources and the illumination at any point can be obtained by the use of the fundamental formula

$$E = \frac{I}{r^2} \cos \theta$$

In practice, however, there are many cases—one might almost say *most* cases—where using the inverse-square law introduces large errors. The increase in use of luminous panels and artificial skylights for interior illumination (the so-called ."architectural" or "built-in" lighting) makes necessary the calculation of illumination from large surface sources. Windows used for daylight illumination of interiors, and illumination resulting from the reflected light from walls and ceilings, are further examples.

In the present chapter, surface sources will be discussed in some detail. First, the characteristics of reflecting and transmitting mediums will be treated briefly, and the particular class of surfaces known as "perfectly diffusing" will be discussed. The remainder of the chapter will be confined to perfectly diffusing surfaces, since imperfectly diffusing surfaces introduce such great· complications in the calculations that no satisfactory method has been developed for treating them. Fortunately, a large number of the materials used in practice (solid-opal and flashed-opal glass, most wall surfaces, etc.) are such that the assumption of perfect diffusion does not introduce large errors. Integration methods will be developed for the determination of illumination from any form of perfectly diffusing surface of known but not necessarily of uniform luminosity.

9.02. Properties of Surfaces.—A knowledge of the reflecting properties of surfaces is a necessity for the illuminating engineer.

One type of reflection is that exhibited by mirrors, each ray of incident light being reflected as a single ray, and the angle of reflection being equal to the angle of incidence.   This type of reflection is called *regular* or *specular*.   It is obtained to a high degree of approximation with a polished metal surface or with the surface of a quiet pool of liquid.   A light source at A (Fig. 9.01) reflected in a specular surface will appear to be at A'.*   The shape and size of the source will be unaltered, but its apparent candlepower will be reduced owing to the fact that some of its luminous flux which strikes the surface is absorbed.   In calculating the illumination at P (Fig. 9.01), therefore, the intensity to

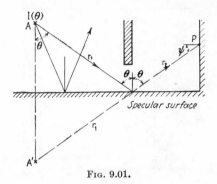

Fig. 9.01.

be used is not the actual intensity $I(\theta)$ of the source but is this intensity times the reflection factor ρ of the surface.   Thus the illumination at P is

$$E_p = \frac{\rho I(\theta)}{(r_1 + r_2)^2} \cos \psi \quad \text{(lumens/sq ft)} \qquad (9.01)$$

Because of minute scratches, dust particles, etc., polished surfaces are never perfect.   These imperfections result in the reflection of a small amount of luminous flux at angles other than the angle given by the law of specular reflection.   As the surface imperfections become more pronounced, the random distribution of flux from the surface increases, and the specular component is correspondingly decreased, until with matt surfaces the specular component may disappear.   Figure 9.02 shows this phenomenon graphically.   The case of specular reflection is shown at (*a*),

* If viewed from the point P.

where the candlepower-distribution curve consists of a single line at $\theta_r = \theta_i$. In (b), the specular component is still large, though there is now also a diffused component. The left-hand diagram of (b) gives the candlepower distribution in polar coordinates, while the right-hand diagram is in rectangular coordinates. The set of graphs (c) shows the characteristics of most matt surfaces, in which there is usually a slight tendency for the candlepower

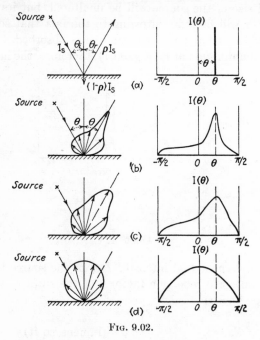

Fig. 9.02.

to be greatest in the neighborhood of $\theta_r = \theta_i$. The diagrams (d) of Fig. 9.02 show the distribution from an ideal matt surface where the distribution is independent of θ_i.

Figures 9.03 a to d give some experimental results on the reflection from a number of diffusing surfaces. The curves give the candlepower at a fixed angle from the normal when the incident radiation strikes the reflecting surface at various angles from 0 to 90 deg. A perfectly diffusing surface would follow the dotted cosine curve (see Sec. 9.03), but the behavior of the actual surfaces is seen to depart somewhat from the ideal. Other interesting curves can be obtained by fixing the angle of incidence and changing the angle at which the candlepower is measured. It is found that nearly all matt surfaces when viewed at large angles from the normal exhibit specular reflection. A black asphalt street pavement, for instance, which reflects hardly any light normal to its surface, acts as a fairly good mirror when

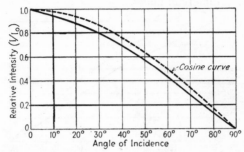

FIG. 9.03a.—Reflecting characteristics of white-matt opal glass viewed normal to surface. (*A. K. Taylor, Proc. Opt. Convention*, 1926, *p.* 350.)

viewed at the usual angles of 87 to 89 deg.[15] This fact is of great importance in street lighting, as has been emphasized by P. S. Millar.[16]

Transmitting surfaces have similar candlepower-distribution curves, as shown in Fig. 9.04. In Fig. 9.04a, a sheet of polished plate glass is interposed between the light source and the observer.

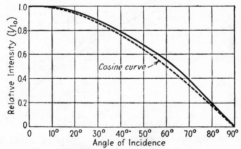

FIG. 9.03b.—Reflecting characteristics of white-matt paint viewed at 30 deg from normal. (*A. K. Taylor.*)

All the luminous flux that emerges from the glass (except for a very small amount due to internal reflections) emerges in a single ray. In Fig. 9.04b, the surface of the glass has been roughened by grinding, sandblasting, or etching. The distribution of the transmitted light now contains a diffuse component but still has a maximum candlepower at the angle $\theta = \theta_i$. Figure 9.04c refers to an opal glass containing a multitude of small particles which prevent a ray of light from passing *directly* through the glass. In this case, the distribution is independent of θ_i, and the light is thoroughly diffused. Figures 9.05 and 9.06 give test results on a number of commercial glasses.

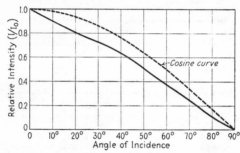

FIG. 9.03c.—Reflecting characteristics of magnesium oxide viewed normal to surface. (*A. K. Taylor.*)

When a ray of light encounters a plane boundary between two transparent media, part of the radiant power is generally transmitted and part reflected (Fig. 9.07). If the two media have indices of refraction n_1 and n_2, and if the incident ray makes an

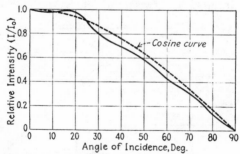

FIG. 9.03d.—Reflecting characteristics of white blotting paper viewed normal to surface. (*A. K. Taylor.*)

angle θ_1 with the normal, the direction of the refracted ray is obtained from Snell's law,

$$n_1 \sin \theta_1 = n_2 \sin \theta_2 \tag{9.02}$$

The reflected ray makes an angle θ_1 with the normal. The classical formula of Fresnel allows the reflected and the trans-

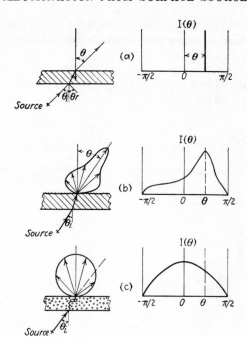

FIG. 9.04.

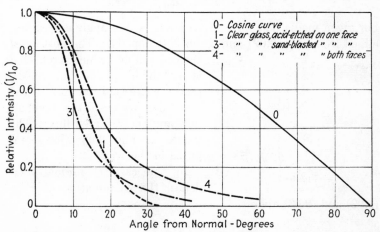

FIG. 9.05.—Transmission characteristics of depolished glasses. (*M. Cohu, C.I.E. Proc.*, 1931, *p.* 440.)

mitted flux to be computed. The ratio of the total flux F_r reflected at the boundary to the flux F_1 incident on the boundary is

$$\frac{F_r}{F_1} = \frac{1}{2}\left\{\frac{\sin\,(\theta_1 - \theta_2)}{\sin\,(\theta_1 + \theta_2)}\right\}^2 + \frac{1}{2}\left\{\frac{\tan\,(\theta_1 - \theta_2)}{\tan\,(\theta_1 + \theta_2)}\right\}^2 \qquad (9.03)$$

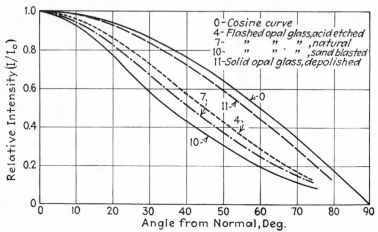

FIG. 9.06.—Transmission characteristics of opal glasses. (*M. Cohu, C.I.E. Proc.*, 1931, *p*. 445.)

For given media and for a given angle θ_1, the angle θ_2 is determined from Eq. (9.02) and Table I (Chap. I). The portion of the original flux which is reflected is obtainable from Eq. (9.03), and the transmitted flux is the difference between the incident flux and the reflected flux. The values of Fig. 9.08 were computed in this way.

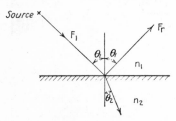

FIG. 9.07.

In the case of normal incidence, the combination of Eqs. (9.02) and (9.03) gives

$$\frac{F_r}{F_1} = \rho = \left(\frac{n-1}{n+1}\right)^2 \qquad (9.04)$$

This formula is a good approximation up to an angle of incidence of about 45 deg, as shown in Fig. 9.08. For ordinary glass,

Eq. (9.04) gives a reflection of about 4 per cent at each glass-air surface.

Problem 78. Derive the expression (9.04) by using Eqs. (9.02) and (9.03).

Problem 79. Reflections in store windows are often found to be very troublesome, making it almost impossible to see the goods displayed behind the glass. A certain store faces a warehouse of buff brick which is on the opposite side of a street having a pavement width of 40 ft and two 10-ft sidewalks. A vertical plate-glass window is used in the store front, and it is found that most prospective purchasers look at the glass within an angle of 30 deg from the normal. When the morning sun illuminates the entire warehouse wall to approximately 6000 lumens/sq ft, it is difficult to see anything within the store window; and the management is considering the use of a high level of artificial illumination of the displayed goods. Assuming for the goods an average reflection factor of 0.50, what illumination on a

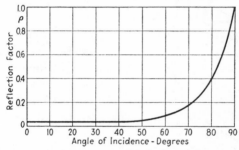

Fig. 9.08.—Reflection from a polished glass surface ($n = 1.5$).

vertical surface within the window will be necessary so that the luminosity of the vertical display surfaces shall not be exceeded by the luminosity of the image of the warehouse wall as reflected in the plate glass?

Problem 80. Another solution of Prob. 79 is to use a slanting glass. At what angle with the vertical must the glass be tilted in order that pedestrians on the sidewalk near the window may not be troubled by images of the warehouse?

Problem 81. A small indoor swimming pool is illuminated by 200-watt lamps in RLM reflectors, which are mounted at the ceiling, 15 ft above the level of the water. What is the illumination of the ceiling at a point 10 ft from a single lamp, due to reflection of the flux from this lamp in the still surface of the pool?

What is the minimum distance between the axis of the RLM reflector and the edge of the pool so that a standing spectator (eyes 7 ft 0 in. above water level) cannot get reflected glare from the water surface?

9.03. Properties of Perfectly Diffusing Surfaces.—Section 9.02 has shown that actual surfaces have markedly different reflecting

characteristics, ranging from an almost perfect mirror to an almost perfect matt surface. In the remainder of the book, we shall confine the discussion to a particular kind of surface called *perfectly diffusing*.

A perfectly diffusing surface may be defined as a surface that emits luminous flux according to the cosine law

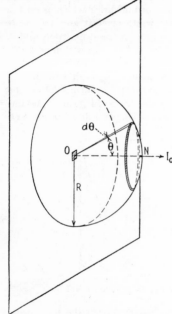

$$I(\theta) = I_0 \cos \theta \qquad (9.05)$$

where I_0 = the candlepower of the surface (or any portion of the surface) normal to itself ($\theta = 0$).

$I(\theta)$ = the candlepower at an angle θ from the normal.

The intensity distribution curve in polar coordinates is thus a circle, as shown in Fig. 9.02. The expression (9.05)—the *cosine law of emission*—is quite distinct from the cosine law of illumination enunciated in Sec. 7.02. The cosine law of illumination is a property of space and is rigorously true. The cosine law of

Fig. 9.09.

emission is an idealized expression which has no theoretical foundation. This law of emission, though closely approximated by many good matt surfaces, is not exactly satisfied by any of them.

Good diffusing reflecting surfaces generally approximate the cosine law except when viewed at angles near 90 deg from the normal. Solid opal glass and flashed opal glass, which are extensively used in architectural lighting elements, produce a thorough diffusion of light, and the candlepower distribution is a close approximation to the cosine law. On the other hand, sandblasted glass and the various figured glasses produce only a slight diffusion and cannot be regarded as perfectly diffusing surfaces. An important attribute of the perfectly diffusing surface, and one that is responsible for much of the mathematical simplicity in its treatment, is that the flux distribution from such a surface is independent of θ_i.

For the perfectly diffusing surface, a simple relation exists between I_0 and the total flux emitted from the surface. Consider a plane source O (Fig. 9.09). Owing to luminous flux reflected by O from another source or to flux transmitted by O, the plane source emits perfectly diffused radiation. Imagine O to be inclosed in a hemisphere of sufficiently great radius R that the illumination on the surface of the hemisphere can be computed by the inverse-square law. Since $I(\theta) = I_0 \cos \theta$, the illumination at any point on the hemisphere is

$$E = \frac{I(\theta)}{R^2} = \frac{I_0}{R^2} \cos \theta \quad \text{(lumens/sq ft)} \qquad (9.06)$$

As the candlepower distribution is symmetrical about the axis ON, an element of surface may be taken in the form of a narrow band, as shown by the shaded area, of area

$$2\pi R^2 \sin \theta \, d\theta \quad \text{(sq ft)}$$

The flux passing through this band is

$$E(2\pi R^2 \sin \theta \, d\theta) = 2\pi I_0 \cos \theta \sin \theta \, d\theta \quad \text{(lumens)}$$

The total flux leaving the plane source O is equal to the total flux passing through the entire hemisphere, or is

$$F = 2\pi I_0 \int_0^{\frac{\pi}{2}} \cos \theta \sin \theta \, d\theta$$

$$= 2\pi I_0 \left[\frac{\sin^2 \theta}{2} \right]_0^{\frac{\pi}{2}} = \pi I_0 \quad \text{(lumens)} \qquad (9.07)$$

Equation (9.07) expresses the important fact that for any plane, perfectly diffusing surface, the number of lumens emitted is equal to π times the intensity normal to the surface. As a special case, we may consider an element dA of a perfectly diffusing surface of *any* form, not necessarily plane. The element considered by itself, however, is essentially plane, and

$$dF = L \, dA = \pi I_0 \qquad (9.07a)$$

As an aid in remembering on which side of the equation the π belongs, one may keep in mind that the number of lumens is always greater than the number of candles. For a uniform spherical source, where $I(\theta) = \text{const}$,

$$F = 4\pi I \quad \text{(lumens)}$$

For a uniform hemispherical source emitting no flux from its plane face, $I(\theta) = \text{const}$, and

$$F = 2\pi I \quad \text{(lumens)}$$

For the perfectly diffusing plane source,

$$F = \pi I \quad \text{(lumens)}$$

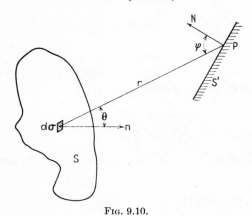

FIG. 9.10.

9.04. The Integration Process, and the Illumination from a Narrow Band Source.—A perfectly diffusing source S of luminosity L illuminates a surface S' (Fig. 9.10). What is the illumination at P on the surface S'?

The source is divided into elements $d\sigma$, each of which may be regarded as a plane, perfectly diffusing source. Since the luminosity is L, the total flux emitted by $d\sigma$ is $L\,d\sigma$, and the intensity normal to the surface element $d\sigma$ is

$$dI_0 = \frac{L\,d\sigma}{\pi} \quad \text{(candles)}$$

The intensity in the direction of P is

$$dI(\theta) = dI_0 \cos\theta = \frac{L\,d\sigma}{\pi}\cos\theta \quad \text{(candles)}$$

Since the dimensions of $d\sigma$ are very small compared with r, the inverse-square law holds, and the illumination at P due to flux from $d\sigma$ is

$$dE_p = \frac{dI(\theta)}{r^2} \cos \psi = \frac{L}{\pi r^2} \cos \theta \cos \psi \, d\sigma \quad \text{(lumens/sq ft)}$$

The total illumination at P from the surface S is obtained by integration:

$$E_p = \frac{1}{\pi} \int_S \frac{L}{r^2} \cos \theta \cos \psi \, d\sigma \quad \text{(lumens/sq ft)} \qquad (9.08)$$

where the integral is taken over the entire surface of S which illuminates P. If the source S is of such form that part of its surface is hidden from P, the limits of integration must be adjusted to take care of this fact. Equation (9.08) is a general expression for the illumination at any point due to a perfectly diffusing source of any form. L may vary from point to point on the luminous surface in a known manner, or it may be a constant. For each shape of surface source and for each type of luminosity variation, a separate integration must be performed. Since the number of shapes used in practice is small, the results of these integrations can be tabulated once for all, and the formulas made available.

As a simple example, consider the illumination from a narrow, luminous panel of diffusing glass lighted by incandescent lamps concealed behind it. Such panels are frequently used in modern interior illumination. The surface is assumed to be perfectly diffusing and of constant luminosity L, and the width of the panel w will be taken small compared with the distance D (Fig. 9.11). The value of the illumination is desired at a point P on the floor, on a line making an angle 90 deg with the wall.

The area of an element is wdh. The intensity of this element perpendicular to the panel is

$$dI_0 = \frac{L}{\pi} wdh \quad \text{(candles)}$$

The illumination of the floor at P due to the flux from this element is

$$dE_p = \frac{Lw}{\pi r^2} \cos \theta \sin \theta \, dh$$

The illumination produced by the whole panel is

$$E_p = \frac{Lw}{\pi} \int_0^H \frac{\cos\theta \sin\theta}{r^2} dh \quad \text{(lumens/sq ft)}$$

Making the substitutions

$$h = D\tan\theta, \qquad dh = D\sec^2\theta\, d\theta, \qquad r = D\sec\theta$$

we obtain

$$E_p = \frac{Lw}{\pi D} \int_0^{\sin^{-1}\frac{H}{\sqrt{H^2+D^2}}} \cos\theta \sin\theta\, d\theta$$
$$= \frac{Lw}{2\pi D}\left(\frac{H^2}{H^2 + D^2}\right) \tag{9.09}$$

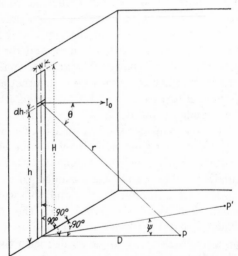

Fig. 9.11.—Illumination from a narrow luminous panel.

It is often convenient to check formulas obtained in this way by seeing if they revert to the inverse-square law when the dimensions become sufficiently small. For a panel of small height $H << D$, Eq. (9.09) reduces to

$$E_p = \frac{LwH^2}{2\pi D^3} \tag{9.09a}$$

This is actually an inverse-square variation, since if H is small, the candlepower of the panel is

$$I_0 = \frac{LwH}{\pi}$$

and the illumination at P is

$$E_p = \frac{I_0}{D^2} \sin \theta = \frac{LwH}{\pi D^2} \cdot \frac{H}{2D}$$

which checks the previous expression, Eq. (9.09a).

In case the illumination is desired at another point on the floor, say at P' of Fig. 9.11, the results are the same as given by Eq. (9.09) except that all candlepower values must be multiplied by $\cos \psi$. Thus

$$E_{p'} = \frac{Lw}{2\pi D}\left(\frac{H^2}{H^2 + D^2}\right) \cos \psi \qquad (9.10)$$

Another special case is where H is very large compared with D. Then the quantity in parentheses approaches unity, and Eq. (9.10) becomes

$$E_{p'} = \frac{Lw}{2\pi D} \cos \psi \qquad (9.10a)$$

It is interesting to note that in this case the illumination has become inversely proportional to the *first* power of the distance, while for the original elements of the area, the illumination was inversely proportional to the second power of the distance. The inverse first-power law will be found to be a characteristic of infinitely-long linear elements and will be treated in greater detail later.

Problem 82.   Consider a perfectly diffusing luminous panel of width w, length H, and uniform luminosity L placed in the ceiling of a room of height D. Derive an expression for the illumination at any point on the floor. Assume $w << H$.

Problem 83.   Obtain an expression for the illumination due to the panel of Prob. 82 when $H >> D$.

Problem 84.   A room 20 by 10 ft with a 9-ft ceiling is illuminated by a luminous panel whose surface is flush with one of the side walls. The panel is 6 in. wide, 20 ft long, and is horizontal, with the bottom edge 8 ft from the floor. Walls, ceiling, and floor have low reflection factors, so their effect may be neglected. The luminosity of the panel is 200 lumens/ sq ft. What is the illumination at a point in the center of the room on a table 30 in. high?

Problem 85. A circular lobby of black marble, 30 ft in diameter and 15 ft high, is illuminated by a built-in luminous element encircling the room, with its bottom edge 12 ft above the floor (Fig. 9.12). The panel is of flashed opal glass 10 in. wide and is lighted by 75-watt incandescent lamps spaced on 10-in. centers and operated at rated voltage. Tests on similar units show that 50 per cent of the lamp lumens can be obtained from the front surface of the glass, the remainder being absorbed by the glass and

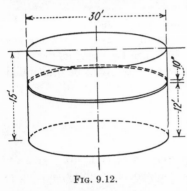

the reflector. What is the illumination on a vertical bulletin board at a point on the center line of the room and 6 ft above the floor?

Fig. 9.12.

9.05. The Circular Disk.

Consider the illumination on a horizontal plane at P (Fig. 9.13) due to a circular luminous source of radius a. The panel is assumed to be of uniform luminosity and perfectly diffusing, and the illumination will be determined for points on the axis OP only. Hence all elements of the disk for a given value of θ will be equally effective in producing illumination at P, and it is therefore permissible to use a circular ring as the element of surface. The area of such a ring of radius ξ and width $d\xi$ will be

$$2\pi \xi \, d\xi = 2\pi D^2 \tan \theta \sec^2 \theta \, d\theta$$

The illumination at P from such a ring is

$$dE = \frac{2LD^2 \tan \theta \sec^2 \theta \, d\theta}{r^2} \cos^2 \theta$$
$$= 2L \sin \theta \cos \theta \, d\theta$$

The illumination due to the whole disk source is

$$E = 2L \int_0^{\sin^{-1} \frac{a}{\sqrt{a^2+D^2}}} \sin \theta \cos \theta \, d\theta = L\left(\frac{a^2}{a^2 + D^2}\right) \quad (9.11)$$

Equation (9.11) gives an exact expression for the illumination on the axis of a circular-disk source. Several interesting conclusions may be obtained from the equation.   In the first place, let us find the error introduced by use of the inverse-square law at short distances.   If D is very large compared with a, Eq. (9.11) reduces to

$$E = \frac{La^2}{D^2} = \frac{I_0}{D^2} \tag{9.11a}$$

and the inverse-square law holds as would be expected.   Since

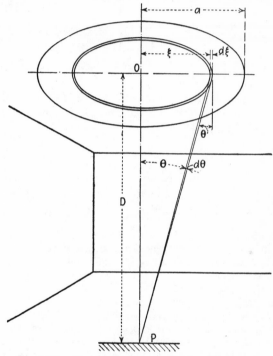

Fig. 9.13.—Illumination from a circular-disk source.

the total flux from the disk is $(\pi a^2)L$, and its candlepower is $(\pi a^2 L)/\pi$, $I_0 = La^2$.   At lesser distances, from Eq. (9.11),

$$E = La^2 \left(\frac{1}{a^2 + D^2} \right) = \frac{La^2}{D^2} \left(\frac{1}{\left(\dfrac{a}{D} \right)^2 + 1} \right) \tag{9.11b}$$

The quantity within the parentheses can be expanded in a series, giving

$$E = \frac{La^2}{D^2}\left[1 - \left(\frac{a}{D}\right)^2 + \left(\frac{a}{D}\right)^4 - \left(\frac{a}{D}\right)^6 + \cdots \right] \quad (9.11c)$$

The first term of thé series is the ordinary inverse-square expression, which is a first approximation even near the source. If an error of 1 per cent is permissible, the second term would be approximately 0.01, or

$$\frac{a}{D} = \sqrt{0.01} = 0.10$$

Thus the inverse-square law holds to within one per cent if $a/D \leq 0.10$, or if D is at least ten times the radius of the disk. Similarly, for a precision of 0.1 per cent, the inverse-square law holds only when $D \geq 32a$.

Another useful result is obtained from (9.11) if a is allowed to become very large. If $a >> D$, the D^2 in the denominator becomes negligible, and

$$E = L \quad (9.12)$$

Thus for a very large diffusing source, such as an overcast sky, the illumination is the same everywhere, independent of the distance from the source, and is equal to the luminosity of the source.

Problem 86. A vertical bulletin board is placed beneath the circular source of Fig. 9.13. Derive an expression for the illumination on the face of the board at a point directly beneath the center of the disk, D ft below it.

Problem 87. A spherical globe of opal glass of radius a incloses an incandescent lamp. The globe is found to be of practically constant luminosity L, and the surface is perfectly diffusing. Candlepower measurements are to be made at various angles, and it is necessary to know at what distance these measurements must be made in order that the candlepower may be calculated from the relation $I = ED^2$. By surface integration, derive an expression for E at any distance and prove that the inverse-square law holds· *at all distances.*

9.06. The Rectangular Source.—Another form of source, even more important from a practical standpoint than either of the previous ones, is the rectangular source. For this case also, the procedure is exactly as before except that a double integral must be evaluated instead of a single one. Consider the perfectly diffusing luminous source shown in Fig. 9.14. The luminosity is L = const, and the illumination will be determined on the opposite wall at a point P which is on a perpendicular erected at one corner of the source.

As element of area, use $dx\ dy$, the candlepower of which in the direction of P is

$$I(\theta) = \frac{L\ dx\ dy}{\pi} \cos \theta$$

The illumination at P is thus

$$E = \frac{L}{\pi} \int_0^H \int_0^W \frac{\cos^2 \theta}{r^2} dx\ dy$$

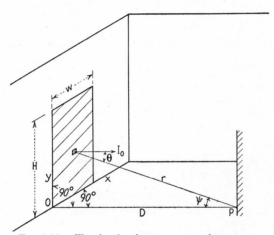

FIG. 9.14.—Illumination from a rectangular source.

But

$$\cos \theta = \frac{D}{r}, \qquad r^2 = D^2 + x^2 + y^2,$$

and

$$E = \frac{LD^2}{\pi} \int_0^H \int_0^W \frac{dx\ dy}{[D^2 + y^2 + x^2]^2} \tag{9.13}$$

The details of the integration are included because they are needed later in the consideration of the case of nonuniform luminosity.

The integration with respect to x is easily performed:

$$\int_0^W \frac{dx}{[(D^2 + y^2) + x^2]^2} =$$
$$\frac{W}{2(D^2 + y^2)[(D^2 + y^2) + W^2]} + \frac{1}{2(D^2 + y^2)^{3/2}}\tan^{-1}\frac{W}{\sqrt{D^2 + y^2}} \quad (9.14)$$

leaving

$$E = \frac{LD^2}{2\pi}\left\{ W\int_0^H \frac{dy}{(D^2 + y^2)[(D^2 + W^2) + y^2]} + \right.$$
$$\left. \int_0^H \frac{1}{(D^2 + y^2)^{3/2}}\tan^{-1}\frac{W}{\sqrt{D^2 + y^2}}dy\right\} \quad (9.15)$$

The second term in the parentheses may be integrated by parts:

$$u = \tan^{-1}\frac{W}{\sqrt{D^2 + y^2}}$$
$$dv = \frac{dy}{(D^2 + y^2)^{3/2}}$$
$$du = -\frac{Wy\,dy}{[(D^2 + W^2) + y^2]\sqrt{D^2 + y^2}}$$
$$v = \frac{y}{D^2\sqrt{D^2 + y^2}}$$

The second integral is therefore

$$\frac{H}{D^2\sqrt{D^2 + H^2}}\tan^{-1}\frac{W}{\sqrt{D^2 + H^2}} +$$
$$\frac{D^2 + W^2}{WD^2}\int_0^H \frac{dy}{[(D^2 + W^2) + y^2]} - \frac{1}{W}\int_0^H \frac{dy}{D^2 + y^2} \cdots \quad (9.16)$$

The first integral is

$$W\int_0^H \frac{dy}{(D^2 + y^2)[(D^2 + W^2) + y^2]} =$$
$$\frac{1}{W}\int_0^H \frac{dy}{D^2 + y^2} - \frac{1}{W}\int_0^H \frac{dy}{[(D^2 + W^2) + y^2]} \quad (9.17)$$

Substituting in Eq. (9.15),

$$E = \frac{LD^2}{2\pi}\left\{ \frac{H}{D^2\sqrt{D^2 + H^2}} \tan^{-1} \frac{W}{\sqrt{D^2 + H^2}} + \right.$$

$$\left. \frac{W}{D^2} \int_0^H \frac{dy}{[(D^2 + W^2) + y^2]}\right\}$$

$$= \frac{L}{2\pi}\left\{ \frac{H}{\sqrt{D^2 + H^2}} \sin^{-1} \frac{W}{r_1} + \frac{W}{\sqrt{D^2 + W^2}} \sin^{-1} \frac{H}{r_1}\right\} \qquad (9.18)$$

where $r_1 = \sqrt{D^2 + H^2 + W^2}$

which gives the illumination (from a rectangular luminous panel of uniform luminosity) on a plane parallel to the panel and at a point that lies on a perpendicular erected at a corner of the panel.

The corresponding equation for the illumination on a plane perpendicular to the luminous panel is derivable in a similar manner.   The result is

$$E = \frac{L}{2\pi}\left\{ \tan^{-1} \frac{W}{D} - \frac{D}{\sqrt{D^2 + H^2}} \sin^{-1} \frac{W}{r_1}\right\} \qquad (9.19)$$

Apparently, Eqs. (9.18) and (9.19) were first derived by Yamauti.[22]   More recently, Higbie[26] and others have made extensive use of them.   Yamauti developed the general equations for the illumination at any point on any plane, of which (9.18) and (9.19) are special cases.   In practice, however, it has been found simpler to restrict conditions to points that lie on a perpendicular erected at the corner of the panel.   The next section will show how Eqs. (9.18) and (9.19) can be used in calculating illumination at any point.

9.07. Tables and Graphs of the Illumination from Rectangular Sources.—The equations (9.18) and (9.19) for the illumination from rectangular sources of constant luminosity can be put in a form more suitable for computation.   The illumination per unit luminosity of source is

$$\frac{E_z}{L} = \frac{1}{2\pi}\left[\frac{H}{\sqrt{D^2 + H^2}} \sin^{-1} \frac{W}{r_1} + \frac{W}{\sqrt{D^2 + W^2}} \sin^{-1} \frac{H}{r_1}\right] \qquad (9.18a)$$

$$\frac{E_y}{L} = \frac{1}{2\pi}\left[\tan^{-1} \frac{W}{D} - \frac{D}{\sqrt{D^2 + H^2}} \sin^{-1} \frac{W}{r_1}\right] \qquad (9.19a)$$

where Eq. (9.18a) refers to the illumination on a plane parallel to the source and Eq. (9.19a), on a plane perpendicular to the source.

In Fig. 9.15,

$$\frac{H}{\sqrt{D^2 + H^2}} = \sin \gamma \qquad \frac{W}{\sqrt{D^2 + W^2}} = \sin \beta$$

$$\sin^{-1} \frac{W}{r_1} = \beta_1 \qquad \sin^{-1} \frac{H}{r_1} = \gamma_1$$

Hence Eqs. (9.18a) and (9.19a) become

$$\frac{E_z}{L} = \frac{1}{2\pi}[\beta_1 \sin \gamma + \gamma_1 \sin \beta] \qquad (9.18b)$$

$$\frac{E_y}{L} = \frac{1}{2\pi}[\beta - \beta_1 \cos \gamma] \qquad (9.19b)$$

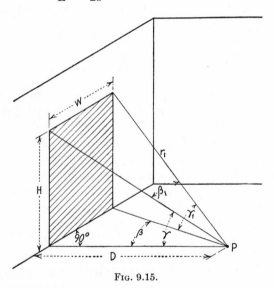

FIG. 9.15.

where β_1 and γ_1 are the angles shown in Fig. 9.15 and are given by the relations

$$\beta_1 = \sin^{-1}\left[\frac{\tan \beta}{\sqrt{\tan^2 \beta + \sec^2 \gamma}}\right] \qquad (9.20)$$

$$\gamma_1 = \sin^{-1}\left[\frac{\tan \gamma}{\sqrt{\tan^2 \gamma + \sec^2 \beta}}\right] \qquad (9.21)$$

The illumination has been expressed in terms of the two angles β and γ subtended by the source. Evidently, (E/L) is entirely independent of the size of the source, as long as these two angles remain the same.

This fact allows values of E/L to be tabulated and to be used for all sizes of sources at all distances. Such a tabulation in

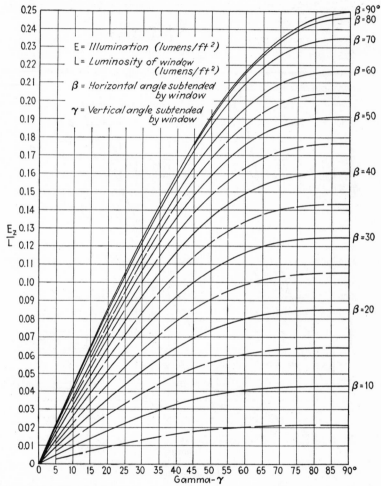

Fig. 9.16.—Illumination from a rectangular window parallel to the illuminated plane.

terms of β and γ will be found considerably quicker and more convenient to use than the corresponding tabulation in terms of H, W, and D. Appendix E gives values of E/L computed from

Eqs. (9.18b) and (9.19b), while Figs. 9.16 and 9.17 give the same data in graphical form. If only a few values of illumination are needed, the values of β and γ can be found easily by use of the trigonometric scales of a slide rule. If a large number of

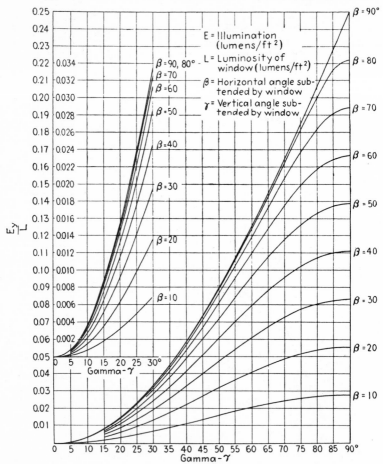

Fig. 9.17.—Illumination from a rectangular window perpendicular to the illuminated plane.

values is needed, however, much time is saved by using scale drawings, measuring β and γ with an ordinary protractor.

But, one asks, of what value are these tables and graphs since they apply only to points on a perpendicular erected at the corner of the source? Higbie[24] and his associates have treated this matter in considerable detail. Suppose, for instance, that the illumination is desired at P (Fig. 9.18) due to the whole window A-B. The illumination is made up of two parts, one from the portion A, and the other from the portion B. Thus one value of γ and two values of β are required. Figure 9.17 gives two values of E/L, one corresponding to each value of β, and the resulting illumination at P is equal to the sum of the values of E/L multiplied by the value of the luminosity of the source.

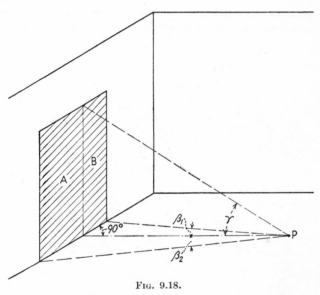

Fig. 9.18.

In Fig. 9.19, the illumination at P, due to the source 1234, is desired. The value cannot be obtained directly because P is not on a perpendicular to the corner of the source. So a fictitious source which *does* satisfy this condition is considered; *i.e.*, the whole area 5794 is taken as source. The resulting value of E/L is obtained from Fig. 9.17 and is recorded. Next, the value of E/L for the fictitious source 5781 is obtained and is subtracted from the value for 5794. The value for 6793 is subtracted from this last result. Now we have subtracted too much, so E/L for the fictitious source 6782 is added. The actual illumination at P is

$$E_p = L[(E/L)_{5794} - (E/L)_{5781} - (E/L)_{6793} + (E/L)_{6782}]$$

In practice, two drawings are desirable, one in each of the planes perpendicular to the plane of the source.   Thus if the illumina-

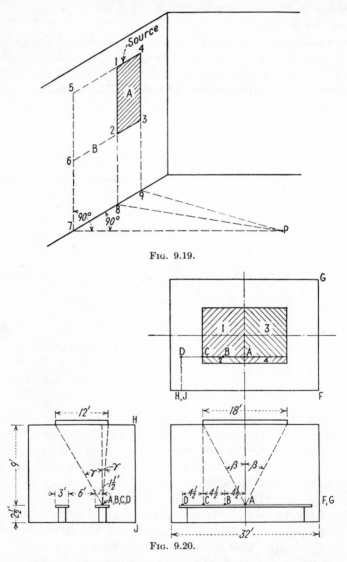

Fig. 9.19.

Fig. 9.20.

tion is desired on a horizontal plane due to a luminous panel or a window in the back wall of a room, the plan and side elevation of the room are needed.   If the problem is the same except that the luminous flux comes from a panel in the ceiling, the plan is no longer useful, but side and front elevations are needed. All angles are found quickly by use of a protractor, and the corresponding values of E/L are tabulated.

As an example, consider the small library shown in Fig. 9.20, lighted by a luminous panel in the ceiling. Here the plan is unnecessary but has been included for convenience in visualizing the problem. The luminosity of the panel is 78.4 lumens/sq ft; and since the walls are paneled in dark oak, reflections from them can probably be neglected. What is the illumination along the middle of a table 30 in. above the floor?

Take the point A, for instance. The source is considered to be divided into four sections 1, 2, 3, 4 (Fig. 9.20) such that each section has a corner directly above A. The four components are then added

Source	β	γ	E/L
1	45.00°	49.40°	0.1473
2	45.00	9.47	0.0336
3	45.00	49.40	0.1473
4	45.00	9.47	0.0336
		Total =	0.3618

The illumination at A is

$$E_A = 78.4 \times 0.3618 = \textbf{28.37 lumens/sq ft}$$

The same procedure can be used for the other points, giving

Point	β	γ	E/L	E (lumens/ sq ft)
A	45.00°	49.40, 9.47°	0.3618	28.4
B	26.57, 56.32	49.40, 9.47	0.3235	25.4
C	63.43	49.40, 9.47	0.2181	17.1
D	26.57, 68.20	49.40, 9.47	0.1054	8.3

Figures 9.21 and 9.22 give additional data. Figure 9.21 shows a plot of the illumination along the desk, while Fig. 9.22 gives the illumination at 16 points for a quarter of the room.

Problem 87a. Prove that if one dimension of the source is very great ($W \rightarrow \infty$), Eqs. (9.18a) and (9.19a) reduce to

$$\frac{E_z}{L} = \frac{1}{4} \sin \gamma \qquad (9.18c)$$

$$\frac{E_y}{L} = \frac{1}{4}(1 - \cos \gamma) \qquad (9.19c)$$

Problem 88. Show that Eq. (9.19a) reduces to Eq. (9.09) if $W << D$.

Problem 89. Compute the illumination on horizontal and vertical planes at the surface of the earth on an overcast day with the luminosity of the clouds equal to 500 lumens/sq ft. Use Eqs. (9.18b) and (9.19b).

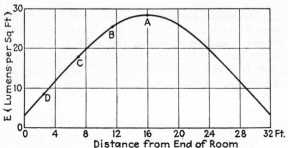

Fig. 9.21.—Illumination in the room of Fig. 9.20.

Problem 90. Plot E along the line *FG* on the table level and along *HJ* on the book stacks in the room of Fig. 9.20.

Problem 91. Check the results of the example (Sec. 9.07) by use of the Higbie protractor (H. H. Higbie, Lighting Calculation, p. 168, 1934).

Problem 92. A device (Fig. 9.23) has been constructed for obtaining instantly the integral of the product of two functions (K. E. Gould, *J.*

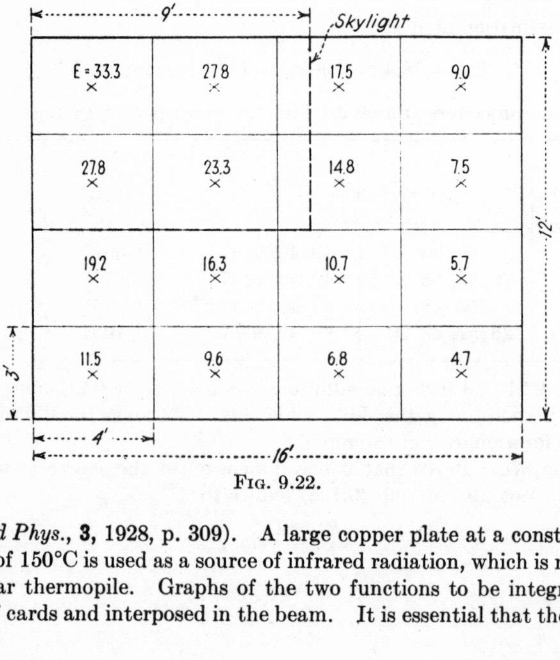

Fig. 9.22.

Math. and Phys., **3**, 1928, p. 309). A large copper plate at a constant temperature of 150°C is used as a source of infrared radiation, which is measured by a linear thermopile. Graphs of the two functions to be integrated are cut out of cards and interposed in the beam. It is essential that the irradiation of screen 2 be uniform.   If the opening in screen 1 is rectangular in shape, 10 by 20 in., how far away must screen 2 be placed for the irradiation of a 10-in. opening on the line AB to be constant to within ± 0.1 per cent?

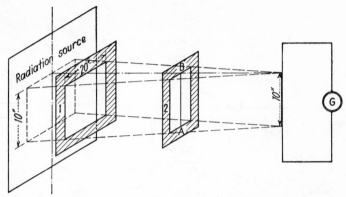

Fig. 9.23.

9.08. The Two-dimensional Case.*—We have considered the general method of integration, giving the illumination due to a perfectly diffusing surface source of any form or size, of uniform or nonuniform luminosity. It sometimes happens that the length of the source is great compared with the distance r, in which case the integration can be performed more easily by considering the problem as a two-dimensional one.

Figure 9.24 shows a portion of a perfectly diffusing surface of uniform luminosity L.   The surface may be curved in any manner in the x and y directions, but the elements are straight in the z direction.   Assume that the surface extends to infinity in both plus and minus z directions.   Consider an element of area

$$d\sigma = ds\,dz$$

The illumination at P on a surface which is normal to r, due to this element $d\sigma$, is

$$dE = \frac{Lds\,dz}{\pi}\frac{\cos\theta_1\cos\psi}{(r\sec\psi)^2}$$
$$= \frac{L}{\pi}\frac{ds\cos\theta\cos^2\psi}{r^2\sec^2\psi}dz$$

* May be omitted in an introductory course.

The illumination due to the whole strip of width ds and of infinite length, is

$$E = \frac{2L\ ds\ \cos\theta}{\pi r^2} \int_0^\infty \cos^4\psi\ dz$$

But
$$z = r \tan\psi$$
$$dz = r \sec^2\psi\ d\psi$$

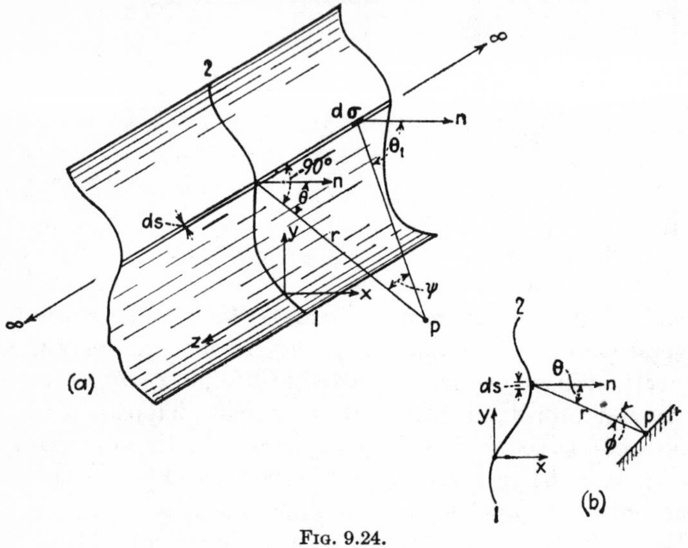

Fig. 9.24.

so

$$E = \frac{2L\ ds\ \cos\theta}{\pi r} \int_0^{\frac{\pi}{2}} \cos^2\psi\ d\psi$$
$$= \frac{L\ ds\ \cos\theta}{\pi r}\left[\psi + \frac{1}{2}\sin 2\psi\right]_0^{\frac{\pi}{2}}$$
$$= \frac{L}{2}\frac{\cos\theta\ ds}{r} \tag{9.22}$$

A cross section is shown in Fig. 9.24*b*, with the luminous surface at 1-2 and the illuminated surface at *P*. Equation (9.22) applies only for $\varphi = 0$. For other values of φ, the illumination due to the element ds, of infinite length, is

$$E = \frac{L}{2}\frac{\cos\theta\ \cos\varphi\ ds}{r}$$

The total illumination from the whole surface 1-2 is given by the line integral

$$E = \frac{L}{2}\int_1^2 \frac{\cos\theta\,\cos\psi\,ds}{r} \tag{9.23}$$

The expression (9.23) may be used to obtain the illumination due to a surface source of infinite length and of any desired contour 1-2. Note that only a single integration is required instead of the double integration, such as Eq. (9.13).

Example. What is the illumination on a vertical plane at P (Fig. 9.14) due to a continuous line of windows of height H and extending to a great distance in both directions?

Here

$$\varphi = \theta$$
$$r = D\sec\theta$$
$$ds = dy = D\sec^2\theta\,d\theta$$

If we make these substitutions in Eq. (9.23)

$$E = \frac{L}{2}\int_0^\gamma \frac{\cos^2\theta\cdot D\sec^2\theta\,d\theta}{D\sec\theta}$$
$$= \frac{L}{2}\sin\gamma \tag{9.24}$$

The same result is obtainable from Eq. (9.18) by letting $W\to\infty$.

Problem 93. Show that the illumination from a window of luminosity L, height H, and extending to infinity in both directions is given by Eq. (9.24). Use Eq. (9.18).

Problem 94. A long corridor is lighted by a half-circular cylinder of radius R of diffusing glass set in the ceiling with the concave surface downward and having a uniform luminosity L due to lamps placed above it. Derive an expression for the illumination at a point in the floor directly beneath the axis of the half cylinder.

9.09. Sources of Nonuniform Luminosity.*—All the preceding work in this chapter has been limited to sources of uniform luminosity. In fact, practically all the theoretical investigations which have ever been made have been based on this same assumption. It sometimes happens, however, that the departure from uniformity is so marked that the assumptions of uniform L will not give even an approximation to the true illumination. Then one can imagine the source to be divided into a number of

* May be omitted in an introductory course.

sections, for each of which the luminosity is assumed to be uniform at its average value. Such a method is still an approximation, but one that can be made as close as desired by increasing the number of sections.

Another way is to derive exact expressions for the illumination with nonuniform L, just as was done with uniform L. Suppose that we consider a rectangular source with luminosity a known function of y. Such sources are often found in practice. A cloudy sky seen through a window, for instance, is of essentially uniform luminosity from side to side (independent of x) but varies from top to bottom of the window. Thus the calculation of the daytime illumination from windows, the ordinary methods of the preceding paragraphs being used, is an approximation. Similarly, one frequently wishes to calculate the illumination caused by luminous flux reflected from a wall of the room; and the luminosity of a wall is usually constant on any horizontal line but decreases in a marked manner from top to bottom of the wall. Such a distribution can be represented by a power series

$$L = L_0 + L_1 y + L_2 y^2 + \cdots \tag{9.25}$$

The coefficients $(L_0, L_1 \ldots)$ are empirical values obtained from the experimental or calculated curve of L for the source in question. To obtain the illumination due to a source of nonuniform luminosity, an integral similar to (9.13) is required for each term of (9.25).

Thus for the $(n + 1)$st term of Eq. (9.25), the illumination at P (Fig. 9.14) on a plane parallel to the source is

$$E_z = \frac{L_n D^2}{\pi} \int_0^H \int_0^W \frac{y^n dx\, dy}{[D^2 + y^2 + x^2]^2} \tag{9.26}$$

For a point on the floor,

$$E_y = \frac{L_n D}{\pi} \int_0^H \int_0^W \frac{y^{n+1} dx\, dy}{[D^2 + y^2 + x^2]^2} \tag{9.27}$$

For a point on a plane perpendicular to the floor and passing through a vertical edge of the source,

$$E_x = \frac{L_n D}{\pi} \int_0^H \int_0^W \frac{x y^n dx\, dy}{[D^2 + y^2 + x^2]^2} \tag{9.28}$$

Note that

$$\frac{E_y}{L_n D^h} = \frac{E_z}{L_{n+1} D^{n+1}} \tag{9.29}$$

This relation reduces the number of integrations that must be made.

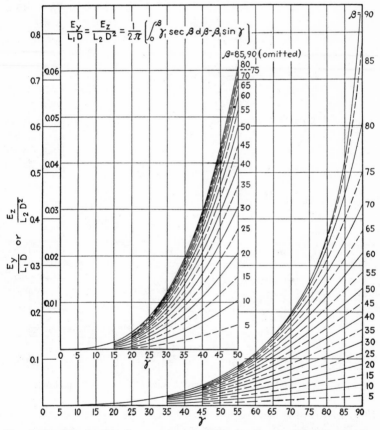

FIG. 9.25.—Illumination from rectangular sources of nonuniform luminosity.
(*C. F. Zee.*)

The integrations are similar to those of Sec. 9.06. In fact, a number of the integrals are evaluated there. C. F. Zee* has calculated values of the quantities $E_x/L_1 D$, $E_x/L_2 D^2$, $E_y/L_1 D = E_z/L_2 D^2$, $E_y/L_2 D^2 = E_z/L_3 D^3$, and has plotted the results in

* Rectangular Windows of Variable Luminosity, M.I.T. thesis, 1935.

Figs. 9.25 to 9.28, inclusive. The results are given as functions of β and γ, as was done for L_0 in Sec. 9.07.

Example. A window 6 ft wide and 8 ft high faces north. The sky is overcast and has a luminosity represented by the curve of Fig. 9.29. The following calculations are based on the data of H. H. Kimball (*I.E.S. Trans.*,

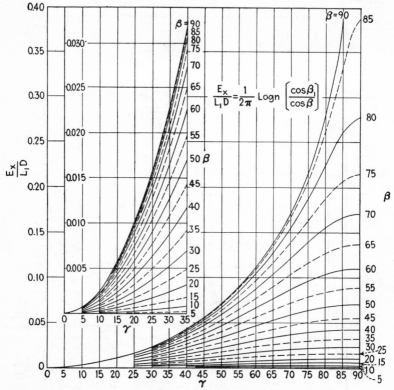

FIG. 9.26.—Illumination from rectangular sources of nonuniform luminosity.
(*C. F. Zee.*)

1921, p. 260, Fig. 8) and were computed by Zee. The illumination is desired at a point on a vertical plane at the level of the bottom of the window. The point is 10 ft from the window and is on a perpendicular erected at the window corner.

As shown in Fig. 9.29, the experimental curve of luminosity is closely approximated by

$$L = 1063 - 76y + 54.4y^2 - 4.33y^3$$

Also,

$$\beta = 31.0°, \qquad \gamma = 38.7°$$

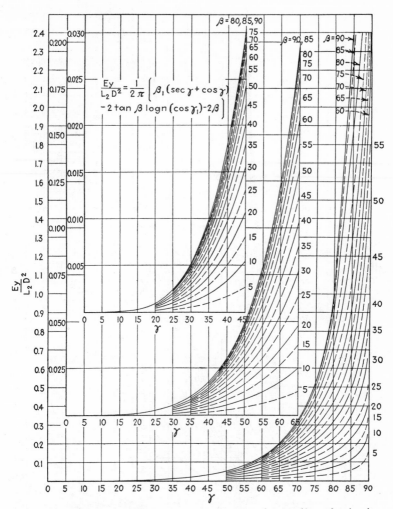

Fig. 9.27.—Illumination from rectangular sources of nonuniform luminosity.
(*C. F. Zee.*)

The values of the illumination components can be obtained from the curves
(Figs. 9.25 to 9.28) giving

$$\frac{E_z}{L_0} = 0.0947, ^* \qquad L_0 = 1063$$

* From Fig. 9.16.

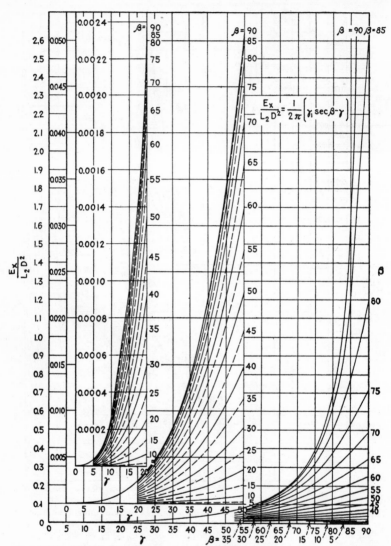

FIG. 9.28.—Illumination from rectangular sources of nonuniform luminosity.
(C. F. Zee.)

$$\frac{E_z}{L_1 D} = 0.033, \dagger \qquad L_1 = -76$$

$$\frac{E_z}{L_2 D^2} = 0.0158, \qquad L_2 = +54.4$$

$$\frac{E_z}{L_3 D^3} = \frac{E_y}{L_2 D^2} = 0.0093, \qquad L_3 = -4.33$$

Thus the illumination on a vertical   plane is

$$E_z = 1063(0.0947) - 76(0.033)10 + 54.4(0.0158)100 - 4.33(0.0093)1000$$
$$= \mathbf{121} \text{ lumens/sq ft}$$

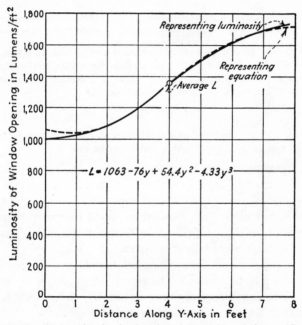

Fig. 9.29.—Luminosity of a cloudy sky viewed through a window.   (*C. F. Zee.*)

The average luminosity is 1360 lumens/sq ft, so if the window is considered to have a uniform L of this value,

$$E_z = 1360 \times 0.0947 = 129 \text{ lumens/sq ft}$$

Thus in this particular example the assumption of uniform luminosity gives practically the same result as the method of nonuniform luminosity. In some cases, however, the difference resulting from the use of the two methods may be much larger.

† From Fig. 9.17, since $\dfrac{E_z}{L_1 D} = \dfrac{E_y}{L_0}$.

Problem 95. Measurements made on a cloudy day gave the following data on sky luminosity:

Angle above Horizon θ (degrees)	L (Lumens/ square feet)
5	975
15	1250
25	1600
35	1730
45	1870
55	2020
65	2120
75	2080
85	2200

Calculate the illumination on a horizontal surface out of doors, using Figs. 9.25 to 9.28. Repeat on the assumption of constant luminosity.

Problem 96. A very long, perfectly diffusing, floodlighted wall, 20 ft in height, has a luminosity given by the equation

$$L = 0.0527y^2$$

What illumination is produced on the sidewalk at a point 8 ft from the base of the wall due to luminous flux reflected from the wall?

9.10. Illumination of Interiors.—Several methods of calculating illumination have been considered, all being classed as "point-by-point calculations." These methods of treatment allow us to calculate the illumination under any circumstances. In practice, we come upon various conditions which may be classified in the order of their complexity:

1. Sources of small dimensions relative to r. No reflection from floor, walls, or ceiling. The simplest case, requiring merely the use of the inverse-square law, Eq. (8.01), or Eq. (8.05).

2. Surface sources of comparatively large size.

    a. Windows, skylights, luminous panels. No reflections from floor, walls, or ceiling.

    b. Ceiling used as a source, illuminated by cove lights or by indirect luminaires. No reflection from walls or floor.

The methods of the present chapter are applied. If luminosity is uniform, the curves or formulas are used directly, or new ones are obtained by integration. If luminosity is nonuniform, integration may be used to derive new formulas, or the source may be divided into sections of essentially uniform luminosity.

3. Sources of any kind. Reflection from ceiling but none from walls or floor. Here we have a more complicated problem but

one that more closely simulates usual conditions.   The illumination direct from the luminaires, windows, or luminous panels is calculated as in (1) or (2).   The distribution of illumination on the ceiling is calculated in a similar manner, and the resulting luminosity is determined.   The illumination on the working plane, due to the ceiling, is now calculated, the ceiling being considered as a luminous-surface source.   The actual illumination is the sum of two components, one due directly to the luminaires, and the other caused by luminous flux reflected from the ceiling.   The calculations, though somewhat tedious, are perfectly straightforward.

4. The case of interreflections.   Suppose that condition 3 is changed slightly by assuming a small amount of reflection from the floor.   This reflected flux will increase the average luminosity of the ceiling and change the luminosity distribution, which will alter the illumination of the floor, which in turn will cause a further increment in ceiling luminosity.   Thus a slight change in the problem enormously increases its complexity and eliminates the possibility of a straightforward solution.   The final result is obtained by successive approximations.

-If the walls have a high reflection factor, the problem is even more complicated, though a solution is possible as shown by the work of A. D. Moore.*   A much more elegant method is the use of integral equations (Chap. X), though this treatment has not been developed thoroughly as yet.   In practice, the accuracy required in the calculations is not very great.   Also, floors are generally dark, and walls are broken up by windows, doors, pictures, bookcases, etc., so that the luminous flux reflected by the walls is not very important.   Thus in many practical cases it is permissible to neglect reflections from the walls and floor. It is very important, however, that the illuminating engineer recognize the approximations that he is making; for there are conditions, such as the illumination of light courts with white-tile walls, where the actual illumination will be many times the value calculated neglecting interreflections.

Example.   A small room (Fig. 9.30) is lighted by a single 300-watt, semi-indirect luminaire whose distribution curve is shown in Fig. 8.02. What is the illumination on a plane 30 in. above the floor?

---

* Interreflection by the Increment Method, *I.E.S. Trans.*, **24,** 1929, p. 629.

For simplicity, walls and floor will be considered to have zero reflection factor. The problem is thus a straightforward one (class 3). Since, according to Fig. 8.02, the distribution is symmetrical about the luminaire axis, it seems natural to divide the ceiling into circular zones and determine the flux in each. If several luminaires were used, a division into rectangles would be preferable probably.

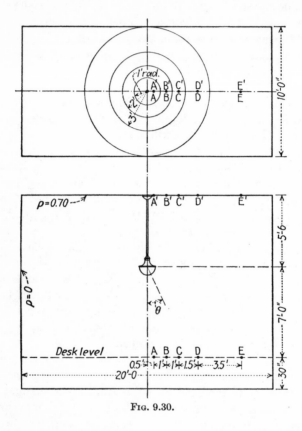

Fig. 9.30.

A circular division with arbitrary diameters (Fig. 9.30) requires the calculation of ceiling illumination at the five points A', B', C', D', E', as tabulated at the top of page 287. The illumination at A', for example, is

$$E = \frac{250}{(5.5)^2}0.987 = 8.16 \text{ lumens/sq ft}$$

Since the illumination is fairly uniform except at the extreme ends of the room, it will probably be satisfactory to consider the whole ceiling as a

ILLUMINATION OF CEILING

Point	θ	$I(\theta)$ (candles)	$\cos^3 \theta$	E (lumens/ sq ft)	Area (sq ft)	F (lumens)
A'	174.8°	250	0.987	8.16	π	8.2π
B'	164.7	325	0.897	9.64	3 π	28.9π
C'	155.5	460	0.753	11.45	5 π	57.3π
D'	144.0	630	0.530	11.04	16 π	176.6π
E'	126.4	790	0.209	5.46	38.7π	211.3π

Total $= 482.3\pi$

single source of uniform luminosity. The average illumination of the ceiling is

$$E_{av} = \frac{F}{A}$$

and cannot be obtained by averaging the foregoing values of E, since the areas of the various rings are different. The total flux on the ceiling is $482.3\pi = 1515$ lumens, and the average ceiling illumination is

$$E_{av} = {}^{1515}\!/_{200} = 7.57 \text{ lumens/sq ft}$$

The average luminosity of the ceiling is

$$L_{av} = 7.57 \times 0.70 = 5.30 \text{ lumens/sq ft}$$

We now consider the ceiling as a uniform source and tabulate the resulting illumination on the desk level as follows:

ILLUMINATION DUE TO LUMINOUS CEILING

Point	β		E/L		E/L (total)	E (lumens/ sq ft)
	Left	Right	Left	Right		
A	40.0°	37.2°	0.069	0.066	0.135	1.43
B	42.6	34.2	0.072	0.063	0.135	1.43
C	45.0	31.0	0.075	0.057	0.132	1.40
D	48.2	25.6	0.077	0.049	0.126	1.34
E	54.5	11.3	0.084	0.022	0.106	1.12

The ceiling has been divided in each case into four panels with

$$\gamma = \tan^{-1} \frac{5}{12.5} = 21.8 \text{ deg}$$

in all cases and with the tabulated values of β. The final values of E are obtained by adding E/L for right and left panels, multiplying by 2 $\times$ 5.30. The illumination due to the ceiling is very uniform, varying from 1.12 to 1.43 lumens/sq ft.

The direct illumination from the luminaire itself is found by using the data from Fig. 8.02.

DIRECT ILLUMINATION FROM LUMINAIRE

Point	θ	$I(\theta)$ (candles)	$\cos^3 \theta$	E (direct)	E (total) (lumens/sq ft)
A	4.0°	220	0.993	4.45	5.88
B	12.0	210	0.936	4.00	5.43
C	19.6	210	0.836	3.59	4.99
D	29.7	190	0.656	2.54	3.88
E	47.0	180	0.317	1.17	2.29

The fifth column gives the illumination due to direct flux from the luminaire, while the sixth gives total values including the effect of the luminous ceiling. Note that the direct illumination varies through a range of almost 4 to 1; but the total illumination, because of the uniformity of the ceiling component, varies by only 2.6 to 1.

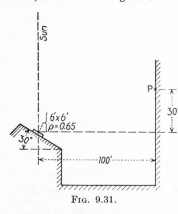

FIG. 9.31.

Problem 97. *a.* A trap door (Fig. 9.31) 6 by 6 ft in a sloping black roof is painted with aluminum paint having reflection factor of 0.65. What is the illumination at P on the wall due to the sun directly overhead? The illumination on a horizontal surface is 8000 lumens/sq ft. Neglect illumination from the sky and assume that the aluminum paint gives a perfectly diffusing surface.

b If a sheet of polished aluminum (reflection factor = 0.65) had been used instead of the matt door surface, what would be the maximum illumination on the wall?

Problem 98. Correct the following description of an automobile showroom:

"This luxurious automobile display room is lighted from above by specially designed luminaires mounted flush in the ceiling. The job consists of 110 units with three 200-watt lamps per unit. Each unit emits a light flux of 320 cp and a brightness of 900 lumens. With all the lamps turned on, the average intensity of light on the sales floor is 70 ft/candle. The buff plastered walls present a pleasing contrast to the brightly colored cars on display. By using a glass area 3 sq ft per unit, the luminosity of

TABLE XXXIV.—REFLECTION FACTORS

For radiation from incandescent lamps incident on surface at 45 deg. in most cases. Values depend greatly upon condition of the surface. The values are generally maximum test results.

Material	ρ	ρ_λ (0.2967μ)	Authority
Metals:			
Aluminum, mill finish	0.53	0.33	Taylor[10] (1934)
surfaced on lathe	0.82	0.78	Taylor[10] (1934)
highly polished	0.72	0.56	Taylor[10] (1934)
highly polished	0.68	....	Paulus & Woodside[8]
etched	0.85	0.82	Taylor[10] (1934)
polished and electrolytically bright-			
ened	0.85	0.69	Taylor[10] (1934)
alumilited	0.88	0.74	Taylor[10] (1934)
Alzak finish, diffusing	0.78	0.58	Taylor[11] (1935)
specular	0.84	0.69	Taylor[11] (1935)
Aluminum foil, plain	0.85	0.64	Taylor[11] (1935)
Sprayed aluminum	0.64	0.65	Taylor[10] (1934)
Aluminum paint	0.75	0.65	Taylor[10] (1934)
Chromium plate	0.66	0.58	Taylor[10] (1934)
Nickel plate	0.63	0.34	Taylor[10] (1934)
Silver plate	0.90	0.13	Taylor[10] (1934)
Silver-plated glass	0.80–0.90	0.04	Taylor[11] (1935)
Tin plate	0.70	0.10	Taylor[11] (1935)
Chromium steel, polished	0.62	....	Taylor[10] (1934)
Stainless steel	0.65	0.30	Taylor[10] (1934)
Allegheny metal	0.60	0.36	Taylor[10] (1934)
Rhodium	0.78	0.45	Taylor[10] (1934)
Eraydo	0.66	0.52	Taylor[10] (1934)
Sprayed cadmium	0.52	0.25	Taylor[10] (1934)
Water Paints:			
Alabastine, white	0.76	0.26	Taylor[10] (1934)
No. 6, cream	0.74	0.25	Taylor[10] (1934)
Devoe kalsomine, white	0.75	0.35	Taylor[10] (1934)
Decotint, white	0.75	0.40	Taylor[10] (1934)
Oil Paints:			
White lead paint, flat	0.80	0.27	Taylor[10] (1934)
Inside white paint, gloss	0.85	0.07	Taylor[10] (1934)
eggshell	0.86	0.09	Taylor[10] (1934)
flat	0.86	0.10	Taylor[10] (1934)
Wall paint, light green	0.69	....	Gamble[7]
light yellow	0.74	....	Gamble[7]
light pink	0.62	....	Gamble[7]
gray	0.68	....	Gamble[7]
Miscellaneous:			
Porcelain-enameled steel	0.75	0.08	Taylor[10] (1934)
Porcelain-enameled steel	0.75	....	Paulus & Woodside[8]
White Plaster	0.65	....	Tyndall
White Plaster	0.85	....	Paulus & Woodside[8]
White Plaster	0.90	0.50	Taylor[10] (1934)
Magnesium oxide	0.98	0.95	Taylor[10] (1934)
Magnesium carbonate	0.98	0.80	Taylor[10] (1934)

TABLE XXXIV.—REFLECTION FACTORS.—(*Continued*)

Material	ρ	ρ_λ (0.2967μ)	Authority
Miscellaneous—(*Continued*)			
Magnesium carbonate..................	0.98	....	Tyndall
Snow...............................	0.93	....	Tyndall
Black velvet........................	0.01	....	Tyndall
Green leaves........................	0.25	....	Tyndall
Ink................................	.01–.04	....	Tyndall
Science Abstracts....................	0.62	....	Tyndall
Saturday Evening Post................	0.63	0.21	Taylor[11] (1935)
Newspaper..........................	0.50	0.07	Taylor[10] (1934)
Munsell cards, gray, N9..............	0.74	....	Tyndall
N7.............................	0.47	....	Tyndall
N5.............................	0.24	....	Tyndall
N3.............................	0.09	....	Tyndall
N1.............................	0.02	....	Tyndall
Rockwool, gray......................	0.45	....	Powell & Dows[3]
Acoustex, white.....................	0.68	....	Powell & Dows[3]
cream..........................	0.62	....	Powell & Dows[3]
Acousti-Celotex, plain................	0.36	....	Powell & Dows[3]
¼ in. holes.....................	0.32	....	Powell & Dows[3]
Corkoustic, natural color..............	0.08	....	Powell & Dows[3]
white..........................	0.66	....	Powell & Dows[3]
with Alabastine No. 26............	0.71	....	Powell & Dows[3]
Insulite, cream......................	0.59	....	Powell & Dows[3]
Macoustic, white....................	0.54	....	Powell & Dows[3]
Masonite, natural color...............	0.15	....	Powell & Dows[3]
Presdwood, brown....................	0.13	....	Powell & Dows[3]
U.S.G. Acoustical tile, brown...........	0.44	....	Powell & Dows[3]
white..........................	0.54	....	Powell & Dows[3]
cream..........................	0.41	....	Powell & Dows[3]
Acoustico, white plaster..............	0.76	....	Powell & Dows[3]
Acoustolith white plaster.............	0.58	....	Powell & Dows[3]
Sabinite white plaster................	0.46	....	Powell & Dows[3]
Glass, clear, hammered...............	0.075		
sandblasted.....................	0.285		
Flashed opal....................	0.37		
solid opal......................	0.56		

the glass is cut down to a value of 300 lumens/sq ft to prevent glare. In order to eliminate shadows and illuminate the under parts of the cars to an intensity of 5 or 10 lumens, footlights are mounted under the windows."

Problem 99. A night club 60 ft square is lighted by a luminous panel 20 ft square over the dance floor. The room has a 14-ft ceiling; the panel is in the center of the room, flush with the ceiling; and walls and ceiling have low reflection factors. The luminosity of the panel is 50 lumens/sq. ft. Draw an isolux map for the floor of the room.

Problem 100. Repeat Prob. 99 but with a circular panel of radius 10 ft having a luminosity

$$L = 10 + 9.0\xi \quad \text{(lumens/sq ft)}$$

where ξ = the distance in feet from the center of the panel.

Problem 101. The room of Fig. 9.20 has been changed so that the reflection factor of the walls is 0.58. Plot the illumination along the line *ABCD*. Neglect interreflections between walls and between luminous panel and walls.

Problem 102. A very long corridor 9 by 9 ft has perfectly diffusing walls of reflection factor 0.37. Ceiling and floor are assumed to be perfectly absorbing. The corridor is lighted by a continuous line of 60-watt Lumiline lamps without reflectors mounted in the middle of the ceiling. Plot the curve of illumination on the floor.

TABLE XXXV.—Transmission Factors

For radiation from incandescent lamps, normal incidence

Material	τ	$\tau\lambda$ (0.3μ)	Authority
Vimlite (wire screen filled with cellulose acetate).............	0.52	0.43	Paulus & Woodside[8]
Cellulose acetate (cloudy).......	0.02–0.42	....	Paulus & Woodside[8]
Urea formaldehyde.............	0.03–0.35	....	Paulus & Woodside[8]
Casein formaldehyde...........	0.46	....	Paulus & Woodside[8]
Solid opal glass................	0.30	....	Paulus & Woodside[8]
Solid opal glass................	0.34–0.60	....	Paulus & Woodside[8]
Flashed opal glass..............	0.40–0.68	....	Paulus & Woodside[8]
Cellulose acetate (etched).......	0.80	....	Paulus & Woodside[8]
Glass, acid etched, one surface...	0.73	....	Paulus & Woodside[8]
double ground..............	0.60		
flashed opal................	0.42		
sandblasted................	0.62		
Silverite	0.75–0.91		
hammered..................	0.80–0.91		
Fused quartz, clear, new........	0.92	0.92	Coblentz, *Bu. Stds. J.R.*, **3**, 1929, p. 644
Corex, D, new................	0.92	0.61	Coblentz, *Bu. Stds. J.R.*, **3**, 1929, p. 644
Neuglas, new.................	0.92	0.63	Coblentz, *Bu. Stds. J.R.*, **3**, 1929, p. 644
Uviol-Jena, new...............	0.92	0.58	Coblentz, *Bu. Stds. J.R.*, **3**, 1929, p. 644
Helioglass...................	0.92	0.58	Coblentz, *Bu. Stds. J.R.*, **3**, 1929, p. 644
Vitaglass....................	0.92	0.48	Coblentz, *Bu. Stds. J.R.*, **3**, 1929, p. 644
Cel-o-glass..................	....	0.30	Coblentz, *Bu. Stds. J.R.*, **3**, 1929, p. 644
Quartzlite...................	0.92	0.005	Coblentz, *Bu. Stds. J.R.*, **3**, 1929, p. 644
Common window glass..........	0.92	0.000	Coblentz, *Bu. Stds. J.R.*, **3**, 1929, p. 644

Table XXXVI.—Light Distribution from Diffusing Glass
(Report of I.E.S. Committee on Illuminating Glasses, 1933)
$I(\theta)/I_0$(per cent)

θ (degrees)	Factro-lite	Ham-mered	Tapes-try	Maze	Silver-ite	Sand-blasted (2 sides)	Flashed opal	Solid opal	Cos θ
0	100	100	100	100	100	100	100	100	100
2.5	86	60	85	91	85	94	100	100	99.9
5.0	63	12	57	64	53	87	99	100	99.6
7.5	33	0.3	30	44	32	81	99	99	99.2
10.0	8.5	0.1	15.5	26	26	74	97	98	98.5
12.5	2.2	0.0	8.7	17	21	65	96	98	97.6
15.0	0.6	....	2.4	7.7	17	52	94	97	96.6
17.5	0.0	....	0.9	3.1	11	39	93	97	95.4
20.0	....	....	0.0	0.5	7.7	32	90	96	94.0
25	....	....	....	0.0	2.9	26	85	95	90.6
30	....	....	....	....	0.6	13	83	91	86.6
40	....	....	....	....	0.0	6	75	77	76.6
50	....	....	....	....	....	3	60	64	64.3

Relative Values of I_0 (Per Cent)

Factrolite.. 100
Hammered.. 212
Tapestry.. 57.5
Maze.. 39.0
Silverite.. 35.0
Sandblasted.. 3.1
Flashed opal.. 0.67
Solid opal.. 0.44

All tests made with light from concentrated source striking glass normal to surface.

Bibliography

Reflection and Transmission

1. H. J. McNicholas: Absolute Methods in Reflectometry, *Bu. Stds. J.R.*, **1**, 1928, p. 29.
2. Powell and Kellogg: Reflecting Properties of White Interior Paints of Varying Compositions, *I.E.S. Trans.*, **21**, 1926, p. 70.
3. Powell and Dows: Light Reflection Factors of Acoustical Materials, *I.E.S. Trans.*, **25**, 1930, p. 882.
4. J. S. Preston: The Reflection Factor of Magnesium Oxide, *Opt. Soc., Trans.*, **31**, 1929–1930, p. 15.
5. A. H. Taylor: Measurement of Reflection Factors in the U.V., *J.O.S.A.*, **21**, 1931, p. 776.
6. Luckiesh and Holladay: Paints for Reflecting Biologically Important U.V. Radiation, *Frank. Inst., J.*, **212**, 1931, p. 787.
7. D. L. Gamble: Reflecting Characteristics of Wall Paints, *I.E.S. Trans.*, **28**, 1933, p. 326.
8. Paulus and Woodside: Illumination Characteristics of Organic Plastics, *I.E.S. Trans.*, **28**, 1933, p. 749.

9. J. D. EDWARDS: Aluminum for Reflectors, *I.E.S. Trans.*, **29**, 1934, p. 351.

10. A. H. TAYLOR: Reflection Factors of Various Materials, *J.O.S.A.*, **24**, 1934, p. 192.

11. A. H. TAYLOR: Light and Ultraviolet Reflection by Various Materials, *I.E.S. Trans.*, **30**, 1935, p. 563.

12. T. K. CHINMAYANANDAM: On the Specular Reflection from Rough Surfaces, *Phys. Rev.*, **13**, 1919, p. 96.

13. E. M. BERRY: Diffuse Reflection of Light, *J.O.S.A.*, **7**, 1923, p. 627.

14. M. COHU: La détermination des caractéristiques réfléchissantes, *R.G.E.*, **35**, 1934, p. 147.

15. G. PERI: Illuminazione e luminosità delle strade, *Elettrotecnica*, **15**, 1928, p. 263.

16. P. S. MILLAR: Brightness of Street Surface as an Element of Effectiveness in Street Lighting, *I.E.S. Trans.*, **23**, 1928, p. 1051.

CALCULATION OF ILLUMINATION

17. E. P. HYDE: Geometrical Theory of Radiating Surfaces, *Bu. Stds. Bull.*, **3**, 1907, p. 81.

18. E. B. ROSA: Photometric Units and Nomenclature, *Bu. Stds. Bull.*, **6**, 1910, p. 543.

19. B. JONES: On Finite Surface Light Sources. *I.E.S. Trans.*, **4**, 1909; **5**, 1910, p. 281.

20. J. C. POLE: Photometry of Mercury-vapor Lamps, *I.E.S. Trans.*, **6**, 1911, p. 306.

21. P. D. FOOTE: Illumination from a Radiating Disk, *Bu. Stds. Bull.*, **12**, 1916, p. 583.

22. Z. YAMAUTI: Geometrical Calculation of Illumination, *Electrot. Lab. Tokyo, Researches*, 148, 1924.

23. Z. YAMAUTI: Further Study of Geometrical Calculation of Illumination, *Electrot. Lab. Tokyo, Researches*, 194, 1927.

24. H. H. HIGBIE: Lighting Calculations, Chap. V, John Wiley & Sons, Inc., New York, 1934.

25. HIGBIE and LEVIN: Prediction of Daylight from Sloping Windows, *I.E.S. Trans.*, **21**, 1926, p. 273.

26. HIGBIE and SZYMANOWSKI: Calculation of Daylighting by Protractor Method, *I.E.S. Trans.*, **25**, 1930, p. 213.

27. HIGBIE and BYCHINSKY: Illumination Distribution Measurements from Surface Sources in Sidewalls, *I.E.S. Trans.*, **29**, 1934, p. 206.

28. H. H. HIGBIE: Illumination Distribution from Surface Sources in Rooms, *I.E.S. Trans.*, **31**, 1936, p. 163.

29. W. TURNER-SZYMANOWSKI: A Rapid Method for Predicting the Distribution of Daylight in Buildings, *Dept. of Eng. Res., U. of Mich. Bull.* 17, 1931.

CHAPTER X

SHORT CUTS IN CALCULATING ILLUMINATION*

Chapter IX has treated the important subject of the calculation of illumination from surface sources. The fundamental method of surface integration has been used and has been applied to various forms of surface sources, of both uniform and nonuniform luminosity. Theoretically, the surface-integration method can always be applied, but it often leads to integrals that are difficult to evaluate. Various short cuts have been developed from time to time, which in certain special cases allow the illuminating engineer to obtain the desired result very easily—in some cases by mere inspection or by simple arithmetic. While most of these short cuts do not have the generality of the surface-integration method, they will be found of real value where they do apply. In the present chapter, therefore, the subject of surface sources is continued, and special methods of calculation are developed.

10.02. The Unit-sphere Method.—In Chap. IX we have seen that the illumination from a rectangular source can be expressed in terms of the two angles (β and γ) subtended by the source, the distance and the size of the source not appearing in the final formulas. One might suspect this to be a manifestation of a more general law, as in fact it is. Consider the perfectly diffusing surface source S of Fig. 10.01. The illumination at P due to an element of surface $d\sigma$ is

$$dE = \frac{L\,d\sigma}{\pi} \frac{\cos\,\theta\,\cos\,\psi}{r^2} \tag{10.01}$$

But since the solid angle $d\Omega$ is equal to the area $d\sigma'$ cut out on a sphere of unit radius about P,

$$d\Omega = d\sigma' = \frac{d\sigma\,\cos\,\theta}{r^2}$$

* May be omitted in an introductory course.

Substitution in (10.01) gives

$$dE = \frac{L}{\pi} \, d\Omega \cos \psi \qquad (10.02)$$

or

$$dE = \frac{L}{\pi} \, d\sigma' \cos \psi \qquad (10.03)$$

Equation (10.03) allows a simple geometrical interpretation as shown in Fig. 10.01. Each element $d\sigma$ of the source produces an illumination at P equal to L/π times the area $d\sigma'$ projected on a plane tangent to the receiving surface at P. Thus dE/L due to

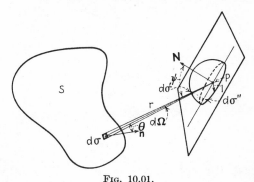

FIG. 10.01.

the element $d\sigma$ is equal to $1/\pi$ times the area $d\sigma''$. Also, if $L = \text{const.}$, the value of E/L for the entire surface S is merely equal to $1/\pi$ times the projection of the total area cut out of the unit sphere by a cone whose base is S and whose apex is at P.*

The important contribution of this analysis is that the source itself has disappeared from the calculations and may be forgotten. We may concentrate our attention on conditions at the point where the illumination is desired. The value of the illumination for any perfectly diffusing source of uniform luminosity is

$$E = \frac{L}{\pi} \int \cos \psi \, d\Omega$$

or

$$E = \frac{L}{\pi} \int d\sigma'' = \frac{L\sigma''}{\pi} \qquad (10.04)$$

*This area may be denoted by σ'', or $\sigma'' = \int d\sigma''$.

which, except for the value of L, requires no information concerning the source. The source may be near P or far away and may have a boundary that is or is not a plane curve. The surface of the source may be plane or curved or crinkled in any manner whatsoever. The value of E/L will be the same as long as the area σ'' is the same.

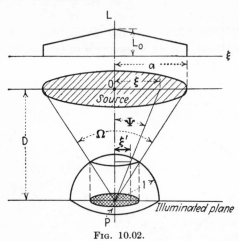

Fig. 10.02.

The method also applies if $L \neq$ const. By the use of Eq. (10.03)

$$E = \frac{1}{\pi}\int L \cos\psi \, d\sigma' = \frac{1}{\pi}\int L \, d\sigma'' \qquad (10.05)$$

This *unit-sphere* method is often useful in visualizing a problem and in estimating the illumination. In most cases, however, it does not lend itself readily to numerical calculation.

As an example whose simplicity is such that the unit-sphere method is advantageous, consider a circular disk source (Fig. 10.02). First assume the luminosity to be uniform over the surface. By Eq. (10.04),

$$\frac{E}{L} = \frac{1}{\pi}\int d\sigma'' = \frac{1}{\pi} \cdot \text{(shaded area on horizontal plane)}$$

The shaded area on the illuminated plane is

$$\pi\left(\frac{a}{\sqrt{D^2 + a^2}}\right)^2 = \frac{\pi a^2}{D^2 + a^2}$$

and

$$E_z = L\left(\frac{a^2}{D^2 + a^2}\right) \tag{10.06}$$

This is the same result as obtained in Chap. IX by integrating over the surface of the source. It will be noted that this method evaluates the integral and gives the result very simply by the use of ordinary geometry.

If the luminosity of the disk is nonuniform, Eq. (10.05) is used. For example, let

$$L = L_0 + L_1\xi$$

The luminosity is the same for all points for which $\psi = $ const., and

$$\xi'' = \frac{\xi}{\sqrt{D^2 + \xi^2}}$$

$$d\sigma'' = 2\pi\xi'' \, d\xi'' = 2\pi D^2 \frac{\xi \, d\xi}{(D^2 + \xi^2)^2}$$

Thus from Eq. (10.05),

$$E = 2D^2L_1\int_0^a \frac{\xi^2 \, d\xi}{(D^2 + \xi^2)^2} = D^2L_1\left[\frac{1}{D}\tan^{-1}\frac{a}{D} - \frac{a}{D^2 + a^2}\right] \tag{10.07}$$

Equation (10.07) gives the component of illumination caused by the term $L_1\xi$. The total illumination at P is, of course, the sum of that given by Eq. (10.07) and that given by (10.06) with $L = L_0$. In this particular case of nonuniform luminosity, the unit-sphere method has no advantages over the direct-integration method.

As another example, what is the illumination at P (Fig. 10.03)

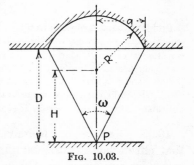

Fig. 10.03.

from a perfectly diffusing ceiling dome of uniform luminosity L? The dome is in the form of a portion of a sphere of radius R. Since the illumination depends only upon the light cone with P as vertex, the illumination in this case is exactly the same as that obtained from a circular disk of the same luminosity and having the same boundary as the dome, or

$$E = L\left(\frac{a^2}{a^2 + D^2}\right) = \frac{L}{2}(1 - \cos \omega) \qquad (10.06)$$

where the result can be expressed in a form that does not contain D, a, R, or H. The replacing disk need not be visualized as of radius a but may be of any size provided it is placed at the proper distance so that it fits into the same light cone.

Problem 103. A dance floor is illuminated by a circular ring-shaped coffer built into the ceiling (Fig. 10.04) and lighted indirectly by lamps along the sides of the coffer. The luminous surface is perfectly diffusing and of uniform luminosity $L = 100$ lumens/sq ft. What is the illumination on the dance floor at P?

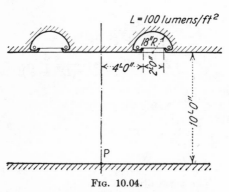

FIG. 10.04.

Problem 104. A piece of iron pipe 5 cm inside diameter and 20 cm long is wound with resistance wire in such a way that in operation each square centimeter of inside surface radiates the same power. Considering the inside surface to be perfectly diffusing, compute the irradiation on a plane perpendicular to the axis at a point on the axis of the pipe 10 cm from its end. The radiosity of the inside of the tube is 2.5 watts/sq cm.

Problem 105. Repeat Prob. 87 (Chap. IX), using the unit-sphere method.

10.03. The Sumpner Method.—Another scheme of calculation that effects considerable simplification in some cases was suggested by Sumpner[6,7] in 1893 and has been developed further by Bartlett, McAllister, and others. Consider a black sphere of radius R, the inside being perfectly *absorbing* except for a small area $d\sigma$ which has the luminosity L. The value of the illumination is desired at an arbitrary point P on the sphere. The three points A, O, and P determine a plane whose intersection with the sphere gives the great circle of Fig. 10.05.

The intensity in the direction AP of the luminous element $d\sigma$ is

$$I(\theta) = I_0 \cos \theta = \frac{L \, d\sigma}{\pi} \cos \theta$$

and the resulting illumination at P is

$$E = \frac{I(\theta)}{(2R \cos \theta)^2} \cos \theta = \frac{L \, d\sigma}{S} \qquad (10.08)$$

where S = total area of sphere. But Eq. (10.08) shows that the illumination at the arbitrary point P is independent of θ, and therefore *the illumination is the same at all points on the surface of the sphere.*

If the luminous element $d\sigma$ be replaced by another element of area $d\sigma'$ and luminosity L', situated anywhere on the spherical surface, the illumination at any point P, due to $d\sigma'$, is

$$E' = \frac{L' \, d\sigma'}{S}$$

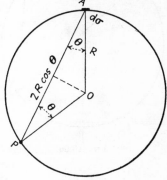

Fig. 10.05.

If, now, both elements are used simultaneously, they will no longer have exactly their former values of luminosity. Owing to interreflections, both luminosities will be slightly higher—say L_1 and L_1', respectively. The illumination at P will be

$$E = \frac{1}{S}(L_1 \, d\sigma + L_1' \, d\sigma')$$

and *remains independent of the position of P.* In the same way, any number of elements of the sphere wall may be made luminous, and the resulting illumination will always remain independent of the position of P. The same conclusion applies if the elements are allowed to fuse together to form a continuous portion of spherical surface.

As a special case, consider a portion ANB of spherical surface as formed by passing a plane through the sphere (Fig. 10.06). The surface is perfectly diffusing, and the luminosity is adjusted to a uniform value L throughout. The rest of the sphere is absolutely black. We wish to find the value of the illumination at P due to this luminous cap ANB. According to the principle enunciated in the preceding section, the illumination from the cap will be exactly the same as that from a circular source AB of the same luminosity L and having the same boundary as the spherical portion ANB. The Sumpner-sphere method allows

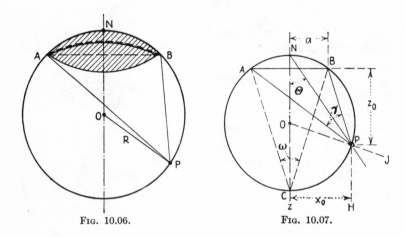

Fɪɢ. 10.06.   Fɪɢ. 10.07.

us to obtain an expression for the illumination at any point due to a circular disk and to obtain it in an absolutely rigorous manner without the use of calculus.

Consider the great circle formed by a plane containing the axis NC and the point P (Fig. 10.07). Before continuing, we state two geometrical theorems which hold for any circle.

Theorem I. The angle γ subtended by the constant arc AB is independent of the position of P on the circular arc below AB.

Theorem II. The line NP bisects the angle HPJ.

We have proved that the illumination at any point P on the sphere wall is the same as at any other point and thus is the same as at C.

$$E_P = E_C$$

By Eq. (10.06), the illumination at C is

$$E_c = L\left(\frac{a^2}{a^2 + D^2}\right)$$

Therefore,

$$E_P = L\left(\frac{a^2}{a^2 + D^2}\right) = \frac{L}{2}(1 - \cos \omega)$$

From Theorem I, $\omega = \gamma$, so the illumination at any point on the sphere wall is

$$E_w = \frac{L}{2}(1 - \cos \gamma) \tag{10.09}$$

where the subscript w has been used to emphasize the fact that we are considering the illumination on the sphere *wall*, not the illumination on the horizontal or vertical planes. According to Eq. (10.09), the simple formula which was previously derived for the special case of points on the axis of the disk holds for all points.

From Eq. (10.09),

$$\frac{E_w}{L} = \frac{1}{1 + \left(\dfrac{D}{a}\right)^2} \tag{10.10}$$

which is the basis of the circle diagram devised by McAllister.[8,9] Since E_w/L is the same for all points on a given sphere, any circle that passes through the point B and that has its center on the axis NC must be a circle of constant illumination, or an *isolux circle*. A series of such circles has been drawn in Fig. 10.08, and the values of E_w/L have been computed from Eq. (10.10). This circle diagram provides a very convenient way of obtaining the illumination from any perfectly diffusing disk source of uniform luminosity.

It will be proved later that E_w is equal to E_z, the illumination on a plane parallel to the disk; so the diagram may be used to obtain the illumination at any point on any plane parallel to the source. For any horizontal plane, values of E_z/L are obtained from the intersections of the plane with the various isolux circles. For a plane ($z_0 = 3a$), for instance, the intersections of

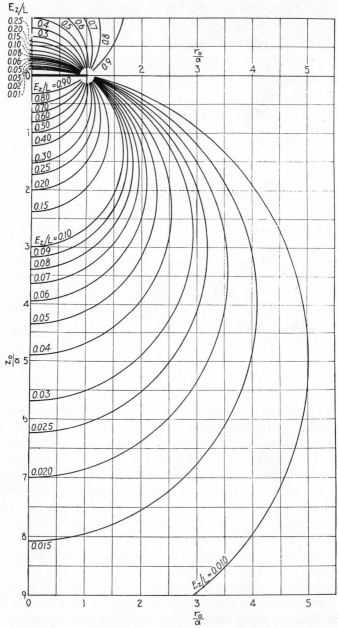

Fig. 10.08.—Circle diagram giving the illumination from a circular-disk source of radius a and luminosity L. r_0 = radial distance from axis of disk; z_0 = distance between illuminated plane and plane of disk.

the line ($z_0/a = 3$) and the circles give the curve shown in Fig. 10.09, where the illumination varies from $0.10L$ directly under the disk to approximately $0.015L$ at $r_0 = 4a$. A few other curves are also shown. Evidently, the circle diagram gives a

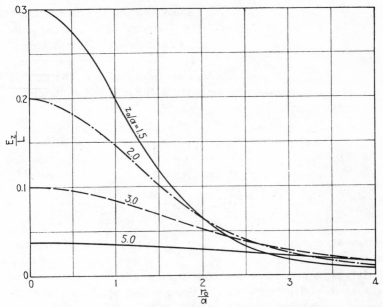

Fig. 10.09.—Illumination from a circular-disk source.

very simple method of obtaining values of illumination, and the results are generally sufficiently accurate for engineering purposes.

Problem 106. A mural painting 30 ft high and 40 ft wide is to be lighted by lamps concealed behind a circular disk of opal glass which is to be set into the opposite wall of the hall, 30 ft away. The axis of the disk passes through the center of the painting. How large a disk must be used so that the maximum illumination at any point on the mural shall not exceed the minimum by more than 50 per cent of the latter?

What glass luminosity must be used to obtain a maximum illumination of 10 lumens/sq ft on the painting?

Problem 107. Draw a circle diagram similar to Fig. 10.08, for $E_z/L = 0.01$ to $E_z/L = 0.001$.

Problem 108. Plot a curve of E_z/L vs r_0/a for a floor with $z_0/a = 4.0$. Draw the lines of equal illumination (isolux diagram).

10.04. The Vector Method.—A point source S is placed at the origin of a system of coordinates (Fig. 10.10). If the intensity of the source in the direction of P is I candles, the illumination at P on a surface parallel to the X-Y plane is

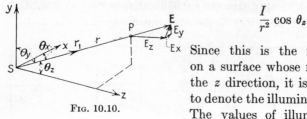

FIG. 10.10.

$$\frac{I}{r^2} \cos \theta_z$$

Since this is the illumination on a surface whose normal is in the z direction, it is convenient to denote the illumination by E_z. The values of illumination on the three planes whose normals are in the x, y, and z directions, respectively, are

$$\left.\begin{aligned} E_x &= \frac{I}{r^2} \cos \theta_x \\ E_y &= \frac{I}{r^2} \cos \theta_y \\ E_z &= \frac{I}{r^2} \cos \theta_z \end{aligned}\right\} \tag{10.11}$$

where θ_x, θ_y, and θ_z are the angles between the line SP and the three coordinate axes.

It will be noted that the coefficient of all the cosine terms is the same and is equal to the illumination at P on a surface normal to the line SP. Calling this value of illumination E_r,

$$E_r = \frac{I}{r^2}$$

and

$$\left.\begin{aligned} E_x &= E_r \cos \theta_x \\ E_y &= E_r \cos \theta_y \\ E_z &= E_r \cos \theta_z \end{aligned}\right\} \tag{10.12}$$

Evidently E_x, E_y, and E_z *are the components of a vector* whose magnitude is E_r and whose direction is from S to P. In vector notation,

$$\boldsymbol{E} = \boldsymbol{i}E_x + \boldsymbol{j}E_y + \boldsymbol{k}E_z \tag{10.13}$$

where $\boldsymbol{i}$, $\boldsymbol{j}$, and $\boldsymbol{k}$ are unit vectors pointing in the positive directions along the three coordinate axes. With $\boldsymbol{r}_1$ denoting a unit vector pointing from S to P (Fig. 10.10),

$$E = r_1 E_r = r_1 \frac{I}{r^2} \qquad (10.14)$$

For a surface source, each element $d\sigma$ provides an illumination vector dE at the point P, and the total illumination vector due to the entire source is the *vector* sum of all the component vectors. For a single element,

$$dE = r_1 \frac{L \cos \theta \, d\sigma}{\pi r^2}$$

where r_1 is a unit vector pointing from the particular element toward P. For the entire surface source,

$$E = \frac{1}{\pi} \int_S r_1 \frac{L \cos \theta \, d\sigma}{r^2} \qquad (10.15)$$

Knowing E, one can obtain its component in any direction by multiplying its magnitude by the cosine of the proper angle, Eq. (10.12). It thus becomes unnecessary to derive a separate formula for each plane on which the illumination is desired. The illumination on any plane is obtained by multiplying $|E|$ by the cosine of the angle between E and the inward-drawn normal to the illuminated surface. This fact constitutes the principal value of the vector method.

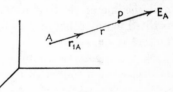

Fig. 10.11.

Perhaps a better picture of the illumination vector may be obtained by considering how it could be measured. Suppose that a source A (Fig. 10.11), is sending out luminous flux in all directions. Imagine a plane loop of wire inclosing one square centimeter of area and place it at P. A certain amount of luminous flux will pass through the wire loop, and the amount (expressed in lumens) will be the illumination (lumens per square centimeter) at P on a surface in the plane of the loop. If we imagine that we have some method of measuring the flux which passes through the loop, and if we turn the loop at P until a maximum amount of flux passes through it, this flux will equal the magnitude of the illumination vector, and the direction of the normal to the loop will give the direction of E. It seems reasonable to consider that E points in the direction of flow of radiant energy, or from A to P, rather than in the opposite direction. This convention will be used throughout the present work; and correspondingly, the inward-drawn normal to the illuminated surface will be used rather than the outward-drawn normal. In practice, the illumination vector could be obtained by using a Photronic cell, or similar device, in place of the imaginary wire loop. The cell could be oriented in various directions

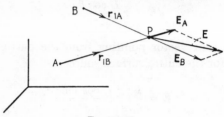

FIG. 10.12.

at P until a direction was found at which maximum current was obtained. An imaginary arrow pointing out of the back of the cell would then give the direction of the illumination vector, and the meter reading would give its magnitude. If the cell is tilted in any other direction, the reading will be reduced by the factor* $\cos \theta$.

Now, suppose two point sources are used (Fig. 10.12) instead of one. From source A alone we obtain an illumination vector

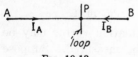

FIG. 10.13.

E_A while for B alone we obtain a vector E_B. If we use the loop as before, we find that a maximum amount of flux is not obtained when the loop is perpendicular to AP or to BP. The maximum value is obtained somewhere between the two, and the resulting magnitude and direction of E can be found experimentally as before. Of course, E could have been obtained also by vectorial addition of E_A and E_B. The same process of vectorial addition may be used for any number of point sources or for surface sources, as noted in Eq. (10.15).

This is all very well as long as the sources are not located too far from each other. Suppose, however, that we have the con-

---

* If it is assumed, of course, that the cell follows the cosine law. Commercial cells are not very good in this respect.

dition shown in Fig. 10.13. Here the source A sends flux through the loop in one direction, while B sends flux through the loop in the opposite direction. We continue to use our previous definition of the illumination vector as a vector whose magnitude is equal to the net flux density passing through the loop and whose direction is the direction of the resulting net flow of radiant energy. If $|E_A| = |E_B|$, the resultant illumination vector is a null vector. This result could be obtained experimentally by using, instead of our single Photronic cell, two identical cells fastened back to back and connected electrically in series opposition.

Consequently, the illumination vector is defined in all cases, irrespective of how the sources are arranged. It is a vector whose magnitude is equal to the net flux density passing through an imaginary loop which has been oriented so that this flux density is a maximum; and whose direction is that of the normal to the loop. Hyde[18] has called this quantity "specific luminous flux," while Yamauti[25] calls it "permeating flux density." Another name would be "flux-density vector"; any one of these names is more appropriate than the name "illumination vector." Fortunately, however, we shall not need to use the vector in its broad definition, since from the practical standpoint of obtaining values of illumination on actual surfaces, E tells us very little unless all of the source or sources are on one side of the illuminated surface. In dealing with the vector method, it is of prime importance to realize that it will *give correct results only when the plane of the illuminated surface does not intersect the source.* Suppose, for example, that a room is illuminated by a disk source in the ceiling and that the illumination is to be calculated on a vertical bulletin board which is somewhere under the source. The vector method gives an answer to this problem, but *it is not the answer that we want.* It gives, in fact, the difference in the illuminations on the two sides of the board, which is of no practical significance. What we are really interested in is not the illumination from a circular disk but the illumination from a circular segment—that segment of the source that is formed by the plane of the bulletin board and is on the side of the board on which we wish to obtain the illumination. Such a value of illumination can be obtained only by integration.

A practical example of the use of the vector method is the determination of the illumination from a sloping window.

Figure 10.14 shows a window in a factory having a saw-tooth roof. The windows are 6 ft high; and since their length is great compared with their height, β will be considered as 90 deg. Taking the origin at the lower corner of the window and the

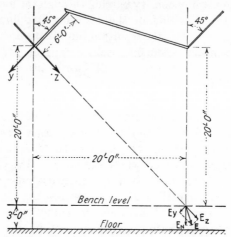

Fig. 10.14.—Illumination from a sloping window in a saw-tooth roof.

z axis normal to the plane of the window, as in Chap. IX, we find that $E_x = 0$ from symmetry. The normal component of the illumination vector, E_N, is

$$E_N = |E| \cos \theta = (jE_y + kE_z) \cos \theta$$

It is probably easier to use the components directly.

$$E_N = E_y \cos 45° + E_z \cos 45° = 0.707(E_y + E_z)$$

The addition is ordinary scalar addition, not vector addition.

10.05. The Circle Diagram (Continued).—We are now in a position to continue the treatment of the circle diagram which was introduced in Sec. 10.03 for the calculation of illumination from perfectly diffusing disk sources of uniform luminosity. As shown previously, the illumination at any point on the wall of an imaginary sphere (Fig. 10.15) is

$$E_w = \frac{L}{2}(1 - \cos \gamma) \tag{10.09}$$

Also, the illumination vector E must be collinear with the line NP, which is the axis of the light cone. From symmetry there can be no component perpendicular to this axis.   The illumination vector may be considered as the sum of two components: the radial vector having the magnitude E_w and the tangential vector having the magnitude E_T (Fig. 10.15).   Or we may divide **E** into the two mutually orthogonal vectors having magnitudes E_z and E_R.   From Theorem II (Sec. 10.03), the angle between

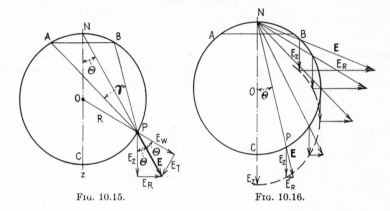

Fig. 10.15.   Fig. 10.16.

E_w and **E** is equal to the angle between E_z and **E**.   Thus E_z must be equal to E_w.   The illumination on a plane which is parallel to the source is therefore always equal to the illumination of the sphere wall at that point and is constant at all points on a given sphere.   This fact has already been made use of in the circle diagram of Fig. 10.08.

Now, consider the illumination E_R, the component radial to the axis NC.   Since E_z is the same for all points of the sphere (Fig. 10.16), it is evident that $|E|$ must be a function of Θ. E_R must have such a value that the sum of the two vectors (having magnitudes E_R and E_z) produces a vector in the direction NP.   Thus the values of E_R must become greater as Θ increases, as shown in Fig. 10.16, and*

$$E_R = E_z \tan \Theta = \frac{L}{2}(1 - \cos \gamma) \tan \Theta \qquad (10.16)$$

* Note that McAllister (*El. World*, 1910, p. 1356) identifies $\tan \Theta$ with r_0/z_0, which is in error owing to the fact that N is not on the line AB.   In most cases, the error is rather serious, though at large distances from the source it becomes negligible.

The circle diagram of Fig. 10.08 may also be used in calculating the illumination on walls. The illumination on a cylindrical wall coaxial with the source and having a radius r_0/a is obtained from the intersections of the circles with an appropriate vertical line, $r_0/a = $ const. This gives values of E_z/L. The corresponding values of E_R/L are obtained by use of Eq. (10.16).

In the case of a circular-disk ceiling source in a rectangular room, the wall illuminations are obtained by a slight modification

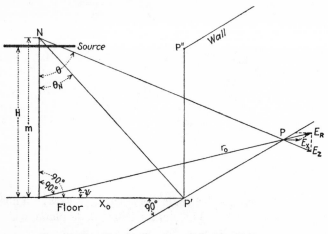

FIG. 10.17.—Illumination from a circular-disk source.

of the method just stated. As can be seen from Fig. 10.17, the illumination E_x on the wall is

$$E_x = E_R \cos \psi = E_z \tan \theta \cos \psi \qquad (10.17)$$

As $\tan \theta \cos \psi = x_0/m = \tan \theta_N$

$$E_x = (E_z)_P \tan \theta_N \qquad (10.18)$$

where the value of E_z is obtained at the point P (not P') by use of the circle diagram and θ_N has the value obtained in a plane perpendicular to the wall.

A simple example is shown in Fig. 10.18. Values of illumination are desired at points A, B, C, and D on the wall at a distance $3a$ below the ceiling. The values of E_z/L are read directly from the curve of Fig. 10.09. We must next obtain θ from the circle diagram (Fig. 10.08). Note that the *vertex of the angle* θ *lies at the top of the circle* $(E_z/L = 0.052)$, *not at the luminous source,* as was erroneously assumed by McAllister. From Fig. 10.08,

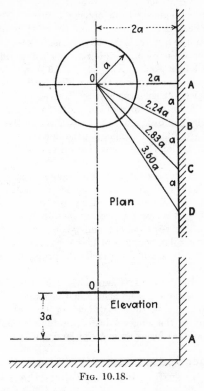

Fig. 10.18.

we find that the point N of this circle is 0.23 above the source; so for point A,

$$\tan \theta = \frac{2}{3.0 + 0.23} = 0.619$$

Similar calculations are made for the other points, giving

Point	E_z/L	E_x/L	E (for $L = 200$) (lumens/square feet)
A	0.052	0.032	6.4
B	0.046	0.028	5.6
C	0.032	0.020	4.0
D	0.020	0.012	2.4

Problem 109. Plot a curve of illumination on the bench level (Fig. 10.14) due to one window ($\beta = 90$ deg. in both $+x$ and $-x$ directions).

Problem 110. A drafting room 15 by 30 ft with a 12-ft ceiling is provided with totally indirect lighting from opaque fixtures. The ceiling is matt white having a reflection factor of 0.75, and the total luminous flux received by the ceiling from the fixtures is 90,000 lumens. Consider a drawing board in the exact center of the room. Its lower edge is 35 in. above the floor and is normal to the longer walls. The slope is 15 deg. Calculate the value of the illumination in the center of the board. Neglect reflections from the walls and also neglect the shadows cast by fixtures.

Problem 111. A rectangular room of width $3a$, height $4a$, and length $6a$ is lighted by a circular disk source in the center of the ceiling. Plot the wall illumination from floor to ceiling on the line $P'P''$ on one of the longer walls (Fig. 10.17). Plot the illumination on one of the longer walls near the floor ($z_0/a = 4.0$).

Problem 112. A sloping desk is built against one of the longer walls of the room (Prob. 111). The surface makes an angle of 30 deg with the horizontal. Plot the illumination along the center line of this desk ($x_0/a = 1.25$, $z_0/a = 3.00$, y_0/a varies from 0 to 3.0).

Problem 113. The z-component and y-component of the illumination vector for a rectangular source are given by Eqs. (9.18b) and (9.19b). Determine the magnitude and direction of the projection of the illumination vector in the yz-plane.

Problem 114. In Prob. 84 (Chap. IX), what are the magnitude and direction of E on a table at the center of the room? What is the value of the illumination on a vertical book held at the center of the table with its surface parallel to the longer sides of the room? On the book if it is tilted so that its surface forms an angle of 30 deg with the horizontal?

10.06. Contour Integration.

—All the formulas of Chap. IX were obtained by surface integration over the source. We now show how it is often possible to save considerable labor by replacing a double integral by a single one. In 1924, Fock[20] proved that for the case of perfectly diffusing surfaces of uniform luminosity, the surface integral can be replaced by an integral along the contour, resulting in a great mathematical simplification. The method cannot be applied to surfaces of nonuniform luminosity except in a few very special cases.

Returning to the fundamental Eq. (10.15), we obtain for constant luminosity,

$$E = \frac{L}{\pi} \int_S r_1 \frac{\cos \theta}{r^2} d\sigma = \frac{L}{\pi} \int_S \frac{r_1}{r^2} (r_1 \cdot n_1) d\sigma \qquad (10.19)$$

What we wish to do is to replace the surface integral by an integral around the contour C. How can this be accomplished? One might guess that a promising mode of attack would be to use Stokes's theorem,* which relates the surface integral of the curl of a vector quantity A to the line integral of the quantity itself:

$$\int_S n_1 \cdot \operatorname{curl} A \, d\sigma = \oint A \cdot ds \qquad (10.20)$$

The integration is performed in the direction indicated in Fig. 10.19, so that an imaginary observer on the positive side of the

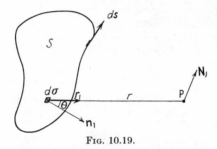

Fig. 10.19.

surface keeps the area always on his left. It is now necessary to show that the integral, Eq. (10.19), is in the form of the left-hand side of Eq. (10.20). This was first done by Fock, but the present derivation follows Gershun,[22] who devised a somewhat more elegant treatment.

Multiplying both sides of Eq. (10.19) by an arbitrary unit vector N_1,

$$N_1 \cdot E = \frac{L}{\pi} \int_S \frac{N_1 \cdot r_1}{r^2} (r_1 \cdot n_1) d\sigma$$
$$= \frac{L}{\pi} \int_S n_1 \cdot \left[\frac{r_1}{r^2} (N_1 \cdot r_1) \right] d\sigma \qquad (10.21)$$

It is easily shown† that

$$\frac{r_1}{r^2}(N_1 \cdot r_1) = \frac{1}{-2} \operatorname{curl}\left(N_1 \times \frac{r_1}{r} \right) = \frac{1}{2} \operatorname{curl}\left(\frac{r_1}{r} \times N_1 \right) \quad (10.22)$$

---

* See, for instance, H. B. Phillips, Vector Analysis, p. 62, 1933.

† Yamauti, *Res. Bull.* 339, p. 19. The negative sign occurs because we have taken *r* as a vector pointing from the variable point toward the fixed point *P* rather than in the usual opposite sense.

Thus,

$$N_1 \cdot E = \frac{L}{2\pi} \int_S n_1 \cdot \operatorname{curl}\left(\frac{r_1}{r} \times N_1\right) d\sigma \tag{10.23}$$

and by Stokes's theorem,

$$N_1 \cdot E = \frac{L}{2\pi} \oint \frac{r_1}{r} \times N_1 \cdot ds \tag{10.24}$$

The terms of a scalar triple product may be commuted cyclically without altering the value or sign, and as N_1 is a constant with respect to the integration,

$$N_1 \cdot E = N_1 \cdot \frac{L}{2\pi} \oint ds \times \frac{r_1}{r}$$

or

$$E = \frac{L}{2\pi} \oint \frac{ds \times r_1}{r} = \frac{L}{2\pi} \oint d\alpha \tag{10.25}$$

where $d\alpha$ is a vector whose magnitude is equal to the angle which intercepts ds,

$$|d\alpha| = \left|\frac{ds \times r_1}{r}\right| = \frac{1}{r} \sin \theta \, ds$$

(where θ is here the angle between the vector ds and the vector r_1) and whose direction is perpendicular to the plane of r_1 and ds.

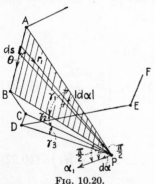

Fig. 10.20.

The vector $d\alpha$ points in the direction of advance of a right-handed screw turned from ds to r_1. Equation (10.25) gives an expression for the illumination due to any perfectly diffusing surface source of uniform luminosity and gives it in the form of an integral taken around the contour of the source.

For sources with polygonal boundaries, the method is particularly advantageous. The $d\alpha$-vectors for a straight-line boundary are all parallel and thus add directly. Consider a source, uniformly luminous and perfectly diffusing, in the form of a polygon of n sides, $ABCD \ldots$ (Fig. 10.20). The contour integration will be performed in the direction shown by the arrow.   Required the illumination vector at P.

The contribution due to the side AB is

$$\Delta_1 = \frac{L}{2\pi} \int_{AB} d\alpha \tag{10.26}$$

But $d\alpha$ is a vector perpendicular to the shaded plane determined by r_1 and ds, and evidently all the $d\alpha$-vectors are collinear.   By the right-hand rule, $d\alpha$ points in the direction shown, always outward from the body of the luminous surface.   Thus the integral becomes an ordinary scalar one.

$$\Delta_1 = \alpha_1\frac{L}{2\pi} \int_0^{\gamma_1} d\alpha = \alpha_1\frac{L}{2\pi}\gamma_1 \tag{10.26a}$$

where α_1 is a unit vector perpendicular to the plane of ds and r_1 and pointing in the direction of advance of a right-hand screw which is turned from ds to r_1.   Similarly, for the side BC,

$$\Delta_2 = \alpha_2\frac{L}{2\pi}\gamma_2, \text{ etc.}$$

Thus the vector illumination at P is

$$E = \sum_{i=1}^{i=n}\Delta_i = \frac{L}{2\pi}\sum_{i=1}^{i=n}\alpha_i\gamma_i \tag{10.27}$$

where α_i is a unit vector, the outward-drawn normal to the ith side of the polygonal boundary cone.   Equation (10.27) was first obtained by Omoto.*   It gives the illumination at any point due to any perfectly diffusing source of uniform luminosity having a polygonal boundary.   Integration is eliminated, and the problem is reduced to one of simple vector addition.

As an example, consider the illumination from a rectangular source (Fig. 10.21).   It is convenient to set this window in a cartesian frame with the origin of coordinates at the window corner and with the unit vectors i, j, and k arranged in a right-handed system as shown.   The illumination vector is required at the point P, which is on the z-axis.   We may start with the

---

* *J. Illuminating Engineering Soc., Japan,* **8**, 1924, p. 285.

vertical side of the window which lies along the y-axis. The vector $d\mathbf{s}$ points downward, and r_1 is in the y-z plane, so the

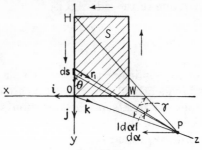

FIG. 10.21.

vector $d\alpha$ is parallel to the x-axis, and

$$d\alpha = \mathbf{i}\, d\alpha$$

The contribution of the side HO of the source is, by Eq. (10.26a),

$$\Delta_1 = \mathbf{i}\frac{L}{2\pi}\int_0^\gamma d\alpha = \mathbf{i}\frac{L}{2\pi}\gamma$$

For the bottom edge OW (Fig. 10.22), the vector $d\alpha$ points downward, and

$$d\alpha = \mathbf{j}\, d\alpha$$

Therefore,

$$\Delta_2 = \mathbf{j}\,\frac{L}{2\pi}\beta$$

For the other vertical edge WV (Fig. 10.23a), affairs are a trifle

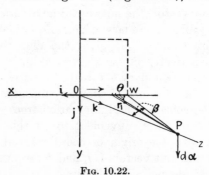

FIG. 10.22.

more complicated, since $d\alpha$ is not parallel to any of the axes. It lies, as shown in the diagram, in the x-z plane; but since it must be perpendicular to the plane formed by ds and r_1, it makes the angle β with the negative x-axis.   Thus,

$$d\boldsymbol{\alpha} = -\boldsymbol{i} \cos \beta + \boldsymbol{k} \sin \beta.$$

The contribution of the side WV is therefore

$$\boldsymbol{\Delta}_3 = \frac{L}{2\pi}[-\boldsymbol{i}\gamma_1 \cos \beta + \boldsymbol{k}\gamma_1 \sin \beta]$$

Similarly, for the side VH,

$$\boldsymbol{\Delta}_4 = \frac{L}{2\pi}[-\boldsymbol{j}\beta_1 \cos \gamma + \boldsymbol{k}\beta_1 \sin \gamma]$$

as shown in Figs. 10.23b and 10.23c.

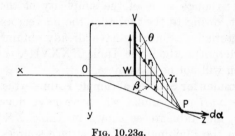

FIG. 10.23a.

FIG. 10.23b.   FIG. 10.23c.

The actual illumination vector at P is the vector sum of the four Δ's, or

$$E = \frac{L}{2\pi}\{\boldsymbol{i}[\gamma - \gamma_1 \cos \beta] + \boldsymbol{j}[\beta - \beta_1 \cos \gamma] +$$
$$\boldsymbol{k}[\beta_1 \sin \gamma + \gamma_1 \sin \beta]\} \quad (10.28)$$

The three components of the illumination vector are

$$E_x = \frac{L}{2\pi}[\gamma - \gamma_1 \cos \beta]$$

$$E_y = \frac{L}{2\pi}[\beta - \beta_1 \cos \gamma] \qquad\qquad (10.29)$$

$$E_z = \frac{L}{2\pi}[\beta_1 \sin \gamma + \gamma_1 \sin \beta]$$

and agree with the results obtained in Chap. IX by surface integration. Thus in a few minutes and without the use of calculus we have obtained more information than was found previously by a tedious integration taking several hours.

The method of contour integration is not limited to sources with polygonal boundaries. For the circular-disk source, for instance, the method allows the calculation of the illumination at any point; though some of the simplicity of the polygonal source is lost, owing to the fact that the $d\alpha$-vectors must now be added vectorially. Since we have already obtained the solution by a different method (see Table XXXVII), the details of the derivation will not be given here.

10.07. Formulas for Sources of Simple Form.—It is convenient to collect the various formulas which we have developed, add a few others, and tabulate as shown in Table XXXVII. All formulas give the illumination from surface sources which are perfectly diffusing and of uniform luminosity. Values of the three components of the illumination vector E_x, E_y, and E_z are tabulated. If the source has axial symmetry, the results are also expressed in cylindrical coordinates, with E_z and E_R given. In these cases, owing to symmetry, the component perpendicular to E_R is always zero.

The first example of Table XXXVII is the spherical source. For any position of P, the illumination vector always points directly out from the center of the sphere and has the magnitude

$$|E| = L \sin^2 \gamma_1 = \frac{La^2}{D^2}$$

where D is the distance from the center of the sphere to P. Thus the illumination follows the inverse-square law, and the sphere acts exactly like a point source at its center, no matter how close it is approached.

The second and third illustrations of Table XXXVII refer to the circular-disk source, which has already been considered in some detail.   The results are equally applicable to any form of coffer with rounded, conical, cylindrical, wrinkled, or any other uniformly luminous surface with perfectly diffusing characteristics.   The broad circular-band source is considered as two disk

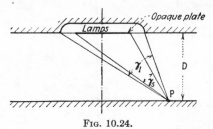

Fig. 10.24.

sources, the illumination that would result from the center one being subtracted from the illumination from the larger one. For convenience, the results are given in the fourth illustration which applies likewise to coffers.   Lighting is sometimes accomplished by an arrangement shown in Fig. 10.24.*   Lamps concealed behind the center plate illuminate the inside of the diffusing coffer. Obviously, this is an illustration of Case IV (Table XXXVII), and to find the illumination at any point on the floor we need determine only the two angles γ_s and γ_l.   A similar case is shown in Fig. 10.25 where a large, circular, domed room is illuminated by floodlights which are mounted in recesses in the top of

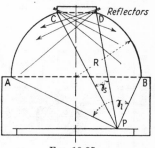

Fig. 10.25.

the dome and are arranged to illuminate the entire dome uniformly.†   Assuming that the surface is perfectly diffusing and that the skylight reflects no appreciable luminous flux, the illumination at P on the tables is

$$E_z = \frac{L}{2}(\cos \gamma_s - \cos \gamma_l)$$

---

* See, for instance, the description of the entrance foyer of the National Broadcasting Studios at Rockefeller Center, Light in Architecture and Decoration, *I.E.S. Trans.*, 1934, p. 36.

† The scheme is used in the M.I.T. central library, also in the Christian Science Church, Boston.

TABLE XXXVII.—ILLUMINATION FROM PERFECTLY DIFFUSING SOURCES OF UNIFORM LUMINOSITY

Source	Diagram	$|E|$	E_z
Spherical source (illumination same as from disk AB).		$L \sin^2 \gamma_1$ $= \dfrac{L}{2}(1 - \cos \gamma)$	0
Circular disk,* illumination at a point on axis.		$L \sin^2 \gamma_1$ $= \dfrac{L}{2}(1 - \cos \gamma)$	0
Circular disk,* illumination at any point.		$E_z \sec \Theta$	$= E_R \cos \Psi$ $= E_z \tan \Theta_N$ (Θ_N = value of Θ for Ψ = 0)
Plane circular band.*			$E_R \cos \Psi$

* Applies also to any form of dome or coffer having the same boundary.

Table XXXVII.—Illumination from Perfectly Diffusing Sources of Uniform Luminosity.—(*Continued*)

E_y	E_z	E_R
0	$L\sin^2\gamma_1$ $=\dfrac{L}{2}(1-\cos\gamma)$	0
0	$L\sin^2\gamma_1$ $=\dfrac{L}{2}(1-\cos\gamma)$	0
$E_R\sin\Psi$	$\dfrac{L}{2}\left[1 - \sqrt{\dfrac{z_0^2+r_0^2-a^2}{(z_0^2+r_0^2+a^2)^2 - 4a^2r_0^2}}\right]$ $=\dfrac{L}{4p_1p_2}[4a^2 - (p_1-p_2)^2]$ $=\dfrac{L}{2}(1-\cos\gamma)$	$\dfrac{Lz_0}{2r_0}\left[\sqrt{\dfrac{z_0^2+r_0^2+a^2}{(z_0^2+r_0^2+a^2)^2 - 4a^2r_0^2}} - 1\right]$ $=\dfrac{Lz_0}{4r_0}\dfrac{(p_1-p_2)^2}{p_1p_2}$ $=E_z\tan\Theta$
$E_R\sin\Psi$	$\dfrac{L}{2}(\cos\gamma_s - \cos\gamma_l)$	$\dfrac{Lz_0}{4r_0}\left[\dfrac{(p_1-p_2)^2}{p_1p_2} - \dfrac{(p_1'-p_2')^2}{p_1'p_2'}\right]$

TABLE XXXVII.—ILLUMINATION FROM PERFECTLY DIFFUSING SOURCES OF UNIFORM LUMINOSITY.—(Continued)

Source	Diagram	$|E|$	E_z
Plane Circular* Band, $w << a$.			$E_R \cos \Psi$
Slender Torus, $\delta << a$.		For general case, see Yamauti, Res. Elec. Lab., Tokyo, 1924, No. 148, p. 11. For P on the z-axis, the formulas reduced to the following: $$L\frac{\delta}{a}(1 - \cos \gamma) \cos \frac{\gamma}{2}$$	0
Narrow Circular Band with surface parallel to axis, $w << a$.			
Elliptical Disk,* illumination at point on axis.		$L \sin b_1 \sin \gamma_1$	0

* Applies also to any form of dome or coffer having the same boundary.

TABLE XXXVII.—ILLUMINATION FROM PERFECTLY DIFFUSING SOURCES OF UNIFORM LUMINOSITY.—(*Continued*)

E_v	E_z	E_R
$E_R \sin \Psi$	$\dfrac{2Lwaz_0^2(z_0^2 + r_0^2 + a^2)}{[(z_0^2 + r_0^2 + a^2)^2 - 4a^2r_0^2]^{3/2}}$ $= \dfrac{2Lwaz_0^2 p_3^2}{(p_1p_2)^3}$ $(p_1^2 = z_0^2 + r_0^2 + a^2)$	$\dfrac{2Lwaz_0r_0(z_0^2 + r_0^2 - a^2)}{[(z_0^2 + r_0^2 + a^2)^2 - 4a^2r_0^2]^{3/2}}$ $= E_z\dfrac{r}{z_0}\dfrac{(z_0^2 + r_0^2 - a^2)}{(z_0^2 + r_0^2 + a^2)}$

For general case, see Yamauti, Res. Elec. Lab., Tokyo, 1924, No. 148, p. 11. For P on the z-axis, the formulas reduce to the following:

E_v	E_z	E_R
0	$L\dfrac{\delta}{a}(1 - \cos \gamma) \cos \dfrac{\gamma}{2}$ $= \dfrac{2L\delta}{a}\sin^2 \gamma_1 \cos \gamma_1$	0
0	$\dfrac{2Lwa^2z_0(z_0^2 + a^2 - r_0^2)}{[(z_0^2 + r_0^2 + a^2)^2 - 4a^2r_0^2]^{3/2}}$	0
	$L \sin \beta_1 \sin \gamma_1$	

TABLE XXXVII.—ILLUMINATION FROM PERFECTLY DIFFUSING SOURCES OF UNIFORM LUMINOSITY.—(*Continued*)

Source	Diagram	$\lvert F \rvert$	E_z
Rectangle,* illumination at a point on perpendicular erected at corner of source.		$\sqrt{E_x^2 + E_y^2 + E_z^2}$	$\dfrac{L}{2\pi}\left[\tan^{-1}\dfrac{H}{z_0} - \dfrac{z_0}{\sqrt{z_0^2+W^2}}\sin^{-1}\dfrac{H}{r_1}\right]$ $= \dfrac{L}{2\pi}[\gamma - \gamma_1 \cos \beta]$
Narrow Rectangle,* $w \ll r_0$.		$\sqrt{E_z^2 + E_R^2}$	$\dfrac{L}{2\pi}\dfrac{W}{r_0}[\cos\gamma\,\sin\gamma + \gamma]\sin\Psi\cos\Psi$
Slender Cylinder, (circular) $\delta \ll r_0$.		$\sqrt{E_z^2 + E_R^2}$	$\dfrac{L}{2\pi}\dfrac{\delta}{r_0}[\cos\gamma\,\sin\gamma + \gamma]\cos\Psi$
Two-dimensional cases. Plane Strip (extends to $\pm\infty$ in z direction).		on y-axis $\dfrac{La}{r_0}$	$\dfrac{Ly_0}{2}\left(\dfrac{p_1 - p_2}{p_1 p_2}\right)$
			0
Circular Cylinder ($\pm\infty$ in z direction).		$L\sin\beta_1$	$E_R\cos\Psi$

* Applies also to any form of coffer having the same boundary.

TABLE XXXVII.—ILLUMINATION FROM PERFECTLY DIFFUSING SOURCES OF UNIFORM LUMINOSITY.—(*Continued*)

E_y	E_z	E_R
$\frac{L}{2\pi}\left[\tan^{-1}\frac{W}{z_0} - \frac{z_0}{\sqrt{z_0^2+H^2}}\sin^{-1}\frac{W}{r_1}\right]$ $= \frac{L}{2\pi}[\beta - \beta_1\cos\gamma]$	$\frac{L}{2\pi}\left[\frac{H}{\sqrt{z_0^2+H^2}}\sin^{-1}\frac{W}{r_1} + \frac{W}{\sqrt{z_0^2+W^2}}\sin^{-1}\frac{H}{r_1}\right]$ $= \frac{L}{2\pi}[\beta_1\sin\gamma + r_1\sin\beta]$	where $r_1 = \sqrt{z_0^2+H^2+W^2}$ $\beta_1 = \sin^{-1}\left[\frac{\tan\beta}{\sqrt{\tan^2\beta+\sec^2\gamma}}\right]$ $\gamma_1 = \sin^{-1}\left[\frac{\tan\gamma}{\sqrt{\tan^2\gamma+\sec^2\beta}}\right]$
$\frac{L}{2\pi}\frac{W}{r_0}[\cos\gamma\sin\gamma+\gamma]\sin^2\Psi$	$\frac{L}{2\pi}\frac{W}{r_0}\sin^2\gamma\sin\Psi$	$\frac{L}{2\pi}\frac{W}{r_0}[\cos\gamma\sin\gamma+\gamma]\sin\Psi$
$\frac{L}{2\pi}\frac{\delta}{r_0}[\cos\gamma\sin\gamma+\gamma]\sin\Psi$	$-\frac{L}{2\pi}\frac{\delta}{r_0}\sin^2\gamma$	$\frac{L}{2\pi}\frac{\delta}{r_0}[\cos\gamma\sin\gamma+\gamma]$
$\frac{L}{2}\left[\frac{(z_0+a)}{p_1} - \frac{(z_0-a)}{p_2}\right]$ $= \frac{L}{2p_1p_2}[p_2(z_0+a) - p_1(z_0-a)]$	0	$\frac{Ly_0}{2}\left(\frac{p_1-p_2}{p_1p_2}\right)\sec\Psi$
$\frac{La}{r_0} = L\sin\beta_1$	0	
$E_R\sin\Psi$	0	$\frac{La}{r_0} = L\sin\beta_1$

We next come to a second class of sources, characterized by a width or diameter small compared with the distance at which they are viewed. The two straight forms given are the narrow rectangle and the slender cylinder. The rectangle is exemplified by many forms of narrow luminous panels, while the cylinder is found in frosted tubular lamps and diffusing glass cylinders. When the narrow source is bent into a circle, we have three forms. In one, the surface is in a plane, as when a narrow diffusing element is built into the ceiling of a circular room. The surface may be parallel to the axis, as when the diffusing glass is mounted in the wall of the circular room. The third form is the slender torus. It should be noted that the ordinary mercury-vapor lamp and the neon lamp do not give a distribution exactly as predicted by these formulas, since their surface is not perfectly diffusing when ordinary clear glass is used.

Two final examples are given of two-dimensional cases. Here the width of the source may be as great as desired, but the length is very great in both $\pm z$ directions. The examples of Table XXXVII do not exhaust the possibilities of the subject. Many other formulas have been developed but are not included, either because of their complexity or because they did not seem of great practical value. If needed, however, they may be found in the literature or may be derived by contour integration. It is advisable, perhaps, to emphasize again the fact that *none of these formulas will give the correct result when the illuminated plane cuts the source.* In such cases, it is necessary to derive new formulas for the particular part of the source which is effective in illuminating the actual surface.

Problem 115. Some of Bel Geddes' theater designs use a hemispherical dome with a circular stage in the center, surrounded by seats. (See design for a repertory theater in "Horizons" by Norman Bel Geddes.) Suppose that the entire dome ceiling is illuminated uniformly by concealed floodlights; illumination of dome = E_D, reflection factor of dome = ρ_D. By means of contour integration, obtain an expression for E on the center of the stage, which is assumed to be in the plane of the circular boundary of the dome.

Problem 116. An I.E.S. student lamp uses a parchment shade with a thoroughly diffusing white inner surface. The shade is in the form of a truncated cone with diameters of 8 and 16 in. and has a vertical height of 8 in. The lower edge is 20 in. above the desk top. At distances beyond 54 in. from the axis of the lamp, the illumination of the desk is due entirely to luminous flux from the *inside* of the shade, which has a luminosity of

700 lumens/sq ft. Plot the desk illumination *vs.* distance from the lamp axis.

Problem 117. Repeat Prob. 82 (Chap. IX), using contour integration.

Problem 118. Repeat Prob. 85 (Chap. IX), using contour integration. What are the magnitude and direction of *E?*

Problem 119. Obtain expressions for the components of the illumination vector at any point on the axis of a circular-disk source of radius *a*.

10.08. Interreflections.—In the previous sections we have omitted the consideration of interreflections. This has been done for the sake of simplicity and because the treatment of interreflections has not been thoroughly developed as yet. The illuminating engineer must exercise a certain amount of caution in omitting the consideration of interreflections. This omission for ordinary rooms will often give calculated values of illumination which are low, while in a few cases (light courts, for instance), the calculated value may be not even of the right order of magnitude. In the present section, the purpose is not to give a complete treatment of the subject but merely to present the elements of a method of attack which has been developed recently by Buckley.[26]

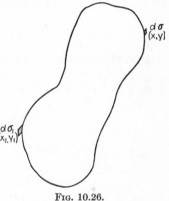

Fig. 10.26.

Consider an inclosure '(Fig. 10.26). Any point on the wall may be specified by two numbers which designate the position of the point on a coordinate system which may be imagined drawn on the walls of the inclosure. Call the two coordinates x and y. A small area of wall $d\sigma_1$ will be held fixed at the point (x_1, y_1), while another area $d\sigma$ is determined in position by the variable point (x, y). The actual luminosity of the area $d\sigma_1$ will be denoted by $L(x_1, y_1)$.

Let $L_0(x, y)$ be the luminosity at the point (x, y), *assuming no interreflections*—i.e., due to the self-luminosity of the surface or to light reflected directly from a concealed source or to a combination of the two. Similarly, at the fixed point (x_1, y_1), omitting interreflections, the luminosity is $L_0(x_1, y_1)$.

In general, besides the component L_0 there is a component due to interreflections. Each element of area $d\sigma$, having the luminosity $L(x, y)$, produces an illumination at (x_1, y_1) equal to

$$L(x, y) \cdot K(x, y; x_1, y_1,)d\sigma$$

where $K(x, y; x_1, y_1)$ = the illumination at (x_1, y_1) caused by unit luminosity of unit area at (x, y).

The illumination at (x_1, y_1) due to the entire inclosure is

$$\Delta E(x_1, y_1) = \int_S L(x, y) \cdot K(x, y; x_1, y_1)d\sigma \qquad (10.30)$$

where the integration is taken over all the surface which is visible from the point (x_1, y_1). The resulting increase in luminosity at (x_1, y_1) is equal to the foregoing multiplied by the reflection factor of the wall at (x_1, y_1), or

$$\Delta L(x_1, y_1) = \rho \int_S L(x, y) \cdot K(x, y; x_1, y_1)d\sigma \qquad (10.30a)$$

The total luminosity at (x_1, y_1) is

$$L(x_1, y_1) = L_0(x_1, y_1) + \rho(x_1, y_1)\int_S L(x, y) \cdot$$
$$K(x, y; x_1, y_1)d\sigma \qquad (10.31)$$

Equation (10.31) is an *integral equation* applicable to all cases. $K(x, y; x_1, y_1)$ is called the *kernel*. The inclosure may be of any shape, and the reflection factor may be a function of x and y.

If symmetry allows the position of a point to be expressed in terms of a single variable x, Eq. (10.31) reduces to the more familiar form of integral equation

$$L(x_1) = L_0(x_1) + \rho(x_1)\int_a^b L(x) \cdot K(x, x_1)dx \qquad (10.31a)$$

10.09. Interreflections in a Sphere.—As a simple example, consider the luminosity of the inside of a sphere having a uniform reflection factor ρ (Fig. 10.27). The illumination at any point ψ_1 due to the area $d\sigma$, of luminosity L, is

$$\frac{Ld\sigma}{\pi} \frac{\cos^2 \theta}{(2R \cos \theta)^2} = \frac{Ld\sigma}{S}$$

Thus the kernel of the integral Eq. (10.31a) is

$$K(x, x_1) = \frac{1}{S}$$

where S = the area of the sphere surface.

Using ψ as our variable, we reduce Eq. (10.31*a*) to

$$L(\psi_1) = L_0(\psi_1) + \rho \int_0^\pi L(\psi) \cdot \frac{1}{S} \cdot 2\pi R^2 \sin \psi \, d\psi$$

$$= L_0(\psi_1) + \frac{\rho}{2} \int_0^\pi L(\psi) \sin \psi \, d\psi \qquad (10.31b)$$

This is the integral equation which must be solved. The

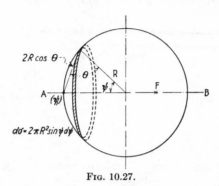

Fig. 10.27.

Fredholm determinant and the Fredholm first minor* are, respectively.

$$D(\lambda) = 1 - \frac{\rho}{2} \int_0^\pi \sin \psi \, d\psi = 1 - \rho$$

$$D(\psi_1, \psi; \lambda) = \frac{\rho}{2} \sin \psi$$

giving

$$L(\psi_1) = L_0(\psi_1) + \frac{1}{D(\lambda)} \int_0^\pi D(\psi_1, \psi; \lambda) L_0(\psi) \, d\psi$$

$$= L_0(\psi_1) + \frac{\rho}{2(1 - \rho)} \int_0^\pi L_0(\psi) \sin \psi \, d\psi \qquad (10.32)$$

Equation (10.32) is the solution of Eq. (10.31*b*). If $L_0(\psi)$ is a known function of ψ, the integral can be evaluated.

If the initial luminosity is a constant, for instance,

$$L_0(\psi_1) = L_0 = \text{const}$$

---

* See any book on integral equations or Whittaker and Watson, *Modern Analysis.*

and

$$L(\psi_1) = L_0\left[1 + \frac{\rho}{2(1 - \rho)}\int_0^\pi \sin\psi \, d\psi\right]$$

$$= L_0\left[\frac{1}{1 - \rho}\right]$$

Thus the resulting luminosity is the same at every point on the surface and, with a high value of ρ, is much greater than the value L_0.

Suppose the initial luminosity is a function of ψ,

$$L_0(\psi_1) = a\psi$$

and

$$L(\psi_1) = a\left[0 + \frac{\rho}{2(1 - \rho)}\int_0^\pi \psi \sin\psi \, d\psi\right]$$

$$= \frac{\pi a}{2}\left[\frac{\rho}{1 - \rho}\right]$$

The resulting luminosity is uniform even though the original distribution (L_0) was decidedly nonuniform.

Suppose the initial luminosity of the wall of the sphere (Fig. 10.27) is due to a lamp of F lumens placed anywhere on the line AB within the spherical enclosure. Then

$$F = 2\pi R^2\int_0^\pi E_0(\psi) \sin\psi \, d\psi$$

$$= \frac{S}{2\rho}\int_0^\pi L_0(\psi) \sin\psi \, d\psi$$

where $E_0(\psi)$ is the initial illumination of the sphere walls due to flux from the lamp alone. We have assumed that E_0 is a function of ψ only.

$$\int_0^\pi L_0(\psi) \sin\psi \, d\psi = \frac{2\rho F}{S}$$

Substitution in Eq. (10.32) gives

$$L(\psi_1) = L_0(\psi_1) + \frac{\rho^2}{(1 - \rho)}\frac{F}{S}$$

The illumination (E_r) due to reflected flux is

$$E_r = \frac{L(\psi_1) - L_0(\psi_1)}{\rho} = \left(\frac{\rho}{1 - \rho}\right)\frac{F}{S} \qquad (10.33)$$

Equation (10.33) shows that with a sphere having a uniform, perfectly diffusing coating with no openings or obstructions, *the illumination due to reflected flux is the same at every point on the sphere and is directly proportional to F.*   Notice that $E_0(\psi)$ is not necessarily a constant. The lamp within the sphere may be at any point on AB and may have any kind of candle-power distribution, provided the illumination is constant on any circle with AB as axis. The proof can be extended readily to any candlepower distribution of a lamp in any position, a result used in the theory of the integrating-sphere photometer (Chap. VII).

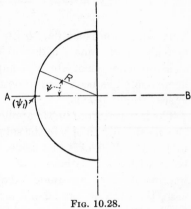

Fig. 10.28.

Similar results can be obtained with a portion of a sphere or with an entire sphere with $\rho \neq$ const.   With a hemisphere, for instance (Fig. 10.28),

$$L(\psi_1) = L_0(\psi_1) + \frac{\rho}{2}\int_0^{\frac{\pi}{2}} L(\psi) \sin \psi \, d\psi$$

$$D(\rho) = 1 - \frac{\rho}{2}$$

$$D(\psi_1, \psi; \rho) = \frac{\rho}{2} \sin \psi$$

Thus,

$$L(\psi_1) = L_0(\psi_1) + \frac{\rho}{2\left(1 - \frac{\rho}{2}\right)}\int_0^{\frac{\pi}{2}} L_0(\psi_1) \sin \psi \, d\psi$$

The total flux reaching the wall of the hemisphere *directly* from the source is

$$F = \frac{1}{2\rho}\int_0^{\frac{\pi}{2}} L_0(\psi) \sin \psi \, d\psi$$

so

$$E_r = \frac{L(\psi_1) - L_0(\psi_1)}{\rho} = \left(\frac{\rho}{1 - \rho/2}\right)\frac{F}{S} \qquad (10.34)$$

This expression is similar to Eq. (10.33) for the sphere, but the increase in illumination due to interreflections is much less for a hemisphere than for a complete sphere. The integrating hemisphere has been used in determining the total luminous flux in searchlight beams.

The integral Eq. (10.31) applies to all interreflection problems. One needs only to obtain the solution that applies to the problem in hand. Buckley[26] has solved the case of circular cylinders, both with and without ends. Analytical solutions of other important cases are undoubtedly possible. In any *numerical* case, the solution can be obtained by mechanical methods, such, for instance, as the use of a differential analyzer.

Problem 120. An integrating sphere of 80-in. diameter is used in measuring the flux from a 1000-watt general-service lamp operated at rated voltage.

a. If the luminous flux were uniformly distributed over the surface of the sphere without interreflections, what would be the illumination of the window W (Fig. 7.30)?

b. What is the illumination at W, using a sphere coating of white paint having a reflection factor of 0.90?

c. For magnesium oxide with $\rho = 0.98$?

Problem 121. A sphere of sandblasted opal glass is lighted from the outside to give a nonuniform luminosity of $L_0(\psi)$, neglecting interreflections. Obtain an expression for $L(\psi_1)$ in terms of $L_0(\psi_1)$, ρ, F, and S.

Problem 122. By use of the integral equations, prove that if the hemisphere of Fig. 10.28 is replaced by any annular ring of uniform reflection factor ρ and having the axis AB, the illumination at ψ_1 due to luminous flux from the ring is directly proportional to the total luminous flux from a source situated on the line AB and having a uniform candlepower distribution.

10.10. The Total Flux.—Thus far in this chapter, our calculations have been concerned with the flux density at a point—the *illumination*. It is often advantageous to work with the *total flux incident on a surface* rather than with conditions at a point, and certain simplified methods have been developed for obtaining the total flux. Such methods are treated in the remainder of this chapter.

As an example, consider the total flux received on a circular area 2 (Fig. 10.29) from a coaxial disk source 1. Such an example occurs when a circular room is lighted from a circular disk source in the ceiling or from a circular dome or coffer.   The disk 2 may be at the floor at any other level where the total flux is desired.   The source is assumed to be perfectly diffusing and of uniform luminosity L.

The illumination at any point on 2 is (Table XXXVII)

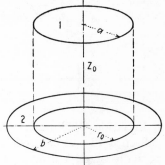

FIG. 10.29.

$$E_z = \frac{L}{2}\left[1 - \frac{z_0^2 + r_0^2 - a^2}{\sqrt{(z_0^2 + r_0^2 + a^2)^2 - 4a^2 r_0^2}}\right]$$

where z_0 is the distance between the disks 1 and 2. E_z is the same at all points on the circumference $r_0 = $ const.   The flux incident on a differential ring of radius r_0 and width dr_0 is

$$dF = 2\pi r_0 E_z\, dr_0 = \pi L r_0\, dr_0\left[1 - \frac{z_0^2 + r_0^2 - a^2}{\sqrt{(z_0^2 + r_0^2 + a^2)^2 - 4a^2 r_0^2}}\right]$$

The total flux received by the disk 2 is

$$
\begin{aligned}
F_{12} &= \pi L \int_0^b r_0\left[1 - \frac{z_0^2 + r_0^2 - a^2}{\sqrt{(z_0^2 + r_0^2 + a^2)^2 - 4a^2 r_0^2}}\right]dr_0 \\
&= \pi L\left\{\frac{b^2}{2} - (z_0^2 - a^2)\int_0^b \frac{r_0\, dr_0}{\sqrt{(z_0^2 + r_0^2 + a^2)^2 - 4a^2 r_0^2}}\right. \\
&\qquad\left. - \int_0^b \frac{r_0^3\, dr_0}{\sqrt{(z_0^2 + r_0^2 + a^2)^2 - 4a^2 r_0^2}}\right\} \quad (10.35)
\end{aligned}
$$

If the variable is changed to $u = r_0^2$, the third term in the parentheses is

$$
\begin{aligned}
&-\frac{1}{2}\int_0^{b^2} \frac{u\, du}{\sqrt{(z_0^2 + a^2)^2 + 2u(z_0^2 - a^2) + u^2}} \\
&= -\frac{1}{2}\left[\sqrt{(z_0^2 + a^2)^2 + 2u(z_0^2 - a^2) + u^2}\,\Big|_0^{b^2}\right. \\
&\qquad\left. - (z_0^2 - a^2)\int_0^{b^2} \frac{du}{\sqrt{(z_0^2 + a^2)^2 + 2u(z_0^2 - a^2) + u^2}}\right] \quad (10.35a)
\end{aligned}
$$

The second term in the parentheses is

$$-(z_0{}^2 - a^2) \int_0^{b^2} \frac{r_0\, dr_0}{\sqrt{(z_0{}^2 + r_0{}^2 + a^2)^2 - 4a^2 r_0{}^2}} = -\frac{1}{2}(z_0{}^2 - a^2)\ \cdot$$

$$\int_0^{b^2} \frac{du}{\sqrt{(z_0{}^2 + a^2)^2 + 2u(z_0{}^2 - a^2) + u^2}} \qquad (10.35b)$$

Thus the integrals in (10.35a) and (10.35b) cancel, and

$$F_{12} = \frac{\pi L}{2}\left\{(z_0{}^2 + a^2 + b^2) - \sqrt{(z_0{}^2 + a^2 + b^2)^2 - 4a^2 b^2}\right\}$$

$$(10.36)$$

Equation (10.36) allows the total flux to be calculated. The subscript 12 will be used to indicate that 1 is the source and 2 is the receiving surface. The average illumination on disk 2 is

$$E_{av} = \frac{F_{12}}{A} \qquad (10.37)$$

where A is the area of 2. Thus if the illuminating engineer desires average illumination (as he often does) rather than illumination at a specific spot, he can obtain it easily by the use of Eqs. (10.36) and (10.37). The alternative is to determine E_z at a large number of points on 2, each point being at the center of an equal area, and average these values. The use of Eq. (10.36) is both quicker and more accurate.

Equation (10.37) applies for any type of source and for any shape of receiving surface, provided that by hook or by crook we can obtain F_{12}. Equation (10.36), however, applies only for a perfectly diffusing source of circular form and of uniform luminosity, a coaxial receiving disk, and no interreflections. The total flux from sources of other shapes can be obtained in similar fashion.

10.11. Total Flux from Rectangular Sources. —Of the various shapes of surface sources, the most important, from the illuminating engineer's standpoint, is the rectangle. Before proceeding to a consideration of the luminous flux incident on a rectangular area from a rectangular source, it is necessary to become acquainted with a reciprocity theorem.

The surface 1 (Fig. 10.30) is a perfectly diffusing source of uniform luminosity L_1. The total flux received by surface 2 is desired.   The illumination at an arbitrary point P_2 on surface 2 is

$$E_{P2} = \frac{L_1}{\pi} \int_1 \frac{\cos \theta_1 \cos \theta_2}{r^2} \, d\sigma_1 \qquad (10.38)$$

due to luminous flux from source 1.   The flux received by the entire surface 2 is

$$F_{12} = \int_2 E_{P2} \, d\sigma_2 = \frac{L_1}{\pi} \int_2 \int_1 \frac{\cos \theta_1 \cos \theta_2}{r^2} \, d\sigma_1 \, d\sigma_2 \qquad (10.39)$$

Suppose that 2 is a source of luminosity L_2 and that we wish to obtain the total flux that passes from 2 to 1.   The illumination

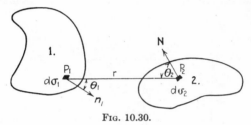

FIG. 10.30.

at a point P_1 is

$$E_{P1} = \frac{L_2}{\pi} \int_2 \frac{\cos \theta_1 \cos \theta_2}{r^2} \, d\sigma_2$$

The total flux received by surface 1 is

$$F_{21} = \int_1 E_{P1} \, d\sigma_1 = \frac{L_2}{\pi} \int_1 \int_2 \frac{\cos \theta_1 \cos \theta_2}{r^2} \, d\sigma_2 \, d\sigma_1 \qquad (10.40)$$

Since the order of integration may be interchanged, Eqs. (10.39) and (10.40) are equal for $L_1 = L_2$, and

$$F_{12} = F_{21} \qquad (10.41)$$

Equation (10.41) is the *reciprocity theorem* for fluxes.   It states that the total flux received by a surface 2 from a luminous surface 1 is exactly the same as the flux that would be received by 1 from 2, were 2 luminous with $L_1 = L_2$.

Suppose, for example, that a room with dark walls and floor is lighted from a star-shaped luminous panel in the ceiling.   We wish to know the total flux received on the rectangular floor of the room.   The usual way of attacking such a problem is first to obtain an expression for the illumination E_2 at any point on the floor due to the star-shaped source.   Then the surface integral

$$\int_2 E_2 \, d\sigma_2$$

taken over the entire floor gives F_{12}, the flux received by the floor.   The same result is obtained by the use of Eq. (10.39). In either case, the integration entails considerable work.

The reciprocity theorem allows a great simplification in the problem.   We interchange the roles of the two areas and consider the problem of finding the total flux received by a star-shaped area from a rectangular luminous panel.   Since the expression for the illumination at any point due to a rectangular source is

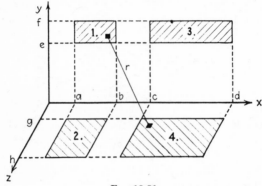

Fig. 10.31.

well-known,* the solution of the problem is obtained merely by integrating this expression over the star-shaped area.   One may even use a contour integral instead of a surface integral, as shown by Fock.   In the present work, however, we shall not go into the further refinement of contour integration for obtaining total flux.

A modified reciprocity theorem, given by Yamauti in *Research Bulletin* 250 of the Electrotechnical Laboratory, Tokyo, will also be useful.   In Fig. 10.31, the illumination at any point in area 4 due to source 1 is

$$E_{14} = \frac{L}{\pi} \int_e^f \int_a^b \frac{\cos \theta_1 \cos \theta_2}{r^2} \, dx \, dy$$

The flux received by the area 4 from the luminous source 1 is

* See, for instance, Yamauti, *Research Bull.* 148.

$$F_{14} = \int_g^h \int_c^d E_{14}\, dx\, dz = \frac{L}{\pi} \int_g^h \int_c^d \int_e^f \int_a^b \frac{\cos\theta_1 \cos\theta_2}{r^2}\, dx\, dy\, dx\, dz$$

$$(10.42)$$

Similarly, the illumination at any point in 2 due to flux from 3 is

$$E_{32} = \frac{L}{\pi} \int_e^f \int_c^d \frac{\cos\,\theta_1\,\cos\,\theta_2}{r^2}\, dx\, dy$$

and the total flux from 3 to 2 is

$$F_{32} = \int_a^h \int_g^b \int_e^f \int_c^d \frac{\cos\,\theta_1\,\cos\,\theta_2}{r^2}\, dx\, dy\, dx\, dz \qquad (10.43)$$

The integrals (10.42) and (10.43) are the same. If the surfaces are of the same luminosity,

$$F_{14} = F_{32} = F_{23} = F_{41} \qquad (10.44)$$

These relations assume perfectly diffusing surfaces of uniform luminosity located as shown in Fig. 10.31. The theorem is not limited to two planes at right angles but applies to planes at any other angle including planes that are parallel.

The reciprocity theorem is especially useful in dealing with rectangular sources. The fundamental formulas are given in Table XXXVIII. The simplest case is shown where the source 1 is perpendicular to the receiving surface 2 and the two surfaces have a common edge of length W. The flux incident on surface 2 from surface 1 is desired. Denoting this flux by F_{12} and using the results of Yamauti's work,*

$$F_{12} = \frac{2W^2 L}{\pi}[\Phi(\beta) - \Phi(\beta_1) + \Phi(\alpha)] \qquad (10.45)$$

where $\alpha = \tan^{-1}\dfrac{W}{H}$, $\quad \beta = \tan^{-1}\dfrac{W}{D}$, $\quad \beta_1 = \tan^{-1}\dfrac{W}{\sqrt{H^2 + D^2}}$,

and

$$\Phi(\omega) = \tfrac{1}{2}[\omega \cot \omega - \tfrac{1}{2}\log \sin \omega + \tfrac{1}{2}\cot^2 \omega \log \cos \omega] \qquad (10.46)$$

Values of this function are given in Table XXXIX.

For the particular case of a square window and a square floor,

$$\tan \beta = \tan \alpha = 1.00$$

$$\tan \beta_1 = \frac{1}{\sqrt{2}} = 0.707$$

---

* The function Φ corresponds to the φ_2 of Yamauti, *Research Bull.* 250.

TABLE XXXVIII

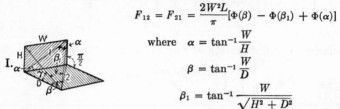

$$F_{12} = F_{21} = \frac{2W^2 L}{\pi}[\Phi(\beta) - \Phi(\beta_1) + \Phi(\alpha)]$$

$$\text{where} \quad \alpha = \tan^{-1}\frac{W}{H}$$

$$\beta = \tan^{-1}\frac{W}{D}$$

$$\beta_1 = \tan^{-1}\frac{W}{\sqrt{H^2 + D^2}}$$

I.

$$\Phi(\omega) = \tfrac{1}{2}(\omega \cot \omega - \tfrac{1}{2}\log\sin\omega + \tfrac{1}{2}\cot^2\omega\log\cos\omega)$$

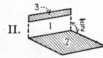

II.

$$F_{32} = F_{(1+3)2} - F_{12}$$

III.

$$F_{14} = \tfrac{1}{2}[F_{(1+3)(2+4)} - F_{12} - F_{34}]$$

IV.

$$F_{1(2+4)} = F_{12} + F_{14}$$
$$= F_{12} + \tfrac{1}{2}[F_{(1+3)(2+4)} - F_{34} - F_{12}]$$
$$= \tfrac{1}{2}[F_{(1+3)(2+4)} - F_{34} + F_{12}]$$

V.

$$F_{3(2+4+6)} = F_{34} + F_{32} + F_{36}$$
$$= \tfrac{1}{2}[F_{(1+3)(2+4)} + F_{(3+5)(4+6)} - F_{12} - F_{56}]$$

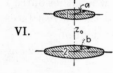

VI.

$$F_{12} = F_{21} = \pi\frac{L}{2}[z_0{}^2 + a^2 + b^2 - \sqrt{(z_0{}^2 + a^2 + b^2)^2 - 4a^2 b^2}]$$

$$F_{12} = \frac{4L}{\pi}[H^2\{\Phi(\gamma_1) - \Phi(\gamma)\} + W^2\{\Phi(\beta_1) - \Phi(\beta)\}]$$

$$\text{where} \quad \gamma_1 = \tan^{-1}\frac{H}{\sqrt{W^2 + D^2}}$$

VII.

$$\gamma = \tan^{-1}\frac{H}{D}$$

$$\beta_1 = \tan^{-1}\frac{W}{\sqrt{H^2 + D^2}}$$

$$\beta = \tan^{-1}\frac{W}{D}$$

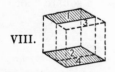

VIII.

$$F_{1(2+4)} = F_{12} + F_{14}$$
$$= F_{12} + \tfrac{1}{2}[F_{(1+3)(2+4)} - F_{12} - F_{34}]$$
$$= \tfrac{1}{2}[F_{(1+3)(2+4)} + F_{12} - F_{34}]$$

Table XXXIX gives the corresponding values of Φ

$$\Phi(\beta) = \Phi(\alpha) = 0.3927$$
$$\Phi(\beta_1) = 0.4712$$

and

$$F_{12} = \frac{2W^2L}{\pi}[2(0.3927) - 0.4712] = \frac{0.6284}{\pi}W^2L$$

For 10-ft. squares and $L = 200$ lumens/sq ft, for instance.

$$F_{12} = \frac{0.6284}{\pi}(100)(200) = 4000 \text{ lumens}$$

If the luminous source does not extend down to the illuminated plane, as shown in II of Table XXXVIII, a scheme similar to that used in calculating illumination from rectangles (Sec. 9.07) may be used. The formula, Eq. (10.45), applies only when the two areas have a common edge. Thus we first take a fictitious source consisting of both 1 and 3. The flux received by area 2 from $(1 + 3)$ is denoted by $F_{(1+3)2}$. From this must be subtracted the flux F_{12} due to the source 1, and

$$F_{32} = F_{(1+3)2} - F_{12} \tag{10.47}$$

Each term on the right-hand side is evaluated by use of Eq. (10.45) and Table XXXIX, taking the proper values for the angle in each case.

Now we come to a slightly more complicated case (III of Table XXXVIII), where the flux received by area 4 from area 1 is to be obtained. Evidently, the only combinations for which we can use Eq. (10.45) are $(1 + 3)$ and $(2 + 4)$, or 1 and 2 or 3 and 4. Since the flux received by $(2 + 4)$ from $(1 + 3)$ is larger than the flux desired, subtract the two fluxes F_{12} and F_{34}, giving

$$F_{(1+3)(2+4)} - F_{12} - F_{34}$$

From the fact that the total flux from area 1 to area $(2 + 4)$ may be considered as the sum of the flux from 1 to 2 plus the flux from 1 to 4, and similarly for the flux from 3,

$$F_{(1+3)(2+4)} = F_{12} + F_{32} + F_{14} + F_{34}$$

Thus,

$$F_{(1+3)(2+4)} - F_{12} - F_{34} = F_{14} + F_{32} \tag{10.48}$$

According to the reciprocity theorem, Eq. (10.44), the two terms on the right-hand side of Eq. (10.48) are equal, so that

$$F_{14} = F_{34} = F_{41} = F_{43} = \tfrac{1}{2}[F_{(1+3)(2+4)} - F_{12} - F_{34}] \quad (10.49)$$

Equation (10.49) allows the calculation of the flux in Case III (Table XXXVIII), by a simple use of Eq. (10.45) and Table XXXIX. Equation (10.49) is also useful in obtaining the flux in more complicated forms, such as the other cases given in Table XXXVIII.

For parallel planes, the methods are exactly the same, and the reciprocity laws apply as before. A somewhat different formula

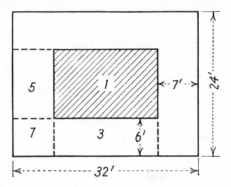

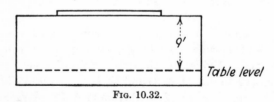

Fig. 10.32.

must be used, however, in computing the flux. As indicated in Case VII of Table XXXVIII,

$$F_{12} = \frac{4L}{\pi}[H^2\{\Phi(\gamma_1) - \Phi(\gamma)\} + W^2\{\Phi(\beta_1) - \Phi(\beta)\}] \quad (10.50)$$

where $\gamma_1 = \tan^{-1}\dfrac{H}{\sqrt{W^2 + D^2}},$ $\beta_1 = \tan^{-1}\dfrac{W}{\sqrt{H^2 + D^2}},$

$\gamma = \tan^{-1}\dfrac{H}{D},$ $\beta = \tan^{-1}\dfrac{W}{D},$

and Φ is the same flux function used previously and tabulated in Table XXXIX. More complicated forms are solved similarly.

As an example of the determination of total flux and average illumination, take the small library which was used in Chap. IX and which is again shown in Fig. 10.32. The luminosity of the ceiling panel is 78.4 lumens/sq. ft, and the value of the average illumination is required on the plane of the table tops.

From Table XXXVIII,

$$F_{1(2+4+\cdots)} = F_{(1+3+5+7)(2+4+6+8)} - F_{(3+7)(4+8)} - F_{(5+7)(6+8)} + F_{78}$$

It is now necessary to consider these four terms, one by one, and to use Eq. (10.50) with each. For the first term, we take a source 18 by 25 ft. Thus,

$$H = 25$$
$$W = 18$$
$$D = 9$$

$$\tan \gamma_1 = \frac{25}{\sqrt{405}} = 1.242 \qquad \Phi(\gamma_1) = 0.3463$$

$$\tan \gamma = \frac{25}{9} = 2.777 \qquad \Phi(\gamma) = 0.2007$$

$$\tan \beta_1 = \frac{18}{\sqrt{706}} = 0.6775 \qquad \Phi(\beta_1) = 0.4811$$

$$\tan \beta = \frac{18}{9} = 2.000 \qquad \Phi(\beta) = 0.2544$$

Therefore,

$$F_{(1+3+5+7)(2+4+6+8)} = \frac{4L}{\pi}[625\{0.3463 - 0.2007\} + 324\{0.4811 - 0.2544\}]$$

$$= \frac{4L}{\pi}(164.45) \text{ lumens}$$

A tabulation of the calculations is as follows:

Quantity	$F_{(1+\cdots)(2+\cdots)}$	F_{78}	$F_{(3+7)(4+8)}$	$F_{(5+7)(6+8)}$
H	25	7	25	7
W	18	6	6	18
D	9	9	9	9
$\tan \gamma_1$	1.242	0.6472	2.311	0.3478
$\tan \gamma$	2.777	0.7778	2.777	0.7778
$\tan \beta_1$	0.6775	0.5265	0.2258	1.579
$\tan \beta$	2.000	0.6667	0.6667	2.000
$\Phi(\gamma_1)$	0.3463	0.4919	0.2293	0.6415
$\Phi(\gamma)$	0.2007	0.4492	0.2007	0.4492
$\Phi(\beta_1)$	0.4811	0.5410	0.7481	0.2981
$\Phi(\beta)$	0.2544	0.4849	0.4849	0.2544
$F/(4L/\pi)$	164.45	4.11	27.36	23.58

The total flux is therefore

$$F_{1(2+\cdots)} = \frac{4(78.4)}{\pi}[164.45 - 50.94 + 4.11]$$
$$= 11,740 \text{ lumens}$$

The average illumination is

$$E_{av} = \frac{F}{A} = \frac{11,740}{32 \times 24} = 15.29 \text{ lumens/sq ft}$$

The average illumination can be approximated by dividing the room into a number of equal areas and averaging the values of illumination at the center of each area. The accuracy is dependent upon the number of equal areas considered.

The results for E_{av} obtained by using 1, 4, 16, and 64 areas (Fig. 9.22) are given below:

Number of Points Considered	E_{av} Lumens/Square Ft
1	34.73
4	16.50
16	16.18
64	15.34
∞ (method of this section)	15.29

Problem 123. Obtain E_{av} on the entire floor of Prob. 99 (Chap. IX), using the method of Sec. 10.11.

Check this result by use of the data obtained in the problem of Chap. IX.

Problem 124. It is proposed to detect the presence of enemy aircraft in night warfare by their temperature radiation. All other sources of radiation being neglected, what would be the irradiation at a distance of one mile due to a spherical balloon of 30 ft diameter, at a temperature of 30°C? Could it be detected by a sensitive radiation-measuring device? Assume that e_λ is approximately unity.

Problem 125. Obtain E_{av} for Prob. 100 (Chap. IX), using the methods of Chap. X.

Problem 126. Calculate the illumination produced on the earth by full moonlight, neglecting atmospheric absorption. Assume that the spectral irradiation of the moon is the same as that of the earth and that the spectral reflection factor of the moon is 0.50 at all wavelengths.

Problem 127. A hot-water radiator is operating at 110°F, and the surface has a spectral radiation factor of 0.80. The radiator can be approximated by 10 elliptical cylinders resting on the floor and having a height of 20 in., a major axis of 10 in., and a minor axis of 2 in., spaced 3½ in. apart (between centers). A wall of the room is 3 ft from the center of the radiator and parallel to the long sides.

Calculate the irradiation at a point on this wall 10 in. above the floor and 10 in. beyond the end of the radiator. (Two significant figures in the answer are sufficient.)

TABLE XXXIX.—FLUX FUNCTIONS

(Based on Yamauti, *Electrot. Lab. Tokyo, Researches* 250)

tan ω	Φ(ω)	Δ	tan ω	Φ(ω)	Δ
0.00	∞	....	0.50	0.55326	476
01	1.5263	1733	51	54850	466
02	1.3530	1013	52	54384	457
03	1.2517	719	53	53927	447
04	1.1798	558	54	53480	438
0.05	1.1240	456	0.55	53042	430
06	1.0784	385	56	52612	422
07	1.0399	333	57	52190	413
08	1.0066	2945	58	51777	406
09	0.97715	2630	59	51371	398
0.10	95085	2378	0.60	50973	392
11	92707	2170	61	50581	384
12	90537	1996	62	50197	377
13	88541	1848	63	49820	371
14	86693	1718	64	49449	364
0.15	84975	1607	0.65	49085	358
16	83368	1509	66	48727	353
17	81859	1422	67	48374	346
18	80437	1344	68	48028	341
19	79093	1274	69	47687	335
0.20	77819	1212	0.70	47352	330
21	76607	1154	71	47022	325
22	75453	1102	72	46697	319
23	74351	1054	73	46378	315
24	73297	1011	74	46063	310
0.25	72286	970	0.75	45753	305
26	71316	933	76	45448	301
27	70383	898	77	45147	296
28	69485	866	78	44851	292
29	68619	835	79	44559	287
0.30	67784	808	0.80	44272	284
31	66976	781	81	43988	280
32	66195	756	82	43708	275
33	65439	733	83	43433	272
34	64706	711	84	43161	268
0.35	63995	690	0.85	42893	264
36	63305	671	86	42629	261
37	62634	652	87	42368	257
38	61982	634	88	42111	254
39	61348	617	89	41857	251
0.40	60731	602	0.90	41606	247
41	60129	586	91	41359	244
42	59543	572	92	41115	241
43	58971	558	93	40874	238
44	58413	544	94	40636	235
0.45	57869	532	0.95	40401	232
46	57337	520	96	40169	229
47	56817	508	97	39940	226
48	56309	497	98	39714	223
49	55812	486	99	39491	221
0.50	55326	476	1.00	39270	220

TABLE XXXIX.—FLUX FUNCTIONS.—(*Continued*)

tan ω	Φ(ω)	Δ	tan ω	Φ(ω)	Δ
1.0000	0.39270		2.0000	0.25439	
1.0101	39050	220	2.0408	25084	355
1.0204	38828	222	2.0833	24726	358
1.0309	38604	224	2.1277	24363	363
1.0417	38378	226	2.1739	23996	367
		227			371
1.0526	38151	230	2.2222	23625	376
1.0638	37921	231	2.2727	23249	381
1.0753	37690	233	2.3256	22868	385
1.0870	37457	235	2.3810	22483	389
1.0989	37222		2.4390	22094	395
		237			395
1.1111	36985	239	2.5000	21699	399
1.1236	36746	241	2.5641	21300	405
1.1364	36505	243	2.6316	20895	410
1.1494	36262	246	2.7027	20485	415
1.1628	36016	247	2.7778	20070	420
1.1765	35769	250	2.8571	19650	426
1.1905	35519	252	2.9412	19224	432
1.2048	35267	254	3.0303	18792	438
1.2195	35013	256	3.1250	18354	443
1.2346	34757	259	3.2258	17911	450
1.2500	34498	261	3.3333	17461	455
1.2658	34237	263	3.4483	17006	462
1.2821	33974	266	3.5714	16544	469
1.2987	33708	269	3.7037	16075	476
1.3158	33439	270	3.8462	15599	482
1.3333	33169	274	4.0000	15117	489
1.3514	32895	276	4.1667	14628	497
1.3699	32619	278	4.3478	14131	504
1.3889	32341	282	4.5455	13627	512
1.4085	32059	284	4.7619	13115	520
1.4286	31775	286	5.0000	12595	528
1.4493	31489	290	5.2632	12067	536
1.4706	31199	293	5.5556	11531	545
1.4925	30906	295	5.8824	10986	554
1.5152	30611	298	6.2500	0.10432	563
1.5385	30313	302	6.6667	[1]98690	5726
1.5625	30011	304	7.1429	92964	5826
1.5873	29707	308	7.6923	87138	5927
1.6129	29399	311	8.3333	81211	6035
1.6393	29088	314	9.0909	75176	6145
1.6667	28774	318	10.000	[1]69031	6260
1.6949	28456	321	11.111	62771	6381
1.7241	28135	324	12.500	56390	6508
1.7544	27811	328	14.286	49882	6640
1.7857	27483	331	16.667	43242	6782
1.8182	27152	335	20.000	[1]36460	6932
1.8519	26817	339	25.000	29528	7093
1.8868	26478	343	33.333	22435	7268
1.9231	26135	346	50.000	15167	7466
1.9608	25789	350	100.000	[2]77013	
2.0000	25439	355	∞	00000	

NOTE.—Decimal points before numbers have been omitted. A superscript 1 or 2 indicates the number of zeros that have been omitted after the decimal point. Thus for tan ω = 100, Φ = 0.0077013. The columns marked Δ give first differences between values of Φ.

Bibliography

GENERAL

1. A. BEER: Grundriss des photometrischen Calcüles, Vieweg, Braunschweig, Germany, 1854, p. 61.
2. H. H. HIGBIE: Lighting Calculations, Chap. V, John Wiley & Sons, Inc., New York, 1934.
3. Z. YAMAUTI: Geometrical Calculation of Illumination, *Electrot. Lab. Tokyo, Researches*, 148, 1924.
4. Z. YAMAUTI: Further Study of Geometrical Calculation of Illumination, *Electrot. Lab. Tokyo, Researches*, 194, 1927.
5. E. B. ROSA: Photometric Units and Nomenclature, *Bu. Stds. Bull.*, **6**, 1910, p. 543.
6. W. E. SUMPNER: The Diffusion of Light, *Phys. Soc., Proc.*, **12**, 1892, p. 10.
7. W. E. SUMPNER: The Diffusion of Light, *Phil. Mag.*, **35**, 1893, p. 81.
8. A. S. MCALLISTER: Graphical Solution of Problems Involving Plane-surface Lighting Sources, *El. World*, **56**, 1910, p. 1356.
9. A. S. MCALLISTER: The Law of Conservation as Applied to Illumination Calculations, *I.E.S. Trans.*, **6**, 1911, p. 703.
10. C. F. ZEE: Rectangular Windows of Variable Luminosity, M.I.T. thesis, 1935.
11. M. COHU: Calcul rapide de l'éclairement moyen dans le cas d'appareils symétriques, *R.G.E.*, **20**, 1926, p. 377.
12. K. HISANO: Calculation of Illumination from an Extended Diffusing Surface, *Electrot. Lab. Tokyo, Researches*, 353, 1933.
13. K. HISANO: Graphical Methods for the Calculation of Light Flux Incident to Illuminated Plane from Surface Source, *Electrot. Lab. Tokyo, Researches*, 367, 1934.
14. J. DOURGNON: Étude sur quelques dispositifs d'éclairage, *R.G.E.*, **23**, 1928, p. 609.
15. DOURGNON and WAGUET: Procédé de calcul des éclairements produits par des sources non ponctuelles, *Comptes Rendus*, **189**, 1929, p. 361.
16. DOURGNON and WAGUET: Les diffuseurs de lumière, *R.G.E.*, **25**, 1929, p. 435.
17. DOURGNON and WAGUET: Optique des surfaces diffusantes, *R.G.E.*, **26**, 1929, p. 863.

VECTOR METHOD AND CONTOUR INTEGRATION

18. E. P. HYDE: Geometrical Theory of Radiating Surfaces, *Bu. Stds. Bull.*, **3**, 1907, p. 81.
19. B. JONES: On Finite Surface Light Sources, *I.E.S. Trans.*, **4**, 1909; **5**, 1910, p. 281.
20. V. FOCK: Освещенностъ от поверхностей произвольной формы, *Opt. Inst. Trans., Leningrad*, **3**, 1924, No. 28.
21. S. O. MAISEL: Освещенностъ от сопъw их поверхностей и применение их к фотометрии, *Opt. Inst. Trans., Leningrad*, **3**, 1923, No. 16.
22. GERSCHUN and GUREVIČ: Световое поте, *Russ. Phys. Chem. Soc. J.*, Physics Section, **60**, 1928, p. 355.

23. M. M. Gurevič: Векторное преꞃставꞃениie основныlх фото-
    метрꙶиуеских веꙶиуꙶн, *Opt. Soc. Trans.*, *Leningrad*, **5**, 1929, No. 44.
24. M. M. Gurevič: Eine Vektordarstellung der photometrischen Grössen,
    Phys. Zeits., **30**, 1929, p. 640.
25. Z. Yamauti: Theory of Field of Illumination, *Electrot. Lab. Tokyo,
    Researches*, 339, 1932.

INTERREFLECTIONS

26. H. Buckley: On the Radiation from the Inside of a Circular Cylinder,
    Phil. Mag., **4**, 1927, p. 753; **6**, 1928, p. 447.
27. H. Buckley: On the Blackness of Black Bodies, *J.O.S.A.*, **18**, 1929,
    p. 216.
28. S. P. Owen: On Radiation from a Cylindrical Wall, *Phil. Mag.*, **39**,
    1920, p. 359.
29. A. C. Bartlett: On Radiation from a Cylindrical Wall, *Phil. Mag.*,
    40, 1920, p. 111.
30. E. T.Whittaker: On the Numerical Solution of Integral Equations,
    Proc. Roy. Soc., **94**, 1918, p. 367.
31. A. D. Moore: Inter-reflection by the Increment Method, *I.E.S. Trans.*,
    24, 1929, p. 629.
32. Manning and White: Brightness Distribution in a Light Well, *I.E.S.
    Trans.*, **25**, 1930, p. 663.

TOTAL FLUX

33. Z. Yamauti: The Amount of Flux through Rectangular Windows,
    Electrot. Lab. Tokyo, Researches, 250, 1929.
34. E. A. Milne: Note on a Geometrical Radiation Problem, *Phil. Mag.*,
    7, 1929, p. 273.
35. A. Gerschun: Uniformly Diffused Light through Two Apertures,
    Phil. Mag., **7**, 1929, p. 419.
36. C. E. Wright: Note on a Geometrical Radiation Theorem, *Phil. Mag.*,
    7, 1929, p. 946.
37. J. W. T. Walsh: Uniformly Diffused Light through Two Apertures,
    Phil. Mag., **8**, 1929, p. 1093.
38. O. A. Saunders: Notes on some Geometrical Radiation Problems,
    Phil. Mag., **8**, 1929, p. 213.
39. Harrison and Anderson: Illumination Efficiencies as Determined in
    an Experimental Room, *I.E.S. Trans.*, **11**, 1916, p. 67.
40. Harrison and Anderson: Coefficients of Utilization, *I.E.S. Trans.*,
    15, 1920, p. 97.
41. Cohu and Dourgnon: Le coefficient d'utilisation d'un espace clos,
    R.G.E., **21**, 1927, p. 531.
42. W. Margoulis: Étude nomographique pour la détermination des
    coefficients d'utilisation, *R.G.E.*, **24**, 1928, p. 439.
43. J. Dourgnon: Nouvelle méthode de prédétermination des coefficients
    d'utilisation, *R.G.E.*, **23**, 1928, p. 271; **33**, 1933, p. 579.

CHAPTER XI

ELEMENTS OF LIGHTING DESIGN

The preceding chapters have treated various methods of calculating illumination. We shall now apply some of this information to the design of lighting systems. The present chapter includes the design of

Interior lighting systems, using commercial luminaires.

Interior lighting systems, using luminous panels or other built-in equipment.

Natural lighting systems for interiors, using windows or skylights.

Floodlight systems.

11.02. The Lumen Method of Calculating Illumination.— Calculation of illumination by the point-by-point method is theoretically possible in all cases, though it may be extremely laborious, particularly if reflections from walls and ceiling are important. Thus there is need for a simple method which will give fairly accurate results with less computation. The *lumen method*, devised by Harrison and Anderson,[1,2] gives less detailed and less accurate information than the point-by-point method; but, because of the simplicity and brevity of its computations, it is used extensively in practice. The point-by-point method and the lumen method are not to be regarded as rivals but rather as mutually supplementary methods. The lumen method is useful in the design of lighting installations and provides a convenient way for obtaining the *average* illumination on a horizontal plane. It gives no information on the variation of illumination from point to point or on the illumination at any given point. If the illumination at a given point is desired, the point-by-point method must be used.

The lumen method is based upon the principle of the conservation of energy. Imagine a room with perfectly reflecting walls and ceiling and a perfectly absorbing floor, lighted by luminaires that absorb no light. The room may be of any size and shape and may be lighted by any number of luminaires arranged in any manner. Irrespective of the distribution of luminous flux emitted by the luminaires or of how many times the flux is reflected by walls and ceiling, all of the flux must eventually reach the floor and there be absorbed. Evidently, the *average* illumination on the floor will be

$$E_{av} = \frac{F_L}{A} \quad \text{(lumens/sq ft)}$$

where F_L = total luminous flux emitted by the lamps.

A = floor area of the room (sq ft).

In an actual room, light will be absorbed by the walls, ceiling, and luminaires, and the average illumination E_{av} will be reduced; so we may write

$$E_{av} = \frac{F_L}{A} k_u \quad \text{(lumens/sq ft)} \quad (11.01)$$

where k_u = a numerical factor called the *coefficient of utilization* This factor is the ratio of the useful luminous flux to the luminous flux emitted by the lamps and is thus a measure of the effectiveness of a given installation in utilizing the lamp lumens. For example, in a certain room lighted by lamps in metal reflectors which throw all the light downward, $k_u = 0.46$; but if a totally indirect unit is used, the coefficient of utilization is found to be reduced to 0.22.

In the ideal room with perfectly reflecting walls and ceiling, the shape of the room and the candlepower distribution of the luminaires have no effect on the resulting illumination. In the actual room, these and other factors have an important bearing on E_{av} and must be included in k_u. This was accomplished experimentally by actually measuring the illumination in rooms of various shapes and with various walls and ceilings, lighted by various luminaires. The final results are tabulated in the *Transactions* of the I.E.S.[*] and have been plotted on (Appendix F) curve sheets 1 to 12. The data are based upon measurements made on a horizontal plane at the average desk level, so that E_{av} calculated from Eq. (11.01) using the experimental values of k_u will be the average illumination on the working plane rather than on the floor.

The Coefficient of Utilization.—The average illumination is calculated by the use of Eq. (11.01), provided k_u is known. The

[*] **15,** 1920, p. 97.

problem thus reduces to one of obtaining k_u for all conditions. The coefficient of utilization depends on

1. Shape of room.
2. Luminaire.
   a. Proportion of light absorbed by luminaire.
   b. Distribution of light from luminaire.
3. Reflection factor of ceiling (ρ_c).
4. Reflection factor of walls (ρ_w).

The coefficient of utilization depends upon the *shape* of the room but not upon its size, the size being taken care of by A in Eq. (11.01). A room whose length l and width w are large compared with the height h will have a coefficient of utilization higher than that of a high, narrow room because less light will be absorbed by the walls in the first room. With *square* rooms of various heights, it is convenient to plot the experimental results against a new variable h/w which we shall denote by k_r.* Tests show that as k_r increase, k_u decreases, though the relation is not a linear one. For rectangular rooms, this definition of k_r no longer applies, but experiment shows that k_r may be defined by the empirical equation

$$k_r = \frac{h}{0.90w + 0.10l} \tag{11.02}$$

where h = height of room, floor to ceiling.
    w = width of room.
    l = length of room.

For a square room, Eq. (11.02) reduces to the previous definition:

$$k_r = \frac{h}{w} \tag{11.02a}$$

For a cubic room, $k_r = 1.00$.

The room shape is thus expressed by a factor k_r against which test results may be plotted. The effects of the type of luminaire and the reflection factors of walls and ceiling are still to be taken into account. Consider, for instance, a room lighted by luminous panels flush with the ceiling. Such lighting units are said to be of the direct type, since all luminous flux is emitted in the lower hemisphere ($0 \leqq \theta \leqq 90$ deg). We therefore turn to curve sheet

* Note that k_r as used in the present treatment is the reciprocal of what is generally termed the "room index."

1 (Appendix F), which gives experimental results for direct-type lighting units. The abscissas represent k_r, while the ordinates are values of

$$f_d = \frac{\text{total flux on working plane}}{\text{total flux emitted by luminaire}}$$

If we represent the efficiency of the luminaire by g_d,

$$g_d = \frac{\text{total flux emitted by luminaire}}{F_L}$$

and

$$k_u = f_d g_d \qquad (11.03)$$

Example. A room 30 by 50 ft with a 15-ft ceiling is lighted by luminous ceiling panels. $F_L = 100,000$ lumens. It is found that 50 per cent of the lamp lumens are emitted by the diffusing glass, so $g_d = 0.50$. The walls reflect 50 per cent while the ceiling reflects practically nothing. What is the average illumination on the working plane?

According to Eq. (11.02),

$$k_r = \frac{15}{0.90(30) + 0.10(50)} = 0.469 \qquad (11.02a)$$

The curve marked $\rho_w = 0.50$ of curve sheet 1 is used, and

$$f_d = 0.747$$

The coefficient of utilization is

$$k_u = f_d g_d = 0.747(0.50) = 0.374$$

The average illumination on a horizontal plane is

$$E_{\text{av}} = \frac{F_L}{A} k_u = \frac{100,000}{30 \times 50} 0.374 = \textbf{24.9 lumens/sq ft}$$

Other Luminaires.—For other luminaires which emit all their flux in the lower hemisphere, the procedure is exactly as in the example just given. It might be expected that the reflection factor of the ceiling would have no effect with such luminaires. Test results, as shown by curves 1 and 2, show a slight effect due to multiple reflections between floor and ceiling. Curves for $\rho_c = 0$ and $\rho_c = 0.80$ have been included. For other values of ρ_c, f_d can be found by linear interpolation. Two other factors may increase the illumination slightly—an unusually low mounting height of the reflector or an unusually narrow beam spread. The curves are for commercial practice, with reflectors within a few feet of the ceiling and having a medium beam spread. In case of concentrated-beam reflectors, it may be advisable to raise the values of k_u by about 0.02; and for very broad spread, the values may be lowered by the same amount. For ordinary conditions, however, the results as given are satisfactory.

For totally indirect units, such as steel-bowl fixtures or for cove lighting, the procedure is the same except that the indirect-component curves (3 to 6) are used. For a fixture with a candle-power-distribution curve represented by

$$I(\theta) = I_{90} \sin \theta \qquad (11.04)$$

the horizontal-component curves (7 to 12) are used.

Most luminaires, however, emit luminous flux in all directions, and in such cases it is necessary to divide the total flux into three components and treat each component separately. The luminaire test data required are

1. Candlepower at 90 deg (I_{90}).
2. Total flux in 0- to 90-deg zone (F_{0-90}).
3. Total flux in 90- to 180-deg zone (F_{90-180}).
4. Lamp lumens (F_L).

The subdivision is then made as follows: The horizontal component of luminous flux is made to conform with Eq. (11.04), with I_{90} equal to the actual value obtained from the luminaire. The horizontal component of flux is

$$F_h = 9.87 I_{90} \qquad (11.05)$$

The downward component of flux F_d must be the difference between the flux in the 0- to 90-deg zone and one-half the horizontal component F_h, or

$$F_d = F_{0-90} - \frac{F_h}{2} \qquad (11.06)$$

Similarly,

$$F_i = F_{90-180} - \frac{F_h}{2} \qquad (11.07)$$

The three components in terms of F_L are

$$g_h = \frac{F_h}{F_L}, \qquad g_d = \frac{F_d}{F_L}, \qquad g_i = \frac{F_i}{F_L} \qquad (11.08)$$

Example. A representative diffusing globe of opal glass gave the following test results (Fig. 11.01):

$$I_{90} = 188 \text{ candles}$$
$$F_{0-90} = 1582 \text{ lumens}$$
$$F_{90-180} = 1153 \text{ lumens}$$
$$F_L = 3283 \text{ lumens}$$

The horizontal component of flux is

$$F_h = 9.87(188) \quad = 1860 \text{ lumens}$$

By Eq. (11.08),

$$g_h = {}^{1860}\!/_{3283} = 0.567$$
$$g_d = \frac{1582 - 930}{3283} = 0.198$$
$$g_i = \frac{1153 - 930}{3283} = 0.068$$

$$\text{Total} = 0.833$$

The total shows that **83.3 per cent** of the lamp lumens are emitted by the globe.

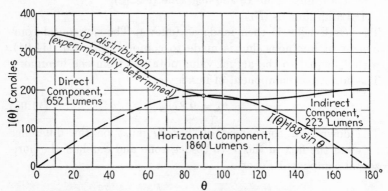

Fig. 11.01.—Candlepower-distribution curve for a typical diffusing-globe luminaire, 200-watt lamp, 3280 lumens.

Values of g_h, g_d, g_i for a number of commercial luminaires are given in Table XL. Values for other luminaires can be obtained as in the example just given. If the values for the coefficients are known, the value of k_u for any given room can be obtained by summing the components.

$$k_u = g_h f_h + g_d f_d + g_i f_i \qquad (11.09)$$

Table XL.—Efficiency Factors for Commercial Luminaires

Values are obtained from tests, made in most cases on single samples. Differences between individual units of the same type made by the same manufacturer, however, are fairly large; so these tables cannot be used to compare the products of different manufacturers, nor can they be expected to hold exactly for a single luminaire or any number of luminaires purchased at random.

Direct Type

Name	Manufacturer	g_h	g_d	g_i	Luminaire total flux/F_L
RLM, clear lamp		0	0.757	0	0.757
RLM, I.F. lamp		0	0.720	0	0.720
RLM, Silvray lamp		0	0.625	0	0.625
"Industrial unit"	Silvray	0	0.685	0	0.685
Glassteel		0.119	0.540	0.010	0.669
Shallow bowl 5509	Benjamin	0	0.788	0	0.788
Deep bowl	Benjamin	0	0.660	0	0.660
Deep bowl PEC-200	Wheeler	0	0.690	0	0.690
Deep bowl (glass)	Curtis	0	0.700	0	0.700
Vapolux RLM		0	0.600	0	0.600
Vapolux bowl		0	0.500	0	0.500
Vaporproof RLM		0	0.620	0	0.620
Vaporproof bowl		0	0.560	0	0.560
Industrial glass shade	Holophane 6583	0.274	0.546	0.034	0.854
Industrial glass shade	Holophane 6543	0.309	0.545	−0.004	0.850
Industrial glass shade	Holophane 622	0.341	0.529	0.020	0.890
Industrial shade	Holophane 661	0	0.620	0.170	0.790
Reflector refractor	Holophane 2180	0.341	0.444	0.061	0.846
Reflector refractor	Holophane 2170	0.311	0.444	0.095	0.850
Reflector refractor	Holophane 2140	0.362	0.409	0.049	0.820
Diffusing ceiling panel	Average	0	0.500	0	0.500
S-2 lamp unit	Holophane SUV-2130	0.161	0.470	−0.030	0.601
Ceiling unit	Holophane FC-5530	0	0.415	0	0.415
Prismatic unit	Holophane 1011	0.413	0.469	−0.094	0.788

Diffusing Type

Name	Manufacturer	g_h	g_d	g_i	Luminaire total flux/F_L
Hyperion 8614	Gill	0.545	0.174	0.092	0.811
Kayline 5728	Kayline	0.654	0.152	0.099	0.905
Graybar 9920	Graybar	0.550	0.222	0.072	0.844
Graybar 7720	Graybar	0.435	0.033	0.320	0.788
Galax 5885	Macbeth	0.491	0.013	0.332	0.836
Galax 12011	Macbeth	0.360	0.124	0.277	0.761
Monax 5297	Macbeth	0.567	0.198	0.068	0.833
Monax 5130	Macbeth	0.554	0.183	0.087	0.824
Monax 5282-A	Macbeth	0.518	0.230	0.105	0.853
Monax 5198	Macbeth	0.604	0.155	0.065	0.824
Monax 3756	Macbeth	0.606	0.164	0.072	0.842
Monax 5290	Macbeth	0.490	0.210	0.083	0.783
Monax 3866-A	Macbeth	0.789	0.105	0.001	0.895
Royalite Type A	Cherniak	0.730	0.144	0.024	0.898
Royalite Type B	Cherniak	0.606	0.203	0.073	0.882
Attalite 5436	Miller	0.450	0.244	0.126	0.820
Ivanhoe 5243	Miller	0.392	0.103	0.213	0.708

Table XL.—Efficiency Factors for Commercial Luminaires.—
(*Continued*)

Name	Manufacturer	g_h	g_d	g_i	Luminaire total flux/F_L
Silvo 5662	Miller	0.426	0.197	0.032	0.655
Saturn 5869	Miller	0.496	0.090	0.248	0.834
Celestialite 5662	Miller	0.414	0.158	0.068	0.640
Heavy opal glass globe	Miller	0.445	−0.103	0.418	0.760
Planetlite	Planetlite	0.643	0.346	−0.169	0.820
Planetlite 1429	Planetlite	0.603	0.255	−0.123	0.735
Planetlite 1229	Planetlite	0.593	0.319	−0.140	0.772
Brascolite W3464	Guth	0.715	0.273	−0.087	0.901
Guth Glo	Guth	0.390	0	0	0.390
Clear lamp	Mazda	0.716	0.150	0.134	1.000
I.F. lamp	Mazda	0.727	0.156	0.117	1.000

Indirect and Semi-indirect Types

Name	Manufacturer	g_h	g_d	g_i	Luminaire total flux/F_L
Super Illuminator R4410	Guth	0	0	0.870	0.870
DM-41 (white inside)	Miller	0	0	0.665	0.665
DM-41 (Al inside)	Miller	0	0.013	0.560	0.573
DM-42 (white)	Miller	0	0.190	0.677	0.867
DM-42 (Al inside)	Miller	0	0.143	0.595	0.738
Duplexalite D-568 (Hancock Disk)	Miller	0.045	0.041	0.527	0.613
Duplexalite D-561 (Irristone)	Miller	0.033	0.030	0.601	0.664
Duplexalite D-561 (Genco)	Miller	0.033	0.041	0.606	0.680
Duplexalite D-561 (Lunistone)	Miller	0.031	0.120	0.537	0.688
Keldon 5363	Miller	0.333	0.039	0.383	0.755
Shirdon	Miller	0.024	0.005	0.708	0.737
Bilite	Silvray	0.129	−0.051	0.850	0.928
Open Bowl No. 16	Graybar	0.151	0.092	0.629	0.872
Semi-indirect 171-G	Wakefield	0.225	0.042	0.489	0.756
Semi-indirect 101-G	Wakefield	0.202	0.076	0.469	0.747
21 in. globe	Wakefield	0.395	0.057	0.318	0.770
Indirect	Holophane	0	0	0.730	0.730
Filterlite F-500	Holophane	0.272	−0.016	0.444	0.700
Filterlite CF-300	Holophane	0.338	0.090	0.398	0.826
Menlo	Spertus	0	0.021	0.755	0.776
Prismatic R-500	Holophane	0	0.050	0.579	0.629
Excelite	Gill	0.291	0.065	0.464	0.820
Silver-plated lamp	Silvray	0.598	−0.258	0.630	0.970
X-ray EC-345	Curtis	0	0	0.840	0.840

For the luminaire (Fig. 11.01) used in a room 10 by 10 by 10 ft and with $\rho_c = 0.70$, $\rho_w = 0.30$, and $F = 3360$,

$$f_h = 0.240$$
$$f_d = 0.579$$
$$f_c = 0.230$$

from the curves.   Thus

$$k_u = 0.567(0.240) + 0.198(0.579) + 0.068(0.230) = 0.266$$

and

$$E_{av} = {}^{3360}\!/_{100}\ 0.266 = \textbf{8.95 lumens/sq ft}$$

Accuracy.—The lumen method as originally developed by Harrison is essentially as just outlined.   For use by the layman, however, it has been simplified* until it has lost some of its original value as an engineering tool.   A complete table of values of k_u is usually given for each type of luminaire, but no method is divulged for obtaining similar tables for luminaires that are not listed.   An unnecessary table of values of "room index" is also given, which, since it confines itself to rather large steps in k_u, introduces error.   For example, consider a room 14 by 14 ft with a 14-ft ceiling, $\rho_c = 0.30$, $\rho_w = 0.10$, lighted from a ceiling panel ($g_d = 0.50$).   Since the room is a cube, $k_r = 1.00$, and, from the table,†

$$k_u = 0.54 \times 0.50 = \textbf{0.270}$$

From curves 1 and 2, we obtain $f_d = 0.538$, and thus

$$k_u = 0.538 \times 0.50 = \textbf{0.269}$$

The two are in excellent agreement, as they should be, since both are based upon the same data.‡

Now, consider another case with everything the same except that the room height is increased to 29 ft.   From the table (*Bull.* LD-6) a value of 0.6 is obtained for the "room index." From *Bull.* LD-12,

$$k_u = 0.35 \times 0.50 = \textbf{0.175}$$

* See, for instance, Illumination Design Data, *Nela Park Dept.*, *General Electric Co.*

† Luminous Architectural Elements, *Nela Park Dept.*, *General Electric Co.*, *Bull.* LD-12, p. 37.

‡ HARRISON and ANDERSON, *loc. cit.*

By Eq. (11.02a),

$$k_r = \frac{h}{w} = \frac{29}{14} = 2.07$$

and from curves 1 and 2 of Appendix F, $f_d = 0.227$, and

$$k_u = 0.227 \times 0.50 = \mathbf{0.113}$$

Since this last value of k_u is based on test, it may be considered correct, and thus the table value is more than 50 per cent high. This is an extreme case. Under most conditions, the error obtained by using the tables (LD-6) will probably not exceed ± 10 per cent. While such an error in the value of k_u may be permissible in some cases, the original data are more accurate than this, and the lumen method is inherently capable of higher accuracy. Thus the use of the curves and formulas based upon the original data seems to be the preferable procedure rather than the use of the approximate tables.

The Depreciation Factor.—It is customary to use values of the luminaire efficiency g_h, g_d, g_i, obtained from tests on new, clean luminaires. In designing lighting installations, it is also customary to use F_L as the *initial* lumens obtained from tables such as those of Chap. VI. Under these conditions, the calculated values of E_{av},

$$E_{av} = \frac{F_L}{A} k_u \quad \text{(initial lumens/sq ft)}$$

will be the initial values obtained with new lamps and clean luminaires. After being in service for some time, the illumination will be reduced owing to blackening of the lamp bulbs, collection of dust, etc., so

$$E_{av} = \frac{F_L}{A} k_u k_d \quad \text{(lumens/sq ft in service)} \qquad (11.10)$$

where k_d is the *depreciation factor*. Its value will depend upon the frequency of cleaning and other conditions but may be taken as about 0.75 for direct reflectors, 0.70 for glass diffusing globes, and 0.60 for open-top indirect units.

Problem 128. Test data on an RLM reflector with 500-watt, white-bowl lamp giving 9700 lumens were as follows:

	$I(\theta)$
θ	(Candlepower)
0°..	2251
5...	2215
15..	2150
25..	2062
35..	1869
45..	1500
55..	1164
65..	806
75..	391
85..	53
90..	0

Calculate the necessary factors so that this reflector can be added to Table XL.

Problem 129. Actual test data on a diffusing glass globe are given below. The globe is of dense opal glass below and of light alabaster glass above, thus giving a larger indirect component than would be obtained with a uniform globe. A 200-watt, 115-volt, PS-30 clear lamp was used, giving 3380 lumens.

θ (degrees)	$I(\theta)$ (candlepower)	θ (degrees)	$I(\theta)$ (candlepower)
180	479	90	149
175	337	85	135
165	287	75	117
155	268	65	113
145	284	55	119
135	337	45	137
125	365	35	156
115	323	25	174
105	272	15	185
95	172	5	191
		0	193

Calculate the values of g_h, g_d, g_i and g (total luminaire flux per lamp lumen).

Problem 130. A room 15 by 30 ft with a 12-ft ceiling is to be lighted by Holophane reflector units 2180 with 200-watt lamps. The centers of the luminaires are 4 ft below the ceiling. Eight luminaires are used, spaced 8 ft apart. Reflection factor of ceiling is 0.7 and of walls, 0.3. What is the initial average illumination on the desk level 30 in. above the floor?

Problem 131. Repeat Problem 130, using the luminaires of Problem 129.

Problem 132. Repeat Prob. 130, using three RLM reflectors (500-watt, Prob. 128) mounted on the ceiling.

Problem 133. Calculate E_{av} in all the rooms of Fig. 8.28, using the lumen method.

Problem 134. Calculate E_{av} for the library considered in the example at the end of Chap. X. Use the lumen method and compare the result with the accurate values given in Chap. X.

11.03. Design of Lighting Systems for Interiors.—The lumen method is particularly useful in the design of general lighting systems which are to provide a fairly uniform illumination over the whole working area. The average illumination is decided upon, as well as the type of luminaire. Then, according to Eq. (11.10), the total lamp lumens must be

$$F_L = \frac{E_{av}A}{k_u k_d} \tag{11.10a}$$

Since the dimensions of the room and type of luminaire are known, A, k_u, and k_d can be obtained, and Eq. (11.10a) gives the total luminous output required from all the lamps.

The value of E_{av} depends upon the kind of visual task to be performed, the reflection factor of the object and its background, and the allowable cost of installing and operating the lighting system. Research on vision proves that seeing continues to improve as E is increased over a very wide range, provided glare does not enter (Chap. XII). The fact that outdoor illumination in the shade is of the order of 1000 lumens/sq ft and that even indoors we are accustomed to about 100 lumens/sq ft near a window during the day indicates that very great increases in the usual low levels of artificial illumination should not cause any discomfort. In fact, if care is taken to eliminate glare, seeing is improved, eyestrain is reduced, and there is a happy psychological effect in the use of higher values of illumination. This improvement appears to continue up to 1000 lumens/sq ft or higher. Thus, in general, it may be said that E_{av} should be as high as is economically feasible. Cost is the limiting factor. As lamps are improved, there is a general movement to higher levels of illumination. Before the advent of the tungsten lamp we were satisfied to light our rooms with the old 60-watt lamp giving about 160 lumens. When the tungsten lamp was introduced, however, it was noticed that instead of using low-wattage lamps with the same luminous output, most people continued to use 60-watt lamps giving much greater luminous flux.

Today, owing to still further increases in the luminous efficacy of lamps and to further education in the importance of adequate illumination, the average home uses many 60-watt lamps giving 750 lumens as well as larger sizes with even higher luminous efficacies. The illumination is correspondingly increased. Twenty years ago, 5 lumens/sq ft was considered high, while now 20 to 30 lumens/sq ft is recommended in all cases where any fine detail is encountered, and values of 50 to 100 lumens/sq ft or even higher are being used in certain applications. Generally, it is not considered economically feasible to light large areas to an E_{av} of more than about 50 lumens/sq ft. High illuminations for exacting work are usually confined to small areas, with a lower level used for the remainder of the illuminated space. It is the general uniform illumination over the whole area with which we are particularly concerned in this chapter.

Tables of recommended values of E_{av} for all sorts of applications have been compiled from time to time, and many people

TABLE XLI.—APPROXIMATE VALUES OF E_{av} USED IN PRESENT PRACTICE
(Subject to Revision Upward)

	E_{av} (Lumens per Square Foot)
Corridors, stairways, and other places where light is needed only to allow people to find their way about	2–5
Lobbies, reception rooms, dining rooms, etc., where some reading may be done but only for short periods	10
Offices, stores, etc.	20–30
Drafting rooms, places where sewing or other close work is done on goods of high reflection factor	30–50
Store show windows	100–500
Machine shops where fine tool work or inspection is done or other places where close work is done on goods of low reflection factor. (Usually requires local lighting on the work, supplemented by a lower level of general illumination)	100–1000

seem to look upon them with almost superstitious awe as results that must be used without question. Actually, however, such tables give only values that have been found economically feasible in recent installations. These values may be helpful to the inexperienced designer in giving him an idea of what others are doing; but there is nothing fixed, immutable, or unique about them. As a very rough guide to present practice, and nothing more, the values of Table XLI are included.

Having decided upon E_{av} and having calculated F_L by the use of Eq. (11.10a), the designer is now ready to determine the number of luminaires. The number is determined by the question of the uniformity of illumination desired. Experience shows that with most commercial luminaires, the spacing between outlets should not be greater than the mounting height of the luminaire above the floor, or the spacing S_L is

$$S_L \leqq H_m \tag{11.11}$$

where H_m = distance (ft) from center of luminaire to floor.

The use of greater spacing will generally result in too great a variation of illumination on the working plane. It is customary to make the distance from luminaire to wall equal approximately to $S/2$. Knowing these empirical rules, the designer quickly determines the number of lamps and the flux required per lamp. Generally, this required flux does not correspond exactly to any commercial size of lamp; and either the next smaller lamp is used with a corresponding readjustment in the number of luminaires, or the next larger size is used with a corresponding increase in the illumination.

The layman seems to have a feeling that the luminaires must be hung as low as possible to get a maximum amount of flux on the working plane. This is by no means true. In fact, a low

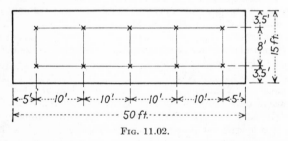

Fig. 11.02.

mounting height is uneconomical for general illumination as a rule because it requires a small spacing, according to Eq. (11.11). Therefore more luminaires of a smaller size must be used, increasing the cost of installation; and since the lamps are smaller, their efficacy is lower. Also, the low mounting height is generally productive of more glare, and the large number of luminaires dangling from long chains gives a cluttered-up, unaesthetic appearance to the room. It would seem that a general lighting scheme (using commercial luminaires) is best accomplished in most locations by mounting the units on the ceiling. If an indirect system is used, H_m is always equal to the ceiling height h, and the mounting height of the luminaires is determined by the desirability of getting a reasonably uniform luminosity of the ceiling. As in any other kind of design, no all-embracing rules can be laid down. Each installation must be considered carefully as an individual problem.

Example. A lunchroom 15 by 50 ft with 10-ft ceiling is to be lighted by diffusing luminaires. Design the lighting system.

It is decided tentatively to use $E_{av} = 10$ lumens/sq ft. Reflection factors are found to be

$$\rho_c = 0.60, \qquad \rho_w = 0.30.$$

Let us select a globe (Table XL) with

$$g_h = 0.545, \qquad g_d = 0.174, \qquad g_i = 0.092$$

From Eq. (11.02),

$$k_r = \frac{10}{0.9(15) + 0.1(50)} = 0.540$$

From Appendix F,

$$f_d = 0.720, \qquad 0.720 \times 0.174 = 0.125$$
$$f_i = 0.280, \qquad 0.280 \times 0.092 = 0.026$$
$$f_h = 0.345, \qquad 0.345 \times 0.545 = 0.188$$

$$\overline{\hspace{2cm}}$$
$$k_u = 0.339$$

Thus the coefficient of utilization is 0.339. Also, $A = 15 \times 50 = 750$ sq ft. and the depreciation factor can be assumed as 0.70. From Eq. (11.10*a*).

$$F_L = \frac{10(750)}{(0.339)(0.70)} = 31,600 \text{ lumens}$$

We now consider the placing of the luminaires. If we decide on ceiling mounting, it will be permissible to use two rows of luminaires spaced 8 ft apart and 3.5 ft from the side walls (Fig. 11.02). At least five luminaires will be needed in each row, giving a spacing of 10 ft, with 5 ft between luminaire and wall at each end. With a total of 10 luminaires, the flux per lamp must be

$$\frac{31,600}{10} = 3160 \text{ lumens}$$

From Table XXIII (page 157), we find that the nearest size lamp is the 200-watt PS-30, giving 3400 lumens. This lamp should be satisfactory. It will give an average illumination under ordinary operating conditions of

$$10 \times {}^{3400}\!/_{3160} = 10.8 \text{ lumens/sq ft}$$

and the initial illumination will be

$$\frac{10.8}{0.70} = 15.4 \text{ lumens/sq ft}$$

Problem 135. A large office is to be 50 by 200 ft with a 15-ft smooth ceiling (no beams). The average reflection factor of the walls will be 0.45 and that of the ceiling will be 0.70.

1. Design a lighting system with luminaires mounted on the ceiling.

2. Repeat for the same type of luminaires hung 8 ft above the floor. Compare number of outlets and total watts in 1 and 2.

Problem 136. Redesign the entire lighting system for all the rooms of Fig. 8.28. Tabulate number of luminaires, type of luminaire, size lamp, average illumination, and kilowatt load for each room. Give careful consideration to the choice of appropriate luminaires for each use and provide a thoroughly satisfactory and modern installation.

Problem 137. Redesign the lighting system of the example at the end of Chap. X, using a commercial luminaire. Plot the actual illumination along *ABCD* with the new design.

11.04. Built-in Lighting.—In the past, it has been customary for the architect to design a building without regard to the lighting, which has been added as an afterthought in the form of a group of more or less nondescript luminaires. Of recent years, however, it is being realized that the artificial lighting is a vital part of the building, fully as important as the ventilating and heating, and that it should be designed as an integral part of the structure. Though luminous panels, columns, etc., can be built *on to* the existing walls, best results are obtained by actually building them in as part of the design. This requires careful planning and a close cooperation between architect and illuminating engineer. The results of the slight added effort are decidedly worth while, both as regards improved conditions for seeing and as regards beauty. It must be admitted that built-in or architectural lighting is relatively high in first cost. Also, it generally requires a large number of small lamps rather than a few large ones. This reduces the obtainable lumens per watt. These disadvantages are in many cases more than compensated by the reduction in glare and by the great freedom which the method gives for producing interesting and varied artistic effects.

Built-in lighting elements can be made in a great variety of forms. Figure 11.03 shows some of them. Also, many different materials are available; general-service, tubular, and Lumiline lamps, various reflecting materials for the box, and various glasses

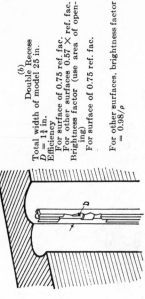

(b)
Double Recess

Total width of model 25 in.
$D = 1\frac{1}{4}$ in.
Efficiency
For surface of 0.75 ref. fac.   39 %
For other surfaces 0.57 × ref. fac.
Brightness factor (use area of opening)
For surface of 0.75 ref. fac.   1.3

For other surfaces, brightness factor
= 0.98/ρ

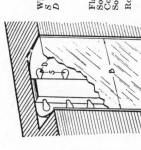

(d)
Flush Panel: 2 Rows of Lamps
Width tested: 24 in.
$S = 1.5\ D$
$D = 0.33\ B$

	Efficiency %	Brightness Factor
Flashed opal	51	1.0
Solid opal #1	37	1.4
Composition	29	1.7
Solid opal #2	22	2.3

Row spacing is one-half of panel width.

(a)
Half Cylinder Recess
Total width of model 25 in.
$S = 1.9\ D$
Efficiency
For surface of 0.75 ref. fac.   43 %
For other surfaces 0.52 × ref. fac.
Brightness factor (use area of opening)
For surface of 0.75 ref. fac.   1.0

For other surfaces, brightness factor
= 0.75/ρ

(c)
Flush Panel: 1 Row of Lamps
Width tested: 12 in.
$S = 1.5\ D$
$D = 0.67\ B$

	Efficiency %	Brightness Factor
Flashed opal	49	1.0
Solid opal #1	34	1.5
Composition	27	1.8
Solid opal #2	18	2.7

For rectangular back, use 0.95 of efficiency
values, and 1.1 of brightness factor values.

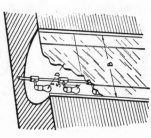

FIG. 11.03.—Luminous architectural elements.
Matt white reflectors, ρ = 0.75
Flashed-opal glass, τ = 0.50
Solid-opal glass No. 1, τ = 0.32
Composition, τ = 0.23
Solid-opal glass No. 2, τ = 0.18
(*Potter and Meaker, Nela Pk. Bull. No. LD-12.*)

Flush Panel: 2 Rows of Lamps (f)
Flashed-opal side, ground glass center panels
Width tested: 24 in.
$S = 1.2 D$
$D = 0.27 B$

	Efficiency %	Brightness Factor
Flashed opal and ground glass	49	1.0

Lamps centered on flashed glass panels. Some spottiness when viewed at an angle.

Double-Window Element: 3 Rows of Lamps (h)
Width tested: 24 in.
$S = D$
$D = 0.33 B$

	Efficiency % (Two Faces)	Brightness Factor*
Flashed opal	65	0.8
Solid opal #1	48	1.0
Composition	38	1.3
Solid opal #2	29	1.7

*Use area of two faces.

Flush Panel: 2 Rows of Lamps (e)
Width tested: 24 in.
$S = 1.2 D$
$D = 0.27 B$

	Efficiency %	Brightness Factor
Flashed opal	49	1.0
Solid opal #1	34	1.4
Composition	27	1.8
Solid opal #2	20	2.5

This form of reflector with lamp rows spaced two-thirds of panel width produces desired transverse uniformity with shallow cavity.

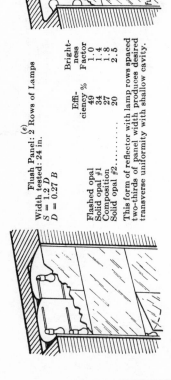

Flush Panel: 3 Rows of Lamps (g)
Width tested: 24 in.
$S = 1.25 D$
$D = 0.27 B$

	Efficiency %	Brightness Factor
Flashed opal	49	1.0
Solid opal #1	34	1.4
Composition	27	1.8
Solid opal #2	20	2.5

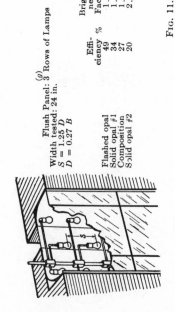

Fig. 11.03.—(*Continued.*)

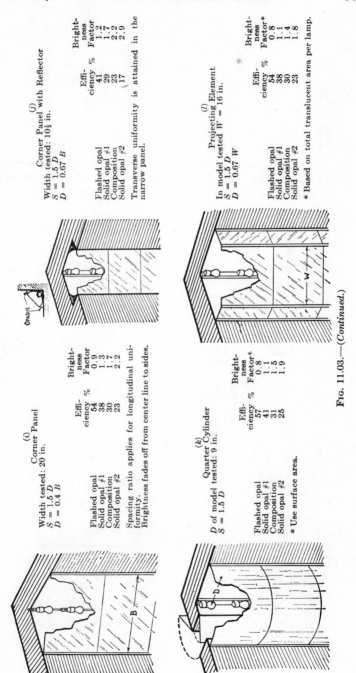

(j)
Corner Panel with Reflector
Width tested: 10½ in.
$S = 1.5 D$
$D = 0.67 B$

	Effi-ciency %	Bright-ness Factor
Flashed opal	41	1.2
Solid opal #1	29	1.7
Composition	23	2.2
Solid opal #2	17	2.9

Transverse uniformity is attained in the narrow panel.

(l)
Projecting Element
In model tested $W = 16$ in.
$S = 1.5 D$
$D = 0.67 W$

	Effi-ciency %	Bright-ness Factor*
Flashed opal	54	0.8
Solid opal #1	38	1.1
Composition	30	1.4
Solid opal #2	23	1.8

* Based on total translucent area per lamp.

(i)
Corner Panel
Width tested: 20 in.
$S = 1.5 D$
$D = 0.4 B$

	Effi-ciency %	Bright-ness Factor
Flashed opal	54	0.9
Solid opal #1	38	1.3
Composition	30	1.7
Solid opal #2	23	2.2

Spacing ratio applies for longitudinal uniformity.
Brightness fades off from center line to sides.

(k)
Quarter Cylinder
D of model tested: 9 in.
$S = 1.5 D$

	Effi-ciency %	Bright-ness Factor*
Flashed opal	57	0.8
Solid opal #1	41	1.1
Composition	31	1.5
Solid opal #2	25	1.9

* Use surface area.

FIG. 11.03.—(*Continued.*)

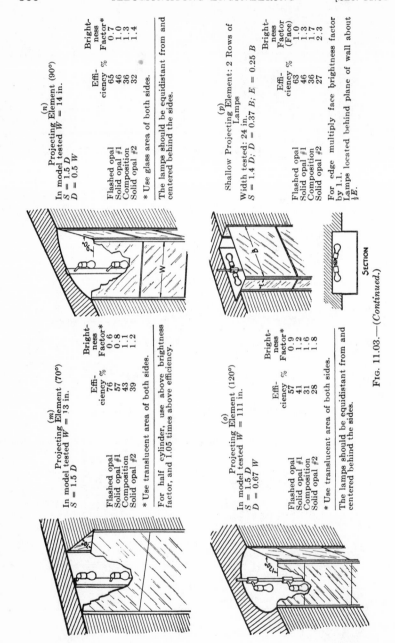

(m)
Projecting Element (70°)
In model tested W = 13 in.
$S = 1.5 D$

	Efficiency %	Brightness Factor*
Flashed opal	76	0.6
Solid opal #1	57	0.8
Composition	43	1.1
Solid opal #2	39	1.2

* Use translucent area of both sides.

For half cylinder, use above brightness factor, and 1.05 times above efficiency.

(n)
Projecting Element (90°)
In model tested W = 14 in.
$S = 1.5 D$
$D = 0.5 W$

	Efficiency %	Brightness Factor*
Flashed opal	65	0.7
Solid opal #1	46	1.0
Composition	36	1.3
Solid opal #2	32	1.4

* Use glass area of both sides.

The lamps should be equidistant from and centered behind the sides.

(o)
Projecting Element (120°)
In model tested W = 111 in.
$S = 1.5 D$
$D = 0.67 W$

	Efficiency %	Brightness Factor*
Flashed opal	57	0.9
Solid opal #1	41	1.2
Composition	31	1.6
Solid opal #2	28	1.8

* Use translucent area of both sides.

The lamps should be equidistant from and centered behind the sides.

(p)
Shallow Projecting Element: 2 Rows of Lamps
Width tested: 24 in.
$S = 1.4 D; D = 0.37 B; E = 0.25 B$

	Efficiency %	Brightness Factor (Face)
Flashed opal	63	1.0
Solid opal #1	46	1.3
Composition	36	1.7
Solid opal #2	27	2.3

For edge multiply face brightness factor by 1.1.
Lamps located behind plane of wall about $\frac{1}{2} E$.

SECTION

FIG. 11.03.—(Continued.)

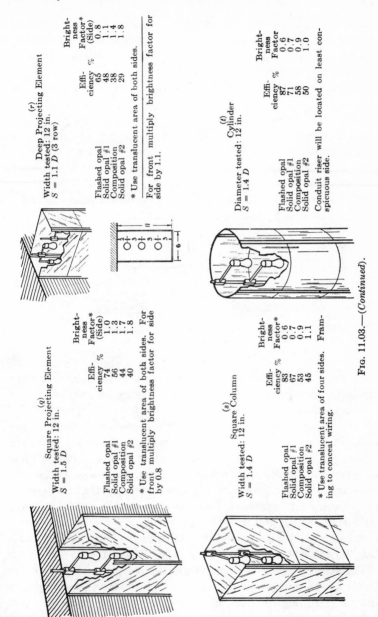

(r)
Deep Projecting Element
Width tested: 12 in.
$S = 1.1 D$ (3 row)

	Efficiency %	Brightness Factor* (Side)
Flashed opal	65	0.8
Solid opal #1	48	1.1
Composition	38	1.4
Solid opal #2	29	1.8

* Use translucent area of both sides.

For front multiply brightness factor for side by 1.1.

(t)
Cylinder
Diameter tested: 12 in.
$S = 1.4 D$

	Efficiency %	Brightness Factor
Flashed opal	87	0.6
Solid opal #1	71	0.7
Composition	58	0.9
Solid opal #2	50	1.0

Conduit riser will be located on least conspicuous side.

(q)
Square Projecting Element
Width tested: 12 in.
$S = 1.5 D$

	Efficiency %	Brightness Factor* (Side)
Flashed opal	74	1.0
Solid opal #1	56	1.3
Composition	44	1.7
Solid opal #2	40	1.8

* Use translucent area of both sides. For front multiply brightness factor for side by 0.8.

(s)
Square Column
Width tested: 12 in.
$S = 1.4 D$

	Efficiency %	Brightness Factor*
Flashed opal	83	0.6
Solid opal #1	67	0.7
Composition	53	0.9
Solid opal #2	45	1.1

* Use translucent area of four sides. Framing to conceal wiring.

FIG. 11.03.—(*Continued*).

and molded plastics for the light-transmitting part.   If the panel is to appear uniform in luminosity, solid-opal or flashed-opal glass is desirable, the flashed glass being preferable because of its higher transmission factor.   Also available are

Depolished glass: sandblasted, acid-etched, or ground (see Fig. 9.05).

"Carved" glass: clear glass with sandblasted pattern.

Figured glass: clear glass with pressed designs, ribs, etc.

Molded glass: a variety of designs and shapes are available (see manufacturer's catalogues).

Tubes and rods.

All these types of glass give much less diffusion than opal glass and for that reason must be used with caution to avoid unpleasant

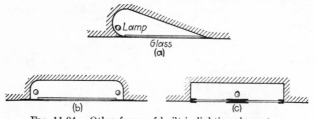

FIG. 11.04.—Other forms of built-in lighting elements.

spotty results and glare.   Handled in an understanding manner, however, they permit a variety of interesting effects.

One of the simplest forms of luminous panels is shown in Fig. 11.03c.   A diffusing reflector of porcelain-enameled steel or other material is used and a sufficiently close lamp spacing to obtain a uniform luminosity.   Data on spacing and distance from the glass to give good results are based on the experiments of Potter and Meaker.[7]   At first glance, it might seem strange that a solid-opal glass having a transmission factor of approximately 0.30 will give an output as high as 0.76 of the lamp lumens.   The explanation is that interreflections increase the luminous output.   Wider panels may be arranged, as in Fig. 11.03 *d, e, f, g*.   Higher efficiency is obtainable by using a larger proportion of glass, as in *i, m, n*. Other schemes, particularly suited to figured or molded glass, are indicated in Fig. 11.04.   A number of standardized forms of light boxes and panels are obtainable from the manufacturers. Other forms can be made specially for the individual job.   In all cases, provision must be made for easy relamping.   Lens plates

(Fig. 8.12) may also be used in the ceiling, as was done, for instance, in lighting the NBC broadcasting studios at Radio City.

The panels of Fig. 11.03 require a large number of small lamps to give uniformity in luminosity.   By using large spacing between lamps and glass, the number of lamps could be greatly reduced, thus taking advantage of the higher luminous efficacy of the larger lamps.   Such a procedure has been used in many cases with skylights, where the loft (Fig. 11.05) is fitted with lamps in reflectors, and the installation can be used for both daylight illumination and artificial illumination.   Such arrangements are

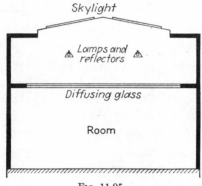

Fig. 11.05.

also well suited for using mercury-vapor lamps, in combination with either incandescent lamps or neon lamps to give an approximation to daylight quality.

Other systems of architectural lighting dispense with the glass entirely.   Figures 11.03a, b, for example, give an effect similar to Fig. 11.03c but use a diffusing reflector and a series of lamps shielded from view by a metal strip.   A similar arrangement, using triangular niches of honed reddish marble, is used in the lobby of the Chrysler building in New York City.   The familiar *cove lighting* (Fig. 11.06) gives very uniform, totally indirect illumination without the use of hanging luminaires.   The ceiling should preferably be vaulted, and to get a really satisfactory result the designer must consider carefully the position of the lamps and the resulting variation in the luminosity of the ceiling.   By recessing the lamps as in Fig. 11.06b, the unpleasantly bright spots above the cove, which mar the effect with so many cove-

lighting systems, are eliminated.   A few other schemes are shown
in Fig. 11.07.

With large ceiling panels or with cove lighting, illumination on
a horizontal plane is fairly uniform, and the lumen method is

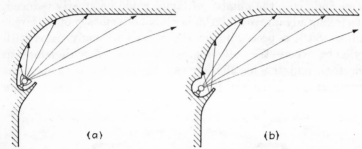

(a)   (b)

FIG. 11.06.—Cove lighting.   (*C. S. Woodside, I.E.S. Trans.*, **31**, 1936, p. 263.)

applicable, at least in the preliminary design.   With small ceiling
panels, however, or with wall panels, the illumination often varies
so widely that E_{av} has little significance, and it is advisable to
calculate the illumination by the methods of the preceding
chapters.[17]   If such calculations ignore interreflections, the results

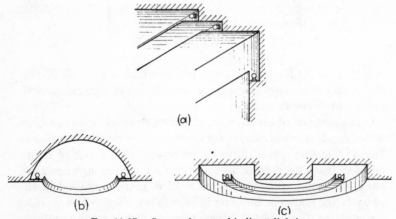

(a)

(b)   (c)

FIG. 11.07.—Some schemes of indirect lighting.

will be pessimistic but will at least give some indication of the
variation in illumination to be expected.   Higbie and his associates have tested panels both in the walls and in the ceiling,[18]
making a large number of photoelectric measurements with a
model room.   The data include the effects of interreflections.

In designing a lighting system using luminous panels of diffusing glass, the illuminating engineer decides upon E_{av} as in Sec. 11.03 and calculates the total area of glass to be used, which is fixed by the allowable luminosity of the glass. One of the principal advantages of built-in lighting is the reduction of glare obtained by the use of large luminous areas of correspondingly low luminosity. Obviously, the allowable luminosity depends upon many factors (Chap. XII), such as the exact location of the panel with respect to the eyes of the people in the room, the luminosity of the surroundings, and the length of time during which the panel is in the field of view. Ceiling panels may be of higher luminosity than wall panels; higher values of L may be used with panels in high ceilings than with panels in low ceilings; higher values of L may be used in corridors than in rooms where work is carried on continuously for long periods. A table is given (Table XLII) for approximate values of panel luminosity

TABLE XLII.—PRESENT PRACTICE IN LUMINOUS PANELS
(POTTER and MEAKER, *I.E.S. Trans.*, **26**, 1931, p. 1025)

	Maximum Luminosity (Lumens per Square Foot)
Ceiling panels 20 ft or more above floor	500
in lower rooms	250
Wall panels in corridors	200
in places of business	125
constantly in field of view	75

used in present practice. As in Table XLI, these values serve merely as a crude guide and if possible should be checked in each case by the methods of Chap. XII. With glass of small diffusion or with lens plates, the glare effect is generally less pronounced, because of a more concentrated beam and consequently less spill light. Thus higher values of L may often be used.

Having decided tentatively on a value of glass luminosity, the designer obtains the minimum glass area by dividing the *total luminous flux emitted by the glass* (not by the lamps) by the allowable value of L. He next decides upon the dimensions of the luminous panels which will give a total area approximately equal to that required. A lamp size is assumed, and the necessary spacing and distance from the glass are calculated from the data of Fig. 11.03. If the resulting dimensions are inconvenient, another size of lamp is assumed, or the panel dimensions are altered. After the completion of the tentative design, it may be advisable to calculate the illumination by the point-by-point method of Chap. IX and to determine if there is too much variation in illumination, if glare is sufficiently reduced, etc.

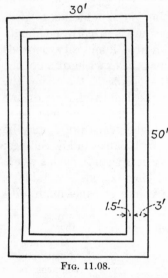

Example. A room of a museum (Fig. 11.08) 30 by 50 ft with a 12-foot ceiling is to be lighted by a flush luminous ceiling panel. The reflection factor of the ceiling is to be 0.70, while the average reflection factor of the walls is to be 0.50.

From a study of similar rooms, the illuminating engineer decides that a value of E_{av} = 20 lumens/sq ft will give satisfactory results, and this value is assumed as a basis for the design. Also,

Fig. 11.08.

A = 1500 sq ft
k_r = 0.375, g_d = 0.50, f_d = 0.843
k_u = 0.42

On the assumption that k_d = 0.80, and by Eq. (11.10a),

$$F_L = \frac{1500 \times 20}{0.42 \times 0.80} = 89{,}300 \text{ lumens from the lamps}$$

Luminous flux from the panel = 89,300 × 0.50 = 44,650 lumens, a luminaire efficiency of 0.50 being assumed. From Table XLII, the allowable luminosity is

$$L = 250 \text{ lumens/sq ft or less}$$

The glass area must be at least

$$\frac{44{,}650}{250} = 179 \text{ sq ft}$$

Such an area can be obtained in an infinite number of ways. Suppose we decide on a narrow ceiling panel running completely around the room, as shown in Fig. 11.08. As the total length of the panel is approximately 130 ft, a width of 18 in. will give a satisfactory luminosity. If the type of panel shown in Fig. 11.03c is used, the distance from the glass to the lamp centers is

$$D = 0.67B = 12 \text{ in.}$$
$$S = 1.5D = 18 \text{ in.}$$

The minimum number of lamps is, therefore,

$$\frac{130}{1.5} = 87, \text{ or about } 90$$

The flux per lamp is

$$\frac{89{,}300}{90} = 1000 \text{ lumens, nearly}$$

which is obtainable in the 75-watt, A-21 I.F. lamp which gives 1035 initial lumens. With flashed-opal glass having a transmission factor of 0.50 and a matt-white reflector, 0.49 of the lamp lumens is delivered (Fig. 11.03c) which is in sufficiently good accord with the original assumption of 0.50.

The final design may consist of a porcelain-enameled box with dimensions shown in Fig. 11.09, flashed-opal glass panels, and 90 lamps of 75 watts

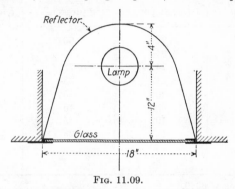

FIG. 11.09.

each. The average illumination on the level of display cases, with depreciation in service allowed for, is

$$E_{av} = \frac{(1035)(90)(0.49)(0.843)(0.80)}{1500}$$

$$= 20.5 \text{ lumens/sq ft}$$

Problem 138. In the example just considered, determine if the illumination is sufficiently uniform on a horizontal plane 36 in. above the floor. Map the isolux lines.

Problem 139. If exhibits are to be hung on the walls, it is necessary to investigate the illumination on these vertical surfaces. Plot the illumination from floor to ceiling near the center of one of the long walls. Is the uniformity satisfactory?

Problem 140. Design a built-in lighting system for the office of Prob. 135.

Problem 141. Repeat Prob. 137 but with some form of built-in lighting system in the walls. Check carefully the uniformity of illumination on the tables and make sure that glare will not be experienced. Use approximately equal wattage of incandescent and high-pressure mercury-vapor lamps to obtain a more nearly white light.

Problem 142. A study room in a dormitory is paneled in dark oak and has built-in book shelves for a length of 22 ft on each side and to a height of

6 ft above the floor. The room is 18 by 25 ft with a 10-ft ceiling. The ceiling has a reflection factor of 0.60. The reflection factor of the walls may be considered as zero.

The room is to be lighted by a built-in luminous panel 3 by 22 ft above each set of bookshelves. Flashed-opal glass is used in conjunction with a white enameled-steel lamp box to obtain a luminaire efficiency of 0.50. Sixty 75-watt Mazda lamps are used in each box.

a. Calculate the illumination distribution on the table level 30 in. above the floor. What is E_{av} for the new installation? Use the point-by-point method.

b. Compute E_{av} by the lumen method.

Problem 143. Test data on a commercial luminaire are as follows:

θ (degrees)	I (candlepower)	θ (degrees)	I (candlepower)
180	212	90	184
175	218	85	187
165	245	75	199
155	217	65	218
145	205	55	242
135	300	45	267
125	192	35	287
115	185	25	300
105	180	15	306
95	180	5	306

Lamp lumens = 3340.

It is decided to light the library of Prob. 142 with four of these luminaires with 200-watt lamps. Using the lumen method, calculate the average illumination on the horizontal plane of the table.

11.05. Solar Illumination.—Until now, we have dealt largely with artificial light. But the illuminating engineer may be called upon to help the architect in the design of natural lighting of buildings through windows or skylights. In the past, the natural lighting of buildings has been left to chance, with the result that artificial light has been required throughout the day in many places where an intelligent consideration of window design would have given adequate daylight illumination under all ordinary circumstances. Recently, there has been a strong trend toward the scientific design of daylighting, and some of the largest companies are now making it a practice to design the windows in their factory buildings with the same care that they take with the manufacturing equipment.

To be able to work intelligently in the field of natural lighting, the illuminating engineeer must know something of solar illumination and how it varies. The illumination may be considered as made of two components:

1. Illumination direct from the sun.
2. Illumination due to skylight.

Table XLIII gives results of direct solar illumination on a surface normal to the sun's rays and with a cloudless sky. The illumination on any other surface is obtained by the cosine law. When direct sunlight enters a room, it produces a tremendous variation in illumination and causes considerable inconvenience, with resulting waste of time in continually adjusting window shades or Venetian blinds. For this reason, some modern factories use windows on the north only and so arranged that no direct sunlight ever enters the building. Even in such cases, however, the data of Table XLIII will be useful, since neighboring buildings may be directly illuminated and may reflect considerable light through the north windows of the building under consideration.

Fortunately, illumination is not confined to direct sunlight. Considerable diffused light reaches us from the sky. A perfectly clear sky devoid of dust is a very deep blue of low luminosity. Assuming that the luminosity of the sky is due to the scattering of light by the molecules of the atmosphere whose dimensions are small compared with a wavelength of visible radiation, Rayleigh showed that only the shorter wavelengths are scattered appreciably, the scattering varying inversely as the fourth power of the wavelength. This accounts for the blue color of the sky. Under ordinary circumstances, light is also scattered by larger particles of dust or of liquid water. Because of their size these particles scatter the radiation of all wavelengths in the visible region. The presence of dust causes the sky to appear lighter in color and more highly luminous. Light clouds generally increase the luminosity still further.

Considerable study has been given to the luminosity of the sky under various conditions. Probably the most complete data (over 85,000 readings) were obtained by H. H. Kimball[44] and his associates at Washington, D. C., and at Chicago. Figures 11.10a, b, c give three typical diagrams showing contour lines of constant luminosity as functions of the azimuth φ from the sun and of the altitude θ. These diagrams illustrate the general characteristics that with cloudless sky or with light clouds the luminosity is greatest near the sun and reaches a minimum approximately 90 deg from the sun. With dense clouds the lumi-

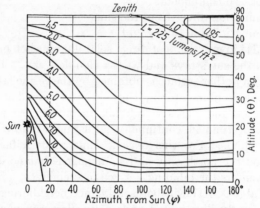

FIG. 11.10a.—Sky luminosity (in terms of luminosity at zenith). Cloudless sky. (*Kimball, I.E.S. Trans.*, **18**, 1923, *p.* 434.)

nosity is practically independent of ϕ but is a function of θ, having its maximum value at the zenith irrespective of the position of the sun. Evidently, the luminosity of the sky is far from

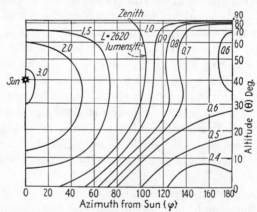

FIG. 11.10b.—Sky luminosity. Dense haze.

uniform. Moreover, the shape of the luminosity-distribution curves shifts with the position of the sun and with the condition of the sky. For any definite condition of the sky such as a dense, cloudy sky, illumination may be calculated by the exact method of

Sec. 9.09, or the sky may be divided into sections of approximately uniform luminosity, and the component illuminations calculated

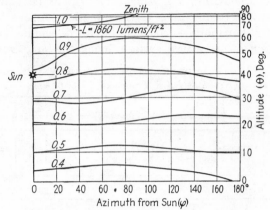

Fig. 11.10c.—Sky luminosity. Dense clouds.

and summed.   For ordinary design, the refinement of nonuniform luminosity is quite unnecessary, and it is customary to assume that L is uniform at its average value.

TABLE XLIII.—SOLAR ILLUMINATION
At normal incidence.   Latitude 42°N, east of Mississippi River.   Cloudless
sky
(From H. H. KIMBALL, *I.E.S. Trans.*, **18**, 1923, p. 457)

Day	Hour angle of sun from meridian							
	0	1	2	3	4	5	6	7
Dec. 21	7600	7300	6640	5190	2460	lumens/sq ft		
Jan. 21	8120	7890	7290	6040	3760			
Feb. 21	9140	9040	8440	7450	6140	2460		
Mar. 21	9270	9110	8710	7910	6700	4650	720	
Apr. 21	9230	9060	8800	8300	7350	5860	3600	
May 21	9070	8990	8630	8140	7480	6260	4700	1200
June 21	9080	9000	8740	8220	7430	6420	4880	2160
July 21	9070	8990	8670	8140	7550	6330	4830	1200
Aug. 21	8810	8710	8390	7830	6880	5460	2990	
Sept. 21	8910	8760	8510	7710	6500	4590	720	
Oct. 21	8510	8420	7960	6910	5220	2100		
Nov. 21	8120	7890	7290	5960	3390			

The total illumination is found by adding to the foregoing values the illumination due to skylight (Table XLIV).

Instead of using the data for the sky luminosity, one may use the derived values of illumination on various surfaces due to skylight (Table XLIV). The first column gives the solar altitude, and the second column gives the illumination (lumens per square foot) on a horizontal surface. The third column shows the illumination on a vertical surface facing the sun ($\phi = 0$). In

TABLE XLIV.—ILLUMINATION FROM SKYLIGHT, WASHINGTON, D.C.
(KIMBALL, *I.E.S. Trans.*, **18**, 1923, p. 443)

Solar altitude θ (deg)	On hori- zontal surface	On vertical surface (lumens/sq ft)							Zenith luminosity lumens/sq ft
		$\phi = 0$ deg	45 deg	70 deg	90 deg	135 deg	180 deg	Av	
Cloudy sky									
0	15.2	5.6	5.8	...	6 4	6.7	7.1	6.3	14.7
20	726	298	280	...	273	273	272	279	919
41	1505	614	608	...	615	622	606	613	1860
61	2150	881	941	...	977	932	929	932	3340
71	2950	1142	1103	...	1118	1122	1203	1138	4500
Clear sky, summer									
20	840	1252	1028	803	526	316	293	......	370
40	1340	1454	1325	932	686	417	358	......	745
60	1600	1420	1255	923	751	559	486	......	1530
70	1600	1291	1074	903	754	542	475	......	2140
Clear sky, winter									
0	67.8	64.6	63.7	...	30.6	30.2	31.5	......	25.2
20	683	1042	873	562	393	265	257	......	261
40	977	1121	936	690	505	325	295	......	505

the third and succeeding columns, ϕ is the azimuth from the sun, *i.e.*, the horizontal angle between the outward-drawn normal to the illuminated vertical surface and the projection of the sun's position on the horizontal plane. Note that with a cloudy sky the illumination on a vertical surface is almost independent of the orientation of the surface but that with a clear sky the illumination is much greater when the surface faces the sun and reaches a minimum value when the surface is turned through 180 deg. All the values of Table XLIV are for skylight alone.

If direct sunlight is also present, the illumination due to it must be determined from Table XLIII, and the components due to skylight and direct sunlight must be added to obtain the actual illumination.

11.06. Daylighting of Buildings.—Consider the illumination at P on a desk (Fig. 11.11) due to an unobstructed sky seen through a window opening A. Assuming that the sky acts as a

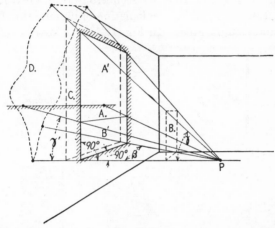

FIG. 11.11.

perfectly diffusing source of uniform luminosity L, we can obtain the illumination at P very easily by use of the curves of Fig. 9.17 or by Eq. (9.19b).

$$E_v = \frac{L}{2\pi}[\beta - \beta_1 \cos \gamma] \tag{9.19b}$$

where β_1 = a function of β and γ, as given by Eq. (9.20).

Note that the formulas and curves for illumination from rectangular sources depend only upon L, β, and γ and require no knowledge of the height and width of the source or the distance from the source, except as these factors affect β and γ. In fact, as shown in Chap. X, the illumination at P due to any form of source depends only upon L and upon the convergent light cone having its vertex at P. The illumination at P in Fig. 11.11 will be exactly the same if window A is replaced by window B of the same luminosity or by window C or by any curved surface D whose boundaries define the same light cone. Thus, instead of considering the actual source—the sky—the actual shapes and distances of the clouds, etc., we are at liberty to focus our attention upon the window A just as if it were an independent perfectly diffusing source of opal glass lighted by lamps behind it. The problem of the calculation of daylight illumination in buildings with unobstructed view of the sky and with windows of any shape reduces to the familiar problems of Chap. IX.

In many cases, the view as seen from P is obstructed by buildings, trees, etc., and the calculation of illumination becomes slightly more complicated. In Fig. 11.11, for instance, if a long

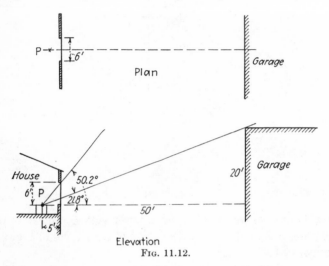

Elevation
FIG. 11.12.

building across the street subtends a vertical angle γ' at P, the illumination at P *due to skylight* is reduced to that obtained from the upper window A' of uniform luminosity L. If the obstructing building is of very low luminosity, the illumination at P is practically that from the window A'. In most cases, particularly if the obstructing building is in direct sunlight, its luminosity L' may be high enough so that its effect at P cannot be neglected. To the illumination from window A' of luminosity L must be added the illumination from the lower window B' of luminosity L' and vertical angle γ'. The resulting illumination at P may be higher in some cases than with an unobstructed window.

Example 1. The value of illumination is desired at P on a table in the house shown in Fig. 11.12. The total window opening is 6 ft square, and a long garage obstructs the view somewhat, as shown by the sketch. The sky is completely covered by clouds, and the sun is at 61 deg. altitude.

From Table XLIV, the illumination on a vertical surface is 932 lumens/sq ft. The luminosity of the window (neglecting the effect of glass, window frames, etc.) is also*

$$L = 932 \text{ lumens/sq ft}$$

First the illumination at P is calculated neglecting the effect of the garage.

$$\gamma = \tan^{-1} \tfrac{6}{5} = 50.2°$$
$$\beta = \tan^{-1} \tfrac{3}{5} = 31.0°$$

From Fig. 9.17 (p. 270),

$$\frac{E_y}{L} = 0.049$$

and thus the illumination from the two halves of the window is

$$E_y = 2(932)(0.049) = 91.4 \text{ lumens/sq ft}$$

We next obtain the illumination at P due to the portion of sky obstructed by the garage.

$$\gamma = 21.8°$$
$$\beta = 31.0°$$
$$\frac{E_y}{L} = 0.0110$$
$$E_y = 2(932)(0.0110) = 20.5 \text{ lumens/sq ft}$$

If the garage were black, the actual illumination at P would be

$$E = 91.4 - 29.5 = 70.9 \text{ lumens/sq ft}$$

The illumination of the side of the garage is 932 lumens/sq ft, if it is assumed that the house is low enough so that it does not shield the garage appreciably. The luminosity of the garage is 932 times 0.30, and the total illumination at P is

$$E_P = 70.9 + 0.30(20.5) = \mathbf{77.1} \text{ lumens/sq ft}$$

Suppose that the window shades are drawn down halfway—apparently an aesthetic necessity, according to the average housewife. In this case,

$$\gamma = \tan^{-1} \tfrac{3}{5} = 31.0°$$
$$\beta = 31.0°$$
$$E_y = 2(932)(0.0215) = 40.0 \text{ lumens/sq ft}$$

and the actual illumination is

$$E_P = 40.0 - 20.5 + 6.2 = \mathbf{25.7} \text{ lumens/sq ft}$$

Thus pulling down the shades to the middle of the windows has reduced the illumination to one-third its original value. Usually, residence surroundings shield the lower part of first-floor windows even more than in

---

* The luminosity of the sky should be taken as *twice* the illumination on a vertical surface. This will double all the values of E in the example.

this example, and the effect of window shades is even more pronounced. It would seem that Venetian blinds, shades operated from the middle of the window, or almost any scheme would be preferable to the customary one.

Example 2. A more complicated example is shown in Fig. 11.13.* The sky is covered with heavy clouds, and the sun is at 20 deg elevation. What is the illumination on a horizontal surface at *P*?

In this case, there is no illumination direct from the sky, but the opposite brick wall ($\rho = 0.44$) acts as a secondary light source. A rough check shows

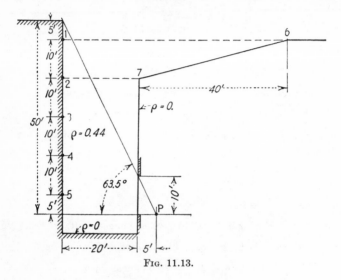

Fig. 11.13.

that the luminosity of the wall varies widely because of the shielding effect of the building on the right. We find it necessary to consider the wall not as a single window but in the form of a set of horizontal strips of different luminosities. Both buildings are so long in the direction perpendicular to the paper that the problem can be considered essentially as a two-dimensional one. The window in the factory building is 10 ft high and extends the whole length of the building. Hence, neglecting window frames, etc.,

$$\gamma = 90° \quad \text{(in both directions)}$$
$$\beta = \tan^{-1} \tfrac{10}{5} = 63.5°$$

There are several ways of obtaining the illumination on the wall, various fictitious windows being used.† Perhaps the simplest way is to consider

* *Cf.* Higbie and Turner-Szymanowski, *I.E.S. Trans.*, 1930, p. 213, App. II.

† Unfortunately, one fictitious window does not give the same result as another. This is due entirely to the fact that we are assuming the sky to be of uniform luminosity.

the wall illuminated by the fictitious window 1 to 6 having the luminosity (Table XLIV)

L = illumination on horizontal plane = 726 lumens/sq ft

The wall at the point 1 is illuminated by two fictitious windows with $\beta = 90°$, $\gamma = 90°$. Thus the illumination at 1 is

$$E = {}^{726}\!\!/_{\!2} = 363 \text{ lumens/sq ft}$$

and the luminosity is

$$L = 363 \ (0.44) = 160 \text{ lumens/sq ft}$$

The luminosity of the wall is determined similarly for the other arbitrarily selected points, with the results given in the second column:

Window	Point	L (lumens per square foot)	γ (degrees)		E_y/L		E
			Upper boundary	Lower boundary	Upper	Lower	
1–6	1	160	63.5	58.0	0.1384	0.1175	6.69
	2	133	58.0	50.2	0.1175	0.0900	7.32
2–7	3	87.5	50.2	38.6	0.0900	0.0546	6.20
	4	46.9	38.6	21.8	0.0546	0.0179	3.44
	5	26.4	21 8	0	0 0179	0	0 95

Total illumination = 24.6 lumens/sq ft

The wall is now considered to be made of five strips each 10 ft high and of great length. The luminosity of each is assumed equal to the value at the center point, and the illumination at P due to each strip is calculated. For the top one, $\gamma = 63.5°$ and $L = 160$. From Fig. 9.17,

$$\frac{E_y}{L} = 0.1384$$

From this must be subtracted the value for the remainder of the wall, $\gamma = 58.0°$:

$$\frac{E_y}{L} = 0.1175$$

Thus the illumination at P due to strip 1 is

$$E = 2(160)(0.1384 - 0.1175) = 6.69 \text{ lumens/sq ft}$$

The results of similar calculations are given in the table, resulting in an illumination at P of

$$E_P = \mathbf{24.6 \text{ lumens/sq ft}}$$

In this example, the wall of the building on the right has such low reflection factors that interreflections across the alley can be neglected. If both walls are of high reflection factor, however, interreflections may be very important and may increase the illumination at P by a factor of three or four. For further information on this subject, the reader is referred to the original papers listed in the bibliography at the close of this chapter.

An excellent application of sound engineering analysis to daylighting is seen in the latest type of saw-tooth construction for factories. The calculation of illumination with different sill heights, window heights, etc., has led to a considerable improvement in the uniformity of illumination and has put the design of such buildings on a much more satisfactory basis. Figure 11.14 *a* shows an older construction and the resulting illumination on

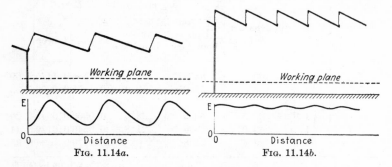

FIG. 11.14*a*.   FIG. 11.14*b*.

the working plane, while *b* shows modern construction such as that used at the Peterboro Works of the Canadian General Electric Company.* The windows face north to avoid direct sunlight. It is found that sloping windows increase the illumination but collect dirt so rapidly as to annul this initial advantage. Vertical windows are now the accepted practice. Uniformity in illumination is improved by raising the sill height. Similar improvements can be effected in the design of windows and skylights for many other types of buildings by the use of logical design instead of haphazard guessing.

Up to this point, we have neglected the effect of the glass and have made our calculations on the basis of unobstructed openings in the walls. The presence of clear glass reduces the luminous flux by about 8 per cent when the radiation is incident normal to the window surface (Fig. 9.08). With diffused light from the sky, the reduction in the flux is considerably greater. Dirty glass reduces the flux still further, as do window frames, shades,

* See discussion by A. Vogel, *I.E.S. Trans.*, **25**, 1930, p. 246.

and other obstructions.   J. E. Ives[48] found that under ordinary conditions the actual illumination was approximately 60 per cent of the calculated value owing to dirty glass, shades, etc.   Typical data are given in Table XLV.   Further changes in the illumination can be expected if ribbed or other figurated glasses are used.

This section would be incomplete without a mention of the economics of daylighting.   Because daylight is free and because

TABLE XLV.—EFFECT OF WINDOW GLASS
On the Illumination in Experimental Room.   Black Walls and Ceiling.
Window 15 Ft. Wide by 9 Ft. High.   Sky Luminosity = 314
Lumens/Sq Ft
(IVES, *U.S. Pub. Health Bull.* 218, p. 41)

Distance from windows (feet)	Illumination (lumens per square foot)		
	Calc.	Calc. × 0.60	Experimental
5	67.8	40.7	33.9
10	26.9	16.1	16.6
15	12.1	7.3	7.4
20	5.6	3.4	3.7
25	2.6	1.6	2.0

windows have always been used in the past, the architect continues to use natural lighting, though it may actually be more expensive in some cases than artificial lighting.   For daylight put into the building is by no means free of cost.   The cost of the windows, window frames, shades, Venetian blinds, of window washing and repair, the large cost of heat wasted through these windows in the winter and the added load on the air-conditioning system in the summer, the waste of valuable space in light courts and in other constructions whose sole purpose is to allow light to enter all the rooms—all these costs should logically be charged against daylighting.   Comparing such costs with the cost of a thoroughly modern artificial lighting system and a windowless building sometimes leads to surprising conclusions* and has resulted in a number of recent windowless stores and factories. Though we shall probably continue to demand windows in our homes, it is probable that the elimination of windows will occur in

* LUCKIESH and HOLLADAY, *I.E.S. Trans.*, 1923, p. 119, give an interesting analysis of the problem.

many factories and stores. There is no reason why artificial lighting cannot be made at least as satisfactory as daylight for visual efficiency and comfort; and the windowless building offers an opportunity to the illuminating engineer to show what he can do in the design of lighting systems of a thoroughly satisfactory nature. It is an opportunity and a challenge.

Problem 144. A living room opening on a porch is lighted through a French window 6 ft wide and 7 ft high. A windbreak of Lombardy poplars

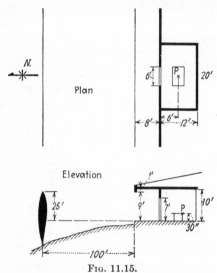

Fɪɢ. 11.15.

100 ft north of the edge of the porch makes a practically uniform wall of foliage extending to a height of 25 ft above the porch-floor level (Fig. 11.15).

Determine the illumination at the center of a table in the middle of the living room. Neglect light reflected from walls and ceiling of room and from porch roof.

a. At 4:00 P.M. on a summer day. Sun at elevation of 30 deg and exactly southwest of house.

b. Same but with porch roof removed.

c. Same as (*a*), but sky covered with light clouds.

Problem 145. A proposed factory building is 80 by 200 ft inside. The brick walls are 17 ft high and 1 ft thick. The view from both sides is practically unobstructed. The manufacturer requires that on a cloudy day with sun at 30 deg elevation, the illumination on the bench level (36 in. above floor) shall be not less than 40 lumens/sq ft at any point.

Specify the size of windows required and the monitor size (if monitor is necessary). It will be sufficient to consider the illumination at the center plane 100 ft from either end.

Problem 146. In Example 2 (page 383), repeat the calculations, (a) using 5- instead of 10-ft strips, (b) considering the opposing wall as a single source. Determine the differences in illumination at P introduced by the new assumptions.

11.07. Floodlighting.*—Floodlighting has been found useful in the lighting of building exteriors for advertising or for ornamental purposes. It is also used for statues, fountains, monuments, and signs. In all these, there is no exacting visual condition to be met, and the value of illumination to be used depends merely upon getting a satisfactory appearance with sufficiently high luminosity to make the object stand out against its background. Floodlighting equipment is also used in the lighting of railroad yards, athletic fields, etc. Here, however, the visual task is the important thing, and the designer must carefully consider the requirements for seeing and for the elimination of glare.

Floodlight projectors are usually weatherproof and consist of a lamp, reflector, and cover glass with trunnion mounting. Two types of lamps are used, the general-service lamp and the floodlight, or spotlight, lamp. The spotlight lamp has a concentrated filament and is used when a very narrow beam is required. Otherwise, the general-service type is advisable. Reflectors are made of silvered glass or of metal such as aluminum or chromium-plated copper. Cover glasses are plain, slightly diffusing to prevent filament images, or fluted to give special beam shapes. Projectors may be classified as:

Narrow beam............................	Up to 15 deg.
Medium beam...........................	15 to 30 deg.
Wide beam..............................	Over 30 deg.

The candlepower distribution from a floodlight projector is shown in Fig. 11.16. It is customary to define the *beam spread* arbitrarily as the total angular distance between points where the candlepower falls to 10 per cent of its maximum. The beam lumens of the projector are defined as the lumens in the portion of the beam given by the 10 per cent limits. Luminous flux outside this zone is called spill light. Its effect is generally ignored unless it is likely to be troublesome, when it can be eliminated by the use of louvers.

* May be omitted in an introductory course.

The lumen method can be used as the basis of floodlighting design, just as it was used as the basis of interior lighting design.

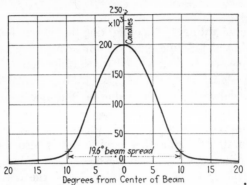

Fig. 11.16.—Candlepower distribution. Permaflector FLC-1001 floodlight. No cover glass, 1000-watt, PS-52 lamp. (*Pittsburgh Reflector Company, Catalog FL-1.*)

A value of E_{av} is selected, either from experience or by use of the rough guide (Table XLVI). The relation

$$E_{av} = \frac{L_{av}}{\rho} \quad \text{(lumens/sq ft)} \quad (11.12)$$

gives E_{av} if the desired luminosity L_{av} is known. The required beam lumens for a surface of area A are

$$F_B = \frac{E_{av}A}{k_d} \quad (11.13)$$

where F_B = total beam lumens required.

A = total illuminated area (sq ft).

k_d = depreciation factor (0.70 is a good assumption).

Some of the beam lumens are always lost by falling outside the area to be lighted; but for the present rough calculation, this loss is assumed to be compensated by the effect of spill light. The manufacturers' data or Table XLVII may be used to determine tentatively the number of projectors and their size.

The question now arises as to how well the tentatively selected projectors will cover the given area—a question of considerable practical importance. Spill light being neglected, each projector is assumed to produce a circular cone of light with sharply defined edges. This cone will illuminate an area with an elliptical boundary on the wall of the building, and the major and minor axes of the ellipse are easily calculated from the beam spread of the projector and the distance to the building. A scale drawing of the building can be used, and the ellipse corresponding to each projector can be drawn, the various ellipses being moved about until all the area is covered. In case the area cannot be covered by the tentatively adopted number of projectors, more projectors with smaller lamps will have to be used, or the beam spread will have to be increased.

The drawing of a large number of ellipses is troublesome, particularly since the size and eccentricity of each ellipse change when the ellipse is moved to make it overlap with adjacent ones. This difficulty has been eliminated by the method developed by Benford.[68] Consider a building (Fig. 11.17) the front of which is to be floodlighted from a station P. Imagine a large hemisphere inclosing the whole arrangement with P at the center. Since the surface of the hemisphere is always normal to the

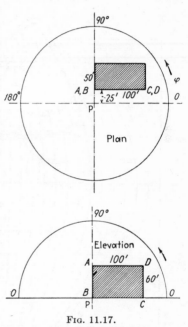

Fig. 11.17.

light rays from the projectors, the area illuminated on the sphere by each projector will have a *circular* boundary. In this way, the former ellipses are replaced by circles which are much easier to draw. Moreover, the circle for a given projector will always be of the same size irrespective of the position of the circle. Instead of using the actual building outline, we project the outline on the hemisphere by straight lines from P and use the projection. Finally, it is desirable to flatten the hemisphere into a plane so that it can be used advantageously. This can be accomplished in a number of ways, one of which is the use of sinusoidal coordinates (Chap. VIII). It is true that shapes are distorted by this method, being correct in the center of the diagram only and being more and more distorted as the edges of the diagram are approached. In most floodlighting installations, however, the portion of the whole sphere which is used is small enough so that the distortion may be neglected, particularly if the position of the building is moved as near the center of the diagram as possible. The position of any point is fixed by the specification of the altitude θ and the horizontal angle ϕ. The altitude must be

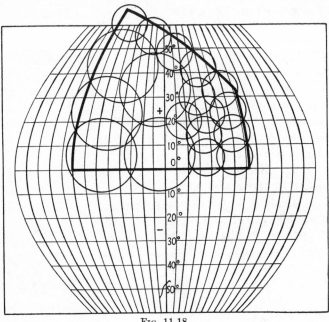

Fig. 11.18.

taken with its zero on the center line of the diagram, but the zero of ϕ may be taken at any convenient place and should be so chosen that the projection of the building is near the center of the coordinate system. If projectors are placed at several widely spaced stations, a separate diagram must be drawn for each station.

Example. To illuminate the front of the building shown in Fig. 11.17, using projectors at P.

The first necessity is to locate the corners of the building on the sinusoidal web of Fig. 11.18. The following angles are easily found either by use of trigonometry or by geometrical construction:

Corner	Degrees	
	ϕ	θ
A	90	67.4
B	90	0
C	14	0
D	14	32.2

Other points along the top edge are considered in a similar manner, giving the building projection shown by the heavy lines of Fig. 11.18.

A sufficient number of projectors must now be used so that the entire area is covered. Many combinations are possible. The diagram shows one arrangement using 30-deg projectors for the near-by parts of the building and 15-deg projectors for the more distant portions. The circles are fixed in diameter according to the scale along the horizontal line at $\theta = 0$ deg, and their positions are altered until the whole area is covered in a fairly uniform manner. In the example, 5 projectors of 30-deg spread and 13 projectors of 15-deg spread are used.

There is a great deal more to floodlighting design than can be considered here. Cornices, columns, and projections of all kinds take on a quite different and often unexpected appearance when illuminated from below. In fact, quite hideous results are often produced. Thus the floodlighting of a building or other object not consisting of simple planes must be considered from the aesthetic standpoint, the architect being consulted. Other installations such as the lighting of tennis courts, railroad yards, and baseball fields, are highly specialized, and each must be studied with reference to its peculiar seeing conditions. Some of these details are discussed in Chaps. XII, XIII, and XIV and in the original papers listed at the end of these chapters.

Problem 147. The entire front (including tower) of a factory building in a city of 25,000 inhabitants is to be floodlighted. The building is of light gray limestone with a rectangular front 180 ft wide and 200 ft high. The depth of the building is 150 ft. A tower 150 ft high and 50 ft square is in the middle of the building front with its front face flush with the building front. The projectors are to be located on the top of another building and are to be 100 ft above the street and 100 ft to the front and 25 ft to the left of the left corner of the structure to be lighted.

Design the lighting system, tabulating number of projectors, beam spreads, lamp sizes, location of each beam, and illumination at center of each beam.

Problem 148. A building of the step construction is to have its top section floodlighted. This section is 30 ft high and 100 ft square. It is to be lighted by a bank of projectors hidden behind the parapet wall which is 10 ft from the wall to be lighted. The building is of tan brick and is in the downtown section of Boston.

Design the installation, specifying the number and size of projectors and checking for uniform coverage.

Problem 149. Descriptions of recent noteworthy buildings are given in the various architectural journals. Select a single room in such a building and design for it a modern lighting system. Any necessary assumptions can be made regarding reflection factors or minor dimensions.

Problem 150. Repeat Prob. 149 for any room described in "Light in Architecture and Decoration."* Calculate E_{av} for the present lighting system. Design a new system and compare the good and bad points of the two.

TABLE XLVI.—PRESENT PRACTICE IN FLOODLIGHTING

Location	L_{av} Approximate Luminosity of Floodlighted Surface (Lumens/square foot)
Downtown, city of 50,000 or over..........	7
5,000–50,000.......................	6
5,000................................	4
Outlying districts, city of 50,000...........	6
5,000–50,000.......................	4

TABLE XLVII.—BEAM LUMENS OF TYPICAL FLOODLIGHT PROJECTORS
(*Nela Park Eng. Bull.* LD-16)

Beam spread	Lamp watts	Beam lumens	Lamp
Narrow (≦15°)................	250 500	1,100 } 2,600 }	Floodlight
Medium (15–30°)...............	300 500 750 1,000 1,500	1,700 3,000 4,900 8,500 12,500	General service
Broad (≧30°).................	300 500 750 1,000 1,500	1,900 3,400 5,200 8,800 13,000	General service

* Published by the Illuminating Engineering Society, New York.

Bibliography

LUMEN METHOD

1. HARRISON and ANDERSON: Illumination Efficiencies as Determined in an Experimental Room, *I.E.S. Trans.*, **11**, 1916, p. 67.
2. HARRISON and ANDERSON: Cofficients of Utilization, *I. E. S. Trans.*, **15**, 1920, p. 97.
3. COHU and DOURGNON: Le coefficient d'utilisation d'un espace clos, *R.G.E.*, **21**, 1927, p. 531.
4. J DOURGNON: Nouvelle méthode de prédétermination des coefficients d'utilisation, *R.G.E.*, **23**, 1928, p. 271; **33**, 1933, p. 579.

MODERN INTERIOR LIGHTING

5. B. JONES: The Lighting of the Allegheny County Soldiers' Memorial, *I.E.S. Trans.*, **6**, 1911, p. 9.
6. BEGGS and WOODSIDE: Technical Aspects of Architectural Lighting, *I.E.S. Trans.*, **26**, 1931, p. 1007.
7. POTTER and MEAKER: Luminous Architectural Elements, *I.E.S. Trans.*, **26**, 1931, p. 1025.
8. C. S. WOODSIDE: Illumination of Structural Glass, *I.E.S. Trans.*, **29**, 1934, p. 878.
9. POWELL and RODGERS: Built-in Lighting, *Lighting*, Nov., Dec., 1930; Jan. 1931.
10. H. L. LOGAN: Modern Lighting with Control Lenses, *I.E.S. Trans.*, **25**, 1930, p. 859.
11. H. L. LOGAN: The Influence of Built-in Lighting Forms on Direct Lighting Methods, *I.E.S. Trans.*, **29**, 1934, p. 686.
12. H. L. LOGAN: The Fenestration of Artificial Light, *I.E.S. Trans.*, **31**. 1936.
13. G. E. SHOEMAKER: Synthetic Lighting, *I.E.S. Trans.*, **27**, 1932, p. 308.
14. A. A. BRAINERD: Tailor-made Lighting, *I.E.S. Trans.*, **25**. 1930, p.867.
15. STAIR and GRAVES: Louvered Lighting, *I.E.S. Trans.*, **31**, 1936, p. 249.
16. H. E. IVES: Some Home Experiments in Illumination from Large Area Light Sources, *I.E.S. Trans.*, **8**, 1913, p. 229.
17. HIGHIE and BYCHINSKY: Illumination Distribution Measurements from Surface Sources in Sidewalls, *I.E.S. Trans.*, **29**, 1934, p. 206.
18. H. H. HIGBIE: Illumination Distribution from Surface Sources in Rooms, *I.E.S. Trans.*, **31**, 1936, p. 163.
19. D. D. PRICE: Room Efficiencies Using a Luminous Panel, M.I.T. thesis, Electrical Engineering Dept., 1932.
20. Illuminating Engineering Society, Light in Architecture and Decoration, 1934 (and other years).
21. Modern Interior Lighting. *Am. Architect*, November, December, 1934.
22. J. L. STAIR: Lighting à la Mode, *I.E.S. Trans.*, **24**, 1929, p. 947.
23. J. M. NESS: Lighting System for the M.I.T. Library, M.I.T. thesis, Electrical Engineering Dept., 1932.
24. E. J. INGRAM: Economic Analysis of Sports Lighting, *I.E.S. Trans.*, **28**, 1933, p. 437.

25. L. A. Gates: Illuminated Fountain, *I.E.S. Trans.*, **27**, 1932, p. 566.

26. Ketch, Sturrock, and Staley: Special Lighting Applications for Industrial Processes, *I.E.S. Trans.*, **28**, 1933, p. 57.

27. G. H. Stickney: Symposium on Office Lighting, *I.E.S. Trans.*, **23**, 1928, p. 51.

28. J. L. Stair: Significant Lighting in Department Stores, *I.E.S. Trans.*, **27**, 1932, p. 361.

29. Powell, Smith, and Rodgers: Practice in Lighting Small Stores, *I.E.S. Trans.*, **29**, 1934, p. 267.

30. Oday and Sturrock: Comfortable High-level Illumination, *I.E.S. Trans.*, **31**, 1936, p. 351..

31. Standards of School Lighting, *I.E.S. Trans.*, **28**, 1933, p. 21.

32. H. B. Dates: Industrial and School Lighting, *I.E.S. Trans.*, **29**, 1934, p. 866.

33. H. L. Logan: Operating Room Lighting, *I.E.S. Trans.*, **28**, 1933, p. 537.

34. Testing Specifications for Lighting Equipment, *I.E.S. Trans.*, **28**, 1933, p. 479.

35. D. R. Grandy: Combining Mercury Vapor and Incandescent Lamps to Produce Commercial White Light, *I.E.S. Trans.*, **28**, 1933, p. 762.

36. W. Harrison: Applications of the New Gaseous-conductor Lamps, *I.E.S. Trans.*, **30**, 1935, p. 190.

37. Oday and Porter: The Use of Ultraviolet Sources for the General Illumination of Interiors, *I.E.S. Trans.*, **28**, 1933, p. 121.

38. M. R. Paul: Surfacing Materials for Light Wells, *I.E.S. Trans.*, **28**, 1933, p. 315.

39. H. P. Cage: Methods of Measuring Visible and Total Energy Transmission of Heat-absorbing Glasses, *I.E.S. Trans.*, **30**, 1935, p. 411.

40. E. H. Hobbie: Glass for Protection from Infrared Radiation, *I.E.S. Trans.*, **28**, 1933, p. 658.

Solar Illumination

41. P. J. Waldram: Daylight Illumination and Sky Brightness, *Illum. Eng., London*, **1**, 1908, p. 811.

42. C. Dorno: Physik der Sonnen- und Himmelstrahlung, Vieweg, Braunschweig, Germany, 1919.

43. Angstrom and Dorno: Registration of the Intensity of Sunshine and Diffuse Sky Radiation, *Monthly Weather Rev.*, **49**, 1921, p. 135.

44. Kimball and Hand: Sky Brightness, *I.E.S. Trans.*, **16**, 1921, p. 255.

45. G. I. Pokrowski: Über die Helligkeitsverteilung am Himmel, *Phys. Zeits.*, **30**, 1929, p. 697.

46. Kunerth and Miller: Visible and Ultraviolet in the Light Obtained from the Sun, *I.E.S. Trans.*, **28**, 1933, p. 347.

47. Ives and Knowles: Brightness of the Clear North Sky in Washington, D.C., *I.E.S. Trans.*, **30**, 1935, p. 281.

48. Ives, Knowles, and Thompson: Studies in Illumination, IV, *Public Health Bull.* 218, Washington, 1935.

49. E. I. Freese: Pathways of the Sun, *Am. Architect*, November, 1934, p. 46.

DAYLIGHTING

50. HIGBIE and MARTIN: A Bibliography of Natural Lighting, *I.E.S. Trans.*, **24**, 1929, p. 315.

51. HIGBIE and BULL: How Glass Affects Your Daylighting, *I.E.S. Trans.*, **26**, 1931, p. 219.

52. HOBBIE and LITTLE: Transmission of Light through Window Glass, *I.E.S. Trans.*, **22**, 1927, p. 258.

53. HIGBIE and LEVIN: Prediction of Daylight from Sloping Windows, *I.E.S. Trans.*, **21**, 1926, p. 273.

54. HIGBIE and SZYMANOWSKI: Calculation of Daylighting by Protractor Method, *I.E.S. Trans.*, **25**, 1930, p. 213.

55. W. TURNER-SZYMANOWSKI: A Rapid Method for Predicting the Distribution of Daylight in Buildings, *U. of Mich., Dept. of Eng., Res. Bull.* 17, 1931.

56. C. H. SHARP: Airshaft Illumination as Studied by Models, *I.E.S. Trans.*, **9**, 1914, p. 598.

57. The Transmission Factor of Commercial Window Glasses, *Dept. of Sci. & Ind. Res. Tech. Paper* 2, 1926.

58. The Natural Lighting of Picture Galleries, *Dept. of Sci. & Ind. Res. Tech. Paper*, 6, 1927.

59. W. S. BROWN: Practical Daylight Calculations for Vertical Windows, *I.E.S. Trans.*, **21**, 1926, p. 225.

60. W. C. RANDALL: Sawtooth Design, *I.E.S. Trans.*, **21**, 1926, p. 241.

61. VOGEL, RANDALL, MARTIN, and BENFORD: Daylighting in Multi-story Industrial Buildings, *I.E.S. Trans.*, **23**, 1928, p. 129.

62. RANDALL and MARTIN: Model Tests and Design Data, *I.E.S. Trans.*, **23**, 1928, p. 135.

63. RANDALL and MARTIN: Predetermination of Daylighting by the Fenestra Method, *I.E.S. Trans.*, **25**, 1930, p. 262.

64. RANDALL and MARTIN: Daylighting in the Home, *I.E.S. Trans.*, **26**, 1931, p. 275.

65. RANDALL and MARTIN: The Window as a Source of Light, *I.E.S. Trans.*, **27**, 1932, p. 275.

66. A. D. MOORE: Inter-reflection by the Increment Method, *I.E.S. Trans.*, **24**, 1929, p. 629.

FLOODLIGHTING

67. HAAS and REID: Floodlighting, *Nela Park Eng. Dept. Bull.* LD-16.

68. F. BENFORD: Methods of Computing Floodlighting, *G.E. Rev.*, **26**, 1923, p. 575.

69. E. B. HALLMAN: Floodlighting Design Procedure. *I.E.S. Trans.*, **29**, 1934, p. 287.

70. W. D. A. RYAN: Illumination of the Panama-Pacific International Exposition, *I.E.S. Trans.*, **11**, 1916, p. 629.

71. GERBER and TILLSON: Color Floodlighting of Buildings, *I.E.S. Trans.*, **19**, 1924, p. 518.

72. BRAINARD and HOEVELER: Advertising Value of Mobile Color Lighting, *I.E.S. Trans.*, **24**, 1929, p. 40.

CHAPTER XII

VISION*

It is recognized to an ever increasing extent that good lighting requires more than a knowledge of applied physics. The purpose of most lighting is to allow people to see, and every lighting system must be designed primarily on the basis of its fitness for promoting good vision. A study of the eye and of the phenomena of vision is therefore of the utmost importance to the illuminating engineer.

In the subject of vision, where original researches already number over 10,000 and where a multivolume treatise is required for an adequate presentation, a single chapter must necessarily omit many interesting and important phases of the subject. Because of the state of our knowledge and the conflicting opinions held by experts, a treatment with the scope of the present one is limited to either a mere tabulation of experimental results, many of them contradictory and confusing, or an account of what seems to be the most satisfactory theory of vision. The author has chosen the latter alternative, fraught with difficulties and colored by personal opinions though it is. An attempt is made to concentrate on the parts of the subject that will be of greatest use to the illuminating engineer and in particular to develop such a concept of the visual mechanism as will help in the visualization of the problems of "design for seeing."

The chapter divides itself into four sections:

1. Structure of the eye.
2. The visual mechanism.
3. Experimental results and their connection with theory.
4. Other methods of attack.

12.02. Structure of the Eye.—The general structure of the eye (Fig. 12.01) has been described so many times and is so well-known that another description seems almost superfluous. There are several details, however, a knowledge of which is particularly

* May be omitted in an introductory course.

necessary for the understanding of this chapter, and these details will be briefly considered.

Light enters the eye through the cornea and, after passing through the various transparent media, falls on the retina. The refractive indices and the sizes of the various parts comprising the optical system need not concern us here. Suffice it to say that the image formed on the retina is essentially the same as that which would be formed by a thin glass lens in air having a focal

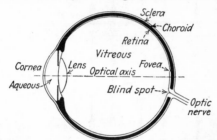

Fig. 12.01.—Section of right eye, viewed from above.

length of about 15 mm. Images of objects focused on the retina appear upside down and much reduced in size; *i.e.*, the retinal image of a person 100 ft away is about 0.9 mm in height. A peculiarity of the eye as an optical instrument is that objects are not generally focused at a point on the optical axis but at a small distance from the axis in a depression in the retina called the *fovea centralis*. The fovea is oval in shape and is approximately 0.30 by 0.24 mm, subtending an angle of very nearly one degree.* The fovea is specially constituted to allow good vision, and most of our seeing and all of our discrimination of fine detail result from focusing the object on the fovea. If the object is so large that it subtends an angle greater than one degree, all of it cannot be seen distinctly at once, and the eye is forced to move rapidly from one part to another of the object. Usually, we are unconscious of these movements and think that our field of exact vision is much greater than it actually is.

Though the field of exact vision is very circumscribed, the total field of hazy vision is large. The retina covers nearly the whole of the inside of the eyeball and is sensitive to light throughout. The part outside the fovea is called the *peripheral region* or the *parafovea*. The retina is a transparent layer 0.22 mm thick and

* The total rod-free area is almost twice this size.

contains a maze of nerve fibers, nerve endings, etc., the functions of many of which are understood only imperfectly. Figure 12.02 gives a greatly simplified diagram of the eye. The radiation

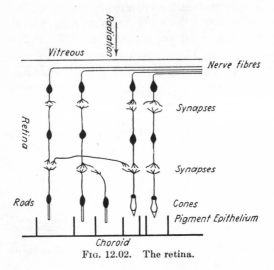

FIG. 12.02.   The retina.

passes completely through the retinal layer until it reaches the sensitive rods and cones, where it apparently produces a photo-

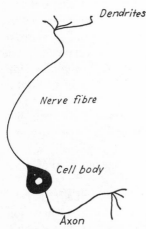

FIG. 12.03.—A neuron.

chemical reaction leading to the excitation of the nerve endings. Radiation that is not utilized in the photochemical process falls on the black *pigment epithelium* where it is absorbed, preventing reflections that might confuse the optical image. The rods contain a photochemical substance of unknown composition called *rhodopsin*, or *visual purple*. This substance has a purple color in the dark but bleaches rapidly in the light. The rate of bleaching depends upon the wavelength of the radiation, the bleaching curve being very nearly the same as the visibility curve for rod vision. Strangely enough, no visual purple has as yet been found in the cones, though this fact certainly does not constitute proof that the action in the case of cone vision is not photochemical.

Since the retina is essentially a layer of nerves, a brief consideration of nerve cells is advisable. The animal body is composed to a large extent of protoplasm which is divided into small units called cells. These cells take various forms, one of the most interesting being the nerve cell. The nerve-cell body, containing the nucleus and other parts necessary for the life of the cell, is provided with long, slender extensions, ending generally in treelike branches or arborizations. The complete cell (Fig. 12.03) is called a *neuron*. In the retina (Fig. 12.02) are three layers of neurons. The neurons farthest from the pupil have specially modified ends—the rods and cones—which act as receptors. The arborizations of these end neurons meet the dendrites of the second layer of neurons, which in turn meet the third set of neurons which make up the optic nerve. Impulses that originate in the rods and cones are communicated through the two layers of arborizations (synapses) and pass through the optic nerve to the central nervous system. To the engineer the structure seems unnecessarily complicated. Perhaps it is so, though our knowledge of the visual mechanism is still so imperfect that it is unwise to make dogmatic statements. The reason for three sets of neurons where one would seem sufficient is not clear, though recent work indicates that there is a "mixing" action in the synapses which probably has a decided effect on the visual sensations. Some neurons run transversely and are evidently important in modifying the messages sent on a given fiber. It was formerly believed that each foveal cone was connected to the brain through its own individual set of neurons and thus had its own "private line to the brain." More recent histological work, however, shows that frequently the arborizations of a number of cones connect to a single neuron in the second layer. The impulses in the second layer are still further modified by contributions from other parts of the retina, impulses from which are sent over the transverse neurons. This interconnection scheme is much less prevalent in the foveal region than in the peripheral region. In the fovea there are no rods, and the cones are of very small diameter tightly packed together and with a large number of independent nerve connections. In the parafovea, on the other hand, the nerve endings are farther apart than in the fovea, rods are more numerous than cones, and inter-connections are numerous.

The cones of the fovea have a diameter of approximately 3.2μ (0.0032 mm), and there are about 130,000 of them per square millimeter. Near the fovea, the cones are somewhat larger and are interspersed with rods. As one goes farther from the fovea, he finds an ever increasing proportion of rods and a corresponding lessening in the number of cones. The total number of cones in the retina is of the order of 3,000,000, while there are about 15,000,000 rods. Approximately 1,000,000 nerve fibers constitute the optic nerve. The retinal area of good vision is confined to the fovea, but the total field of vision covers a considerably larger area. Despite a certain amount of shielding by the bony structure of the head, the field of vision of the two eyes covers approximately 180 deg in the horizontal plane, 50 deg upward, and 70 deg downward. In the outer part of the field, vision is indistinct, and there is no color sensation.

By study of the eye under various lighting conditions, it has been found that the rods and cones have certain noteworthy differences in their operating characteristics. The rods are considerably more sensitive than the cones, but sensations of color are obtained only through the cones. Ordinary daylight vision, or *photopic vision*, uses the foveal cones almost exclusively. In photopic vision, color sensations are produced; and since the foveal cones are closely spaced, a high degree of visual acuity is obtained. Night vision, or *scotopic vision*, is used when the luminosity of the objects viewed is of the order of 0.001 lumen/sq ft or less. The cones are entirely inoperative in scotopic vision, and objects focused on the fovea are invisible. To take care of this condition, the eye automatically moves the images into the peripheral region where rod vision obtains. Owing to the comparatively coarse structure of the peripheral retina, fine details can no longer be distinguished. Color sensations are absent, all objects appearing gray. These and many other facts point to the existence of two distinct receptors in the eye—the rods, sensitive in weak light; the cones, insensitive in weak light but capable of exciting the sensation of color with high illuminations.

THE VISUAL MECHANISM

12.03. Effect of Pupil Area.—Having considered the rudiments of the structure of the eye, we are in a position to study the nature

of the visual process, with particular emphasis on those facts
which will be useful to us as illuminating engineers.   In any such
study, it is evident that the illumination of the retina is important, since upon it depends the operation of the receptor organs.
In previous chapters, we have spent considerable time in calculating the value of the illumination on surfaces due to sources of
various forms.   Yet the visual effect produced by such illuminated surfaces is by no means dependent upon the value of their
illumination alone.   More closely is it related to the surface
luminosity.   For a large, perfectly diffusing surface of uniform

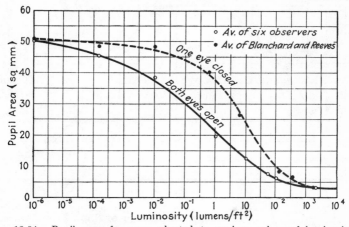

FIG. 12.04.—Pupil area for eyes adapted to various values of luminosity.[5]

luminosity, it is the value of the luminosity that determines the
retinal illumination, all other factors being constant.   But as
the luminosity of the surface is varied, all other factors do *not*
remain constant.   One of the obvious variables is the size of the
pupil, which automatically changes when the luminosity is
changed.   Figure 12.04 shows that the pupil diameter varies
from approximately 2 to 8 mm (3 to 50 sq mm area), depending
upon the luminosity of the extended surface in the field of vision.
The measurements were made from flashlight photographs of the
eye, sufficient time having been allowed before each picture
for the pupil to become adjusted to the specific value of luminosity used.

Until very recently, it was assumed universally that the retinal
illumination was always directly proportional to the pupil area,

and it was customary to plot experimental results against the so-called "retinal illumination" obtained by multiplying the luminosity by the pupil area.* For the usual cases met in practice, a little consideration shows that the "retinal illumination" can be only an approximation at best. The recent experimental results of Stiles and Crawford indicate that it has no justification whatever.[6] Stiles and Crawford have found that rays entering the pupil near the edge are much less effective in producing a

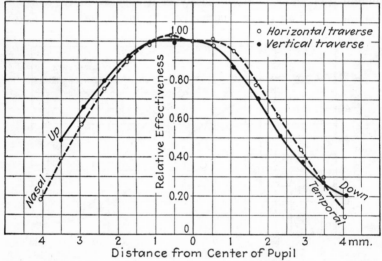

Fig. 12.05.—Relative effectiveness of rays entering the pupil at different points.[6]

visual sensation than rays entering the pupil near the center. One of their experimental curves is reproduced in Fig. 12.05 and shows that rays near the edge of the pupil may have an effect as small as 20 per cent of what the effect would have near the center of the pupil. Thus pupil area has less effect than was formerly believed.

It is somewhat difficult to see what function the change of pupillary diameter has. The layman believes usually that the contraction of the pupil protects the eye from the effect of bright lights and that the change in size allows the eye to adapt itself to a wide range of luminosities. However, its effect in this way

* This conception led to various bastard units such as the "meter-candle-millimeter" which is used by Houstoun (Vision and Color Vision, p. 9.) and the "photon" unit used by Troland.

is very limited. The eye adapts itself to white surfaces in direct sunlight, $L = 10,000$ lumens/sq ft, and to values of less than 0.01 lumen/sq. ft, a range of over 1,000,000 to 1. But under this variation in luminosity the pupil area varies through a range of only 16 to 1, and its effectiveness in altering retinal illumination is even less than this ratio. An assumption that the function of the change in pupil diameter is to allow greater visual acuity at high illuminations by decreasing the optical aberrations is also disproved. Cobb showed that visual acuity is practically unaffected by a change in pupil diameter from 2 to 6 mm.[48]

Although pupil diameter does have an effect on retinal illumination, the reason for the marvelous ability of the human eye to adapt itself to a wide range of luminosities must be sought elsewhere than in change in pupil diameter. A great deal of evidence has been collected by various investigators to show that the seat of this adaptation process is the retina.

12.04. The Photochemistry of the Retina.—After passing through the optical system of the eye, radiant energy falls on the retina, and there it reacts with matter. Since all reactions between radiant energy and matter are quantum phenomena, we should expect the first stage of the complex physicopsychological progress of vision to occur in discrete quanta. There is considerable evidence that this first step in the process is a photochemical one, though the chemical constitution of the various products is still unknown. The brilliant researches of Hecht give support to the photochemical theory and show that its predictions are in fairly good agreement with experiment for both human beings and lower forms of animal life.

Assume that each receptor element (rod or cone) has either in it or associated with it a certain small amount of photochemical substance, which for want of exact knowledge we shall call S. When a quantum of radiant energy is absorbed by S, one of the complex molecules of S breaks into two other substances A and B, which are not light-sensitive. The reaction may be written

$$S \xrightarrow{\text{light}} A^+ + B^-$$

One or the other of these decomposition products is capable of exciting the nerve ending. The phenomena of nerve excitation are but imperfectly understood. One may assume that the two products A and B are in the ionic state and that one of them is capable of migrating into the rod or into the cone and exciting it electrically. That the nerve ending is not immediately excited is shown by oscillographic studies (Fig. 12.11) which indicate that a definite time elapses between the absorption of the quanta and the excitation of the nerve ending. Flicker studies also seem to require the hypothesis of a comparatively slow diffusion of the ions into the rod or cone. We assume two steps in the retinal process,

1. A photochemical reaction, where each quantum absorbed produces one ion of A and one ion of B.

2. A diffusion process of the ions,* which results in the excitation of the nerve ending.

To return now to the initial process, what happens when a single flash of homogeneous radiation reaches the retina? The flash consists of a large number of quanta, some of which are absorbed by the pigment layer while others lose their energy in forming the products A and B. We should expect the quantum nature of the phenomenon to be most marked in very weak light with the eye in its most sensitive condition; and under these circumstances we should expect the visual effect to be dependent not upon the retinal illumination alone or upon the duration of time of the flash alone but upon their product. This is exactly what is obtained by experiment. Bloch's law (1885) states that for a barely perceptible flash,

$$E_{ret} \times \Delta t = \text{const}$$

for durations of flash up to about 0.2 sec.

Here E_{ret} = the *retinal* illumination.

Δt = the duration time of the flash.

A similar indication of a quantum relation seems to be given by Ricco's law.† If a small luminous disk is displayed continuously with perfectly dark surroundings, the disk is perceptible so long as the product of its diameter and its luminosity is a constant for all sizes of disk up to about 6 deg visual angle. In other words, the disk becomes visible when the total number of photons entering the eye per second reaches a definite value. In the case of

---

* Hecht's experiments on the effect of temperature in *Mya* and *Pholas* do not seem to agree with the assumption of a diffusion process, however.[15]

† See, for instance, Houstoun, Vision and Colour Vision, p. 49.

flashes, visibility is obtained when the total number of photons in the flash reaches a certain threshold. Stiles estimates that 50 quanta of homogeneous radiation are required to excite vision at $\lambda = 0.52\mu$. At other wavelengths, larger numbers of quanta are required.

In the case of a single flash, an inappreciable amount of S is decomposed. But suppose that radiation streams into the retina continuously from a steady source of fairly high intensity. The substance S will be changed continuously into A and B; and unless there is some process for the production of S it will soon be exhausted, and vision will cease. Actually S is being renewed, probably by elements carried by the blood stream. Hecht has found that the assumption of a bimolecular reaction between A and B fits the experimental data and has the advantage of simplicity. Whenever A and B are present, an ordinary chemical reaction occurs to form S:

$$A^+ + B^- \longrightarrow S$$

The velocity of the reaction is zero when the amounts of A and B are zero, and the velocity increases as the amounts of A and B increase. Thus there are two opposing reactions, the photochemical reaction where radiant energy is absorbed to produce A and B, and the ordinary chemical reaction which tends to decrease the amounts of A and B. For any given constant retinal illumination, an equilibrium state will be reached when the rate of production of A and B is just equal to the rate of recombination of A and B.

Let us consider the matter in somewhat greater detail.

Let $x =$ number of molecules of A, expressed in terms of the maximum possible number that is associated with one receptor element.

$E_{ret} =$ retinal illumination at this receptor element.

The number of molecules of A produced in the time Δt is directly proportional to E_{ret}. The probability of a photon's colliding with any molecule of S is directly proportional to the number of molecules of S present. We might expect, therefore, that the amount of A produced in time Δt would be directly proportional to the number of molecules of S, or to $(1 - x)$. Thus

$$\Delta x = k_1 E_{ret}(1 - x)\Delta t \qquad (12.01)$$

The rate of production of A is

$$\frac{dx}{dt} = k_1 E_{\text{ret}}(1 - x) \qquad (12.01a)$$

where $k_1 = \text{const.}$

There is also the chemical reaction occurring between A and B to form S. The velocity of this reaction is independent of E_{ret} but dependent upon the number of molecules of A and B. For a bimolecular reaction,

$$\frac{dx}{dt} = -k_2 x^2 \qquad (12.01b)$$

The resulting reaction velocity is the sum of Eqs. (12.01a and b), or

$$\frac{dx}{dt} = k_1 E_{\text{ret}}(1 - x) - k_2 x^2 \qquad (12.02)$$

The solution of this differential equation will give x as a function of time, while dx/dt might reasonably be expected to be proportional to the number of nerve impulses produced per second by the A^+ or B^- ions which excite the ending.

The solution of Eq. (12.02) is complicated by the fact that the equation is not linear. For certain special cases, however, it yields important results very simply.

1. If the eye has been in the dark for some time just previous to the retinal excitation and is thus thoroughly *dark-adapted*, $x = 0$; and the second term on the right-hand side of Eq. (12.02) vanishes. Then, according to Eq. (12.01),

$$\Delta x = k_1 E_{\text{ret}} \Delta t \qquad (12.03)$$

or the photochemical effect depends only on the product of illumination and the duration of the flash. This result is in accordance with Bloch's law.

2. For the special case of equilibrium $dx/dt = 0$, and Eq. (12.02) becomes

$$\left(\frac{k_1}{k_2}\right) E_{\text{ret}} = \frac{x^2}{1 - x} \qquad (12.04)$$

Equation (12.04) has been used in plotting the curve of Fig. 12.06. The amount of A present in equilibrium is seen to increase with an increase in retinal illumination.   Note that a change in the values of k_1 and k_2 merely shifts the entire curve to the right or left without changing its shape, so the single curve of Fig. 12.06 applies for any value of k_1 and k_2.   The theory predicts a gradual change in the amount of A over a very wide range of retinal illumination—a range strikingly similar to that obtained experimentally for the adaptation range of the human eye.   This

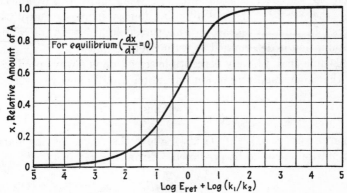

FIG. 12.06.—Calculated characteristic of the photochemical reaction.

retinal adaptation, then, rather than the change of pupil area, is the explanation of how the eye adjusts itself to the range of luminosities found in nature.

3. If, after the eye has become light-adapted, the radiation is suddenly cut off, the first term on the right-hand side of Eq. (12.02) becomes zero, and

$$\frac{dx}{dt} = -k_2 x^2$$

The solution of this differential equation is

$$x = \frac{1}{k_2 t + \dfrac{1}{x_0}} \tag{12.05}$$

where x_0 = the value of x at $t = 0$.

By selecting an arbitrary value of x_o and plotting x as a function of $(k_2 t)$ from Eq. (12.05), it will be found that x changes very slowly at first, then more rapidly, and finally approaches zero.   This means that the concentration of the A ions in the retina which has had the equilibrium value x_o now decreases until it finally reaches zero.

The shape of the curve cannot be checked directly, since there is no straightforward experimental way of measuring x. However, the concentration of ions determines the sensitivity of the retina, which can be evaluated experimentally. After the steady radiation has been cut off and the retina has started to adapt itself to the dark surroundings, a weak light is introduced; and the resulting retinal illumination is increased until the threshold value is reached. This threshold value E_t of retinal illumination is determined as a function of time.

Assume that a barely perceptible sensation is always produced by the same small rate of ion formation; *i.e.*, E_t always gives

$$\frac{dx}{dt} = \Delta = \text{const}$$

Then Eqs. (12.01) and (12.05) allow the forms of the dark-adaptation curve to be predicted. From Eq. (12.01a),

$$\frac{dx}{dt} = \Delta = k_1 E_t (1 - x) \qquad (12.06)$$

Note that Eq. (12.01a) is used, not Eq. (12.02), since we are interested here in the actual rate of ion production due to E_t. From Eq. (12.06),

$$\left(\frac{k_1}{\Delta}\right) E_t = K E_t = \frac{1}{1 - x} \qquad (12.07)$$

where K is a constant. Thus $1/(1 - x)$ is directly proportional to the threshold illumination. Values of x can be taken from Eq. (12.05), and a curve of $1/(1 - x)$ against $(k_2 t)$ should give the shape of the experimental dark-adaptation curves, provided the theory is correct. A curve for $x_o = 1.0$, calculated from Eqs. (12.07) and (12.05), is shown in Fig. 12.07 and is seen to be a straight line over most of the range of $k_2 t$.

An experimental curve obtained by Hecht for foveal dark adaptation is given in Fig. 12.08. The eyes of the observers were adapted to a given level, and then the room was suddenly darkened. The eyes immediately started to change to the dark-adapted state $(x \to 0)$. The progress of the adaptation was determined by exposing a small red cross and increasing its

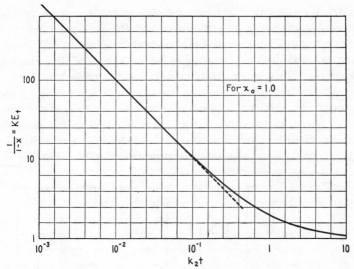

FIG. 12.07.—Dark adaptation (calculated), showing how the threshold illumination varies with time.

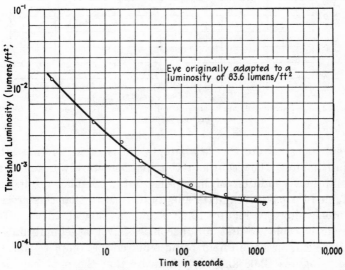

FIG. 12.08.—Foveal dark adaptation.[18]

luminosity until it could just be seen. At first, a fairly high threshold luminosity was required, but the required luminosity gradually diminished as the eye adapted itself more fully to the dark surroundings. Precautions were taken to minimize the disturbing effect of the test light. The red cross was used as test object in order to obtain dark adaptation for the *foveal* region. In the dark, the tendency is to use the rods of the para-foveal region rather than the cones of the fovea; but since the rods are comparatively insensitive to red and not well-suited for distinguishing form, the red cross presumably gave results for the

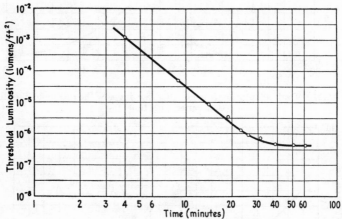

Fig. 12.09.—Parafoveal dark adaptation.[4] (*From W. Nagel in Helmholtz, Vol.* II, *p.* 320.)

foveal cones. Note that the adaptation is rapid, so that after approximately 100 sec the retina has practically reached an equilibrium condition of high sensitivity. Similar results are obtained for parafoveal dark adaptation except that this process is much slower. Figure 12.09 shows a typical curve. The change is rapid at first but becomes slower as equilibrium is approached, almost an hour being required for complete adaptation. Figures 12.08 and 12.09 indicate that the photochemical substances in the rods and cones are quite different and that k_2 for the rods is much smaller than for the cones. Note that for both foveal and parafoveal adaptation the results are in excellent qualitative agreement with the theory, though of course this does not *prove* that the theory is correct.

The practical significance of these experimental results to the illuminating engineer seems obvious.   Where rapid changes in illumination are necessary, the observer can be expected to adapt himself to the new conditions within a minute or two, provided cone vision is used.   In coming into an artificially lighted store on a bright day, for instance, the customer may be inconvenienced slightly for a minute or two by the change in illumination, but this effect quickly disappears.   The illuminating engineer can improve matters by arranging a fairly high level of illumination in the store; and if he uses a higher level near the door, with gradually decreasing values inside, the customer may be unconscious of the change.   On the other hand, in the relatively infrequent cases where the observer must change from cone vision to rod vision, such graded illumination is of little use.   In coming into a cinema theater in the daytime, for instance, one is able to see the screen (cone vision) but is quite unable to see the seats or the people near him (rod vision), and this state of affairs may last for a long time—30 min. or more.

Problem 151.   Plot a family of curves of x against $k_2 t$ and of $1/(1 - x)$ against $k_2 t$ for $x_o = 1.00$, 0.10, and 0.01.   Use logarithmic scales with $k_2 t$ from 10^{-4} to 10^3.

Problem 152.   Determine the approximate values of k_2 to fit the dark-adaptation data for the rods and the cones (Figs. 12.08 and 12.09).

12.05. Visibility Curves.—In every receptor system for radiant energy, the first stage in the process (in which reaction takes place between radiant energy and matter) has a characteristic behavior in regard to the wavelength of the radiation.   We have considered a number of such spectral-response curves in Chap. II. These wavelength-response characteristics are determined only by the first stage of the receptor system, since after the initial reaction has taken place the resulting impulses no longer possess the characteristic of wavelength.   In a photocell, for instance, the spectral-response curve is a function of the structure and chemical constitution of the sensitive layer of the cell and is entirely independent of the kind of circuit that the cell feeds.

Similarly for the eye; the nature of the photochemical substance or substances utilized in the first step of the visual phenomenon determines the wavelength range over which the eye is operative.   The ordinary curve for daylight vision has been called the *visibility curve* and has been discussed in Chap. III and elsewhere.   The curve is evidently a characteristic of the photochemical substances associated with the cones.

If the retinal illumination is very low the standard visibility curve is no longer applicable, and our photometric units, all of which are based upon the standard visibility curve, are meaningless as far as visual comparisons go.   This fact may be of considerable importance in the measurement of street illumination or luminosity or in other applications where extremely low illuminations are used.   Fortunately, most of the work of the illuminating engineer is done at levels above the photopic threshold, where the standard visibility curve applies.   If the luminosity L is above approximately 0.01 lumen/sq ft, vision is photopic.   If L is less than approximately 0.001 lumen/sq ft, vision is scotopic, and an entirely new visibility curve must be used.   Between 0.001 and 0.01 lumen/sq ft, both cones and rods are active and there is a gradual transition from one to the other with a gradual shift of the visibility curve.   This transition region is called the *Purkinje region* (pronounced Pur' kin yee).

When the luminosity of the observed surface falls below approximately 0.01 lumen/sq ft, the customary visibility curve no longer applies.   The use of a Macbeth illuminometer, for instance, at such values of luminosity will still give correct results provided the spectral radiosity curve of the surface is of the same shape as that of the comparison lamp.   If this requirement is not satisfied, the readings of the instrument may not have the slightest relation to the values obtained from the spectroradiometric curve in conjunction with the standard visibility function.   Conditions of low illumination are also obtained with the bar photometer when using a long bar and lamps of low candlepower.   Photometers of the physical type continue to give readings based on their response curves, which in the ideal case are the same as the standard visibility curve and are independent of the illumination.   It should be realized that the reading of physical photometers at illumination levels below the photopic threshold have little relation to *vision*.

Figure 12.10 shows the standard photopic visibility curve having its peak at 0.555μ.   The circles give the experimental results of Hecht and Williams at low luminosities and constitute the best available visibility data on scotopic vision.[23]   The scotopic curve is drawn of exactly the same shape as the standard visibility curve but is shifted to the left by 0.048μ so that the maximum comes at 0.507μ instead of at 0.555μ. The curve is seen to fit the data within the limits of experimental error; and until more complete data are available, this shifted curve may be taken as the visibility curve for rod vision. It would seem that the photosensitive substances associated with the rods have a different chemical composition from the substances associated with the cones, and the response curves for the rods and the cones are therefore different. The scotopic curve applies from the

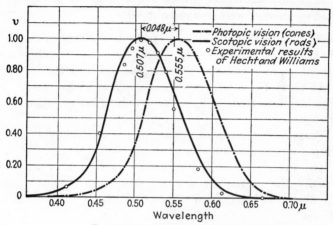

FIG. 12.10.—Visibility curves.[23]

lowest limits (order of 10^{-5} lumen/sq ft, the *absolute threshold*) to approximately 0.001 lumen/sq ft. Between 0.001 and 0.01 lumen/sq ft, there is a transition from rod vision to cone vision and a resulting gradual shift of the visibility curve from its scotopic position with peak at 0.507μ to its photopic position with peak at 0.555μ. This shift is called the *Purkinje phenomenon*. With very low illuminations, the eye discriminates in favor of blue and violet and becomes almost blind to red. This fact would lead us to expect that the mercury-vapor lamp would be particularly well-suited to the lighting of highways and places where the illumination is commonly below the photopic threshold.

Problem 153. A small experimental sodium-vapor lamp is being balanced on a bar photometer against a source of homogeneous radiation of wavelength 0.450μ. Both sources produce irradiations of 1.60×10^{-4} watt/sq ft at a distance of one foot. Assume that the radiation from the sodium lamp is homogeneous and that the inverse-square law holds. The source of 0.450μ is used as a candlepower standard.

a. What value of candlepower is obtained for the sodium lamp, using a one-foot bar?

b. Repeat for a 16-ft bar.

Problem 154. Three test sections of street are illuminated by three kinds of sources: incandescent lamps operating at 2800°K, high-pressure mercury-vapor lamps, and sodium-vapor lamps. In each case, the illumination of the pavement directly beneath the lamp is 1.0 lumen/sq ft. At 200 ft from the lamp, the illumination is again measured with a Macbeth illuminometer having a test lamp operating at 2800°K. The illumination due to the incandescent street lamp is 0.001 lumen/sq ft. What readings are obtained for each of the other two lamps?

12.06. Stimulation of Nerve.—The understanding of the visual mechanism has been greatly aided by recent oscillographic studies of nerve impulses. These researches show the following:

1. All nerve fibers transmit the same kind of messages. The interpretation as heat, pain, taste, sound, or light is made in the brain.

2. These messages consist not of slow variations but of discrete, separated pulses which travel along the nerve fibers.

3. The magnitude of the pulses in a given fiber is always essentially the same. At a given instant, a definite portion of the fiber is either excited or not excited; there is no halfway condition.

4. The number of pulses per second varies with the stimulation. A very weak stimulus may result in only a single pulse. In most cases, a succession of pulses results, the frequency increasing up to 100/sec or more as the stimulus is increased. It seems probable that the intensity of the resulting sensation becomes greater as the number of pulses per second increases.

Perhaps the most beautiful oscillographic results have been obtained by Hartline and Graham.[28] The eye of the horseshoe crab, or *Limulus polyphemus*, was used because of its comparative simplicity. There are no synapses, the receptor neurons apparently going directly into the optic nerve. The eye and optic nerve were removed from the animal, and the nerve dissected until a single fiber was obtained. This fiber rested on two slender electrodes connected to the input of a vacuum-tube amplifier, the output of which operated the oscillograph. When light fell on the retina of the eye, impulses were sent over the nerve fiber, and the oscillograph recorded the result. Figure 12.11 gives some of the oscillograms. The magnitude of the impulses is about 0.3 millivolt. The results are omitted for several seconds in each case, as is indicated by the gap in the record. The duration of the exposure to light is shown by the heavy bands beneath the oscillograms. Illuminations outside the eye were *A*, 5900; *B*, 590; *C*, 59; *D*, 5.9 lumens/sq ft.

The eye was dark-adapted in each case. Note that for a short interval after the light is admitted (near $t = 0$), nothing

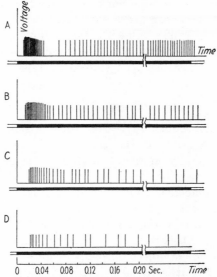

FIG. 12.11.—Oscillograms showing nerve impulses in a single fiber.[28]
Limulus polyphemus. Complete dark adaptation.
A. 5900 lumens/sq ft illumination at eye
B. 590 lumens/sq ft
C. 59 lumens/sq ft
D. 5.9 lumens/sq ft

happens. This cannot be due to the finite velocity of the impulses, since the distance traveled by these impulses is only a few centimeters, and their velocity is of the order of the velocity of sound in air. It is apparently due to the diffusion into the nerve endings of the ions formed by the photochemical reaction. As the retinal illumination decreases, the time of lag is seen to increase. Adaptation is also evident. At first, the dark-adapted eye responds with a burst of impulses, but the frequency gradually decreases until a fairly steady rate is obtained. The frequency in the equilibrium condition is seen to increase as the illumination is increased. The oscillograms also show that the impulses continue for a short time after the light is shut off.

That the nerve impulses from the human eye are probably very similar to those of Fig. 12.11 is indicated by the numerous researches on nerve impulses of all kinds and also by the oscillographic work of Adrian and Matthews[27] on the eye of the conger eel. The eye of the eel has synapses and is otherwise similar to the human eye though with a much smaller number of elements. The results were similar to those on the Limulus. The impulses travel along the nerve fibers, reach the central connections, evoke sensations. Beyond the pulses in the fiber we cannot go. The propagation of these pulses is an interesting field, however, which has been studied by Lillie, Raschevsky,[31] and others.

EXPERIMENTAL RESULTS

12.07. Contrast Sensitivity.—How does vision vary as the luminosity is changed? In the past, the attempt to answer this question has generally entailed two kinds of tests:

1. Tests to determine the minimum difference in luminosity which can be detected, using two large, uniform, contiguous surfaces.

2. Tests to determine the minimum size of object which can be seen, using small, black test objects on a white ground.

In test 2, the size of object is usually expressed in terms of the visual angle that it subtends. With low luminosity of the background, the test object must subtend a rather large visual angle before it becomes visible; but as the luminosity of the background is increased, the minimum-perceptible visual angle becomes much smaller. In plotting the results, it is found that the curves appear simpler if the reciprocal of the visual angle is used, and this procedure gives a number which increases as vision improves. Thus it is customary to speak of *visual acuity* Υ, meaning the reciprocal of the minimum-perceptible visual angle expressed in minutes of arc.

$$\Upsilon = \frac{1}{\text{min visual angle}} \quad \text{(reciprocal minutes)} \quad (12.08)$$

In 1, two large surfaces are used, subtending several degrees at the eye, and the luminosity of one is adjusted until a barely perceptible difference in brilliance is detected.   One type of field uses a circular disk of luminosity L_O and a surrounding ring of luminosity L_B.   The *minimum-perceptible contrast* $c_{\min}$ is

$$c_{\min} = \frac{L_B - L_O}{L_A} \qquad (12.09)$$

where L_A = the luminosity to which the eye is adapted.

For two large fields of equal area, the adapting luminosity may be considered as the average of the two, or $L_A = \frac{1}{2}(L_B + L_O)$. If the object of luminosity L_O is very small compared with the background (which has the luminosity L_B), $L_A \cong L_B$.   For other conditions, intermediate values of L_A may be used.   In most tests on contrast sensitivity, the difference between L_B and L_O is so small that L_A may be considered equal to either.

Just as with visual acuity it is more convenient to have a number that increases as vision improves, so we use the reciprocal of minimum-perceptible contrast and call it *contrast sensitivity* (S_c):

$$S_c = \frac{1}{c_{\min}} = \frac{L_A}{L_B - L_O} \qquad (12.10)$$

Section 12.07 deals with contrast sensitivity and the effect upon it of variations in the luminosity L_B.   First consider what might be expected to happen with variation of L_B, on the basis of our knowledge of vision.   The whole fovea is illuminated uniformly.   Some of the cones are probably excited to a lesser degree than others, and consequently the frequency of the pulses in the individual nerve fibers will vary to some extent.   Because of the large numbers of cones involved, however, such statistical variations are negligible.   At high illuminations, the frequency of the pulses due to both L_B and L_O is high, perhaps 100 per second. One might expect that a variation of one or two pulses per second could be detected, giving a contrast sensitivity of 50 to 100, which is in agreement with experiment.   Now, suppose that the illumination is greatly reduced so that only three or four pulses per second occur in a single fiber.   If we are still able to detect a difference of one pulse per second, it is clear that the contrast sensitivity has dropped to the low value of 3 or 4.   Thus, we might expect the luminosity of the field to have a decided effect on S_c.

The principal experimental results on contrast sensitivity are shown in Fig. 12.12. Further results showing the effect of using homogeneous radiation are given in Fig. 12.13. A logarithmic scale is used for luminosity because of the very wide range of

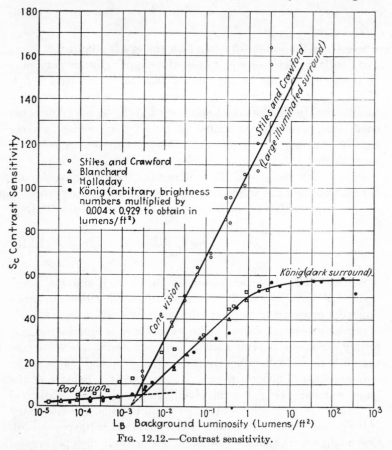

Fig. 12.12.—Contrast sensitivity.

values involved. The classical results of König are shown by the solid circles, and the curve is seen to consist of two parts: a straight-line part of small slope at luminosities below approximately 0.003 lumen/sq ft and a rapidly rising part at higher values of luminosity.[35] There is considerable evidence that the first part is due to rod vision while the second part is due to cone vision. A linear relation is obtained between S_c and log L_B from about 0.01 to 1 lumen/sq ft. At still higher values of L_B, the König results decrease with increasing L_B.   The more recent results of Blanchard, Holladay, and others check the König values fairly well, though they do not show this decrease of S_c at higher values of L_B.*   Today, it is felt generally that the König results are open to criticism because of the completely dark surroundings which were used about the test field.   These conditions do not generally

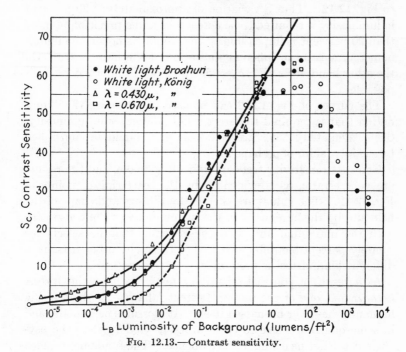

Fig. 12.13.—Contrast sensitivity.

obtain in ordinary visual tasks.   It is undoubtedly true that with dark surroundings and high field luminosity there is a distinct sensation of glare, which makes seeing difficult.   Stiles[59] illuminated the surroundings so that the entire retina was filled with light.   The resulting curve (Fig. 12.12) is seen to increase linearly to the highest value of luminosity used.   The results (Fig. 12.12) as well as many other results in related fields have led to the belief that if the surroundings are illuminated, vision continues to improve as luminosity is increased up to at least 1000 lumens/sq ft.

* See also the results of S. Hecht, *J. Gen. Physiol.*, **18**, 1935, p. 767; *Nat. Acad. Sci., Proc.*, **20**, 1934, p. 644.

The results of Fig. 12.12 apply directly to visual photometry and indicate why such poor results are occasionally obtained. In using a Macbeth illuminometer, for instance, to measure the illumination of street pavements at night, where the illumination may be of the order of 0.001 lumen/sq ft, we cannot expect to obtain a contrast sensitivity of greater than about 5, according to Fig. 12.12. Thus a variation of approximately ± 20 per cent in luminosity is required to be detectable, and a precision of more than 20 per cent is impossible. The trouble is not in the illuminometer; it is in an inherent limitation of the human eye. On the other hand, if $L_B = 1$, $S_c = 50$ and a precision of 2 per cent is possible.

The curves of Fig. 12.12 can be used to determine the illumination that is required to detect small differences in luminosity. Such calculated values are *thresholds* and should be multiplied by a safety factor of perhaps 10.

Contrast-sensitivity tests are difficult to make, and the results are very erratic, as is evidenced by the scattering of points in Fig. 12.12. The values are affected by the size and shape of the field and by the luminosity of the surroundings. They also vary with the individual and with the criterion that he selects for "barely perceptible difference." For these and other reasons, a different kind of test is preferable.

As a result of contrast-sensitivity tests, we have the *Weber-Fechner law*, one of the most persistent fallacies to which erring humanity has ever harnessed itself. It blossoms perennially and in some quarters seems to be regarded as God's gift to the psychologist. Let us examine the evidence. The fundamental idea of this law seems to have originated in the fertile brain of Pierre Bouguer, who found, about 1729, that two surfaces could be distinguished if their contrast was $\frac{1}{64}$. Various other investigators, including Weber (1834), checked this result with luminosities varying through a range of 10 to 1, or greater, and with c_{min} from about $\frac{1}{50}$ to $\frac{1}{150}$. Such values were evidently considered to be nearly constant, so that Weber's law

$$c_{min} = \text{const}$$

was adopted. The law can hardly be regarded as even an approximation. The trouble seems to be that the data were invariably plotted with c_{min} against log L_B instead of using S_c.

The resulting curves start with high values in the scotopic region and fall almost to the axis throughout most of the photopic region. Thus it *looks* as if c_{min} were *almost* constant over a wide range of luminosities. That this conclusion is false, particularly with the more modern data, is shown by Fig. 12.12. If c_{min} were a constant, its reciprocal S_c would also be a constant, and the curves of Fig. 12.12 would be horizontal lines.

The real criticism, however, is not of the Weber law but with what Fechner did to it in 1858. The difference $(L_B - L_o)$ was replaced by ΔL, an apparently innocuous change but one that is certainly quite unjustified. L_B and L_o are two separate quantities appearing side by side and causing the illumination of two separate patches of the retina, while ΔL is an increment in a single quantity. The next step on the downward path is to equate the ratio $\Delta L/L$ to a just perceptible increment ΔS in sensation

$$\Delta S = k\frac{\Delta L}{L}$$

We now imagine that S is infinitely divisible and so replace the expression for finites by one for differentials and then integrate, obtaining

$$S = k \ln L + K$$

Here is the Weber-Fechner law which is responsible for all the talk about sensation's being a logarithmic function of the stimulus.

Thus the Weber-Fechner law is obtained by doing some thoroughly reprehensible things to an erroneous statement that c_{min} is a constant. Perhaps the worst step in the process is the assumption that sensation can be measured and can be equated to physical quantities. We have become accustomed to measuring physical quantities, representing them by symbols, and manipulating the resulting equations. It is perhaps natural to forget that between the familiar world of physics and the world of consciousness yawns an immense abyss and that the methods of one world cannot be applied in the other.

Sensation cannot be measured, in the sense that physical quantities are measured. True, such things as pain, happiness, love, and the sensations produced by radiant energy can be great or small, but there is no way of setting up a unit or of evaluating in terms of a unit. Any equation like the Weber-Fecher one is pure nonsense.*

When there are so many important subjects to discuss, it seems a waste of space to include the Weber-Fechner law, which has been criticised by such authorities as Helmholtz[4] and has been thoroughly damned by Cobb,[37] Guild, and others. However, the frequency with which one encounters references to the "well-known logarithmic law of response" makes it worth while to warn the illuminating engineer of this fallacy.

Problem 155. A Macbeth illuminometer is used in measuring the luminosity of street pavements by sighting directly at the pavement and adjusting the surrounding photometer field to the same luminosity as that of the pavement. If absorption and reflection of light in the instrument are neglected, what precision can be obtained, with L for the pavement equal to 0.0001 lumen/sq ft—*i.e.*, what is the minimum percentage change in luminosity of the photometer field that can be detected? Repeat for 10 lumens/sq ft.

Problem 156. In chromium plating, it is often very difficult to detect flaws in the plating. If a plated surface ($\rho = 0.650$) has an unplated portion $\frac{1}{2}$ in. in diameter with $\rho = 0.640$, how much illumination is necessary for its detection, using well-shaded lamps?

Plot a curve of necessary illumination for detecting the flaw with base metals having reflection factors from 0 to 1.00. Assume (*in this problem only*) that a change in sign in Eq. (12.10) has no effect on the experimental results.

12.08. Resolving Power of the Eye.—We have considered the ability of the eye to discriminate between two extended surfaces of slightly different luminosities. Another property of the eye is its ability to detect small objects and to distinguish fine detail when there is a large contrast between object and background. The resolving power of the eye is found to vary widely, depending upon the kind of test object, spectral distribution of radiant energy, luminosity of background, contrast between object and background, and the criterion used to determine whether the object is seen or is not seen. Two stars, for instance, separated by an angle of approximately one minute, can be distinguished as separate stars, while if the angle is much less the two stars appear as one. This datum, in addition to the results of tests with black letters on white grounds, has led to the common statement that the normal eye is capable of resolving two objects separated by a

* See also J. Guild, Discussion on Vision, or Appendix B of the present volume.

visual angle of one minute.   The subject is not so simple as that.
Recent tests show that visual angles of ½ or ⅓ min are obtainable
under certain conditions with black letters on a white ground,
while other test objects show still smaller visual angles.

TABLE XLVIII.—APPROXIMATE RESOLVING POWER OF THE EYE

Object	Minimum visual angle		Distance on retina
	Minutes	Radians	
Two stars........................	1.0	2.90×10^{-4}	4.3μ
Two black bars on white ground......	0.5	1.45	2.1
Vernier...........................	0.15	0.43	0.65
Spider web or black wire on self-luminous white ground...............	0.13	0.38	0.57

Table XLVIII gives some average values obtained with various
test objects, using white light, high luminosity of background, and
high contrast.   It is well-known
that high precision is obtainable in
judging collinearity in two line segments, a fact used in the vernier.
The angular separation between the
two line segments can be adjusted to
within about 0.15 min, or about one-
sixth the angle between two stars.
Even better results are found in the
ability to see a dark line against a
bright background, such as a flagpole or a wire silhouetted against
the sky.   With a self-luminous
background, values of approximately 0.13 min are obtainable.

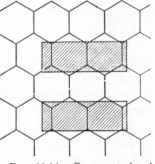

FIG. 12.14.—Geometrical image of a test object on the retina.

What is the explanation of the high resolving power of the eye
with certain test objects and the much lower resolving power with
others?   It has been commonly assumed that the eye is able to
resolve two black objects on a white ground provided their
images on the retina are sufficiently far apart for an excited cone
or row of excited cones to fall between the unexcited cones.
Figure 12.14 shows a portion of the fovea.   The cones are small
in size (approximately 3.2μ), are packed tightly together, and
assume a hexagonal shape.   If the eye is focused on the test

object, a perfect image of which is assumed to be formed on the retina, it would be expected that the smallest detectable gap would be approximately as shown in Fig. 12.14, with the image of the gap measuring approximately 3μ (0.003 mm) on the retina. Since the focal length of the optical system of the eye is approximately 15 mm, this corresponds to a visual angle of about 2.1×10^{-4} radian, or 0.7 min. This value is in good agreement with experiment, especially when one considers that histological information regarding the size of the cones is somewhat inexact. But no explanation is offered for the large changes in resolving power with different test objects.

The principal argument against this naïve picture of vision is that it assumes that a perfect image of the test object is formed on the retina, an assumption contrary to fact. Actually, the image is blurred, owing principally to two factors:

1. Chromatic aberration.
2. Diffraction.

There may be other imperfections of the optical system of the normal eye— slight irregularities in the optical surfaces and scattering of light in the media of the eye—but there seems to be considerable evidence that such factors do not have a marked effect. The imperfections of the abnormal eye will not be considered. It is well-known that the normal eye suffers from chromatic aberration. Rays of different wavelengths come to a focus at different distances from the lens of the eye. When a white point source (a star, for instance) is viewed, the eye adjusts itself so that the yellow of the spectrum is sharply focused. The red then comes to a focus slightly beyond the plane of the yellow and forms on the retina a red disk of about 24μ diameter. The blue and violet come to a focus in front of the retina and produce a large disk on the retina, with a maximum diameter of approximately 55μ. These values are for a 2-mm pupil. With larger pupils, the disks increase in diameter in direct proportion to the pupil diameter.

Thus the images formed on the retina are considerably modified representations of the objects themselves. Chromatic aberration occurs in every case where the radiant energy covers a reasonably large part of the visible spectrum but can be completely eliminated by using homogeneous radiation. Even the attainment of an ideal lens system would not give an ideal image. Diffraction

enters—an inherent property of the wave nature of electromagnetic radiation. Rays entering at different parts of the
pupil may arrive at a given point on the retina with differences
in phase and may combine either to increase or to decrease the
illumination. Owing to diffraction, the image of a point source
of homogeneous radiation is not a point but a disk surrounded by
alternate dark and bright rings. The effect is small with large
pupil diameters but increases rapidly as the pupil size is decreased,

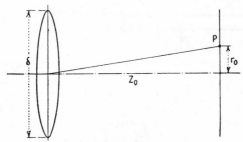

FIG. 12.15.

the diameter of the disk and rings due to a point source of
homogeneous radiation being inversely proportional to the pupil
diameter and directly proportional to the wavelength. The
illumination at any point P (Fig. 12.15) is given by the relation*

$$E = E_0 \left[\frac{J_1(2m)}{m} \right]^2 \qquad (12.11)$$

where $m = \dfrac{\pi \delta}{2\lambda} \cdot \dfrac{r_0}{z_0}$.

E_0 = illumination for $r_0 = 0$.

r_0 = displacement from center of image (microns).

z_0 = 15 mm, approximately.

δ = pupil diameter (mm).

λ = wavelength (microns).

$J_1(2m)$ = Bessel function of the first order.†

Since the Bessel function has an infinite number of zeros, there
must be theoretically an infinite number of dark rings surrounding

---

* See, for instance, SLATER and FRANK, Theoretical Physics, p. 325,
McGraw-Hill Book Company, Inc., New York, 1933.

†Tables are given in JAHNKE and EMDE, Funktionentafeln, p. 229,
Leipzig, 1933.

the central disk.   The first dark ring has a radius of

$$m = 0.6098\pi = 1.916.$$

The first bright ring has a maximum illumination of only 1.7 per cent of the illumination in the center of the disk, while the second ring reaches only 0.7 per cent.   The rings are therefore negligible

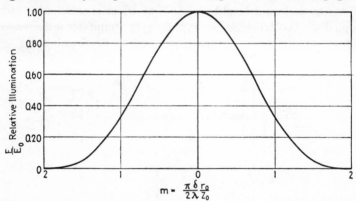

FIG. 12.16.—Calculated retinal illumination caused by a point source of homogeneous radiation.

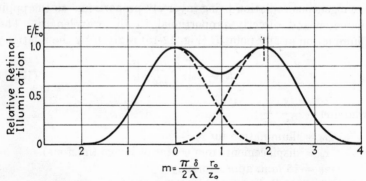

FIG. 12.17.—Calculated retinal illumination caused by two point sources of homogeneous radiation.

so far as seeing is concerned, and one needs to consider only the center disk, the illumination for which is plotted in Fig. 12.16. An interesting question immediately arises as to the resolving power of the eye in the case of two point sources of homogeneous radiation. Astronomers have found that two stars can be resolved when the center of one image falls on the first dark ring of the other. This condition is plotted in Fig. 12.17. Each

source produces its own diffraction disk, and since the two illuminations can be added directly, the resulting illumination is as
shown by the heavy line. Evidently, the idea of sharp images
and unilluminated cones (Fig. 12.14) must be abandoned.
Actually, the illumination of the retina follows a smooth curve,
and no great difference in the illumination of adjacent cones is
possible.

We have seen in Sec. 12.07 that with very large test objects
subtending angles of one minute or more and with high retinal
illumination, the number of pulses per second in the nerve fibers
may be in the neighborhood of 100, and a difference of 1 in the
frequency for the two half-fields is sometimes detectable. Thus
contrast sensitivities as high as 100 are sometimes obtainable.
We cannot expect such good results, however, if the test object is
small. Figure 12.11 shows that the pulses from a single receptor
are not spaced at exactly equal intervals. With large numbers of
cones in operation, such random variations in the individual
fibers have no appreciable effect, but when we come to a single
cone or to a small group of cones, conditions are quite different.
The random variation in frequency would be expected to make
it impossible to discriminate so closely regarding differences in
retinal illumination, and tests seem to indicate that with small
numbers of receptors a variation of about 10 per cent is the
smallest that we can distinguish instead of a variation of approximately one per cent with the large fields. Thus if we find from a
diagram such as Fig. 12.17 that the total luminous flux on one
cone is approximately 10 per cent less than on the adjacent cones,
we may predict that this represents approximately threshold
conditions with high illuminations. With low illuminations,
conditions will be much poorer. For homogeneous radiation
or 0.5μ and with $\delta = 2$ mm, the 10-per cent criterion holds
approximately for the condition given in Fig. 12.17.

A consideration of the theoretical curves of retinal illumination
gives an explanation of the phenomena of the resolving power
of the eye. This is according to the interesting theory of
Hartridge.[39,40] One might argue that a large number of simplifying assumptions have been made which are not too well-
substantiated by experiment and that we are treating the
recondite mysteries of vision with a familiarity that savors of con-
tempt. The fact remains, however, that the Hartridge theory

offers a simple picture of what is possibly happening, that it is in agreement, at least qualitatively, with experiment, and that it is the only theory that appears to be tenable.

Point sources of homogeneous radiation have been considered. Hartridge has also treated white-light surface sources, taking into account both diffraction and chromatic aberration. Figure 12.18a shows the calculated illumination, expressed in terms of the maximum value, due to an extended luminous source with

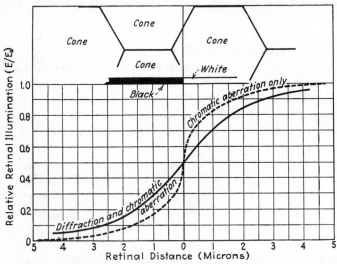

Fig. 12.18a.—Calculated retinal illumination for a semi-infinite surface source of white light. (Based on calculations of Hartridge,[39,40] 2-mm pupil.)

a straight boundary. It will be noted that the retinal illumination does not fall abruptly at the geometrical image of the boundary but decreases slowly over a considerable distance. The curve of Fig. 12.18a can be utilized in a number of problems. In Fig. 12.18b, for instance, a black bar has been placed on a white, self-luminous background. Each edge produces an effect (dotted curves) like that shown in Fig. 12.18a, and the resulting retinal illumination is given by the sum of the two curves, as shown by the heavy curve. The geometrical image of the black bar has a width of 2μ on the retina, corresponding to a visual angle of about 0.5 min. A few cones are sketched to scale in the upper part of the diagram. The difference in luminous flux received by adjacent cones will be more than 10 per cent, and thus the black bar will be easily visible at high illuminations. The result of decreasing the width of the bar to 0.5μ is shown in

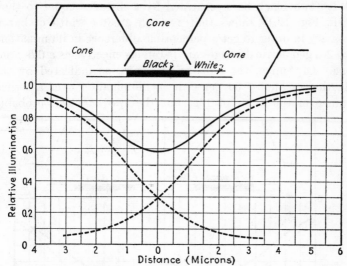

FIG. 12.18b.—Retinal illumination.   Black bar on a white background.

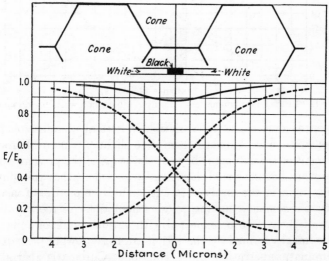

FIG. 12.18c.—Retinal illumination.   Narrow black bar on white background.

Fig. 12.18c.   The variation in illumination is now seen to be about 10 per cent, and thus we can predict that a single black bar will be barely perceptible with high illumination if it subtends an angle of 0.12 min. This prediction is in agreement with experiment, as shown in Table XLVIII.

With two black bars separated by a distance equal to their width, Fig. 12.19 shows that a much greater width of bar is necessary in order to get a perceptible difference in illumination. Two 2-μ geometrical images are barely as effective as a 0.5-μ one alone. Of course, the bars will be seen, as indicated by the reduction of almost 50 per cent in illumination over a retinal distance of the order of 10μ; but the two bars will probably

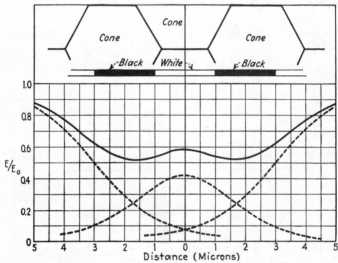

Fig. 12.19.—Retinal illumination. Two black bars on a white background.

be seen as one, since the variation in retinal illumination due to the white space between them is so slight. A more thorough treatment of the subject is beyond the scope of the present work. From what has been said, however, it is evident that the illuminating engineer can easily obtain a qualitative picture of visual-acuity phenomena, making rough calculations of the resolving power of the eye to be expected with various kinds of objects.

The images formed on the retina are fuzzy, owing principally to chromatic aberration and diffraction. Chromatic aberration becomes more pronounced as the pupil diameter increases, while with diffraction the reverse effect occurs. One might predict that with white light the two effects would give a resolving power which would not alter greatly as the pupil diameter changed.

Apparently, this is the fact, as is shown by the experimental curve of Cobb (Fig. 12.20). A diaphragm was placed in front

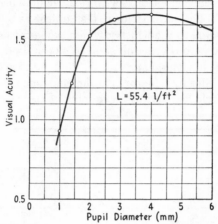

FIG. 12.20.—Visual acuity as a function of pupil diameter. Artificial pupil used, dark surround, black bars on white ground.[48]

of the eye, and the size of a circular opening in the diaphragm was changed from 1 to 6 mm. The curve of visual acuity is fairly constant with diameters of opening greater than 2 mm. With large openings, diffraction is practically negligible, but chromatic aberration becomes pronounced. At diameters less than 2 mm, chromatic aberration is very small, but diffraction becomes so important that the visual-acuity curve falls sharply.*

12.09. Visual Acuity.—As indicated in Table XLVIII, the

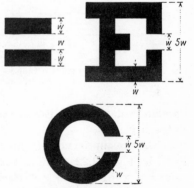

FIG. 12.21.—Test objects.

minimum detectable visual angle depends to a considerable degree upon the kind of test object, being much smaller for a single black bar on a white ground than for two bars on a white ground. In order to obtain consistent results, it is necessary to standardize the conditions of test. Test objects commonly used

* The portion of the curve below 2 mm diameter is, of course, never obtained in ordinary vision.

are shown in Fig. 12.21.   One consists of two parallel black bars of width w separated by a white space of the same width. Another is the Snellen letter E with relative dimensions as shown in the figure.   The international test object is a broken circle with the gap equal to the width w which is one-fifth of the outside diameter.   Numerous other objects have been used, and the data so obtained are in general agreement, though the actual values of visual acuity differ by a factor that depends upon the test object. The broken circle has been used in most of the recent work, and

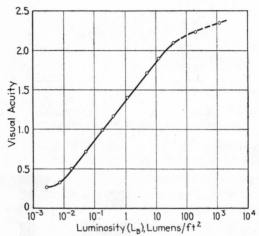

Fig. 12.22.—Visual acuity as a function of the luminosity to which the eye is adapted.[45]

standardized testing with it seems advisable for the sake of uniformity.

The best results on visual acuity appear to be those of Lythgoe,[45] given in Fig. 12.22.   The black broken-circle test object was used on a white ground, and the entire visual field was adjusted, except at the highest luminosities, to a luminosity approximately equal to that of the background.   The test object was oriented at different angles, and the observer was required to state where the opening was.   The criterion for "seeing" was taken as 4.5 correct answers out of 8.   The eye was accommodated to each level of luminosity.   Figure 12.22 shows that the visual acuity continues to rise even at the highest values of the test—over 1000 lumens/sq ft.

The results of several investigators are given in Fig. 12.23, and
all of the curves are seen to be more or less of the same character.
The long, straight rise in each is characteristic for values of

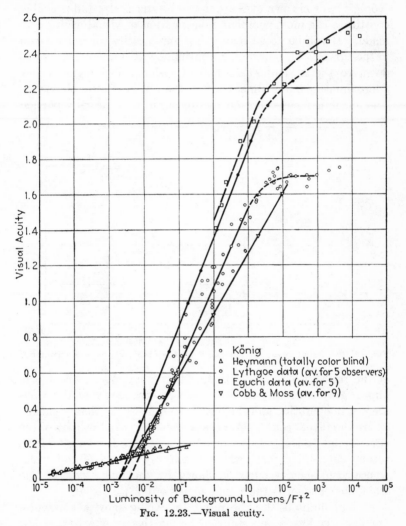

FIG. 12.23.—Visual acuity.

L_B from approximately 0.01 up to 30 lumens/sq ft.   The slopes
obtained by different investigators are somewhat different owing,
principally, to the use of different test objects or different criteria
for seeing.   It is to be noted, however, that if all the ordinates

for any one curve are multiplied by a constant, the straight-line
portion of this curve can be made practically to coincide with the
straight-line portion of any other curve.   The classical results of
König[34,35] for his own eyes are shown by the circles and probably
constitute the most complete investigation of visual acuity ever
made.   It will be noted that at low luminosities there is a break
in the curve.   The curve then continues with a much lower slope
down to the absolute threshold of vision.   The region below
approximately 0.001 lumen/sq ft is the region of scotopic vision.
The image is focused not on the fovea but on a near-by portion

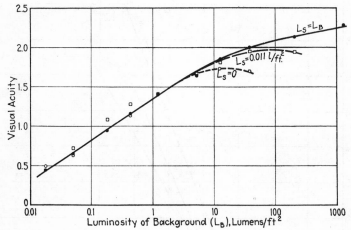

Fig. 12.24.—Visual acuity as influenced by the luminosity of the surround.[45]

of the retina where the rods are fairly numerous.   All objects
appear gray with hazy outlines, owing to the fact that the cones
are not in operation and the rods are not nearly so closely packed
as are the foveal cones.   Another indication that this part of the
curve is due to the rods is shown by the results of König[34,35] for a
totally color-blind man, who was entirely devoid of cones and
whose visual-acuity curve is shown by the long, straight line
which never reaches the visual acuity of 0.2.

At high luminosities the results of König show a horizontal
portion.   It has been established that this is due to the low
luminosity of his surrounds.   In more recent tests, the entire
visual field is illuminated, and this eliminates the sense of glare
and increases visual acuity.   Figure 12.24 gives some results
showing the effect of illuminating the surround.   As the effect

becomes marked only at high values of luminosity, we can conclude that the König results are probably essentially correct up
to approximately 10 lumens/sq ft.   The Lythgoe results continue
to rise for all values of L_B up to 1000 lumens/sq ft.   The Eguchi
results also continue to rise even up to values of double the
luminosity of white paper in direct noon sunlight.   Unfortunately, neither Lythgoe nor Eguchi succeeded, at the highest
values of L_B, in illuminating the surround to the luminosity
of the test-object background.   Thus we have no proof that the
straight-line relation may not continue upward considerably
beyond the point at which even the Eguchi tests indicate a bend.
We may conclude that visual acuity continues to improve up
to the highest values of L_B obtained in nature.   This conclusion
requires that the surroundings be well illuminated so that the
entire retina can adapt itself to the high values of luminosity.
This means that in artificial lighting, a distinct gain in ability to
distinguish fine detail can be obtained by increasing the illumination well above the usual values.

All the foregoing experimental data were obtained with continuous spectra, usually from incandescent lamps.   The question
often arises as to the effect of using homogeneous radiation.   A
number of tests have been made recently on visual acuity with
sodium-vapor light.   The visual-acuity results for sodium light
are somewhat higher than for incandescent-lamp light (10 to
20 per cent usually), as would be expected because of the elimination of chromatic aberration.   The improvement is not phenomenal, however, and there is the possibility that with scotopic
vision the visual acuity will be lower for sodium light than for the
light from incandescent lamps.   With red light, visual acuity is
lower than with white light (Fig. 12.29), and with blue or violet
light vision is very poor.

Problem 157.   An automobile license plate with white ground ($\rho = 0.75$)
and black letters having ½-in. bars is illuminated by the tail light ($E = 2.0$
lumens/sq ft).   At what distance can it be read at night?

Problem 158.   A vertical black flag pole 2 in. in diameter is used on the
roof of an isolated building on a hilltop.   At what distance can a person with
normal vision see the flagpole on a cloudy evening with the sun at the
horizon?   At noon on a cloudy day with the sun at 70 deg elevation?

Problem 159.   An advertising sign with white ground ($\rho = 0.78$) and
black letters is to be illuminated so that it can be read easily at night by
motorists at a distance of 200 ft.   The smallest letters have bars ⅝ in. wide.
What value of illumination do you recommend for the sign?

12.10. Other Factors Affecting Vision.—We have considered visual acuity for black objects on a white ground—*i.e.*, for a contrast of essentially 100 per cent. But in practice, most visual tasks deal with lesser contrasts, and it is essential that we consider visual acuity as a function of both luminosity and contrast. Figure 12.25 shows the retinal illumination due to a gray bar

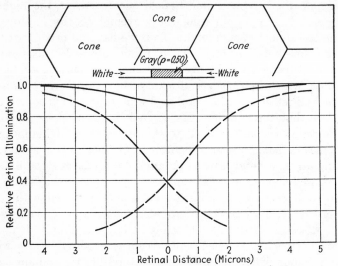

Fig. 12.25.—Retinal illumination for a gray bar on a white background.

($\rho = 0.50$) against a white background. Comparison of this with Fig. 12.18 for a black bar on a white ground shows that the size of the bar must be increased considerably as contrast is reduced. As we decrease the contrast between object and background, we may expect the visual acuity to decrease.

Contrast may be defined by the equation

$$c = \frac{L_B - L_O}{L_B} \qquad (12.12)$$

which is essentially the same as Eq. (12.09). Since the background is very large compared with the object, the adapting luminosity L_A is practically equal to L_B. If L_O becomes greater than L_B, c becomes negative. Unfortunately, there seem to be no data for this condition.

The desirability of obtaining visual acuity as a function of both luminosity and contrast was first recognized by Cobb and

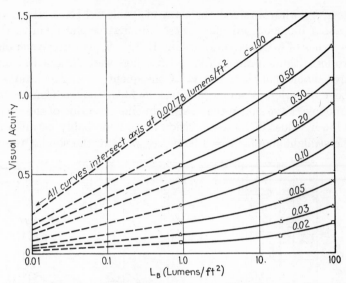

FIG. 12.26.—Visual acuity for gray objects on a white ground.   Cone vision only.   (Based on data of Cobb and Moss.[53])

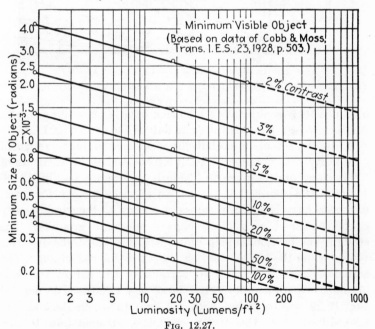

FIG. 12.27.

Moss,[53,54] who obtained the data of Table XLIX as the result
of about 100,000 readings.   These data may be plotted in various
ways, one of which is shown in Fig. 12.26.   The results cover only
two logarithmic units in L_B, and readings were obtained at only
three values of luminosity.   Consequently, extrapolation in
either direction is somewhat questionable, though Conner and
Ganoung[55] have shown that a straight-line extension of the curves
to lower values of L_B (cone vision only) is probably permissible.
The straight line for $c = 1.00$ corresponds to the similar results

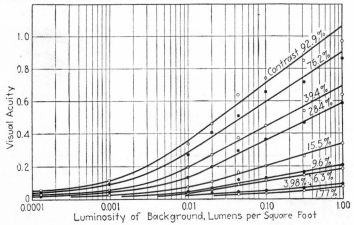

FIG. 12.28.—Visual acuity as a function of contrast and background luminosity.[55]

obtained for visual acuity with black objects on white grounds.
Another way of plotting the same data is shown in Fig. 12.27.

A similar set of data, but for a wider and lower range of
luminosity, was obtained recently at Massachusetts Institute of
Technology and is given in Table L and shown in Fig. 12.28.
Figure 12.28 shows that the curves of visual acuity for lower
contrasts have essentially the same shapes as the visual-acuity
curves obtained with black objects on white grounds.   The
straight-line portion sloping upward to the right indicates cone
vision, while the low portion on the left is for rod vision.   The
actual separation of the two portions of the curves was also
obtained experimentally (Figs. 12.29 and 12.30).   The data of
Fig. 12.29 were obtained with red light to which the rods are
insensitive.   Thus the curves continue as straight lines to zero
visual acuity, and no measurable results could be obtained for L_B

less than approximately 0.003 lumen/sq ft. Figure 12.30 was
obtained by keeping the test object focused on the periphery
of the retina 5 deg. from the fovea. This was accomplished by
using a tiny red fixation lamp placed 5 deg. from the test object.
The observer kept this lamp focused on the fovea throughout
the test. The results show that the rods continue to respond
along a linear function of log L_B far beyond the place where the

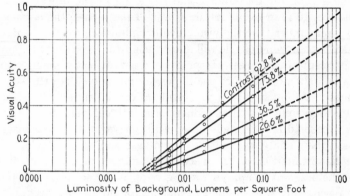

Fig. 12.29.—Visual acuity. Cone vision only. Obtained with red light.[55]

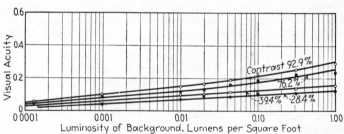

Fig. 12.30.—Visual acuity for rod vision. Obtained by use of offset-fixation
method.[55]

foveal cones would normally be operative. The slight upward
bend at high values of luminosity is due probably to the action
of the cones, some of which are present even in the peripheral
region.

Results of visual acuity as a function of luminosity and contrast are of considerable value to the illumination engineer.
They allow him to determine the minimum illumination required
for each visual task. Another factor to be considered, besides
luminosity and contrast, is the time of exposure of the test

object.   In most cases, as shown by Cobb and Moss,[53,54] exposure time is not very important; though of course if this time is very short (less than approximately 0.01 sec), exposure time may be of importance.

For short distances such as are used in reading, visual acuity appears to be reduced somewhat* below its value for long distances, and higher values of illumination should be used for reading than for the same visual angle where the object is, for instance, 10 ft or even farther away.   In any case, the engineer must remember that the visual acuity values are *threshold values* which with normal people will allow the object to be seen in about 50 per cent of the cases.   In practice, we want better seeing than this and should therefore use higher illumination than threshold values.   We must take into consideration the subnormal vision of many people as well as reduction in fatigue.   A safety factor of at least 10 is indicated.   The study of various typical visual tasks, their analysis in terms of contrast and visual angle, and the determination of the necessary amount of luminous flux and the best way of applying it to give optimum seeing conditions are fascinating subjects and promising for further research.

Problem 160.   Repeat Prob. 159 for the same sign but with a background of 0.50 reflection factor and letters of 0.10 reflection factor.

Problem 161.   Illumination recommendations given for inspecting gloves in a factory are

$$\text{Light goods } (\rho = 0.60), \qquad E = 10 \text{ lumens/sq ft.}$$
$$\text{Dark goods } (\rho = 0.08), \qquad E = 25 \text{ lumens/sq ft.}$$

What are your recommendations for E in these cases?   Assume that a 2 per cent contrast is to be detected in objects $\frac{1}{20}$ in. in smallest dimension. Neglect effect of nearness of object.   Criticize the recommended values.

Problem 162.   From the data of Tables XLIX and L, plot a family of curves, similar to Fig. 12.26, for L_B from 10^{-4} to 10^{+2} lumens/sq ft.

12.11.   Effect of Luminosity of the Surround.—We have already stated in connection with the experimental results on contrast sensitivity and on visual acuity that the eye does not perform best when the object has dark surroundings.   Lythgoe,[45] for instance, has shown a marked effect of surround luminosity on visual acuity (Fig. 12.24).   The effect is shown even more clearly in Fig. 12.31 where visual acuity is plotted against L_s, the

* Luckiesh and Moss, *J.O.S.A.*, **23**, 1933, p. 25.

luminosity of the surround, for a constant background luminosity
to which the fovea is adapted. With a surround of zero luminosity, the visual acuity is seen to be 1.8, or 10 per cent less than
with correctly illuminated surroundings. Best results appear
to be obtained with L_s slightly less than L_B, but when the luminosity of the surround is raised above the luminosity of the
background, the visual acuity shows a rapid drop. These
results indicate that in practical lighting the best results will be
obtained when the entire field of view is illuminated. But the
luminosity of the surroundings must never exceed the luminosity
of the work, for which the fovea is adapted, and should preferably
be somewhat less. According to Fig. 12.31, best results will be

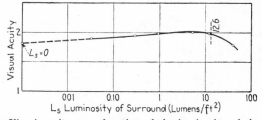

Fig. 12.31.—Visual acuity as a function of the luminosity of the surround.[45]
Background luminosity held constant at 12.6 lumens/sq ft.

obtained if the luminosity of the surroundings is approximately
one-half the luminosity of the work and should not drop below
0.1 the luminosity of the work. When reading at a desk, for
instance, the eyes adapt themselves to the luminosity of the
printed page L_B. The rest of the desk, the walls, etc., constitute the surround of luminosity L_s. With the surroundings in
darkness, we can expect some diminution in seeing ability, and
for this and other reasons experts agree that the entire room
should be illuminated, though the illumination can be lower than
the illumination of the printed page.

It would be expected that the curve of Fig. 12.31 would
continue to decrease rapidly as L_s is increased beyond the values
shown and would approach the zero axis asymptotically. Figure
12.32 shows a sketch of the general form of results to be expected
for any kind of visual test, the visual property (visual acuity,
contrast sensitivity, etc.) being given as a function of the ratio
of surround luminosity to foveal adapting luminosity. The curve
can be divided into three parts:

1. A region of low surround luminosity (L_s/L_B less than approximately 0.1) where vision is poorer than it would be with L_s/L_B equal to unity.

2. A region of moderate surround luminosity where $L_s/L_B \leqq 1.0$ where optimum visual conditions obtain.

3. A region of high surround luminosity ($L_s/L_B > 1.0$) where vision is very poor.

The sensation produced in 3 is generally called *glare*. Thus, the very important subject of glare is merely a special case of the effect of surround luminosity. The term glare is used loosely in practice with several meanings. It seems best to consider it as any unpleasant *sensation* produced by large spatial variations in

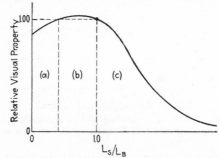

Fig. 12.32.—Effect of surround luminosity.

luminosity. Glare is usually thought of as produced by point sources, but the same reduction in vision can be produced by large surface sources as well. It is difficult, for instance, for an observer outside a building in the daytime to see details within a room through the open door or window. Here the opening is framed by a surround of high luminosity which interferes with vision. If the same scene is viewed at night when the luminosity of the surround is greatly reduced but the interior illumination is the same as before, the details in the room are clearly perceived.

Stiles [59] has developed a theory of glare based on the idea of light scattered by the media of the eye. A more recent point of view seems to be, however, that the effect is due to conduction of impulses over the lateral neurons (Sec. 12.02) between the peripheral region and the fovea and that these impulses interfere with the normal messages being sent out by the foveal cones and thus confuse vision.

An experimental study of region 3 was made by Holladay,[56] and further work of the same nature was done by Stiles.   In both cases, a large white surface, used for background and surround, was uniformly illuminated and had a test spot at its center.   A glare source could be introduced into the field of view, and the size and intensity of this source could be varied at will.   Figure 12.33a shows the field of view of one eye.   The area A, sub-tending a visual angle of approximately two degrees, is called

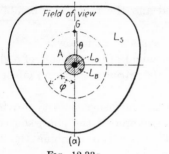

FIG. 12.33a.

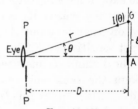

FIG. 12.33b.

the background.   On it is placed the test object.   Under normal conditions of photopic vision, the background illuminates the entire fovea.   The test object of luminosity L_O is placed on the background of luminosity L_B, and a surround of luminosity L_s illuminates the remainder of the retina.   A point glare source may be introduced at G.   Since we are interested here in *relative* values of contrast sensitivity, as affected by glare, rather than in absolute values, it is convenient to use the ratio

$$S_c/S_{1.0},$$

where S_c = the actual contrast sensitivity.

$S_{1.0}$ = the value obtained with the same L_B but with a uniform surround of $L_s = L_B$ and with no glare sources.

Let us make a list of the factors that might reasonably be expected to affect the relative contrast sensitivity $S_c/S_{1.0}$ when a glare source is placed in the field of view.   Evidently, $S_c/S_{1.0}$ depends upon

1. Candlepower I_G of the glare source in the direction of the eye.

2. Angle θ between the line of sight and the line drawn from the eye to G.

3. Angle φ measured around the line of sight as an axis.

4. Distance D from the test object to the eye.

5. Luminosity L_B of the background.

6. Luminosity L_s of the surround.

It might be expected, therefore, that S_c would have to be obtained experimentally as a function of these six independent variables. Fortunately, however, the experimental data show that a number of these factors can be neglected and the remainder combined into a single independent variable.

The experimental results may be stated as follows:

a. Contrast sensitivity is independent of the position of a glare source on a circle about A; *i.e.*, the variable φ has no effect on contrast sensitivity.

b. The distance D has no effect on contrast sensitivity provided θ is kept the same and the candlepower of the glare source is varied as the square of D. Thus we can combine the two variables 1 and 4 into a single variable:

$$E_G = \frac{I_G}{r^2} \cos \theta = \frac{I_G}{D^2} \cos^3 \theta$$

the glare illumination at the eye. Evidently, E_G is the illumination at the eye on a plane perpendicular to the line of sight.

c. Luminosity L_B of the background has no effect on S_c, provided E_G is varied directly with L_B. For a constant value of θ, therefore, items 1, 4, and 5 can be lumped in a single independent variable

$$\frac{E_G}{L_B} = \frac{I_G}{L_B D^2} \cos^3 \theta$$

d. Experiment shows that a variation in θ has a marked effect on glare. To keep S_c constant while varying θ, E_G must be varied as approximately the three-halves power of θ. This experimental fact allows us to combine the variables 1, 2, 4, and 5 into one variable, which for a single point glare source is

$$\Lambda = \frac{ME_G}{\theta^{3/2} L_B} = \frac{MI_G}{\theta^{3/2} L_B D^2} \cos^3 \theta \qquad (12.13)$$

where M = an arbitrary constant.

The new variable Λ is called the *surround factor*. According to the experimental results, then, we need not try the difficult feat of plotting S_c as a function of six independent variables. A single curve of S_c vs. Λ will give us all the information regarding the effect of a single point glare source having any candlepower and situated anywhere in the field of view. One word of caution: The experimental results of Holladay and of Stiles, stated in items *a* to *d*, were obtained at low illuminations rarely exceeding one lumen per square foot. There is considerable reason to believe that at higher values of illumination, some of the conclusions no longer apply.

e. Equation (12.13) evaluates Λ for a single point source. For a number of point sources, Stiles has found that the values of Λ_i for the individual sources are directly additive. As long as the total value

$$\Lambda = \sum_{i=1}^{n} \Lambda_i$$

remains constant, it makes no difference how many sources are used or where they are placed.

This fact allows us to calculate the effect of a surround of any kind whatever. For an element $d\sigma$ of perfectly diffusing surface of luminosity L_s, in the plane AG (Fig. 12.33),

$$I_G = \frac{L_s \, d\sigma}{\pi} \cos \theta$$

and Eq. (12.13) becomes

$$d\Lambda = \frac{M \cos \theta}{\theta^{3/2} L_B D^2} \cdot \frac{L_s \, d\sigma}{\pi} \cos^4 \theta \qquad (12.14)$$

For a perfectly diffusing surround of any luminosity $L_s(\theta, \varphi)$, which may be nonuniform in any way desired, the surround factor is

$$\Lambda = \frac{M}{\pi L_B D^2} \int_S \frac{L_s(\theta, \varphi) \cos^4 \theta \, d\sigma}{\theta^{3/2}} \qquad (12.15)$$

where the integral is taken over the entire surround.

In the special case of a uniform surround, $L_s(\theta, \varphi) = L_s = \text{const}$, and the surround factor is

$$\Lambda = \frac{M L_s}{L_B} \int_{\theta_B}^{\theta_r} \frac{2 \sin \theta \cos \theta \, d\theta}{\theta^{3/2}} \qquad (12.16)$$

where θ_B = the angle corresponding to the outline of the background.

θ_c = the angle corresponding to the outside contour of the field of view.

The integral is a constant. For simplicity, set it equal to $1/M$, since M is purely arbitrary. Then the surround factor Λ for a uniform surround reduces to

$$\Lambda = \frac{L_s}{L_B} \qquad (12.17)$$

For a surround of any uniform luminosity L_s with superposed glare sources, we may combine Eqs. (12.13) and (12.17) to obtain

$$\Lambda = \frac{L_s}{L_B} + \frac{ME_G}{\theta^{3/2}L_B} \qquad (12.18)_I$$

Stiles has found that $M = 13.1$ when θ is expressed in degrees. Thus,

$$\Lambda = \frac{L_s}{L_B} + \frac{13.1}{\theta^{3/2}} \cdot \frac{E_G}{L_B} \quad \text{(numeric)} \qquad (12.18a)$$

Consider now the effect of changing the surround. If $E_G = 0$, $\Lambda = L_s/L_B$, and a curve similar to Fig. 12.32 is to be expected. Visual conditions are poor if $L_s << L_B$, rise to an optimum condition as L_s approaches L_B, and fall rapidly as L_s exceeds L_B. Exactly the same result will be obtained by fixing L_s and introducing one or more glare sources to give an additional illumination E_G at the eye. Suppose that $L_s = 0$. Then, according to Fig. 12.32, visual conditions are rather poor if $E_G = 0$; but by introducing a glare source which is of not too high intensity, seeing is actually improved. The experimental results of Lythgoe[45] with point sources and a dark surround bear out this conclusion. When the last term of Eq. (12.18) exceeds unity a rapid decrease in vision results. The conclusion implied in Eq. (12.18) is an important one and appears to be well-substantiated. Let us state it again: *Glare sources in the field of view have the same effect on visual acuity or contrast sensitivity as a uniform luminous surround having the same value of Λ.*

The effect of the glare sources may be either beneficial or deleterious. It should be realized that the tests on which our conclusions are based were made in such a way as to minimize fatigue, and no attempt was made to measure fatigue or psychological effects. It can hardly be doubted that the effort required in performing a given visual task is greater where concentrated glare sources are present than with these sources absent. The condition is somewhat analogous to the effort required in listening to a musical composition when a pneumatic riveter is in operation in the vicinity. The music can be heard and appreciated even, but the effort required is very great. This conclusion is in accord with the work of Harlinson and Bartlett, who found subjects "gripping the sides of the chair in which they sat, moving restlessly, getting breathless and flushed or pale and

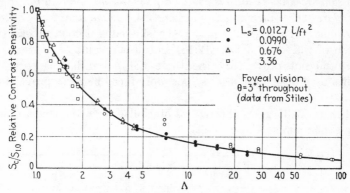

Fig. 12.34.—Effect of surround.[59,60]

tense" when they were observing under glare conditions. Thus, it is necessary to remember that the laboratory tests, though undeniably valuable, do not tell the whole story. They are useful in the predetermination of what glare will do in affecting visual acuity or contrast sensitivity, but they say nothing about the increased fatigue and strain caused by the glare sources. It is certainly best for the illuminating engineer to eliminate, if possible, all concentrated luminous sources which may appear in the field of view, and this is particularly necessary if people are to use the installation for long periods of time each day.

We shall now continue with the experimental results of introducing glare sources. Most of the research of this nature has been done with contrast sensitivity, but the same general results appear to be obtained with visual acuity. A large surround is used having the same luminosity as the background.

Thus, the values of Λ are never less than unity. The results of Stiles[59,60] are given in Fig. 12.34, where the ordinates are values of contrast sensitivity expressed in terms of $S_{1.0}$ the contrast sensitivity obtained with $\Lambda = 1.00$. The abscissas were calculated from Stiles's experimental values, using Eq. (12.18) with $M = 13.1$.

$$\Lambda = \frac{L_s}{L_B} + \frac{13.1}{\theta^{3/2}}\left(\frac{E_G}{L_B}\right) \qquad (12.18a)$$

It will be noted that despite the large range of surround luminosity (300:1), practically all the points are close to the curve, and *the same results are always obtained provided the illumination from the glare source increases in the same ratio as the luminosity of the surround.* These results may be considered as a good substantiation of the form of Eq. (12.18) and of the value of M, though they do not prove that the three-half power law is correct. Stiles used other test results (not reproduced here) to prove this law.

Figure 12.35 gives the results of Holladay,[56,57] plotted in the same manner as those of Stiles. The curve is that of Stiles—

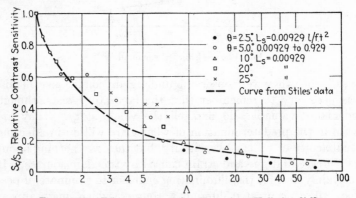

Fig. 12.35.—Effect of surround.   (Data from Holladay.[56,57])

the same one used in Fig. 12.34. It is a fairly good approximation to the data, despite the fact that quite different apparatus and different observers were concerned in the two researches. The results of Cobb and Moss[62] are also of interest (Fig. 12.36). Unlike the previous investigations, this one was made with comparatively small objects having greater contrast. The condition most nearly like that of Stiles is with the 16-min test object, and the resulting curve is not far different from that of Stiles. As the size of object is reduced, however, the change in $S_c/S_{1.0}$ becomes less pronounced. The curve for 1.17 min corresponds roughly to a visual-acuity test with maximum contrast and shows that visual acuity and contrast sensitivity exhibit the same downward trend due to glare, though visual acuity is less affected than contrast sensitivity.

Example. As a simple example of the use of the curves of Figs. 12.34, 12.35, and 12.36, consider a typist working in a large office lighted by diffusing luminaires on 10-ft centers. For the sake of definiteness, consider

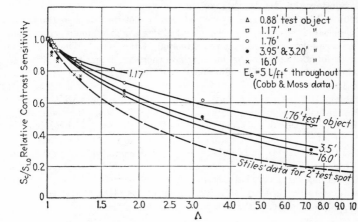

Fig. 12.36.—Effect of surround.[62]

that she is looking horizontally at her copy and that the line of sight is directly beneath a row of luminaires, the other luminaires being neglected. With the typist directly beneath a lamp, a distance of 3.5 ft between lamp and line of sight, the four luminaires make angles of 19.3, 10.0, 6.9, and 5.0 deg. with the line of sight, $L_s = 1.2$, and the intensity of each luminaire is 200 candles. The calculations are tabulated below:

Luminaire	θ	$\theta^{1.5}$	E_G	$\dfrac{E_G}{L_B}$	$\dfrac{13.1}{\theta^{1.5}}\left(\dfrac{E_G}{L_B}\right)$
1	19.3°	85	1.71	1.42	0.219
2	10.0	31.6	0.49	0.40	0.166
3	6.9	18.2	0.22	0.19	0.137
4	5.0	11.2	0.13	0.10	0.117
				Sum =	0.639

If the work has a luminosity equal to that of the surround, Eq. (12.18a) gives

$$\Lambda = 1.0 + 0.639 = 1.639$$

and Fig. 12.34 shows that *the luminaires in the field of view reduce seeing ability to* **0.58** of its value with shielded lamps.

Problem 163. *a.* The reading of small print (six-point type) requires the distinguishing of 0.007-in. details. If a book is held 14 in. from the eyes and is printed with black ink on diffusing white paper of reflection factor 0.82, what is the absolute minimum illumination required for reading? A desk lamp with metal shade is used over the book, and the rest of the room is in darkness.

b. Repeat where the luminosity of the desk and remainder of room are approximately the same as those of the paper.

Problem 164. The shade is removed from one of the lamps in Prob. 156, leaving a bare lamp 8 in. from the eyes, 2½ deg from the line of vision, and having a candlepower of 60 in the direction of the eyes. What reflection factor of foundation metal is detectable if there are large imperfections in the chromium plate? The illumination of the metal is the same as in Prob. 156.

Problem 165. A concrete pavement ($\rho = 0.30$) having a width of 60 ft is illuminated by 6000-lumen lamps placed opposite each other with 100-ft spacing on each side of the street and 2 ft back of the curb, with a mounting height of 30 ft. A pedestrian (height 6 ft 0 in., width 18 in.) dressed in a gray suit ($\rho = 0.25$) is midway between the lamps and 15 ft from the curb. The observer is at the same distance from the curb and is approaching the pedestrian in a car. At what distance can the pedestrian be seen? Assume all surfaces to be perfectly diffusing. Neglect the glare from street lamps. Neglect all lamps except the four nearest the pedestrian.

UPRIGHT ORNAMENTAL SYMMETRIC REFRACTOR WITH 6000-LUMEN LAMP

θ	I (Candlepower)
0	120
10	100
20	120
30	150
40	240
50	350
60	500
70	980
75	1240
80	920
85	600
90	400

Problem 166. Another car is approaching, and its head lamps are at the same distance from the observer as the pedestrian is, but the head lamps are about 10 ft to the left of the pedestrian. The total candlepower of the

head lamps is 20,000 in the direction of the observer.   At what distance
can the pedestrian be seen by the observer?

12.12. Flicker.—We have now considered the aspects of vision
that seem to be of greatest practical use to the illuminating
engineer:

Contrast sensitivity.

Visual acuity.

Visual acuity as a function of c and L_B.

Effect of surround (glare).

Flicker is another factor which is sometimes of importance.

H. E. Ives[77] has shown that many of the complicated visual
phenomena obtained with flickering light can be predicted by
postulating that the second step in the visual process is a diffusion
of ions which follows the ordinary differential equation of
diffusion.   We have an analogy to the flow of heat or to the
propagation of electric impulses through an unloaded submarine
cable.   It is well-known that rapid periodic fluctuations in the
emf applied to a long cable will finally result in a constant current
at the receiving end.   Similarly, we might expect that a periodically flickering light of sufficiently high flicker frequency would
produce a constant sensation.   The production of ions from the
photosensitive substances in the retina would follow the instan-
taneous fluctuations of the retinal illumination, but the slow
diffusion of these ions into the nerve endings would result in a
steady stimulation of nerve and a steady sensation.

Experiment shows this to be true.   A photometric match will
be obtained between a steady luminosity L_1 and a rapidly
flickering one $L_2(t)$ when the arithmetic average of the latter is
accurately equal to L_1 or when

$$\frac{1}{T}\int_0^T L_2(t)\,dt = L_1 \tag{12.19}$$

$L_2(t)$ = a periodic function of time.

T = one complete period of the fluctuation.

Equation (12.19) is usually known as *Talbot's law.*[65]   It is used
in visual photometry, particularly when a large lamp is to be
compared with a small one.   A motor-driven flicker disk is
interposed between the large lamp and the photometric screen,
the apparent luminosity of the screen being determined by the
size of openings in the disk.[68]

At high speeds, a lamp seen through such a flicker disk appears to be perfectly steady; but as the frequency of flicker is reduced, a sensation of flicker gradually appears until at low frequencies we perceive distinct dark and light periods. It is found that the *critical frequency* f_c at which flicker appears is approximately 50 cycles/sec at high luminosity and falls to low values as the luminosity is reduced. The *Ferry-Porter law*[66,67] states that f_c is a logarithmic function of L. Figure 12.37 shows some recent results which plot as a straight line against log L_B for foveal vision except at the highest luminosities. The curve for peripheral

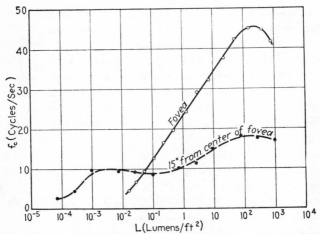

Fig. 12.37.—Critical frequency at which flicker is detected.[73] Test field 2°, surround 10°.

vision is low throughout, and the two have a striking resemblance to curves for contrast sensitivity and for visual acuity.

The preceding results are for a rectangular wave with equal periods of light and darkness. An approximation to this condition is obtained with sodium lamps operating on alternating current. We need expect no trouble from flicker at 60 cycles. A great many other types of light variation were studied by Ives, in most or all of which the critical frequency was lower than for the rectangular variation.[77] With incandescent lamps, for instance, only slight cooling of the filament is experienced between cycles, and f_c may be lower than 25 cycles, even with high luminosity.

OTHER METHODS OF ATTACK

12.13. Fatigue and Other Factors.—The scheme used in all scientific research is to reduce the problem to its simplest terms, carefully tie down all the independent variables but one, and allow this one variable to vary in a known manner. This method has been so successful in physics that it is applied also to the psychophysiological problems of this chapter. Here, however, various personal factors enter and can be controlled only with difficulty so that immense numbers of readings must be taken by a large number of observers. To reduce variations in the data, fatigue is eliminated as much as possible. The results are threshold values obtained by average observers who are not suffering from fatigue and who are concentrating upon a single given task. As has been pointed out, such results cannot be obtained continuously for long periods of time and cannot be obtained under the distracting conditions of ordinary work.

Such considerations as these have led some investigators to condemn all the results and to attempt a radically different attack on the problem. A study of fatigue as a function of illumination is a research of genuine importance. Luckiesh and Moss[83,86] have tried to correlate fatigue with pupil size and with finger pressure and to find how these quantities vary with illumination.

Other investigators have transferred the research from the laboratory to the factory and have made a tremendous number of tests to determine the effect on production of varying the illumination. Such a transfer of locale greatly increases the number of variables over which the investigator has no control, such as details in the lives of the workers and many factors in connection with their work. A valid test must use a great number of individuals for a considerable length of time, as well as a *control* consisting of a like number of individuals for whom the illumination is kept constant. Such fragmentary results as are available are surprisingly unconvincing.

Most people who have given the matter any attention arrive inevitably at the conclusion that present values of illumination are inadequate and that an increase in illumination to at least 100 lumens/sq ft would make seeing more pleasant. Measurements of various kinds have been made to substantiate this idea but with the peculiar result that either the assertion seems to be

TABLE XLIX.—DATA OF COBB AND MOSS ON VISUAL THRESHOLDS
(Geometric mean of nine observers, exposure time 0.170 sec, illumination
from incandescent lamps)
(*Frank. Inst., J.*, **205**, 1928, p. 831)

Visual angle (minutes)	Contrast		
	$L = 0.93$ lumen/sq ft	$L = 18.6$	$L = 92.9$
0.80	......	......	0.448
0.99	......	0.485	
1.17	......	0.301	0.152
1.35	0.603	0.209	
1.63	0.405	0.141	0.0813
1.93	0.279	0.0996	
2.41	0.172	0.0687	0.0467
3.20	0.109	0.0492	
3.95	0.0739	0.0371	0.0243
5.67	0.0443	0.0271	
7.98	0.0320	0.0216	0.0150
11.31	0.0242	0.0180	
16.02	0.0195	0.0157	0.0114

TABLE L.—VISUAL ACUITY AT LOW LUMINOSITY
(Geometric Mean of seven observers, illumination from incandescent lamps)
(CONNER and GANOUNG, *J.O.S.A.*, **25**, 1935)

Contrast	Luminosity of background (lumens per square foot)							
	1.30×10^{-4}	9.83×10^{-4}	9.93×10^{-3}	0.020	0.044	0.100	0.312	1.00
0.929	0.055	0.114	0.335	0.459	0.638	0.741	0.850	0.965
0.762	0.044	0.089	0.268	0.404	0.508	0.657	0.715	0.863
0.394	0.030	0.055	0.194	0.267	0.370	0.443	0.538	0.632
0.284	0.023	0.041	0.131	0.198	0.291	0.359	0.464	0.584
0.155	.....	0.025	0.071	0.105	0.160	0.198	0.258	0.335
0.096	.....	.....	0.040	0.064	0.114	0.125	0.158	0.203
0.063	.....	.....	0.034	0.054	0.087	0.119	0.141	0.186
0.0398	.....	.....	.....	0.036	0.039	0.048	0.060	0.085
0.0177	.....	.....	.....	.....	0.028	0.033	0.046	0.071

denied or the test proves nothing.   In the latter class is the very popular scheme of letting the customer adjust the illumination for himself until he finds the most satisfactory value, which is then measured.   The value chosen depends largely upon adaptation; and by a wise choice of the available range and the method of manipulation, the salesman can get almost any desired answer from the customer.

Statistics are often cited to show that low illumination levels are responsible for poor eyesight.   Certainly there can be no criticism of a belief in the deleterious effect of poor lighting; but let us be frank about it—admit that our belief is a matter of faith and that it is not *proved* by the fortuitous result of some half-baked experiment.

Bibliography

STRUCTURE OF THE EYE

1. CADY and DATES: Illuminating Engineering, p. 229, New York, 1928
2. R. A. HOUSTOUN: Vision and Colour Vision, p. 41, London, 1932.
3. J. D. LICKLEY: The Nervous System, London, 1919.
4. H. V. HELMHOLTZ: Physiological Optics (translation), *Opt. Soc. Am.*, 1924.

THE VISUAL PROCESS

5. P. REEVES: Response of the Pupil to Various Intensities of Light, *J.O.S.A.*, **4**, 1920, p. 35.
6. STILES and CRAWFORD: Luminous Efficiency of Rays Entering the Eye Pupil at Different Points, *Proc. Roy. Soc.*, **112B**, 1933, p. 428.
7. J. PARSONS: Some Problems of Vision, Discussion on Vision, *Phys. Soc., Proc.*, 1932, p. 272.
8. HOUSTOUN and SHEARER: The Quantum and Vision, *Nature*, **126**, 1930 p. 437.
9. J. JOLY: A Quantum Theory of Vision, *Phil. Mag.*, **41**, 1921, p. 289.
10. P. LASAREFF: Application of the Theory of Quanta to Peripheral Vision, *J. Gen. Physiol.*, **8**, 1926, p. 189.
11. W. S. STILES: Discussion on Vision, 1932, p. 326.
12. A. K. DAS: On Collisions of Photons, *Phys. Rev.*, **37**, 1931, p. 94.
13. S. HECHT: Die physikalische Chemie und die Physiologie des Sehaktes, *Ergeb. Physiol.*, **31**, 1931, p. 243.
14. S. HECHT: The Photic Sensitivity of *Ciona Intestinalis*, *J. Gen. Physiol.*, **1**, 1918, p. 147.
15. S. HECHT: Sensory Equilibrium and Dark Adaptation in *Mya Arenaria*, *J. Gen. Physiol.*, **1**, 1919, p. 545.
16. S. HECHT: The Photochemical Nature of the Photosensory Process, *J. Gen. Physiol.*, **2**, 1920, p. 229.

17. S. HECHT: The Dark Adaptation of the Human Eye, *J. Gen. Physiol.*, **2**, 1920, p. 499.

18. S. HECHT: The Nature of Foveal Dark Adaptation, *J. Gen. Physiol.*, **4**, 1921, p. 113.

19. S. HECHT: Sensory Adaptation and the Stationary State, *J. Gen. Physiol.*, **5**, 1923, p. 555.

20. S. HECHT: The Kinetics of Dark Adaptation, *J. Gen. Physiol.*, **10**, 1927, p. 781.

21. P. W. COBB: Dark Adaptation with Especial Reference to the Problems of Night Flying, *Psychol. Rev.*, **26**, 1919, p. 428.

22. H. PIPER: Über Dunkeladaptation, *Zeits. psychol. u. physiol. Sinnes.*, **31**, 1903, p. 161.

23. HECHT and WILLIAMS: The Visibility of Monochromatic Radiation and the Absorption Spectrum of Visual Purple, *J. Gen. Physiol.*, **5**, 1922, p. 1.

24. K. TANSLEY: Factors Affecting the Development and Regeneration of Visual Purple in the Mammalian Retina, *Proc. Roy. Soc.*, **114B**, 1933, p. 79.

25. S. HECHT: Photochemistry of Visual Purple, *J. Gen. Physiol.*, **3**, 1920, pp. 1, 285; **6**, 1924, p. 731.

26. E. D. ADRIAN: The Messages in Sensory Nerve Fibers, *Proc. Roy. Soc.*, **109**, 1931, p. 1.

27. ADRIAN and MATTHEWS: The Action of Light on the Eye, *J. Physiol.*, **63**, 1927, p. 378; **64**, 1927, p. 279; **65**, 1928, p. 273.

28. HARTLINE and GRAHAM: Nerve Impulses from Single Receptors in the Eye, *J. Cell. and Comp. Physiol.*, **1**, 1932, p. 277.

29. C. H. GRAHAM: The Relation of Nerve Response and Retinal Potential to Number of Sense Cells Illuminated in an Eye Lacking Lateral Connections, *J. Cell. and Comp. Physiol.*, **2**, 1932, p. 295.

30. R. GRANIT: Comparative Studies on the Peripheral and the Central Retina, *Am. J. Physiol.*, **94**, 1930, p. 41; **95**, 1930, p. 211; **95**, 1930, p. 229.

31. N. RASHEVSKY: Some Physico-mathematical Aspects of Nerve Conduction, *Physics*, **4**, 1933, p. 341.

32. N. RASHEVSKY: On the Theory of Nervous Conduction, *J. Gen. Physiol.*, **14**, 1931, p. 517.

33. H. A. BLAIR: Conduction of Nerve Fibres, *J. Gen. Physiol.*, **18**, 1934, p. 125.

34. KÖNIG and BRODHUN: Experimentelle Untersuchungen über die psychophysiche Fundamentalformel in Bezug auf den Gesichtssinn, *Sitz. d. Preussischen. Akad. Wissen.*, Berlin, 1888, p. 917.

35. A. KÖNIG: Reprint of preceding in *Gesammelte Abhandlungen*, Leipzig, 1903, p. 135.

36. S. HECHT: Visual Discrimination of Intensity and the Weber-Fechner Law, *J. Gen. Physiol.*, **7**, 1924, p. 235.

37. P. W. COBB: Weber's Law and the Fechnerian Muddle, *Psych. Rev.*, **39**, 1932, p. 533.

38. R. A. Houstoun: New Observations on the Weber-Fechner Law, Report of a Joint Discussion on Vision, *Phys. Soc., London*, Cambridge University Press, 1932, p. 167.

Visual Acuity

39. H. Hartridge: Visual Acuity and the Resolving Power of the Eye, *J. Physiol.*, **57**, 1922, p. 52.
40. H. Hartridge: Chromatic Aberration and Resolving Power of the Eye, *J. Physiol.*, **52**, 1918, p. 175.
41. Banister, Hartridge, and Lythgoe: Influence of Illumination on Visual Acuity, *Proc. Opt. Convention, London*, 1926, Part II, p. 551.
42. H. Hartridge: Visual Acuity and the Resolving Power of the Eye, Discussion on Vision, *Phys. Soc., London*, Cambridge University Press, 1932, p. 309.
43. R. S. Creed: Visual Acuity and Retinal Structure, discussion on vision, *Phys. Soc., London*, Cambridge University Press, 1932.
44. A. König: Die Abhängigkeit der Sehschärfe von der Beleuchtungsintensität, *Gesammelte Abhand. zur Physiol. Optik.*, 1903.
45. R. J. Lythgoe: The Measurement of Visual Acuity, *Med. Res. Council, Spec. Rep.* 173, 1932, p. 85.
46. H. Eguchi: Über die Sehschärfe unter starker Helligkeit, *C.I.E. Proc.*, **1**, 1932, p. 36.
47. S. Hecht: Relation between Visual Acuity and Illumination, *J. Gen. Physiol.*, **11**, 1928, p. 255.
48. P. W. Cobb: The Influence of Pupillary Diameter on Visual Acuity, *Am. J. Physiol.*, **36**, 1915, p. 335.
49. Luckiesh and Moss: Dependency of Visual Acuity upon Stimulus-distance, *J.O.S.A.*, **23**, 1933, p. 25.
50. Luckiesh and Moss: Seeing in Sodium Vapor Light, *J.O.S.A.*, **24**, 1934, p. 5.
   Visual Acuity and Sodium Vapor Light, *Frank. Inst., J.*, **215**, 1933, p. 401.
51. Burnap and Jackson: Illumination of Snellen Charts, *I.E.S. Trans.*, **23**, 1928, p. 1153.

Visual Thresholds

52. Cobb and Moss: Relation between Extent and Contrast in the Liminal Stimulus for Vision, *J. Exp. Psychol.*, **10**, 1927, p. 350.
53. Cobb and Moss: The Four Variables of the Visual Threshold, *Frank. Inst., J.*, 205, 1928, p. 831.
54. Cobb and Moss: Four Fundamental Factors in Vision, *I.E.S. Trans.*, **23**, 1928, p. 503.
55. Conner and Ganoung: Experimental Determination of the Visual Thresholds at Low Values of Illumination, *J.O.S.A.*, **25**, 1935, p. 287.

Effect of Surround

56. L. L. Holladay: Fundamentals of Glare and Visibility, *J.O.S.A.*, **12**, 1926, p. 271.

57. L. L. Holladay: Action of a Light Source in the Field of View in Lowering Visibility, *J.O.S.A.*, **14**, 1927, p. 1.

58. U. Bordoni: Alcune Richerche sopra i Fenomeni di Abbagliamento, *Elettrotecnica*, 11, 1924, p. 585.

59. W. S. Stiles: Effect of Glare on the Brightness Difference Threshold, *Proc. Roy. Soc.*, **104B**, 1929, p. 322.

60. W. S. Stiles: The Scattering Theory of the Effect of Glare on the Brightness Difference Threshold, *Proc. Roy. Soc.*, **105B**, 1929, p. 131.

61. W. S. Stiles: Effect of Glare on the Brightness Difference Threshold, *C.I.E. Proc.*, 1928, p. 220.

62. Cobb and Moss: Glare and the Four Fundamental Factors in Vision, *I.E.S. Trans.*, **23**, 1928, p. 1104.

63. Millar and McK. Gray: Glare—Its Manifestations, *C.I.E. Proc.*, 1928, p. 239.

64. J. W. T. Walsh: Reduction of Glare from Automobile Headlights, *J.O.S.A.*, **18**, 1929, p. 202.

Flicker

65. H. F. Talbot: Experiments on Light, *Phil. Mag.*, **5**, 1834, p. 321.

66. E. S. Ferry: Persistence of Vision, *Am. J. Sci.*, **44**, 1892, p. 192.

67. T. C. Porter: Contribution to the Study of Flicker, *Proc. Roy. Soc.*, **70**, 1902, p. 313.

68. E. P. Hyde: Talbot's Law as Applied to the Rotating Sectored Disc, *Bu. Stds. Bull.* 2, 1906, p. 1.

69. Arnold and Winsor: On the Theoretical Significance of Talbot's Law, *J. Gen. Physiol.*, **18**, 1934, p. 97.

70. Wolf and Zerrahn-Wolf: Validity of Talbot's Law for the Honey Bee, *J. Gen. Physiol.*, **18**, 1935, p. 865.

71. Granit and Harper: Comparative Studies on the Peripheral and Central Retina, *Am. J. Physiol.*, **95**, 1930, p. 211.

72. Hecht and Wolf: Intermittent Stimulation by Light, *J. Gen. Physiol.*, **15**, 1932, p. 369.

73. Hecht, Shlaer, and Verrijp: Intermittent Stimulation by Light, *J. Gen. Physiol.* **17**, 1934, pp. 237, 251, 269.

74. Hecht and Verrijp: The Influence of Intensity, Color and Retinal Location of the Fusion Frequency. *Nat. Acad. Sci. Proc.*, **19**, 1933, p. 522.

75. Lythgoe and Tansley: Relation of the Critical Frequency of Flicker to the Adaptation of the Eye, *Proc. Roy. Soc.*, **105B**, 1929, p. 60.

76. E. Wolf: Critical Frequency of Flicker for the Eye of the Bee, *J. Gen. Physiol.*, **17**, 1934, p. 7.

77. H. E. Ives: A Theory of Intermittent Vision, *J.O.S.A.*, **6**, 1922, p. 343.

78. P. W. Cobb: Dependence of Flicker on the Dark-light Ratio of the Stimulus Cycle, *J.O.S.A.*, **24**, 1934, p. 107.

79. P. W. Cobb: Some Comments on the Ives Theory of Flicker, *J.O.S.A.*, **24**, 1934, p. 91.

80. P. Lasareff: The General Theory of Flicker in Peripheral and Central Vision, *Phil. Mag.*, **2**, 1926, p. 1170.

OTHER METHODS OF ATTACK

81. L. T. TROLAND: An Analysis of the Literature Concerning the Dependency of Visual Functions upon Illumination. *I.E.S. Trans.*, **26**, 1931, p. 107.

82. J. H. CLARK: Lighting in Relation to Public Health, Williams and Wilkins Company, Baltimore, 1924.

83. LUCKIESH and MOSS: Seeing—A Partnership of Lighting and Vision, Williams & Wilkins Company, Baltimore, 1931.

84. LUCKIESH and MOSS: Lighting for Seeing, *G.E. (Nela Park) Bull.* LD-2, 1931.

85. LUCKIESH and MOSS: Recommended Foot-Candles, *I.E.S. Trans.*, **26**, 1931, p. 1061.

86. LUCKIESH and MOSS: The Human Seeing-Machine, *Frank. Inst., J.*, **215**, 1933, p. 629.

87. R. J. LYTHGOE: Illumination and Visual Capacities, *Med. Res. Council, Spec. Rep.* 1, 1926.

88. M. D. VERNON: The Movements of the Eyes in Reading, *Med. Res. Council, Spec. Rep.* 8, 1930.

89. VERNON and PICKFORD: Two Studies in the Psychology of Reading, *Med. Res. Council, Spec. Rep.* 3, 1929.

90. I. G. PRIEST: Reading by Artificial Daylight, *J.O.S.A.*, **15**, 1927, p. 131.

91. Report of the Committee of Inquiry into Problems Connected with Defective Vision in School Children, London, Board of Education, 1931, pp. 1–54.

92. FLEISCHER and HOFFMAN: A New Approach to School Lighting, *I.E.S. Trans.*, **31**, 1936, p. 389.

93. H. M. JOHNSON: Reaction-time Measurements, *Psychol. Bull.*, **20**, 1923, p. 562.

94. ODAY and STURROCK: Comfortable High-level Illumination, *I.E.S. Trans.*, **31**, 1936, p. 351.

95. P. W. COBB: Some Experiments on the Speed of Vision, *I.E.S. Trans.*, **19**, 1924, p. 150.

96. FERREE and RAND: Studies in Physiological Optics, Vols. I and II, Wilmer Ophthal. Inst., Baltimore, 1934.

CHAPTER XIII

COLOR*

In the foregoing chapters, we have considered the calculation of illumination and the elements of the design of lighting installations. We have concerned ourselves exclusively with the magnitude and not with the quality of the effects. In fact, the design of lighting installations outlined in Chap. XI is really only the crude beginning of a broad and fascinating field, which for its satisfactory development requires a knowledge of the psychological and physiological aspects, a knowledge of color and color harmony, and an artistic sense. The aesthetic factors, as well as many intangible effects which have not yielded to scientific analysis, cannot and should not be included in an introductory course on the *scientific basis of illuminating engineering*. But beyond the scientific aspects, which are stressed in this volume, lie a great many other factors which affect the beauty and utility of a lighting installation.

A study of color from the standpoint of both the artist and the physicist will be found valuable to the illuminating engineer. The artist has obtained a great deal of qualitative information in regard to color. The physicist is placing some of this information upon a scientific basis and has developed exact methods of specifying color. The modern trend toward a heightened use of color in daily life and the growth of mass-production of colored materials have stimulated the interest in color. Yet the average illuminating engineer seems to use color with the same carelessness that characterizes most of his work; and whether the job is the illumination of Niagara Falls, the floodlighting of an exterior, or the interior lighting of a "movie palace," he invariably uses crude red, green, and blue with no attempt at the production of beautiful and delicate harmonies. It is hoped that a more imaginative as well as a more analytical approach may develop in the near future.

* May be omitted in an introductory course.

13.02. Sensations and Stimuli.—Much of the confusion existing in the literature on color is caused by lack of proper discrimination between *color stimuli* and *color sensations,* many terms being used loosely in both senses.

If one thinks of all the varied sensations of color that he has experienced, he will find that they have three attributes or properties which distinguish one from another. In the first place, there is the attribute of *brilliance,* without which the sensation cannot exist. The wall of a house in direct sunlight gives the sensation of greater brilliance than the same wall in shadow. On a dark night, one might not be able to see the wall, in which case the sensation (brilliance) would be zero. Another characteristic of the color sensation is *hue.* We speak of reddish, purplish, yellowish, etc., sensations. A still different set of sensations might be called "pale or unsaturated colors," and the third attribute of color is *saturation.* The saturation of a homogeneous radiation is high, while the sensation produced by sunlight is said to have little or no saturation. Sometimes it is convenient to lump hue and saturation together under the term *quality* or *chromaticity* of the sensation.*

It is important to remember that saturation, hue, and brilliance are psychological quantities. These concepts are obtained by pure introspection and give convenient though qualitative names for our visual sensations. Since we have no method of measuring sensation, these terms have no quantitative significance and must be carefully differentiated from exact physical quantities such as irradiation, illumination, etc.

The usual stimulus for the sensation of color is radiant power; and the complete specification of radiant power is given (as seen in Chap. II) by the spectroradiometric curve, which gives the watts per square centimeter per micron plotted against wavelength. The specification of radiant power in general requires the specification of a large number of ordinates. There is an infinite number of spectroradiometric curves for all of which the same sensation is produced. To specify the sensation-evoking characteristics of a given radiation, three numbers are generally necessary and are always sufficient. The present chapter will treat of three methods of specification:

* See also Appendix B for definitions.

1. Specification in terms of the amounts of three primaries. The three numbers may be called *trichromatic coefficients,* and the method is usually designated as the *trichromatic specification.*

2. Specification in terms of *luminosity, dominant wavelength,* and *purity,* corresponding roughly to the sensation attributes of brilliance, hue, and saturation, respectively.

3. Specification by *luminosity* and *color temperature.* The methods 1 and 2 are general and can be used to specify *any* color stimulus. Number 3 applies only in special cases.

While it is true that the exact sensation depends not only upon the radiation but also upon a number of other factors such as the state of adaptation of the eye, the presence or absence of other radiations, the peculiarities of the individual, etc., we shall consider a fictitious standard observer working under standard conditions.

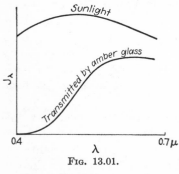

Fig. 13.01.

13.03.   Spectroradiometric Curves.—The most fundamental basis for any specification of color is the spectroradiometric curve, from which all other methods of specification can be derived. Such a curve may represent the radiosity of a source or the radiant power transmitted by a filter or reflected by a surface. Figure 13.01, for instance, shows the spectral distribution of average noon sunlight, also the spectral distribution of this sunlight after it has passed through a piece of amber glass. We know that the sensations produced by the two radiations are quite different.

The spectral distribution of radiant energy is also changed when the radiation is reflected from most surfaces. Figure 13.02 shows again the spectral distribution of noon sunlight, also the distribution curve of this radiation after it has been reflected from a surface. The skin of an orange, for instance, has the property of absorbing a large proportion of the energy at short wavelengths and reflecting well at longer wavelengths. Thus, the radiation curve obtained when sunlight is reflected from an orange is not greatly different from the lower curve of Fig. 13.01. Figure 13.03 gives data on the reflecting charac-

teristics of a paper which reflects at both ends of the spectrum
and which therefore produces a sensation of purple when illuminated by sunlight.

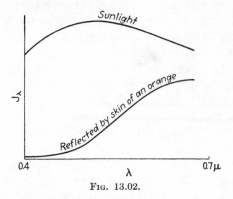

FIG. 13.02.

It is evident that the same sensation is evoked by a given
distribution irrespective of whether this radiation is produced

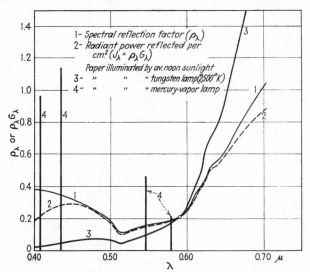

FIG. 13.03.—Reflection from a purple paper. (Milton-Bradley paper "VR.")

directly from a light source, is obtained by transmission through
colored glass, or is reflected from a colored surface. Many
artists do not seem to realize the fact and persist in considering

their paints as the fundamental quantities instead of thinking in terms of light. This has led to erroneous rules of color mixture based upon the mixture of pigments instead of upon the mixture of lights. For instance, in his interesting book "The Art of Color," Jacobs gives complements which he obtains by mixing pigments and which are not true complementary hues.[66]

Notice, also, that the color evoked by reflected and by transmitted radiation depends not only upon the characteristics of the transmitting or reflecting media but also upon the spectral distribution of the source. Figure 13.03 gives the spectral reflection factor ρ_λ of a colored paper. A curve is also given of the distribution obtained when sunlight is reflected from this paper, the resulting sensation being purple. Now, place the same paper under artificial light obtained from an incandescent lamp operating at 2500°K. The spectral radiosity of the paper is found by multiplying the spectral irradiation G_λ by ρ_λ for each wavelength and has its higher values at the longer wavelengths. The paper no longer appears purple but is now *red*. Place the paper under a mercury-vapor lamp, and the spectral distribution given by the heavy vertical lines results. The eye sees the paper now as a bright blue.

Here is an interesting field for the illuminating engineer, which he has largely neglected up to the present time. The whole subject of interior decoration and color harmony depends quite as much upon the spectral distribution of the radiation which the illuminating engineer furnishes as upon the reflection factors of the various paints, fabrics, and papers used. Is it too sanguine to hope that in the near future the illuminating engineer, in designing important lighting installations, will consider carefully the spectral reflection factors of the walls, ceiling, etc., with reference to the spectral distribution from the luminaires and will evolve a colorful, harmonious, and beautiful whole? We are entering the domain of art, and no amount of plotting distribution curves or determination of reflection factors can take the place of artistic talent and artistic experience. Nevertheless, a knowledge of the scientific basis of color will allow the ambitious illuminating engineer and interior decorator to predict and to produce new and lovely effects which he could otherwise obtain only as the fortuitous result of a long series of trials and errors.

Problem 167. Plot the distribution curve of radiant power obtained when light from 200-watt Mazda lamps operating at rated voltage is reflected from the paper considered in Fig. 13.03.

Problem 168. A travel bureau wishes to duplicate in its office as nearly as possible the psychological effect of strong summer sunlight. It plans to build the office interior as an exact reproduction of a certain Spanish patio and expects to use a high level of illumination obtained from an artificial skylight. The possibility of filtering the light from incandescent lamps to obtain a spectral distribution like tropical sunlight has been considered but has been abandoned because of the low efficacy of such a method. The possibility still remains of making the walls, floor, etc., of the office with such reflecting properties that the reflected radiation has exactly the same spectral distribution as obtains in the Spanish patio, and this phase of the problem is now under consideration. Data for the spectral radiosity of the actual patio walls on a summer afternoon are found to be as follows:

λ	$J_{\lambda\ rel}$	λ	$J_{\lambda\ rel}$	λ	$J_{\lambda\ rel}$	λ	$J_{\lambda\ rel}$
0.40μ	0.05	0.48	0.25	0.56	0.80	0.64	1.25
0.42	0.06	0.50	0.60	0.58	0.85	0.66	1.30
0.44	0.08	0.52	0.65	0.59	1.00	0.68	1.30
0.46	0.15	0.54	0.70	0.60	1.20	0.70	1.30
				0.62	1.25		

Determine the necessary curve of ρ_λ vs. λ to give the same distribution of reflected radiation from the office walls as is given in the table, assuming a maximum value of ρ_λ of 0.80 and assuming 200-wall Mazda lamps above a skylight of white frosted glass.

13.04. Color Matching.—We have seen that a color stimulus is completely specified by a spectroradiometric curve or by a table of a large number of ordinates from which the curve may be plotted. The curve, per se, however, tells very little about the sensation that will be produced. In one respect, it is *too* specific, since an infinite number of spectral distributions can be found, all of which evoke the same sensation. Figure 13.04*a* shows a simple distribution—the *equal-energy spectrum*, which gives a sensation of almost neutral gray. It will be found, however, that exactly the same sensation is produced by all the other distributions on the page, though from a *physical standpoint* they are entirely different. Homogeneous radiations at 0.48 and 0.58μ, with radiant power in the ratio 1.00 to 0.78, for example, evoke the same quality of sensation as the equal-energy spectrum. Another example consists of homogeneous radiations at 0.700 and 0.495μ with radiant power in the ratio 1.00 to 0.0338 (Fig. 13.04c). The three radiations of Fig. 13.04d also produce the same sensation, as does the continuous curve in Fig. 13.04e. The spectroradiometric curve itself gives

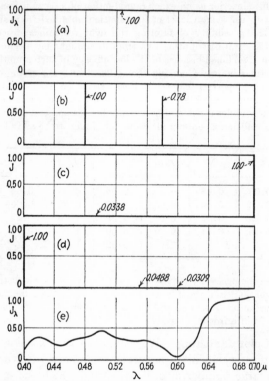

Fig. 13.04.—Some spectral distributions which evoke the same sensations.

very little idea of the sensation, though the ability of the radiation to evoke a sensation can be obtained from the spectroradiometric curve by a process similar to the one used in obtaining luminous flux from this curve.

Consider a white screen (Fig. 13.05) irradiated on the left half-field by any visible radiation whatsoever, homogeneous or otherwise. The right half-field is irradiated by three sources having fixed wavelengths but of variable magnitude. It is also possible to shift any one or two of the variable elements to the left half-field if that should be desirable. The observer adjusts the radiosity J_1, J_2, J_3 due to the three components until the two half-fields appear the same. The fundamental law of color matching, based on the experiments of a great number of observers, is that with any spectral distribution whatsoever on the left half-field, *it is never necessary to adjust more than three controls to get a perfect match.* In special cases, a smaller number of controls suffices, but three is always sufficient. *At very low illuminations* where vision is scotopic (Chap. XII), any two of the components can be set at zero radiosity, and matches obtained by the manipulation of the remaining single control. In most cases all three components will have to be adjusted, and some-

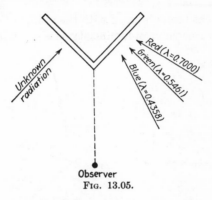

Observer
Fig. 13.05.

times one or two must be transferred to the left half-field to get a match.

The three components are often called *primaries* or *primary stimuli.* Some psychologists and most artists seem to believe that there is something unique about a particular set of primary colors, such as a certain red, green, and blue, and that any other set will fail in many cases. But actual experiment shows this idea to be quite erroneous. An infinite number of sets of primaries can be used in color matching, and there is nothing that places one of these sets apart from its fellows. The sole requirement imposed upon a set of primary stimuli is that *no match shall be possible in the absence of the unknown; i.e.,* no two of the primaries shall be the same, and no combination of two shall be capable of matching the third. Subject to this one restriction, any three primaries will allow matching all possible radiations. The primaries may be homogeneous or may be obtained from an incandescent lamp with filters.

Suppose that homogeneous primaries of wavelengths λ_1, λ_2, λ_3 are used and that when a match is obtained it is found that the radiosities of the right half-field due to the separate primaries are J_1, J_2, and J_3 watts/sq cm. Then the component luminosities of the right half-field due to these three radiations are $v_1 J_1$, $v_2 J_2$, and $v_3 J_3$ lightwatts/sq cm, where v_1, v_2, and v_3 represent values of the visibility function at the wavelengths λ_1, λ_2, and λ_3. The total luminosity of the right half-field is the sum of these three components, or

$$L = v_1 J_1 + v_2 J_2 + v_3 J_3 \tag{13.01}$$

Since a match has been obtained with the unknown, the unknown must have the same value of luminosity as is given by Eq. (13.01).

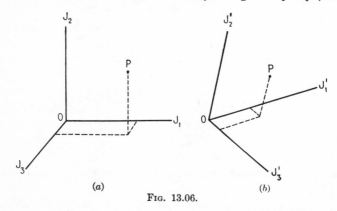

(a)   (b)

Fig. 13.06.

The three experimental values J_1, J_2, J_3 give a complete specification of the unknown radiation as regards its color-matching properties, while Eq. (13.01) indicates how its luminosity is also obtainable from the same three values. If filters are used in obtaining the primaries, the values of v in the foregoing equation must be replaced by integrated values obtained exactly as the luminous efficacy was obtained in Chap. III.

Since any color stimulus whatsoever can be matched by suitable amounts of three primaries, each radiation can be represented, as regards its sensation-evoking qualities, by a point in three-dimensional space (Fig. 13.06). Here J_1, J_2, J_3 represent the radiosity components (watts per square centimeter) of the right half-field, and P represents an arbitrary radiation. As the magnitude of the arbitrary radiation is increased, P moves

outward, away from the origin which represents darkness; while
if the quality of the stimulus is changed at constant magnitude,
P moves about at approximately fixed distance from the origin.
In some cases, a match may require the shift of one or of two of
the primaries to the left half-field. The values are then considered to be negative, and the point P moves into another
quadrant.

There is nothing unique about the coordinate system of Fig.
13.06a. Each set of primaries will have the effect of giving a
new set of coordinates such as J_1', J_2', J_3' of Fig. 13.06b. A
point of zero luminosity will always be matched by zero values
of all primaries, irrespective of what the primaries may be, and
will thus lie at the origin of all coordinate systems. A linear
transformation allows us to express results obtained with one
set of primaries in terms of any other set or to pass from one
coordinate system to any other.

We need not limit ourselves to primaries that can actually be
obtained, but we may use imaginary primaries. It is found that
such a step is of some practical advantage, since it makes possible
the elimination of negative values. In using imaginary primaries, there is clearly no reason why we must express values
in watts per square centimeter. Different arbitrary linear scales
for the three components will allow the placing of *white* so that
it is expressed in *equal numbers* on all three axes. This is not
necessary but is convenient, since a glance at the numbers shows
whether the unknown is bluish, reddish, or greenish. Finally,
the three imaginary primaries can be so chosen that the luminosity coefficients of Eq. (13.01) are 0, 1, and 0, respectively.
All these changes were incorporated in the standard system
adopted by international agreement in 1931 and called the C.I.E.
(Commission Internationale de l'Éclairage) system. In the
C.I.E. system, the luminosity of the unknown is expressed
simply by a single term instead of by the sum of Eq. (13.01).

13.05. Color-mixture Data.—Consider how a set of curves
may be obtained for color matching similar to the single curve of
visibility (Fig. 3.02). The procedure is similar to that used in
obtaining the visibility curve except that we use three radiations
on the right half-field instead of one and obtain an exact match
instead of only a brilliance match. Homogeneous radiation of
wavelength λ is used on the left half-field. The radiosity of the

left half-field is kept constant throughout the experiment, say at one milliwatt per square centimeter. Three homogeneous radiations of variable magnitudes and fixed wavelengths 0.7000, 0.5461, and 0.4358μ are used on the right. The experimental data obtained in this way by Wright[11] and Guild[13] are shown in Fig. 13.07.

When λ = 0.4358μ for the radiation on the left half-field, it is found that a match requires zero red, zero green, and one

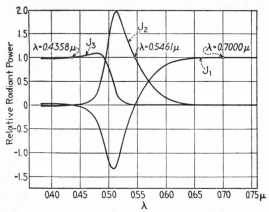

FIG. 13.07.—Color-mixture data.[11,12,13,14]   (*Adopted by C.I.E.*, 1932.)

milliwatt per square centimeter of blue on the left half-field Hence, $J_1 = 0$, $J_2 = 0$, and $J_3 = 1$, as shown by the curves. Similar results are obtained at 0.5461μ and at 0.7000μ. Negative values indicate that a primary has been transferred from the right side to the left side of the screen. We have just considered a method of obtaining the fundamental color-mixture data experimentally. In practice, the procedure and apparatus may be modified somewhat, but the principle is essentially the same.

The international standard data are obtained from the color-mixture data of Fig. 13.07 by suitable transformations, yielding the results of Fig. 13.08 and Appendix G. The ordinates of the curves are designated by $\bar{x}$, $\bar{y}$, and $\bar{z}$. Note that all negative values have been eliminated and that the values of $\bar{y}$ correspond to the standard visibility values v.

It is comparatively easy to build instruments (called *colorimeters*) using the principle of Fig. 13.05. Any convenient primaries are used, and the results are expressed in terms of the C.I.E. standards by suitable algebraic transformations. Such colorimetry suffers from the usual weakness of visual methods.   It depends upon the observer, though this dependence is less marked than in heterochromatic photometry.   Also, the adjustment is a peculiarly arduous one, since three independent controls must be adjusted more or less simultaneously to obtain a set of unique values corresponding to an exact match.   It

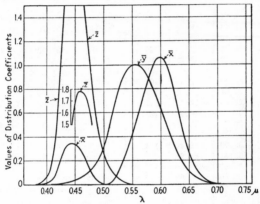

Fig. 13.08.—Distribution coefficients for equal-energy stimulus.   See Appendix G.

appears to be much better to place colorimetry upon a physical basis and to obtain the trichromatic coefficients from the spectro-radiometric curve, as has been done with marked success by A. C. Hardy.*

A homogeneous radiation can be specified in the C.I.E. trichromatic system by reading the proper values of $\bar{x}$, $\bar{y}$, and $\bar{z}$ from Fig. 13.08 or from the table of Appendix G and multiplying each by the watts per square centimeter.   For a continuous spectrum, the methods of Chap. III are used, giving the trichromatic coefficients:

$$\left. \begin{aligned} x' &= \int_0^\infty \bar{x} J_\lambda \, d\lambda \\ y' &= \int_0^\infty \bar{y} J_\lambda \, d\lambda \\ z' &= \int_0^\infty \bar{z} J_\lambda \, d\lambda \end{aligned} \right\} \tag{13.02}$$

* See Bibliography, 25, 26, 27, 28.

TABLE LI.—Relative Spectral Radiosity of C.I.E. Standard
Illuminants *A*, *B*, and *C*
(Judd, *J.O.S.A.*, **23**, 1933, p. 361)

λ (microns)	A	B	C	λ (microns)	A	B	C
0.380	9.79	22.40	33.00	0.580	114.44	101.00	97.80
0.385	10.90	26.85	39.92	0.585	118.08	100.07	95.43
0.390	12.09	31.30	47.40	0.590	121.73	99.20	93.20
0.395	13.36	36.18	55.17	0.595	125.39	98.44	91.22
0.400	14.71	41.30	63.30	0.600	129.04	98.00	89.70
0.405	16.15	46.62	71.81	0.605	132.70	98.08	88.83
0.410	17.68	52.10	80.60	0.610	136.34	98.50	88.40
0.415	19.29	57.70	89.53	0.615	139.99	99.06	88.19
0.420	21.00	63.20	98.10	0.620	143.62	99.70	88.10
0.425	22.79	68.37	105.80	0.625	147.23	100.36	88.06
0.430	24.67	73.10	112.40	0.630	150.83	101.00	88.00
0.435	26.64	77.31	117.75	0.635	154.42	101.56	87.86
0.440	28.70	80.80	121.50	0.640	157.98	102.20	87.80
0.445	30.85	83.44	123.45.	0.645	161.51	103.05	87.99
0.450	33.09	85.40	124.00	0.650	165.03	103.90	88.20
0.455	35.41	86.88	123.60	0.655	168.51	104.59	88.20
0.460	37.82	88.30	123.10	0.660	171.96	105.00	87.90
0.465	40.30	90.08	123.30	0.665	175.38	105.08	87.22
0.470	42.87	92.00	123.80	0.670	178.77	104.90	86.30
0.475	45.52	93.75	124.09	0.675	182.12	104.55	85.30
0.480	48.25	95.20	123.90	0.680	185.43	103.90	84.00
0.485	51.04	96.23	122.92	0.685	188.70	102.84	82.21
0.490	53.91	96.50	120.70	0.690	191.93	101.60	80.20
0.495	56.85	95.71	116.90	0.695	195.12	100.38	78.24
0.500	59.86	94.20	112.10	0.700	198.26	99.10	76.30
0.505	62.93	92.37	106.98	0.705	201.36	97.70	74.36
0.510	66.06	90.70	102.30	0.710	204.41	96.20	72.40
0.515	69.25	89.65	98.81	0.715	207.41	94.60	70.40
0.520	72.50	89.50	96.90	0.720	210.36	92.90	68.30
0.525	75.79	90.43	96.78	0.725	213.26	91.10	66.30
0.530	79.13	92.20	98.00	0.730	216.12	89.40	64.40
0.535	82.52	94.46	99.94	0.735	218.92	88.00	62.80
0.540	85.95	96.90	102.10	0.740	221.66	86.90	61.50
0.545	89.41	99.16	103.95	0.745	224.36	85.90	60.20
0.550	92.91	101.00	105.20	0.750	227.00	85.20	59.20
0.555	96.44	102.20	105.67	0.755	229.58	84.80	58.50
0.560	100.00	102.80	105.30	0.760	232.11	84.70	58.10
0.565	103.58	102.92	104.11	0.765	234.59	84.90	58.00
0.570	107.18	102.60	102.30	0.770	237.01	85.40	58.20
0.575	110.80	101.90	100.15	0.775	239.37	86.10	58.50
0.580	114.44	101.00	97.80	0.780	241.67	87.00	59.10

TABLE LII.—COMPUTATION OF TRICHROMATIC SPECIFICATION
(Surface Irradiated by Standard Illuminant B)
(SMITH and GUILD, *Opt. Soc., Trans.*, **33**, 1931–1932, p. 104)

λ	$\bar{x}J\lambda$	$\bar{y}J\lambda$	$\bar{z}J\lambda$	λ	$\bar{x}J\lambda$	$\bar{y}J\lambda$	$\bar{z}J\lambda$
0.380	0.0015×10^{-4}	0.0000×10^{-4}	0.0070×10^{-4}	0.580	4.4218×10^{-4}	4.1984×10^{-4}	0.0082×10^{-4}
0.385	0.0028	0.0001	0.0135	0.585	4.6790	3.9030	0.0067
0.390	0.0063	0.0001	0.0301	0.590	4.8644	3.5880	0.0052
0.395	0.0131	0.0003	0.0626	0.595	4.9701	3.2684	0.0047
0.400	0.0282	0.0008	0.1340	0.600	4.9736	2.9546	0.0037
0.405	0.0517	0.0013	0.2455	0.605	4.8999	2.6561	0.0028
0.410	0.1083	0.0030	0.5163	0.610	4.7185	2.3672	0.0014
0.415	0.2139	0.0061	1.0236	0.615	4.4415	2.0882	0.0009
0.420	0.4058	0.0121	1.9495	0.620	4.0700	1.8149	0.0009
0.425	0.7017	0.0238	3.3944	0.625	3.6031	1.5392	0.0005
0.430	0.9916	0.0405	4.8394	0.630	3.1000	1.2788	0.0000
0.435	1.2134	0.0621	5.9951	0.635	2.6296	1.0530	0.0000
0.440	1.3446	0.0888	6.7448	0.640	2.1871	0.8545	0.0000
0.445	1.3878	0.1188	7.1067	0.645	1.7765	0.6804	0.0000
0.450	1.3718	0.1551	7.2308	0.650	1.4074	0.5312	0.0000
0.455	1.3229	0.1993	7.2399	0.655	1.0929	0.4078	0.0000
0.460	1.2269	0.2531	7.0422	0.660	0.8273	0.3060	0.0000
0.465	1.0807	0.3181	6.5769	0.665	0.6085	0.2239	0.0000
0.470	0.8589	0.4000	5.6599	0.670	0.4381	0.1604	0.0000
0.475	0.6365	0.5044	4.6670	0.675	0.3177	0.1159	0.0000
0.480	0.4348	0.6323	3.6980	0.680	0.2323	0.0844	0.0000
0.485	0.3667	0.7784	2.8332	0.685	0.1617	0.0585	0.0000
0.490	0.1475	0.9590	2.1449	0.690	0.1102	0.0398	0.0000
0.495	0.0672	1.1826	1.6156	0.695	0.0758	0.0273	0.0000
0.500	0.0221	1.4538	1.2242	0.700	0.0540	0.0194	0.0000
0.505	0.0106	1.7976	0.9370	0.705	0.0378	0.0135	0.0000
0.510	0.0403	2.1798	0.6856	0.710	0.0267	0.0097	0.0000
0.515	0.1246	2.6052	0.4785	0.715	0.0185	0.0068	0.0000
0.520	0.2707	3.0361	0.3344	0.720	0.0129	0.0044	0.0000
0.525	0.4735	3.4272	0.2476	0.725	0.0087	0.0030	0.0000
0.530	0.7291	3.7973	0.1859	0.730	0.0060	0.0021	0.0000
0.535	1.0186	4.1292	0.1345	0.735	0.0042	0.0017	0.0000
0.540	1.3445	4.4168	0.0940	0.740	0.0029	0.0012	0.0000
0.545	1.7042	4.6445	0.0635	0.745	0.0020	0.0008	0.0000
0.550	2.0915	4.8016	0.0420	0.750	0.0012	0.0004	0.0000
0.555	2.5006	4.8840	0.0278	0.755	0.0008	0.0004	0.0000
0.560	2.9200	4.8872	0.0192	0.760	0.0008	0.0004	0.0000
0.565	3.3360	4.8122	0.0133	0.765	0.0004	0.0000	0.0000
0.570	3.7359	4.6669	0.0103	0.770	0.0004	0.0000	0.0000
0.575	4.1019	4.4568	0.0088	0.775	0.0000	0.0000	0.0000
0.580	4.4218	4.1984	0.0082	0.780	0.0000	0.0000	0.0000
				Totals =	99.0930	100.0000	85.3125

These three coefficients completely specify the radiation as regards its sensation-evoking ability under standard conditions for color matching. Since in the C.I.E. system, $\bar{y} = v$, the second integral gives the luminosity, or

$$y' = L = \int_0^\infty \bar{y} J_\lambda \, d\lambda \qquad (13.03)$$

Example. Table LI gives the values of $J_{\lambda \text{ rel}}$ for the three standard illuminants recommended by the C.I.E. for use in the colorimetry of materials. Standard illuminant A is an incandescent lamp operating at 2842°K,* while B and C are obtained with the same lamp and suitable liquid filters. What, for example, is the trichromatic specification of the radiation emitted by a white surface which is illuminated by B, the spectral radiosity of the surface at 0.59μ being 4.74×10^{-4} watt/sq cm per micron?

Either the three curves of $\bar{x} J_\lambda$, $\bar{y} J_\lambda$, and $\bar{z} J_\lambda$ can be plotted and the integrals of Eq. (13.02) evaluated, or the ordinates can be added in the usual manner† as shown in Table LII. The sums of the ordinates are divided by 20 because the unit step was not a micron but $\frac{1}{20}\mu$, and the trichromatic specification of the radiation emitted by the surface is thus

$$\begin{cases} x' = 4.9546 \times 10^{-4} \\ y' = 5.0000 \times 10^{-4} \\ z' = 4.2656 \times 10^{-4} \end{cases}$$

The luminosity of the surface is 5.00×10^{-4} lightwatt/sq cm, or 0.311 lumen/sq cm.

Problem 169. Express the irradiation of a surface 2 meters from a 220-volt high-pressure quartz mercury lamp by giving the trichromatic coefficients.

Problem 170. Repeat Prob. 169 for Fig. 2.06.

13.06. The Color Triangle.—The trichromatic coefficients can be plotted in a three-coordinate system as in Fig. 13.06. If a two-dimensional representation could be obtained, it would be much more convenient, though of course it could not possibly give all the information given by the three coefficients x', y', and z'. It is an experimental fact that a match obtained at one value of luminosity remains a match over a wide range of luminosity. Thus in many cases, particularly in specifying reflecting or transmitting properties of materials, it is advantageous to consider the quality attributes as distinct from the magnitude. The quality can be specified by *two* numbers and can be plotted in two dimensions.

* For $C_2 = 14,320$. Originally specified as 2848° with $C_2 = 14,350$.

† *Cf.* HARDY and PINEO, The Computation of Trichromatic Excitation Values by the Selected Ordinate Method, *J.O.S.A.*, **22**, 1932, p. 430; D. NICKERSON: Disc Colorimetry, *J.O.S.A.*, **25**, 1935, p. 253.

The trichromatic coefficients x', y', and z' are expressed in terms of their sum, defining the *unified trichromatic coefficients*:

$$\left. \begin{array}{l} x = \dfrac{x'}{x' + y' + z'} \\[2mm] y = \dfrac{y'}{x' + y' + z'} \\[2mm] z = \dfrac{z'}{x' + y' + z'} \end{array} \right\} \qquad (13.04)$$

Obviously, $x + y + z = 1.0$, and only two therefore are independent. Any two, such as x and y, may be represented in

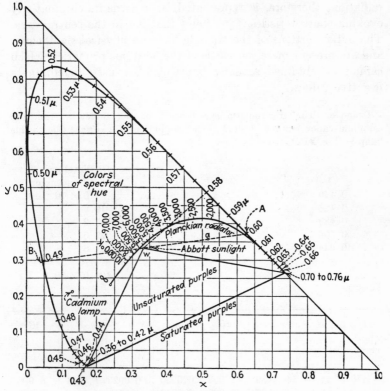

Fig. 13.09.—The color triangle.

ordinary rectangular coordinates; and each radiation is represented by a point. Such a diagram is shown in Fig. 13.09.

The upper point of the triangle represents 100 per cent green in the system of standardized fictitious primaries; the lower right-hand corner is 100 per cent red; while the lower left-hand corner represents 100 per cent blue. Any radiation is represented by a single point in the triangle. The locus of all points representing homogeneous radiations is a smooth curve (Fig. 13.09). The coordinates are tabulated in Table LIII. We also experience sensations that we call purples, which cannot be evoked by a single homogeneous radiation. They can be obtained by a mixture of reds with blues or violets. The most highly saturated purples are obtained by mixing deep spectral red with spectral violet and can be represented by points on a straight line connecting red and violet (Fig. 13.09). Every radiation, therefore, is represented, as regards its chromaticity evoking characteristics, by a point that lies in the central area. The outer portions of the triangle have no physical significance and are present merely because of the fictitious primaries, which cannot be obtained actually but which are used to eliminate negative values.

Example. The trichromatic specification of the radiation from the cadmium-vapor lamp is desired. The irradiation of a surface due to this lamp is (Fig. 2.02)

λ	G (Watts per Square Centimeter)
0.440	4.0×10^{-6}
0.468	19.6
0.480	37.2
0.509	27.6
0.644	11.6
	$\overline{100.0 \times 10^{-6}}$

Thus,

λ (microns)	G	$\bar{x}$	$\bar{x}G$	$\bar{y}$	$\bar{y}G$	$\bar{z}$	$\bar{z}G$
0.440	4.0	0.3483	1.393	0.0230	0.092	1.7471	6.988
0.468	19.6	0.2177	4.267	0.0842	1.650	1.3838	27.123
0.480	37.2	0.0956	3.556	0.1390	5.171	0.8130	30.243
0.509	27.6	0.0079	0.218	0.4839	13.356	0.1690	4.664
0.644	11.6	0.3782	4.387	0.1456	1.689	0.0000	0.000
Sums			13.821	......	21.958	......	69.018

TABLE LIII.—Unified Trichromatic Coefficients for Homogeneous
Radiation

(Smith and Guild, *Opt. Soc., Trans.*, **33**, 1931–1932, p. 96)

λ	x	y	λ	x	y
0.380	0.1741	0.0050	0.420	0.1714	0.0051
0.381	0.1741	0.0050	0.421	0.1712	0.0052
0.382	0.1741	0.0050	0.422	0.1710	0.0053
0.383	0.1740	0.0050	0.423	0.1708	0.0055
0.384	0.1740	0.0050	0.424	0.1706	0.0056
0.385	0.1740	0.0050	0.425	0.1703	0.0058
0.386	0.1739	0.0050	0.426	0.1700	0.0060
0.387	0.1739	0.0050	0.427	0.1698	0.0062
0.388	0.1739	0.0049	0.428	0.1695	0.0064
0.389	0.1739	0.0049	0.429	0.1692	0.0066
0.390	0.1738	0.0049	0.430	0.1689	0.0069
0.391	0.1738	0.0049	0.431	0.1685	0.0072
0.392	0.1737	0.0049	0.432	0.1681	0.0075
0.393	0.1737	0.0049	0.433	0.1678	0.0078
0.394	0.1736	0.0049	0.434	0.1673	0.0082
0.395	0.1736	0.0049	0.435	0.1669	0.0086
0.396	0.1735	0.0049	0.436	0.1664	0.0090
0.397	0.1735	0.0049	0.437	0.1660	0.0094
0.398	0.1734	0.0049	0.438	0.1655	0.0099
0.399	0.1734	0.0048	0.439	0.1650	0.0103
0.400	0.1733	0.0048	0.440	0.1644	0.0109
0.401	0.1733	0.0048	0.441	0.1638	0.0114
0.402	0.1732	0.0048	0.442	0.1632	0.0120
0.403	0.1731	0.0048	0.443	0.1626	0.0125
0.404	0.1731	0.0048	0.444	0.1619	0.0131
0.405	0.1730	0.0048	0.445	0.1611	0.0138
0.406	0.1729	0.0048	0.446	0.1603	0.0145
0.407	0.1728	0.0048	0.447	0.1595	0.0152
0.408	0.1728	0.0048	0.448	0.1586	0.0160
0.409	0.1727	0.0048	0.449	0.1576	0.0169
0.410	0.1726	0.0048	0.450	0.1566	0.0177
0.411	0.1725	0.0048	0.451	0.1556	0.0186
0.412	0.1724	0.0048	0.452	0.1545	0.0196
0.413	0.1723	0.0048	0.453	0.1534	0.0205
0.414	0.1722	0.0048	0.454	0.1522	0.0216
0.415	0.1721	0.0048	0.455	0.1510	0.0227
0.416	0.1720	0.0049	0.456	0.1497	0.0239
0.417	0.1719	0.0049	0.457	0.1484	0.0252
0.418	0.1717	0.0050	0.458	0.1469	0.0266
0.419	0.1716	0.0050	0.459	0.1455	0.0281
0.420	0.1714	0.0051	0.460	0.1440	0.0297

Table LIII.—Unified Trichromatic Coefficients for Homogeneous Radiation.—(*Continued*)

λ	x	y	λ	x	y
0.460	0.1440	0.0297	0.500	0.0082	0.5384
0.461	0.1425	0.0313	0.501	0.0063	0.5628
0.462	0.1409	0.0331	0.502	0.0049	0.5868
0.463	0.1392	0.0351	0.503	0.0040	0.6102
0.464	0.1374	0.0374	0.504	0.0037	0.6328
0.465	0.1355	0.0399	0.505	0.0039	0.6548
0.466	0.1335	0.0427	0.506	0.0047	0.6760
0.467	0.1313	0.0459	0.507	0.0061	0.6962
0.468	0.1290	0.0495	0.508	0.0081	0.7154
0.469	0.1267	0.0534	0.509	0.0107	0.7334
0.470	0.1241	0.0578	0.510	0.0139	0.7502
0.471	0.1215	0.0626	0.511	0.0178	0.7655
0.472	0.1187	0.0678	0.512	0.0223	0.7793
0.473	0.1158	0.0735	0.513	0.0274	0.7917
0.474	0.1128	0.0798	0.514	0.0329	0.8027
0.475	0.1096	0.0868	0.515	0.0389	0.8120
0.476	0.1062	0.0945	0.516	0.0453	0.8194
0.477	0.1027	0.1029	0.517	0.0521	0.8250
0.478	0.0991	0.1120	0.518	0.0593	0.8292
0.479	0.0953	0.1219	0.519	0.0667	0.8322
0.480	0.0913	0.1327	0.520	0.0743	0.8338
0.481	0.0870	0.1444	0.521	0.0821	0.8341
0.482	0.0826	0.1570	0.522	0.0899	0.8334
0.483	0.0780	0.1706	0.523	0.0979	0.8317
0.484	0.0734	0.1851	0.524	0.1060	0.8292
0.485	0.0687	0.2007	0.525	0.1142	0.8262
0.486	0.0640	0.2175	0.526	0.1223	0.8228
0.487	0.0594	0.2354	0.527	0.1305	0.8191
0.488	0.0547	0.2543	0.528	0.1386	0.8150
0.489	0.0500	0.2742	0.529	0.1467	0.8105
0.490	0.0454	0.2950	0.530	0.1547	0.8059
0.491	0.0407	0.3170	0.531	0.1625	0.8013
0.492	0.0361	0.3401	0.532	0.1702	0.7966
0.493	0.0317	0.3638	0.533	0.1778	0.7918
0.494	0.0275	0.3880	0.534	0.1854	0.7868
0.495	0.0235	0.4127	0.535	0.1929	0.7816
0.496	0.0198	0.4378	0.536	0.2003	0.7764
0.497	0.0163	0.4630	0.537	0.2077	0.7711
0.498	0.0132	0.4883	0.538	0.2151	0.7656
0.499	0.0105	0.5134	0.539	0.2224	0.7600
0.500	0.0082	0.5384	0.540	0.2296	0.7543

Table LIII.—Unified Trichromatic Coefficients for Homogeneous Radiation.—(*Continued*)

λ	x	y	λ	x	y
0.540	0.2296	0.7543	0.580	0.5125	0.4866
0.541	0.2369	0.7485	0.581	0.5191	0.4800
0.542	0.2441	0.7426	0.582	0.5256	0.4735
0.543	0.2514	0.7366	0.583	0.5321	0.4671
0.544	0.2586	0.7305	0.584	0.5385	0.4607
0.545	0.2658	0.7243	0.585	0.5448	0.4544
0.546	0.2729	0.7181	0.586	0.5510	0.4482
0.547	0.2801	0.7118	0.587	0.5572	0.4421
0.548	0.2873	0.7054	0.588	0.5633	0.4360
0.549	0.2944	0.6989	0.589	0.5692	0.4301
0.550	0.3016	0.6923	0.590	0.5752	0.4242
0.551	0.3088	0.6857	0.591	0.5810	0.4184
0.552	0.3159	0.6791	0.592	0.5866	0.4128
0.553	0.3231	0.6724	0.593	0.5922	0.4072
0.554	0.3302	0.6657	0.594	0.5976	0.4018
0.555	0.3373	0.6589	0.595	0.6029	0.3965
0.556	0.3445	0.6520	0.596	0.6080	0.3914
0.557	0.3517	0.6451	0.597	0.6130	0.3865
0.558	0.3588	0.6383	0.598	0.6178	0.3817
0.559	0.3660	0.6314	0.599	0.6225	0.3770
0.560	0.3731	0.6245	0.600	0.6270	0.3725
0.561	0.3802	0.6175	0.601	0.6315	0.3680
0.562	0.3874	0.6105	0.602	0.6359	0.3637
0.563	0.3945	0.6036	0.603	0.6402	0.3594
0.564	0.4016	0.5966	0.604	0.6443	0.3553
0.565	0.4087	0.5896	0.605	0.6482	0.3514
0.566	0.4158	0.5826	0.606	0.6520	0.3477
0.567	0.4229	0.5756	0.607	0.6557	0.3440
0.568	0.4300	0.5686	0.608	0.6592	0.3405
0.569	0.4371	0.5616	0.609	0.6625	0.3372
0.570	0.4441	0.5547	0.610	0.6658	0.3340
0.571	0.4510	0.5478	0.611	0.6689	0.3309
0.572	0.4580	0.5409	0.612	0.6719	0.3279
0.573	0.4650	0.5339	0.613	0.6747	0.3251
0.574	0.4719	0.5270	0.614	0.6774	0.3224
0.575	0.4788	0.5202	0.615	0.6801	0.3197
0.576	0.4856	0.5134	0.616	0.6826	0.3172
0.577	0.4924	0.5066	0.617	0.6849	0.3149
0.578	0.4991	0.4999	0.618	0.6872	0.3126
0.579	0.5058	0.4932	0.619	0.6894	0.3104
0.580	0.5125	0.4866	0.620	0.6915	0.3083

TABLE LIII.—UNIFIED TRICHROMATIC COEFFICIENTS FOR HOMOGENEOUS RADIATION.—(*Continued*)

λ	x	y	λ	x	y
0.620	0.6915	0.3083	0.660	0.7300	0.2700
0.621	0.6935	0.3064	0.661	0.7302	0.2698
0.622	0.6954	0.3045	0.662	0.7305	0.2695
0.623	0.6972	0.3027	0.663	0.7307	0.2693
0.624	0.6989	0.3010	0.664	0.7309	0.2691
0.625	0.7006	0.2993	0.665	0.7311	0.2689
0.626	0.7022	0.2977	0.666	0.7313	0.2687
0.627	0.7037	0.2962	0.667	0.7315	0.2685
0.628	0.7051	0.2948	0.668	0.7317	0.2683
0.629	0.7066	0.2933	0.669	0.7318	0.2682
0.630	0.7079	0.2920	0.670	0.7320	0.2680
0.631	0.7092	0.2907	0.671	0.7321	0.2679
0.632	0.7105	0.2894	0.672	0.7323	0.2677
0.633	0.7117	0.2882	0.673	0.7324	0.2676
0.634	0.7129	0.2870	0.674	0.7326	0.2674
0.635	0.7140	0.2859	0.675	0.7327	0.2673
0.636	0.7151	0.2848	0.676	0.7329	0.2671
0.637	0.7161	0.2838	0.677	0.7330	0.2670
0.638	0.7171	0.2828	0.678	0.7331	0.2669
0.639	0.7181	0.2818	0.679	0.7333	0.2667
0.640	0.7190	0.2809	0.680	0.7334	0.2666
0.641	0.7199	0.2800	0.681	0.7335	0.2665
0.642	0.7208	0.2792	0.682	0.7337	0.2663
0.643	0.7216	0.2784	0.683	0.7338	0.2662
0.644	0.7223	0.2777	0.684	0.7339	0.2661
0.645	0.7230	0.2770	0.685	0.7340	0.2660
0.646	0.7237	0.2763	0.686	0.7341	0.2659
0.647	0.7243	0.2757	0.687	0.7342	0.2658
0.648	0.7249	0.2751	0.688	0.7342	0.2658
0.649	0.7255	0.2745	0.689	0.7343	0.2657
0.650	0.7260	0.2740	0.690	0.7344	0.2656
0.651	0.7265	0.2735	0.691	0.7344	0.2656
0.652	0.7270	0.2730	0.692	0.7345	0.2655
0.653	0.7274	0.2726	0.693	0.7345	0.2655
0.654	0.7279	0.2721	0.694	0.7346	0.2654
0.655	0.7283	0.2717	0.695	0.7346	0.2654
0.656	0.7287	0.2713	0.696	0.7346	0.2654
0.657	0.7290	0.2710	0.697	0.7346	0.2654
0.658	0.7294	0.2706	0.698	0.7347	0.2653
0.659	0.7297	0.2703	0.699	0.7347	0.2653
0.660	0.7300	0.2700	0.700	0.7347	0.2653

The radiation is specified by the three numbers

$$\begin{cases} x' = 13.82 \times 10^{-6} \\ y' = 21.96 \times 10^{-6} \\ z' = 69.02 \times 10^{-6} \end{cases}$$

and the luminosity of the surface is

$$L = y' = 21.96 \times 10^{-6} \text{ lightwatt/sq cm}$$

The three unified values are

$$\begin{cases} x = \dfrac{13.821}{104.8} = 0.132 \\[2mm] y = \dfrac{21.958}{104.8} = 0.209 \\[2mm] z = \dfrac{69.018}{104.8} = 0.659 \end{cases}$$

This point is shown in Fig. 13.09.

An interesting application of the trichromatic method of color specification is the determination of the positions in the triangle of the radiation from a Planckian radiator at various temperatures. Table LIV gives the data computed by Eq. (13.04), and the results are plotted in Fig. 13.09. At 2000°K, the light from the Planckian radiator, though not a saturated orange like the pure spectral color, has a distinctly orange hue. As the temperature is raised, the color approaches white, and above about 6000°K it becomes bluish like the light from some of the high-temperature stars or the light from a clear sky. The light from all ordinary incandescent lamps lies very nearly on this curve, and the color temperature corresponds to the Planckian-radiator temperature marked on the curve. Now we see why a specification of T_c cannot be used for all colors. The Planckian-radiator locus is one-dimensional, while colors in general require for their quality specification a two-dimensional plot such, for instance, as the color triangle.

Problem 171. Prepare a large color triangle, at least 20 by 20 in., for use in the following problems. Plot the locus for homogeneous radiation, locate the point for equal-energy spectrum and the curve for Planckian radiators, indicate the divisions between the purples and the colors of spectral hue.

Problem 172. Show that the statement of Sec. 13.04 (the "sole requirement imposed upon a set of primary stimuli . . . ") is true.

Problem 173. Calculate x, y, and z for the light from the ordinary mercury-vapor lamp and show its position in the color triangle.

Problem 174. One method of obtaining pictures in natural colors requires the taking of three negatives of the same scene: one through a red, one through a green, and one through a blue filter. The three black-and-white positives may then be projected on a screen by means of three separate lenses, each provided with a filter. The Eastman Kodak Company recommends Wratten filters 29, 61, and 47 for this purpose.

Using tungsten lamps operating at 2800°K, determine x, y, and z for the radiation from a white screen illuminated under the following conditions:

  a. Positive films behind Nos. 29 and 61 are opaque, while film behind No. 47 is perfectly transparent.

  b. Film behind No. 29 transparent, others opaque.

  c. Film behind No. 61 transparent, others opaque.

Ordinary pictures will have a considerable variation in the densities of all three positives, which will give a great variety of colors on the screen. On a color triangle show the area representing all possible colors obtainable on the screen.

Problem 175. If a two-color process using filters 29 and 61 had been used instead of a three-color process, indicate on the color triangle all possible colors which could be produced on the screen.

13.07. Monochromatic Specification.—We have seen that the color-matching characteristics of a given radiation can be completely specified by three numbers: the trichromatic coefficients x', y', and z', or the unified coefficients x and y plus the luminosity

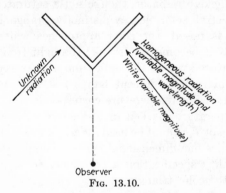

Observer

Fig. 13.10.

L. An equally valid system specifies all color stimuli in terms of *luminosity*, *dominant wavelength*, and *purity*. These terms can best be identified by considering an experiment for determining them for any given radiation. A white screen (Fig. 13.10) is used, one side of it illuminated by the unknown radiation. On the other side is placed a source of white light of variable luminosity and a source of homogeneous radiation of variable wavelength λ_d and variable luminosity. The observer will find that any unknown color of spectral hue can be completely matched by a variation of the two component radiations on the right. To match purples, the homogeneous stimulus must be transferred to the left half-field.

After a match has been obtained, the value of λ_d is read. This is called the *dominant wavelength* of the unknown radiation. The *colorimetric purity* of the unknown is defined as the luminosity of the homogeneous radiation in terms of the total, or

$$p = \frac{\text{luminosity of homogeneous radiation}}{\text{total luminosity}} \qquad (13.05)$$

When the homogeneous stimulus is transferred to the left half-field in matching purples, the purity is said to be negative.

We do not actually use this procedure, because of the experimental difficulty of obtaining a balance and because we prefer to use a physical basis. Dominant wavelength and purity are obtainable, however, from the color triangle. The unknown radiation is specified in terms of x and y and is represented by a point such as a in Fig. 13.09. Radiation represented by the point a may be color matched by mixing in proper proportions a pure spectral stimulus A with white light. On the triangle, this means that A, a, and the point representing white light W must all lie on the same straight line. Thus, a straight line drawn through W and a must determine the dominant wavelength by the point A at which this line cuts the spectral curve. Some idea of the purity can be obtained by inspection: If a is near W, the purity is not far from zero; if a is near A, the purity is near 1.00. The exact purity values cannot be obtained by direct measurement on the chart, since the scale is not linear. Colorimetric purity of a given radiation may be computed by use of the equation*

$$p = \frac{y - fy_w}{y} \qquad (13.06)$$

where

or

$$\left.\begin{aligned} f &= \frac{x - X}{x_w - X} \\ f &= \frac{y - Y}{y_w - Y} \end{aligned}\right\} \qquad (13.07)$$

---

* Judd, *J.O.S.A.*, **23**, p. 367.

X and Y = coordinates of the intersection with the spectral locus of a straight line drawn in the color triangle through W and the point representing the given radiation.

x_w and y_w = the coordinates of the white point W.

As an example, suppose we wish to obtain the purity of the *C.I.E.* standard illuminant B, using the equal-energy spectrum as the white point. From Table LII,

$$\begin{cases} x = 0.3485 \\ y = 0.3518 \end{cases}$$

These coordinates locate the point on the color triangle. A line is drawn through W, and this point and is found to cut the spectral locus at $\lambda_d = 0.5756\mu$ with $Y = 0.5159$. Thus

$$f = \frac{y - Y}{y_w - Y} = \frac{0.3518 - 0.5159}{0.3333 - 0.5159} = 0.8996$$

and the colorimetric purity is

$$p = \frac{0.3518 - (0.8996)0.3333}{0.3518} = +0.147$$

Thus the radiation has a dominant wavelength of 0.5756μ and a purity of 0.147 and will appear as a very pale yellow.

The dominant wavelength is a physical quantity which is related (roughly, not exactly) to the sensation attribute of hue, while purity is a physical quantity related to the sensation attribute of saturation. White is considered to have zero purity; while homogeneous radiations are said to have a purity of 100 per cent, or 1. The curve that incloses the central area of Fig. 13.09 represents the highest possible purity, while all radiations represented by points within their central area have less purity and appear as more diluted (less saturated) colors.

Complementary hues are also easily obtained from the color triangle. Two stimuli are said to be *complementary* if their mixture in proper proportions results in the sensation of white or gray. Suppose that we have a radiation whose dominant wavelength is 0.60μ. What is the dominant wavelength of its complement? The complement must be such that a straight line passed through its point and A on the color triangle must also pass through W. We therefore draw a line through A and

W and find that it cuts the locus for spectral colors at 0.49μ. Thus the dominant wavelength of the complement of the radiation at a is $\lambda_d = 0.49\mu$, and any radiation represented by a point on the line between W and B will give a gray sensation *when mixed in proper proportions* with the radiation represented by a. The proper proportions may be found by the use of the fundamental data given in Appendix G.

For example, suppose it is desired to find in what proportions homogeneous radiations of 0.40, 0.55, and 0.60μ must be mixed to get the same sensation quality as that evoked by the equal-energy spectrum (Fig. 13.04). A few trials with arbitrarily selected values leads to the following:

λ	$J_{\lambda\,rel}$	$\bar{x}J_{\lambda\,rel}$	$\bar{y}J_{\lambda\,rel}$	$\bar{z}J_{\lambda\,rel}$
0.40μ	1.000	0.0143	0.0004	0.0679
0.55	0.0488	0.0211	0.0486	0.0004
0.60	0.0309	0.0328	0.0195	0.0003
		0.0682	0.0685	0.0686

Since the sum for each of the three columns is approximately the same, the three radiant energies must be mixed in the proportions 1.00 to 0.049 to 0.031 to give the same sensation as that evoked by an equal-energy spectrum.

A brief review of the methods of specification may be helpful. Radiation is completely specified by the spectroradiometric curve. The spectroradiometric curve alone tells very little about the ability of this radiation to evoke a visual sensation. Other specifications obtainable from the spectroradiometric curve are

1. *Trichromatic Specification.*—Three primary stimuli are used, allowing a perfect match to be obtained with any radiation.

    a. Color-matching properties completely specified by the trichromatic coefficients J_1, J_2, and J_3 (watts/sq cm). Also,

$$L = v_1 J_1 + v_2 J_2 + v_3 J_3$$

The three coefficients depend upon the particular primaries used, and there is nothing unique about any set of primaries. By deciding upon definite primaries, all radiations can be expressed by the trichromatic coefficients J_1, J_2 and J_3. Such a scheme is not used, however.

b. The C.I.E. Specification—Trichromatic coefficients x', y', z' based on fictitious primaries. Luminosity is

$$L = \int_0^\infty \bar{y} J_\lambda \, d\lambda$$

c. Unified Coefficients (C.I.E.).—Specification by the luminosity and the two coefficients

$$x = \frac{x'}{x' + y' + z'}$$
$$y = \frac{y'}{x' + y' + z'}$$

Allows use of color triangle.

2. *Monochromatic Specification.*—Specification in terms of luminosity, dominant wavelength, and purity. Gives a better idea of the sensation than 1 but cannot be obtained from the spectroradiometric curve except through the color triangle of 1c.

3. *Color-temperature Specification.*—Specification in terms of luminosity and color temperature. Of very limited use, since it applies strictly only to radiations which can be exactly matched by radiation from a Planckian radiator.

Problem 176. A modern method of lighting large rooms is by a combination of mercury-vapor lamps and incandescent lamps behind a panel of diffusing glass. If white glass, commercial low-pressure mercury-vapor lamps, and 100-watt Mazda lamps are used, how many incandescent lamps must be used with one mercury-vapor lamp to give the nearest approach to average noon sunlight?

Problem 177. What is the dominant wavelength of the light from high-pressure and from low-pressure mercury-vapor lamps? From the hot-cathode neon lamp?

Problem 178. To get light that will exactly match the color of the low-pressure mercury-vapor lamp, what two homogeneous radiations may be used, and in what proportions must they be mixed?

Problem 179. Prove that the mixture of homogeneous radiation of wavelength λ_d with equal-energy radiation in any proportion will give a point lying on a straight line drawn between W and the spectral point in the color triangle.

13.08. The Color of Daylight.—Since so much of our time is spent under natural daylight, its color is of considerable interest. Fabrics that match under one kind of light may not match under another kind, and color harmonies made with daylight may be

distorted under artificial light.   The incandescent lamp produces
light that is distinctly more yellow than daylight; and though
this is not displeasing in many cases, it is probable that a more
nearly white light would be used extensively if it could be
obtained economically.   It is important, therefore, to consider
the color of daylight and how such color can be reproduced by
artificial illuminants.

Sunlight is usually spoken of as "white" (or, more properly,
gray).   When one attempts to make such a definition more

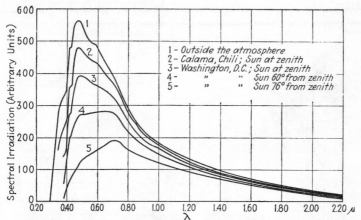

Fig. 13.11.—Spectral irradiation from the sun.   (*Kimball, C.I.E. Proc.*, 1928,
p. 503.)

specific, he encounters the difficulty that sunlight is an extremely
variable thing.   Figure 13.11 gives the spectroradiometric curves
of sunlight under various conditions.   Curve 1 refers to sunlight
outside the atmosphere and has a maximum at 0.475μ.   Curve 2
is for high altitude with the sun at the zenith.   The peak of
this curve is still in the blue.   At sea level (curve 3), the shape
of the curve has been changed considerably owing to atmospheric
absorption.   In curves 4 and 5, the peak shifts to orange and
red, respectively, representing the condition of late afternoon
sunlight.   Evidently, the color of direct sunlight is a highly
variable quantity, depending upon time of day, altitude of the
observer, condition of the atmosphere, etc.   Abbot has given
data on average noon sunlight at Washington (Table LV), and
this distribution of radiant power is sometimes considered as
standard white light.   O ers have suggested that white light

be defined as the light from a complete radiator at a definite temperature, which has been variously fixed from 5000 to 6500°K. Perhaps the simplest method would be to select arbitrarily the equal-energy spectrum as white, at least until more conclusive data are obtained as to exactly what kind of stimulus evokes a hueless sensation. Such a method is used in this chapter, the point W (Fig. 13.09) representing the equal-energy spectrum.

North skylight, which is used extensively for color matching, actually shows great variation in both luminosity and chromaticity. On overcast days the color temperature is about 6500°K,

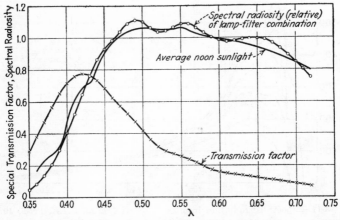

Fig. 13.12.—Characteristics of a liquid filter. Incandescent lamp at 2700°K. (*Davis and Gibson, Bu. Stds. Misc. Pub.* 114, p. 140.)

while on clear days it may range from about 10,000 to 25,000°K or even higher at high altitudes (see Chap. V).

If incandescent lamps could be operated at temperatures of 5000°K or higher, the question of how to obtain light of approximately the quality of sunlight would be settled. With existing limitations in filament temperature, a convenient method is to use an incandescent lamp operating at any arbitrary temperature with a filter to cut out the superabundance of long wavelengths. Various glass filters have been produced for this purpose. Davis and Gibson have made a thorough study of liquid filters, and an example of the distribution obtained from such a filter is shown in Fig. 13.12. The filter was designed to duplicate average noon sunlight when used with a lamp operating at 2700°K, and the curves show that a good approximation is obtained. The principal objection to the method is its poor economy. The filter in Fig. 13.12, for instance, passes only 22 per cent of the luminous flux incident on it, so that with a tungsten lamp operating at 15 lumens/watt, the luminous output of the lamp-filter combination cannot exceed 3.3 lumens per input watt. The ordinary "daylight" Mazda lamp using a light-blue glass globe emits usually about 66 per cent as much light as with

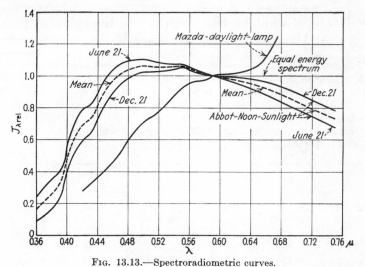

FIG. 13.13.—Spectroradiometric curves.

a clear globe, but the distribution curve (Fig. 13.13) has little resemblance to that of daylight.

Another way of obtaining light which appears white is by means of gaseous-conduction lamps. The CO_2 lamp gives a light whose color is between that of direct sunlight and skylight, and it has been used in some cases for color matching in order to eliminate the variable quality which occurs in natural daylight. The $ZrCl_4$ and $TiCl_4$ lamps are also possible sources for color matching. Combinations of mercury-vapor lamps with incandescent lamps or with neon lamps can be used where the requirements are not too severe. It must be realized that though lamps producing line spectra can be made to give subjective white, they can never be relied on in color matching. For example, two homogeneous radiations which separately evoke the sensations of red and blue-green, when mixed in the proper proportions will give the sensation of white; and when the light is reflected from a gray surface, this surface may appear exactly as if illuminated by sunlight. But most colored surfaces will appear quite different, and color matches made in daylight will generally not match under such an artificial light. A blue surface exposed to the preceding radiation will appear almost black because the light source emits no blue rays. Orange and red surfaces will appear red, etc. Combinations of gaseous-conduction sources which give a subjective white with line spectra must be used with caution. Sources with band spectra, such as the CO_2 lamp, are better in this respect.

Problem 180. Plot the required spectral transmission-factor curve for a blue filter to be used with a 200-watt Mazda lamp to give a light whose color temperature is 6500°K. How many lumens will be obtained with the lamp-filter combination, assuming that the filter completely incloses the lamp?

Problem 181. A Davis and Gibson filter designed to change 2450 to 6500°K. color temperature has transmission factors as follows:

λ	τ_λ	λ	τ_λ	λ	τ_λ
0.38	0.489	0.51	0.169	0.63	0.0477
39	0.578	2	0.1395	4	0.0447
40	0.637	3	0.1264	5	0.0426
1	0.676	4	0.1196	6	0.0402
2	0.695	5	0.1122	7	0.0373
3	0.672	6	0.1020	8	0.0343
4	0.611	7	0.0898	9	0.0309
5	0.523	8	0.0778	70	0.0279
6	0.437	9	0.0675	1	0.0251
7	0.375	60	0.0598	2	0.0225
8	0.322	61	0.0546		
9	0.271	2	0.0508		
50	0.215				

Determine the point on the color triangle representing the radiation from a lamp operating at 3000°K when viewed through this filter. Is it permissible to use color temperature to specify the color of the resulting radiation?

Problem 182. A stage set is illuminated by 200-watt, 115-volt Mazda lamps behind Corning-glass filters 554, 408, and 245. Five lamps are used with the red, five with the green, and ten with the blue filters. With $V = 115$ volts, determine the values of R, G, and B for the resulting radiation; also the dominant wavelength and purity.

The operator now desires gradually to dim the light on the set, keeping the color quality the same. He gradually moves all three dimmer handles at the same rate until the voltage on all lamps is 80 volts. Specify the chromaticity of the radiation at 115 and at 80 volts. Has the quality changed? If so, what can be done to keep the quality the same?

13.09. Color Harmony.—Some artists are able to give the observer the keenest delight by their subtle use of colored pigments, though such pigments are very imperfect and can give neither the range of brilliance nor the range in hue and saturation that are obtained in nature. Since the retina is stimulated only by light reflected by the pigments, it is evident that the painter in applying paint to canvas is using an indirect method of obtaining his result. The illuminating engineer, on the other hand, deals with light directly and has at his command not only a much greater range of luminosity but stimuli of greater purity than can possibly be obtained by the painter. Painting directly with light undoubtedly has a great future, the basis for which is perhaps being laid by the colorama, etc.[55] The rules of color harmony laid down by various artists, though often contradictory, will give the student of illumination food for thought and subject for experiment.

One kind of color harmony consists in using two or more radiations whose dominant wavelengths are not too far apart, such as red and yellow or violet and blue. Apparently, the observer obtains a certain satisfaction in sensing a relationship between colors not too far apart. Actually, such harmonies must be used with caution, as they will often appear unpleasantly glaring unless the colorimetric purity is kept low, *i.e.*, unless delicate tints are used rather than saturated colors.

Another type of harmony consists in using a number of colors of the same dominant wavelength but of different purities. For instance, a wall might be flooded with a delicate tint of yellow ($x = 0.39$, $y = 0.38$) enlivened by wall brackets which give a light of the same λ_d but of greater purity ($x = 0.450$, $y = 0.433$). It will be found that large areas of delicate tints will be required to balance a small area of pure color and that the areas should be adjusted approximately in inverse ratio to the purities. Such harmonies may be further extended by varying the luminosity as well as the purity but keeping the dominant wavelength the same in all cases. The combinations just considered are called *harmonies of analogy*, since there is an element of similarity in all the colors used in a given harmony.

Another class of harmonies is called *harmony of contrast*. It is well-known that the most striking effects are obtained by using contrasting colors, such, for example, as the complements red ($x = 0.650$, $y = 0.285$) and blue-green ($x = 0.10$, $y = 0.37$). If one wishes to obtain a combination that will attract immediate attention, he uses a pair of complements of high purity; but for general use, such harmonies are too sensational unless the purity of the radiations is reduced. A pleasing combination might be a delicate blue-green ($x = 0.250$, $y = 0.345$) and a pink

TABLE LIV.—UNIFIED TRICHROMATIC COEFFICIENTS FOR RADIANT POWER
FROM PLANCKIAN RADIATORS
($C_2 = 14,320$)
(Data from D. B. JUDD, *J.O.S.A.*, **23**, 1933, p. 366)

T (°K)	x	y	z
100 or less	0.7347	0.2653	0.0000
298.9	0.7341	0.2659	0.0000
598.7	0.7090	0.2909	0.0001
997.0	0.6524	0.3448	0.0028
1,497	0.5852	0.3934	0.0214
1,896	0.5372	0.4114	0.0514
2,355	0.4893	0.4150	0.0957
2,842	0.4476	0.4075	0.1449
3,493	0.4049	0.3906	0.2046
4,790	0.3506	0.3560	0.2933
6,486	0.3133	0.3235	0.3632
9,979	0.2806	0.2883	0.4311
23,950	0.2532	0.2532	0.4936
∞	0.2399	0.2342	0.5259

($x = 0.41$, $y = 0.32$); or a large area of the pale blue-green might be balanced by a small area of pure red. Evidently, a great variety of such combinations is possible, the particular one to be used depending upon the effect that the designer wishes to secure.

Jacobs makes extensive use of what he calls "split complementaries."[66] Two radiations whose dominant wavelengths are not too far apart are balanced by a single radiation whose dominant wavelength is not complementary to either but lies between the two complements. Thus, a red (whose complement is a blue-green) and a violet (whose complement is a yellow-green) may be used with a green midway between the two complements.

In the same way, three or more radiations which lie on one side of the color triangle may be balanced by one "average" or split complement. Any of these radiations can be used in a number

TABLE LV.—RELATIVE IRRADIATION FROM DIRECT NOON SUNLIGHT AT
WASHINGTON, D. C.
(Data Furnished by C. G. Abbot)

λ (microns)	June 21	Dec. 21	Mean	λ (microns)	June 21	Dec. 21	Mean
0.36	0.240	0.094	0.167	0.55	1.073	1.054	1.063
0.37	0.300	0.128	0.214	0.56	1.054	1.037	1.046
0.38	0.350	0.174	0.262	0.57	1.034	1.023	1.028
0.39	0.404	0.225	0.315	0.58	1.018	1.014	1.016
				0.59	1.000	1.000	1.000
0.40	0.560	0.385	0.472				
0.41	0.693	0.506	0.599	0.60	0.988	1.002	0.995
0.42	0.784	0.593	0.689	0.61	0.975	0.996	0.986
0.43	0.815	0.632	0.723	0.62	0.957	0.991	0.974
0.44	0.897	0.729	0.813	0.63	0.940	0.987	0.963
				0.64	0.921	0.982	0.952
0.45	0.991	0.825	0.908				
0.46	1.039	0.890	0.965	0.65	0.902	0.973	0.937
0.47	1.077	0.950	1.014	0.66	0.885	0.966	0.926
0.48	1.092	0.979	1.035	0.67	0.859	0.947	0.903
0.49	1.098	1.005	1.051	0.68	0.836	0.935	0.885
				0.69	0.815	0.914	0.865
0.50	1.102	1.026	1.064				
0.51	1.092	1.023	1.057	0.70	0.791	0.893	0.842
0.52	1.087	1.029	1.058	0.71	0.765	0.867	0.816
0.53	1.078	1.035	1.057	0.72	0.743	0.848	0.795
0.54	1.073	1.037	1.055	0.73	0.720	0.826	0.773
				0.74	0.700	0.805	0.753
				0.75	0.679	0.785	0.732

of different purities and luminosities, so the greatest variety of effects is possible. In fact, one begins to wonder if there is any combination of colors that does not constitute a harmony. Cutler and Pepper[65] say *no:*

The one consideration an artist should have in selecting his color scheme is its suitability for the picture he has in mind. Will it give the

emotion he desires, will it be in sympathy with the rest of the picture?
. . . These are the things for an artist to think of when selecting his
color scheme, not some abstract rules from a fantastic theory that lies
like so much rubbish and lumber in his path.   And behind all this lies
the fact, which the experience of artists themselves will substantiate,
that all color combinations are pleasing under the right circumstances.

The "right circumstances" can be determined only by experience. For the beginner in color, it is probably safest to stick to
some of the very simple harmonies already outlined, using
radiations of not too great purity. Some examples of beautiful
and delicate harmonies, such as those given in "Color Problems"
by Vanderpoel or in other works mentioned in the Bibliography,
may be found helpful.

Problem 183. Transform the following quotation into a reasonably
exact engineering statement:

"We find that the normal spectrum of an incandescent lamp, while continuous qualitatively, varies quantitatively from the proportion of 150 units
of red light down to approximately 20 units of blue light. We find that
white light, or the black-body radiator, at 5000°K has a light-sensation value
as though it were made up of one-third each of red, green, and blue" (*I.E.S.
Trans.*).

Bibliography

General

1. L. T. TROLAND: Report of Committee on Colorimetry, *J.O.S.A.*, **6**,
   1922, p. 527.
2. J. GUILD: A Critical Survey of Modern Developments in the Theory
   and Technique of Colorimetry, *Proc. Opt. Convention, London*, I,
   1926, p. 61.
3. T. SMITH: A Reading of Elementary Colorimetric Theory, *Opt. Soc.,
   Trans.*, **33**, 1931–1932, p. 214.
4. H. E. ROAF: Color Vision, *Physiol. Rev.*, **13**, 1933, p. 43.
5. H. E. ROAF: Normal and Abnormal Color Vision, *Nature*, **134**, 1934,
   p. 442.
6. D. NICKERSON: Color Measurements in Psychological Terms, *J.O.S.A.*,
   21, 1931, p. 643.
7. S. HECHT: Development of Thomas Young's Theory of Color Vision,
   J.O.S.A., **20**, 1930, p. 231.
8. S. HECHT: Interrelation of Various Aspects of Color Vision, *J.O.S.A.*,
   21, 1931, p. 615.

Color-mixture Data

9. KÖNIG and DIETERICI: Die Grundempfindungen in normalen und
   anomalen Farbensystemen, *Zeit. psychol. u. physiol. Sinnes.*, **6**, 1892,
   p. 241.

10. W. D. Wright: A Trichromatic Colorimeter with Spectral Primaries, *Opt. Soc., Trans.*, **29**, 1928, p. 225.

11. W. D. Wright: A Redetermination of the Trichromatic Coefficients of the Spectral Colors, *Opt. Soc., Trans.*, **30**, 1928–1929, p. 141.

12. W. D. Wright: A Redetermination of the Mixture Curves of the Spectrum, *Opt. Soc., Trans.*, **31**, 1929–30, p. 201.

13. J. Guild: The Colorimetric Properties of the Spectrum, *Proc. Roy. Soc.*, **B 108**, 1931, p. 576.

14. J. Guild: The Colorimetric Properties of the Spectrum, *Roy. Soc., Phil. Trans.*, **A 230**, 1932, p. 149.

15. D. B. Judd: Comparison of Wright's Data on Equivalent Color Stimuli with the O.S.A. Data, *J.O.S.A.*, **21**, 1931, p. 699.

Transformations

16. H. E. Ives: The Transformation of Color-mixture Equations from One System to Another, *Frank. Inst., J.*, **180**, 1915, p. 673.

17. C. L. Froelich: Algebraic Methods for the Calculation of Color Mixture Transformation Diagrams, *J.O.S.A.*, **9**, 1924, p. 31.

18. J. Guild: The Transformation of Trichromatic Mixture Data: Algebraic Methods, *Opt. Soc., Trans.*, **26**, 1924–1925, p. 95.

19. J. Guild: The Geometrical Solution of Color Mixture Problems, *Opt. Soc., Trans.*, **26**, 1924–1925, p. 139.

20. Smith and Guild: The C.I.E. Colorimetric Standards and their Use, *Opt. Soc., Trans.*, **33**, 1931–1932, p. 73.

21. J. Guild: On the Fixed Points of a Colorimetric System, *Opt. Soc., Trans.*, **32**, 1930, p. 1.

22. T. Smith: Condensed Tables for Color Computation, *Phys. Soc., Proc.*, **46**, 1934, pp. 372, 478.

23. J. G. Holmes: Rapid Mathematical Methods for Trichromatic Colorimetry, *Phys. Soc., Proc.*, **47**, 1935, p. 400.

24. D. B. Judd: A Maxwell Triangle Yielding Uniform Chromaticity Scales, *J.O.S.A.*, **25**, 1935, p. 24.

Miscellaneous

25. A. C. Hardy: A Recording Photoelectric Color Analyzer, *J.O.S.A.*, **18**, 1929, p. 96.

26. A. C. Hardy: A New Photoelectric Spectrophotometer, *J.O.S.A.*, **25**, 1935, p. 305.

27. R. D. Nutting: The Detection of Small Color Differences, *J.O.S.A.*, **24**, 1934, p. 135.

28. R. D. Nutting: Interpretation of Data Obtained with Spectrophotometers of the Polarizing Type, *J.O.S.A.*, **25**, 1935, p. 211.

29. I. G. Priest: Note on the Relation between the Frequencies of Complementary Hues, *J.O.S.A.*, **4**, p. 402, 1920; **5**, p. 513, 1921.

30. I. H. Godlove: Wave Lengths of Complementary Hues, *J.O.S.A.*, **20**, 1930, p. 411.

31. D. B. Judd: Chromatic Sensibility to Stimulus Differences, *J.O.S.A.*, **22**, 1932, p. 72.

32. E. Genberg: Some Complementary Color Relations, *Phys. Soc., Proc.*, **45,** 1933, p. 836.

33. E. P. T. Tyndall: Chromatic Sensibility to Wavelength Difference as a Function of Purity, *J.O.S.A.*, **23**, 1933, p. 15.

34. D. B. Judd: Sensibility to Color-Temperature Change as a Function of Temperature, *J.O.S.A.*, **23**, 1933, p. 7.

35. I. H. Godlove: Complementarism of the Standard O.S.A. and I.C.I. Observers, *J.O.S.A.*, **24**, 1934, p. 264.

36. D. B. Judd: Saturation Scale for Yellow Colors, *J.O.S.A.*, **23**, 1933, p. 35.

37. D. B. Judd: Spectral Energy Distributions Produced by Rotary Mixing of Complementary Papers, *J.O.S.A.*, **9**, 1924, p. 95.

38. I. G. Priest: The Computation of Colorimetric Purity, *J.O.S.A.*, **9**, 1924, p. 503.

39. D. B. Judd: A General Formula for the Computation of Colorimetric Purity, *J.O.S.A.*, **21**, 1931, p. 729.

40. D. B. Judd: A General Formula for the Computation of Colorimetric Purity, *Bu. Stds. J.R.*, **7**, 1931, p. 827.

41. D. B. Judd: The 1931 I.C.I. Standard Observer and Coordinate System for Colorimetry, *J.O.S.A.*, **23**, 1933, p. 359.

42. W. Peddie: The Essence and Present Position of the Trichromatic Theory, p. 102, Discussion on Vision, Physical and Optical Society, Cambridge University Press, 1932.

43. J. Guild: The Interpretation of Quantitative Data in Visual Problems, p. 60, Discussion on Vision, Cambridge University Press, London, 1932.

44. J. Guild: Some Problems of Visual Reception, p. 1, Discussion on Vision, Cambridge University Press, London, 1932.

45. H. E. Ives: Simultaneous Color Measurements by Trichromatic and Monochromatic Analysis, *J.O.S.A.*, **7**, 1923, p. 287.

46. I. G. Priest: A Proposed Scale for Use in Specifying the Chromaticity of Incandescent Illuminants, *J.O.S.A.*, **23**, 1933, p. 41.

47. T. Smith: The Color Triangle and Color Discrimination, p. 212, Discussion on Vision, Cambridge University Press, London, 1932.

48. S. Hecht: A Quantitative Formulation of Color Vision, p. 126, Discussion on Vision, Cambridge University Press, London, 1932.

APPLICATIONS

49. A. H. Taylor: The Color of Daylight, *I.E.S. Trans.*, **25**, 1930, p. 154.

50. L. A. Jones: The Color of Illuminants, *I.E.S. Trans.*, **9**, 1914, p. 687.

51. M. Luckiesh: White Light *vs.* North Skylight for Color Discrimination, *Frank. Inst., J.*, **205**, 1928, p. 566.

52. K. S. Gibson: Filters for Producing the Color of Equal-energy Stimulus, *Bur. Stds. J.R.*, **12**, 1934, p. 263.   (RP652)

53. L. J. Buttolph: Gaseous Conduction Lamps and Light, *I.E.S. Trans.*, **30**, 1935, p. 147.

54. W. Harrison: Applications of the New Gaseous-conductor Lamps, *I.E.S. Trans.*, **30**, 1935, p. 190.

55. F. J. Cadenas: Colorama Lighting, *I.E.S. Trans.*, **25**, 1930, p. 282.

56. H. E. Ives: Thomas Young and the Simplification of the Artist's Palette, *Phys. Soc., Proc.,* **45,** 1934, p. 16.

57. A. H. Munsell: A Color Notation, Geo. H. Ellis Company, Boston, 1907.

58. Munsell Book of Color, Munsell Color Company, New York.

59. Priest, Gibson, and McNicholas: An Examination of the Munsell Color System, *Bu. Stds. Tech. Paper,* 167, 1920.

60. I. H. Godlove: Neutral Value Scales, *J.O.S.A.,* **23,** 1933, pp. 394, 419.

61. W. Ostwald: Color Science, trans. by J. S. Taylor, Winsor and Newton, Ltd., London, 1931.

62. W. Ostwald: Die Farbenlehre, I, Leipzig, 1918; II, 1919; Der Farbenatlas, 1918; Der Farbkörper, 1919.

63. R. Ridgway: Color Standards and Color Nomenclature, Washington, 1912.

64. Maerz and Paul: Dictionary of Color, McGraw-Hill Book Company, Inc., New York, 1930.

65. Cutler and Pepper: Modern Color, Harvard University Press, Cambridge, Mass., 1923.

66. M. Jacobs: The Art of Color, Doubleday, Doran & Company, Inc., New York, 1931.

67. F. F. Rupert: A Study of Pigment Primaries and Mixtures, *J.O.S.A.,* **20,** 1930, p. 661.

68. E. N. Vanderpoel: Color Problems, Longmans, Green & Company, New York, 1902.

69. M. Luckiesh: Color and its Applications, D. Van Nostrand Company, Inc., New York, 1921.

70. J. M. Holmes: Colour in Interior Decoration, Charles Scribner's Sons, New York, 1932.

71. D. L. MacAdam: The Specification of Whiteness, *J.O.S.A.,* **24,** 1934, p. 188.

72. G. A. Shook: Design of Mobile Color Apparatus, *I.E.S. Trans.,* **29,** 1934, p. 425.

73. Three Monographs on Color, 1. Color Chemistry; 2. Color as Light; 3. Color in Use, International Printing Ink Corporation, New York, 1935.

74. A. C. Hardy: Handbook of Colorimetry, The Technology Press, Cambridge, Mass., 1936.

CHAPTER XIV

DESIGN FOR SEEING*

In Chap. XI, we considered the elements of lighting design. The subject was approached from the physical standpoint, to determine merely a lighting system that would give a uniform illumination of the desired value on a horizontal plane. A really satisfactory design cannot be based exclusively on purely physical considerations, important as these may be. The person who is to use the light must be taken into account—the kind of visual task that he is to perform, his visual peculiarities, his position in the room, and a host of physiological and psychological factors. Design becomes immensely complex—and immensely fascinating. It is the purpose of the present chapter to point out a few of the salient factors which must be considered.

To clarify thinking, the designer may find it desirable to classify lighting systems as

1. Purely utilitarian.
2. Purely aesthetic.
3. Combination of 1 and 2.

Strictly speaking, one might argue that all systems fall in class 3, since every installation is made to give light and thus has a utilitarian function, while there is little excuse for an *ugly* lighting system no matter how much the utilitarian aspects must be stressed or how little money is available for ornament. There are certain cases, such as the floodlighting of a public building or much of the lighting in a theater, where aesthetic considerations are paramount. On the other hand, most installations belong primarily under 1. Every lighting installation that is to be used for seeing, for doing visual work of any kind—reading, clerical work, manufacturing, sports, etc.—*must be considered first from its functional standpoint*. The lighting must be designed to make vision easy, to prevent glare and eyestrain. Only after the designer has considered this all-important phase is he at liberty to turn to the idea of making the lighting beautiful.

* May be omitted in an introductory course.

14.02. Functional Design.—An emphasis on function by no means precludes the attainment of beauty. In the nineteenth and early part of the twentieth century, there appears to have been a general confusion of the terms "beauty" and "ornament" and a feeling that everything pertaining to our machine civilization was inherently ugly unless, perchance, it could be completely covered by scrolls, ribbons, or cupids. Thus, early lathes and steam engines were provided with Doric columns and absurd scrollwork.* Metal furniture was carefully painted in imitation mahogany or walnut instead of exhibiting the honest beauty of metal. Glass, linoleum, and wallboards are still made to imitate marble and tile. The contemporary American landscape is turned into a mad kind of museum by a hodge-podge of tawdry imitations of French chateaux, Italian villas, and early-American homes. Lighting fixtures are still made to imitate old Roman oil lamps, Louis XIV chandeliers, or early-American sconces, with imitation wax carefully molded on the sides of imitation candles, with openings carefully arranged in shades for the smoke that never appears, with drip pans carefully placed to catch the melted wax that never flows. All for Art's sake!

Over forty years ago, a revolt against this idiocy was begun by Louis Sullivan.[3] Sullivan taught that "form follows function," that the outward form should be a natural outgrowth of the function of the object. Being an architect, Sullivan spent a great deal of time in ridiculing the prevalent scheme of forcing a bank into an imitation Greek temple or a library into an imitation Italian palace, the important functions of the building being entirely subordinated to the outward appearance. The same principle applies in other fields. Perhaps the best example of functional design is the modern airplane whose form was determined completely by engineering considerations. The design involves no glance at the Roman chariot or the covered wagon and contains no pink ribbons or cupids yet possesses a clean, breath-taking beauty.

The modern movement toward built-in lighting is also a step in the same direction—toward functionalism and away from eclecticism. The essence of the advance is a frank realization

---

* H. Read[6] in his book Art and Industry gives some very interesting illustrations. Also see Bel Geddes, Horizons.[8]

that we are no longer dealing with candles or oil lamps but with electric lamps possessing quite new possibilities. This realization has opened up the whole field of luminaire and lighting design. A consideration of function, an honest and sincere expression of this function in the lighting system can hardly help being beautiful to the discriminating taste. Functionalism does not preclude ornament, but the ornament must be sincere.

Considerations of aesthetics are beyond the scope of the present volume, the purpose of which is to treat of the basis of the *engineering* of illumination. The design of lighting fixtures must also be omitted. It is a fact, however, that many extremely useful and incidentally truly beautiful things have been produced by the crude engineer, who, though knowing nothing of the art of Greece and Rome, has used his innate originality in designing something that is fine and genuine. Any engineer who will attack the problem of lighting design in the same fearless, straightforward manner that he uses in other engineering problems and will shun ostentatious ornamentation will produce results that are not only infinitely superior for seeing but are also satisfactory from the aesthetic standpoint. This does not mean that a study of art is unnecessary or that the lifelong process of trial and error which develops a feeling for form and color is undesirable; but it does mean that *in design for seeing, the functional aspect must always be considered first and must be treated as a straight engineering problem before it is permissible to give any thought to beauty of outward form or decoration.*

14.03. Eight Important Factors.—In designing a lighting system to produce the best possible conditions for seeing, it is necessary to give careful attention to a number of factors. Among them are the following:

1. Illumination of object and its background.
2. Illumination of surround.
3. Glare from light sources.
4. Glare due to reflected light.
5. Reduction in contrast due to specularity.
6. Shadows.
7. Illumination ratio.
8. Spectral distribution of radiant power.

Such a specific list of items will be found helpful, since consulting it usually eliminates the possibility of forgetting considerations which are not obvious but which are important for visual comfort. Some of the factors may be inapplicable to a particular problem, but by checking through the list one makes fairly sure that important considerations are not being forgotten. An honest consideration of the eight factors, using the results of the previous chapters, will show the possible positions of the light sources, their approximate physical size, their luminous output, etc., required to meet the visual requirements of the problem.

The question of cost then enters, and the illuminating engineer may find it necessary to modify his design, making it somewhat less ideal in order to reduce its cost. Considerations of cost are best learned in practice and will not be discussed here. After having made the necessary sacrifices at the altar of economy, the designer can then proceed to details. Detailed engineering analysis of a lighting problem is much more difficult than the older method of conventional design given in Chap. XI but in most cases will give a vastly superior result. Even when rigid economy forces the modern designer to reduce his system to the simplest possible terms, he is likely to produce a more satisfactory result than his predecessor produced.

In the list of eight factors, we have eliminated any specific reference to aesthetics. Psychological effects are also ignored. Nothing has been said about the fact that a totally indirect lighting system may satisfy all the requirements and still produce an unpleasant gloomy sensation in the consciousness of the beholder. That dominant wavelength and purity of color stimuli have a distinct psychological effect is well-known. Both aesthetic and psychological effects are important but are not subject to engineering analysis. In the following paragraphs, we shall consider the eight factors and their use in the design of lighting systems.

14.04. Adequate Illumination.—In Chap. XII, we have considered the effect on vision of the luminosity to which the eye is adapted and have found that with proper surround conditions, vision improves as the luminosity is increased up to 1000 lumens per sq ft or even higher. Economy precludes the general use of such high luminosities, and for most work they are unnecessary. The value of luminosity to be used depends upon the visual task that is to be performed. Knowing the minimum size of detail which must be seen and the contrast between this detail and its background, one can obtain the minimum allowable value of L_B from the experimental curves of Chap. XII. Then, a knowledge of the reflection factor of the background gives the minimum required illumination. This value is the lowest illumination that will allow the detail to be detected by a person with normal vision. But a surprising proportion of the population has subnormal vision and requires higher illumination for a given visual task than the curves of Chap. XII indicate. The data were obtained with careful provisions to prevent fatigue. In offices and factories where the visual task is usually continued for long periods with very little rest, fatigue and eyestrain may greatly reduce efficiency. Such fatigue can be reduced by a decided increase in luminosity above the visual threshold. Thus it is evident that the application of the experimental data of Chap. XII requires a safety factor. Moreover, a factor near unity is of no use whatsoever. A factor of at least two or three is necessary to show any discernible effect. Tables of recommended values of illumination for various applications have been published from time to time, but such recommendations can be regarded only as the roughest kind of guide.

The illuminating engineer must consider not only the illumination of the work but also the illumination of the whole field to be viewed. We have seen that visual acuity is actually reduced if the surround is dark but reaches its highest value with the luminosity of the surround between 0.1 and 1.0 times the luminosity of the background. Other considerations usually necessitate the lighting of the surroundings. This allows the eyes to be focused occasionally on comparatively distant objects in order to rest them. Reasonably good illumination of the whole space is required to allow movements of people with ease and certainty. Many factory accidents have been traced to the inadequate illumination of passageways, etc. On the other hand, to illuminate the entire space to the level needed for fine machine work or inspection would be uneconomical and is unnecessary.

14.05. Glare.—An ideal lighting system must be absolutely free from glare, due to both direct and reflected light. We have seen in Chap. XII that an increase in the surround luminosity above that of the background causes a decided decrease in the

ability to see. The same result is produced for $L_S = L_B$ by
small, bright sources in the field of view. Even when experiment
shows no marked effect of the glare sources, it is almost certain
that they introduce an additional nervous strain analogous to
the effect of extraneous noise on our ability to appreciate music.
The annoyance of glare sources and the fatigue engendered by
them are difficult factors to measure but are none the less real.
The ideal lighting system will have a uniformly luminous work
area, a surround which is also essentially uniform in luminosity,
and an entire absence of spots of high intensity in the surround.

Most interior lighting systems installed in the past were
glaring to some extent, the glare sources ranging from clear
bulbs of high wattage, hanging directly in the field of view, to
lamps in inclosing globes of opal glass mounted near the ceiling.
Most people do not think of diffusing luminaires as glare sources
but admit that they can work more effectively and with less
eyestrain by daylight. Undoubtedly, the reason for this is
compounded of many factors, one of which is glare. There is
no reason why human beings should submit to the annoyance
of working or playing under the stupidly designed lighting
systems of the past. Sufficient is known about vision, sufficient
is known about the production and control of light, so that by
the application of sound engineering principles, seeing by artificial
light can be made at least as good as seeing by daylight.

The methods of eliminating glare from light sources in the
field of view require but little comment. If bare lamps are used,
they should be shielded so that they cannot be seen from any
position in which a person normally has his eyes. Actual
installations often show a striking carelessness in regard to this
obvious requirement. For example, clear bulbs in silvered-glass
reflectors illuminating a ceiling are carefully shielded from the
view of people on the main floor of a hotel lobby while no thought
is given to people on the mezzanine. The lighting of many store
windows shows a similar lack of rudimentary planning. Even if
the lamps are concealed behind diffusing glass or by lens plates,
it is desirable that such sources be shielded from view. This can
be accomplished by a molding at the edge of the glass or plate
or by louvers.

Glare due to reflected light is a more insidious danger and one
that is more often overlooked. The image of light sources

reflected in a mirror or in polished-metal trim is almost as bad a source of glare as the lamp itself. A less intense, but nevertheless annoying, potential source of glare is a polished glass surface, such as a glass desk top, a window, bookcase glass, etc. Varnished and enameled surfaces are almost as bad as polished-glass surfaces. Even such diffusing surfaces as painted walls when viewed at large angles from the normal (Chap. IX) have a surprising propensity for appearing in the guise of mirrors.

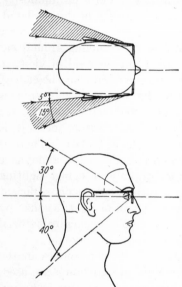

FIG. 14.01.—Reflections from eyeglasses.

There are generally a great many possible sources of glare due to reflection, and it is important that the light sources be so arranged with reference to the reflecting surfaces that trouble from glare is not encountered. In all these cases, the use of the law of regular reflection—the angle of reflection is equal to the angle of incidence—gives the position in which glare may result, while a consideration of the reflection characteristics of the surface allows the calculation of the glare illumination at the eye.

Eyeglasses introduce another source of reflections which may be bothersome to the wearer. Some measurements made at Massachusetts Institute of Technology indicate that no glare will exist if the light source is 30 deg or more above the line of sight, 40 deg or more below the line of sight, or outside the two 15-deg zones shown in Fig. 14.01. The number of people wearing glasses is sufficiently large, and the glare effect is sufficiently severe so that reflections from eyeglasses should be considered in the placing of the light sources.

A scale drawing will be found of great assistance in the study of a proposed lighting system from the glare standpoint. The positions of the observer's eyes under all ordinary conditions can be noted, and a "glare zone" containing all these possible positions

can be located. It is then an easy matter to find the possible
positions of the sources such that direct or reflected rays of light
shall not enter the glare zone or, if they enter it, shall do so at
such angles that glare will not be experienced. That rays may
enter the glare zone and still not produce glare depends upon the
fact that the normal field of view covers approximately 180 deg
horizontally, 50 deg above the line of vision, and 70 deg below
the line of vision.

An example is shown in Fig. 14.02 which is concerned with
the lighting of a desk. The height of the glare zone is equal to

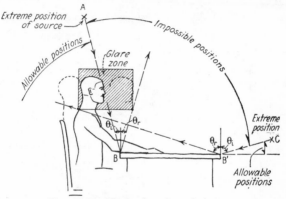

Fig. 14.02.—Reflections from desk top.

the variation in eye level to be expected with various individuals,
while the width of the glare zone is determined by the range
encountered in the ordinary movements of a person seated at
the desk. In the present case, no consideration is given to glare
experienced in the standing position, though that position would
have to be considered if the person spent much time standing.
A simple analysis shows that to prevent glare from reflections in
the desk top, it is necessary that the sources be behind the line
AB (otherwise the person will see the source reflected in the
desk top when he leans forward and looks down); or else the
light must strike the desk from the front at an angle such that
the reflected rays do not enter the glare zone. The use of light
sources below the line $B'C$ is a possibility, though such positions
would require a carefully-designed louver system. The region
between AB and CB is forbidden, since any source placed in this
region will produce glaring reflections in the desk top, and in

most cases *direct glare* will also be experienced. This means that the common practice of using desk lamps in front of the reader or lamps hung over the desk is absolutely unsound. The only permissible positions are *behind* the desk and *in a low position on the front or sides* of the desk. Figure 14.02 analyzes the problem in only one plane. The general conclusions are not altered if a similar analysis is made in other planes.

14.06. Reduction of Contrast Due to Specularity.—We have seen that the light reflected from most surfaces does not follow

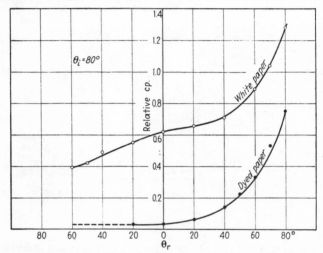

Fig. 14.03.—Reflecting characteristics of paper.[15]

the cosine law of emission. There is a tendency for even the best diffusing surfaces to exhibit a higher candlepower along the ray for which the angle of reflection is equal to the angle of incidence. In Sec. 14.05 we have considered this point with respect to the surround, now we consider the corresponding effect with respect to the background.

A very simple experiment shows the decidedly bad effect of specularity in reducing contrast and thus increasing the difficulty of seeing. Try reading a printed page on calendered paper, using a desk lamp at your side as a source of light. If the sheet is flat, the results will be good; but move the lamp in front of you, and for at least some positions of your head the printing will merge into the paper in a uniform sheen. That is, when the angle of reflection is equal to the angle of incidence, the brightness of the inked paper becomes almost as high as that of the white paper. Figure 14.03 gives some results obtained on a white paper with the light incident at 80 deg. The curve indicates that the paper is slightly glossy, and this property results in a high candlepower at $\theta_r = 80$ deg. The same paper was then dyed, which greatly reduced the reflection factor. Near $\theta_r = 80$ deg, however, the candlepower rises rapidly so that the material when viewed in this direction looks almost as white as the original white paper. This phenomenon of reduced contrast has a marked effect on seeing and must be taken into account in designing the lighting for desks and tables. Much of the paper now used does not show this phenomenon to a high degree, but all papers exhibit it to some extent, and there is enough glossy paper in use so that light sources must be placed to eliminate any possibility of trouble. The importance of this factor of reduced contrast due to specularity can hardly be overemphasized. It is the cause of a great amount of visual fatigue, yet its presence does not seem to be generally recognized.

Cases where specular reflection is a benefit instead of a hindrance are frequent in the inspection departments of factories. Specular reflection may allow the detection of scratches, dents, etc., which would be invisible otherwise. Each case constitutes a separate problem, requiring a knowledge of the manufacturing process and the faults to be detected.*

14.07. Shadows.—Glare and shadows constitute the Scylla and Charybdis of engineered lighting. In illuminating the table of Fig. 14.02, for instance, our Odysseus clears by a wide margin the danger of shadows by placing the source over the table, only to run into unavoidable glare from light reflected in the table top. Or he safely negotiates the glare danger by placing the source behind the line AB but comes perilously near to trouble from shadows cast by the person's head.

A shadow may be defined as an area of reduced illumination, generally with fairly sharp boundaries, caused by an opaque object located between the light source and the illuminated surface. In some cases we may be satisfied to know merely the shape and position of the shadow, while in others we need to

---

* For an excellent discussion of the subject, see a paper by Ketch, Sturrock, and Staley, Special Lighting Applications for Industrial Processes, *I.E.S. Trans.*, **28**, 1933, p. 57.

know the actual quantitative variation in illumination which constitutes the shadow. An effort should be made to place the light sources so that shadows are eliminated for any ordinary position of the observer. Occasionally such a desirable condition may be impossible of attainment. In such cases, it is necessary to use a large luminous source or a multiplicity of sources to diffuse the shadow and reduce its variation in illumination. The illuminating engineer must be able to answer two questions: first, how large a variation is permissible in the illumination of the object and its background; second, how can the position and density of the shadow be predetermined. Regarding the first, it is doubtful if there is a definite answer. With good illumination a one per cent difference may be detectable, but certainly most people would not regard a difference of 1 or 2 per cent as objectionable. A few experiments indicate that the border line is in the neighborhood of 5 to 10 per cent when the shadow is fairly sharp in outline. Such differences are distinctly appreciable, and most people find them annoying. If the shadow is fuzzy, a somewhat greater variation may be allowed. It would seem that if shadows cannot be avoided, the designer should limit their variation in illumination to less than 10 per cent.

The second question is most conveniently answered by the use of scale drawings. As an example, consider the illumination of the electric switchboard shown in Fig. 14.04. The problem is to light the board in such a way that the shadows cast by an operator who is adjusting a field rheostat or throwing a switch will not appreciably reduce the illumination of the panel in front of him. In this particular installation, owing to structural reasons, it happens to be convenient to place the lamps in a line 8 ft above the floor and 4 ft from the face of the board. Observation shows that an operator usually stands about 24 in. from the board, and he is sketched in that position. Since the lighting installation is to be satisfactory for men of all heights, we take the maximum dimensions usually found (see Sec. 14.10) and draw the man 6 ft 4 in. tall and with a corresponding width of head and shoulders. Because of the wide range of human dimensions as well as the variations in posture, there is no need for considering details of anatomy and clothing and the exact shapes of shadows cast by them. The work is considerably simplified by the use of the block outline shown in the front elevation of Fig.

14.04.   It is probably accurate enough to replace the man by a "cardboard figure" with rectangular contours, as shown in the drawings.   Even if the exact shape of the shadow cast by the head becomes of importance, it is best to start with the rectangular shape of object to produce a shadow with straight-line boundaries, after which the curve boundaries can be sketched in.

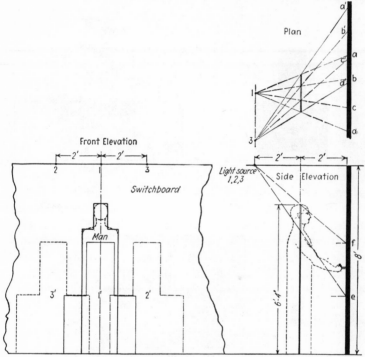

Fig. 14.04.—Shadows when point sources are used.

First consider the worst case, a single concentrated lamp at 1 directly behind the operator.   Pass a plane through point 1 and the vertical line representing one side of the man.   This plane will cut the face of the switchboard in a vertical line which represents the extreme limit of the shadow (*a* on the plan, Fig. 14.04).   Similar construction gives the line *d*.   Now pass a plane through 1 and the horizontal line representing the operator's shoulders.   The intersection of this plane and the front of the switchboard is the horizontal line *e* representing the upper boundary of the shadow cast by the operator's shoulders.   A similar construction gives the horizontal line f and the vertical lines b and c, which determine the boundaries of the shadow of the head. The complete shadow cast on the board is shown in $1'$ of the front elevation (Fig. 14.04). For a similar lamp 3 displaced to the side, the shadow edges are determined by a', b', c', d' and e, f. The shadow is outlined at $3'$.

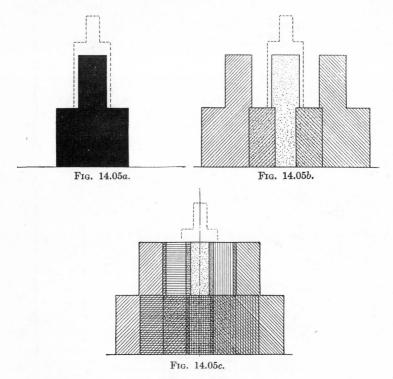

Fig. 14.05a.   Fig. 14.05b.

Fig. 14.05c.

The appearance of the shadows with several arrangements of lamps is shown in Figs. 14.05 *a, b, c.* The first diagram (Fig. 14.05a) indicates the shadow cast on the board by a single lamp behind the operator. If there are no other lamps and no reflections from walls or other objects, the illumination within the shadow area will be zero, and there will be a sudden transition from high illumination to no illumination at the edge of the shadow. Figure 14.05b shows the result of using the lamps 1, 2, 3 spaced 2 ft apart. Three shadows of the head appear, but they are not very dense because the board is now illuminated always by at least two of the three lamps. The shadows cast by the body are in most cases of the same density as those cast by the head, but two small zones will be noted where shadows overlap, leaving an illumination from only one lamp. The result for five lamps spaced one foot apart is shown in Fig. 14.05c. If we ignore the very narrow regions of overlap, we find the entire head shadow illuminated by four of the five lamps, the head obscuring the light from only one lamp. The body shadow is seen to consist of a single shadow near the edges followed by double shadows and with a shadow of triple density over the whole central portion. It should be noted, however, that even the triple shadow is illuminated by two lamps and is therefore much less dense and troublesome than the shadow in Fig. 14.05a. If reflectors or lens plates are used, the effective size of the source is increased, resulting in a blurring of the shadow edges. This effect can be taken into account, though usually the additional refinement is unnecessary.

There is another way of treating shadows. With numerous luminous sources the superposition of all the shadows becomes somewhat complicated, and interest shifts naturally from a consideration of the *size and shape* of the shadow to a consideration of the *illumination curve*. Figure 14.06 shows the same arrangement as Fig. 14.04 except that a large number of lamps is used on the line $a'd'$. Irrespective of the number of lamps, the upper boundaries of the head shadow and the body shadow are at the same levels as before, as shown by the dotted lines of the front elevation. Take a point as O on the switchboard at which the illumination is desired. This point will be illuminated by all the lamps except those hidden by the operator's head; *i.e.*, all the lamps excluded by two vertical planes passed through the sides of the head and through O. The candlepower distribution of the sources being known, the illumination at O due to each source is determined, and the resulting illumination at O is the sum of all the component illuminations except those due to sources in the length bc. Other points, such as 1, are taken, and the illumination calculated in a similar manner, excluding lamps within the length $b'c'$. For points in the lower shadow cast by the operator's body, the procedure is the same except that the boundary planes now cut off the illumination from a greater length, ad or $a'd'$.

A *continuous* source, such as a narrow luminous panel or a mercury-vapor tube along $a'd'$ is treated in the same manner, and the methods of Chap. IX are used in calculating the illumination. The resulting variation in illumination along a horizontal line on the switchboard is shown in Fig. 14.07d, which is compared with the results previously obtained by using from one

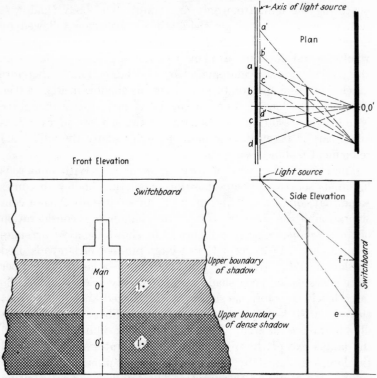

Fig. 14.06.—Shadows when linear source is used.

to three *concentrated* sources. All sketches are for the shadows cast by the head, though similar diagrams are easily made for the illumination in the body shadow.

When a large surface source is used instead of a narrow one, the method of Fig. 14.06 is used. The outline of the operator is projected back upon the luminous panel, using conical projection from the point where the illumination is to be computed; and the portion of the panel that is not useful in illuminating this point is thus determined. The remaining portions of the luminous panel are divided into rectangles and triangles, and the illumination is calculated by the use of the tables or graphs of Chap. IX. A projection must be made for each point at which the illumination is desired. In many cases, however, one such projection is sufficient. Assume, for example, that an artificial skylight of diffusing glass is used to illuminate the switchboard of Fig. 14.06.

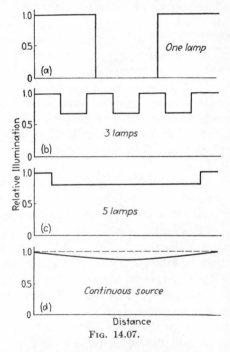

FIG. 14.07.

We wish to determine how large a variation in illumination exists due to the presence of the operator. We are not interested in the variation of illumination near the floor, since there is no necessity of distinguishing fine details below a certain level on the board, determined by the arrangement of the instruments. The lowest illumination will probably occur directly in front of the operator. We confine our attention, therefore, to a single point such as O. The value of the illumination at this point and with no operator is easily obtained by the methods of Chap. IX. The boundaries of the conventionalized figure of the operator are now projected from O upon the luminous panel, and the areas useful in illuminating O are obtained.   If a large percentage change of illumination at O is found, due to the presence of the operator, one can conclude without further calculation, that the lighting system will be unsatisfactory and can then proceed to make suitable changes in the design.

14.08. Illumination Ratio.—We have already considered the direction of the radiant energy with reference to its possible production of glare and reduction of apparent contrast.   Still another question sometimes arises concerning the direction of the light: Is there too large a difference between the values of the illumination of various surfaces?   It is customary to design the lighting to produce satisfactory illumination on the principal surface of the object being viewed; and there is a tendency to forget that the illumination levels on other surfaces of the object, though perhaps of lesser interest, are nevertheless of some importance.   In general, therefore, it is advisable to keep the ratio of illuminations on the various surfaces at a reasonable figure not to exceed three or four.

For example, one way of lighting a table used for bookkeeping is by throwing a wedge of light over the table from the side, the lamps being placed below the eye level.   Under these conditions and with correct design, there is no possibility of glare from the lamps or from reflections in the table top.   Also, if the papers are always flat on the table, reasonably constant illumination can be obtained.   But if the sheets of paper are not flat, as is always the case when books are used, a great difference in illumination is found, ranging from perhaps ten times normal on a portion of the page that bulges so that it is normal to the light rays to a very low value of illumination on portions that are thrown into shadow.   The trouble is not experienced if the light sources are placed near the ceiling.

14.09. Spectral Distribution of Radiant Power.—In most cases, incandescent light, unmodified as to color, is used without question and produces satisfactory results.   Occasionally, it is necessary to consider modification of the light by the use of filters or the use of other types of sources.   For color matching, the light from ordinary tungsten lamps is much too yellow and must be modified by special blue filters, or else gaseous-conduction lamps such as the CO_2 lamp may be used instead of incandescent lamps. For ordinary interior illumination, some people prefer light having the approximate color of noon sunlight, particularly when very high levels of illumination are used. The high-pressure mercury lamp in combination with incandescent lamps offers an attractive means of obtaining an approximate daylight quality with relatively high efficacy. On the other hand, there are advocates of a restricted spectrum. Some prefer a continuous spectrum with the blue and violet eliminated by use of a yellow filter,* while others point out the increased visual acuity obtained with homogeneous radiation. The sodium lamp is a source of homogeneous radiation and is being used with apparent satisfaction in the lighting of highways. Because of the monochromatic nature of its radiation and its high luminous efficacy, this lamp should be considered seriously for certain interiors where severe visual tasks require high visual acuity but no color discrimination. The ordinary mercury-vapor lamp also acts essentially as a source of homogeneous radiation and is used in many factories.

We have considered the spectral distribution in the visible region. In some cases, it may be desirable to consider also the remainder of the spectrum. Lamps are available for the production of biologically effective ultraviolet radiation in combination with radiation in the visible region. Such dual-purpose lighting has an undeniable beneficial effect and should be considered seriously in many cases. The infrared radiation, on the other hand, is usually undesirable due to its heating effect. This is particularly true in air-conditioned buildings in summer if high values of illumination are necessary. The infrared radiation from the lamps will place an added load on the cooling system.† If the light sources are in the room, it is evident from the conservation-of-energy principle that the total energy consumed by the lamps must all appear in the room as heat, irrespective of how much of this input is radiated or at what wavelengths. Thus a room lighted by ten 200-watt lamps receives from them the same heat that it would obtain from a 2000-watt heater. If the lamps are used behind built-in glass panels with the light boxes connected to a ventilating system, some of the heat can be

---

* A discussion of the effect on visual acuity of eliminating the blue and violet is given by Luckiesh and Moss, *J.O.S.A.*, **10**, 1925, p. 275.

† See Sturrock and Walker, The Heating Effect of Artificial Lighting, *I.E.S. Trans.*, **29**, 1934, p. 23.

removed by the air stream and thus prevented from entering the room.   Such a scheme is not very effective, however, unless liquid or glass filters are used to cut off the large amount of radiant energy beyond $\lambda = 0.7\mu$.

Not only does the radiation from the lamps raise the temperature of the air, but each person absorbs most of the radiant energy which strikes him.   In extreme cases, the sensation produced is decidedly unpleasant.   Table LVI shows the watts per square foot falling on a surface when the illumination is 100 lumens/sq ft.   Note that with radiation having the spectral energy distribution of noon sunlight, 1.2 watts of radiant power is incident on each square foot of surface when $E = 100$.   With homogeneous radiation at 0.555μ, only 0.161 watt is incident on a square foot; while with tungsten lamps, much higher values of irradiation are obtained.   Irradiation values corresponding to other values of illumination are obtained by direct proportion.   The values were calculated from the data of Chaps. II and V.

TABLE LVI.—IRRADIATION FOR A CONSTANT ILLUMINATION OF 100 LUMENS/SQ FT

Type	Lumens per radiated watt	G (watts/sq ft)
Homogeneous radiation at $\lambda = 0.555\mu$	621	0.161
Noon sunlight	85	1.2
Planckian radiator (°K) at:		
6500	85	1.2
5000	74	1.4
3200	25	4.0
3000	19	5.3
2600	9	11
Tungsten lamp (°K) at:		
3200	35	2.9
3000	27	3.7
2800	20	5.0
2600	14	7.1

At present, no data seem to be available as to the watts of radiant power that can be absorbed by a human being without discomfort.   Midsummer noon sunlight on a clear day gives an irradiation of 0.120 watt/sq cm, or 112 watts/sq ft, corresponding to an illumination of approximately 9000 lumens/sq ft.   Experience indicates that such values of irradiation are decidedly noticeable and would be unpleasant in many circumstances, though it would seem that values about one-tenth as high, 10 watts/sq ft, would be permissible. Discomfort due to irradiation is of importance when high values of illumination are used and cannot be neglected in the design of an ideal lighting system. If there is any possibility of trouble from this source, the illuminating engineer should attempt to control accurately the edge of his high-intensity light beam so that the desired area is illuminated without irradiating the people concerned.

14.10. Dimensions of the Human Figure.—In any careful design of lighting, the illuminating engineer finds that he needs one or more dimensions of human beings, such as the height of the eyes above the floor, sitting height, or arm length. Not only should the average value be known but also the variation to be expected in a reasonably large sample of the population. The magnitude of this variation is of particular importance in the positioning of light sources to eliminate glare, since it determines the height of the glare zone. We have seen how some of the dimensions are used in the consideration of shadows and reflected glare. We now turn to a tabulation of further information which will be found useful in practice.

A large number of data have been collected by the anthropometrists, and the various sources[*] of data have been used freely in writing the present section. Figure 14.08 shows typical data on stature of the male figure. The points represent the number of men whose height fell within a variation of ± 0.5 in. from a given height. The curve is the *normal*, or *Gaussian*, probability curve[†] expressed by the equation

$$y = \frac{N}{\sigma\sqrt{2\pi}}e^{-\frac{1}{2}\left(\frac{x-x_m}{\sigma}\right)^2}$$

where N = the total area under the curve.
x and y = abscissa and ordinate.

[*] See, for instance, Karl Pearson, The Chances of Death, and various papers in *Biometrika*.

[†] See, for instance, T. C. Fry, Probability and its Engineering Uses, New York, 1928; or Raymond Pearl, Medical Biometry and Statistics, Philadelphia, 1930.

x_m = the mean stature (x_m = 67.70 in.).

σ = the *standard deviation*.

In Fig. 14.08, σ = 2.585 in. It will be noted that the curve fits the points fairly well, and it will be found that similar curves are obtained with many other dimensions of the human figure. The stature of the female was obtained from Pearson's data on 1078

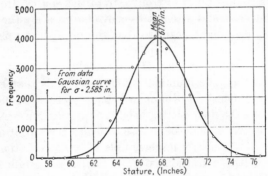

Fig. 14.08.—Stature of 25,878 U.S. Army recruits. (*Data from K. Pearson.*)

British married couples. The fact that the average height of the 1078 British husbands was 67.68 in. with a standard deviation of 2.70 in., which is in good agreement with the data of Fig. 14.08 on U.S. recruits, gives us confidence in the use of these figures for the population of the United States.

Some other data are given in Table LVII.

TABLE LVII.—SOME HUMAN DIMENSIONS

Dimension	Number of individuals	Male		Female	
		Mean	σ	Mean	σ
Stature..............	25,878	67.70 in.	2.585 in.		
Stature..............	{1078 {1078	67.68	2.70	62.48 in.	2.39 in.
Sitting height........	{1013 { 775	36.0	1.41	33.9	1.21
Span..............	{ 881 { 770	69.9	3.06	63.0	2.77
Length of forearm....	{1078 {1078	18.31	0.96	16.51	0.86
Length of foot........	3000	10.1	0.46		

It is interesting to consider how the values of σ may be used. What we wish to know is how large a variation in the dimensions should be considered in order that the lighting system may satisfy most people. The information could be used also to good advantage by furniture makers and architects. Probability theory states that with the normal distribution function the probability

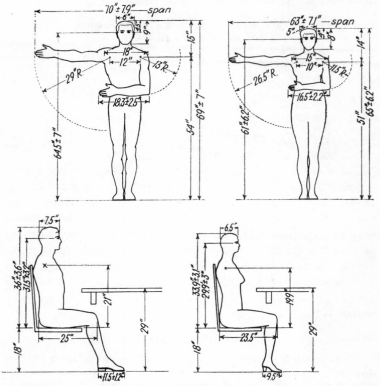

FIG. 14.09.—Some human dimensions.

that a given individual will approach the mean within $\pm0.67\sigma$ is 0.50; that is, if an individual is taken at random, there is a 50-50 chance that his dimensions will lie within these limits. This is not a large enough variation in dimensions for our purpose. Other possibilities are indicated in Table LVIII, which shows that on the average 1 person in 100 will fall outside a region having a width of 2.575σ on each side of the mean and only 1 person in 1000 will fall outside the range $\pm3.30\sigma$. If we adopt arbitrarily as our criterion, the value 2.575σ, it is evident from Table LVII that the height of men will vary between 67.68 ± 6.95 in., or from 60.73 to 74.63 in., while the height of women will vary from 56.32 to 68.64 in. For our purpose, it is more convenient to have the heights when shoes are worn, so an average value of 1.3 in. has been added to the male stature and 2.5 in. to the female stature to obtain the standing heights of Fig. 14.09.

TABLE LVIII.—VARIATION TO BE EXPECTED IN DIMENSIONS THAT FOLLOW
THE NORMAL DISTRIBUTION FUNCTION

Number of People outside Range	Range of Variation from Mean Value
500 in 1000	$\pm 0.67\sigma$
317 in 1000	± 1.00
100 in 1000	± 1.645
10 in 1000	± 2.575
2.6 in 1000	± 3.00
1.0 in 1000	± 3.30

The dimensions of the human figure,* which are needed for the engineering design of lighting installations, are given in Fig. 14.09. The principal dimensions are accompanied by their values of $\pm 2.575\sigma$. For the smaller dimensions, the averages only are given usually, though the approximate variation can be found, if desired, by considering the standard deviation to be roughly proportional to the mean value and thus scaling down the σ belonging to one of the larger dimensions. Suggested chair and table heights are also given in Fig. 14.09, though some variation from these values can be expected in practice.

LIGHTING PROJETS†

The purpose is to obtain a lighting system that is ideal for seeing and that is carefully designed to meet the specific requirements of the problem. The eight requirements for good lighting are to be satisfied. Particular attention is to be paid to the absolute elimination of direct and reflected glare.

The lighting fixtures should also present a pleasing appearance. No dangling luminaires will be used. Light will be obtained from one or more of the following:

Built-in luminous panels of diffusing glass ⎱either built into the walls or
Built-in lens plates   ⎰   applied to the walls.

---

* See also E. I. FREESE, Geometry of the Human Figure, *Am. Architect*, July, 1934, p. 57.

† One projet may be assigned to each member of the class. Several weeks should be allowed for its completion.

Reflectors (metal or silvered glass) shielded from view by louvers or by
obscuring glass

Cove lighting

Illuminated coffers

Cost is not of prime importance, though high levels of illumination should
be used only in the parts of the room where they are needed.

In your report on the projet, give a complete discussion of the requirements, the possible solutions of the problem, why you chose the one you did,
and how it satisfies the eight requirements. Specify material, color, reflection factor, surface finish (matt, semimatt, polished) of all surfaces. Calculate luminosity of object, background and surround, illumination in shadows,
etc. Give total kilowatt load.

Include scale drawings of completed room, giving principal dimensions,
glare zones, etc. Give scale drawings of lighting fixtures, specify size and
bulb number of lamps, manufacturer's number for reflectors and lens
plates, dimensions of glass panels and louvers.

PROJET A. LIGHTING A MACHINE SHOP

You are arranging a small machine shop for your personal use. The
available room will be 12 by 18 ft with a 9-ft ceiling. The building is not
constructed yet but will be of concrete, and the room will have one door and
one window. Arrange bench and cabinets as desired. Specify finish of
walls and ceiling. Design ideal lighting system for the room.

Particular attention is to be paid to the illumination of the engine lathe to
allow accurate work on metals at night without glare or eyestrain.

References

SHOEMAKER: *I.E.S. Trans.*, **27**, 1932, p. 308.
LOGAN: *I.E.S. Trans.*, **29**, 1934, p. 686.

PROJET B. LIGHTING A CONFERENCE ROOM

Room — is to be lighted in the best possible manner to provide adequate
illumination on the table with absolutely no reflected glare. Also, the front
blackboard must be lighted so that it can be read easily, both at night and
in the daytime from any seat at the table (no daytime reflections due to
light from the windows).

References

Am. Architect, November and December, 1934.
CUTLER: *Magazine of Light*, November, 1933.
LOGAN: *I.E.S. Trans.*, **29**, 1934, p. 686.
SHOEMAKER: *I.E.S. Trans.*, **27**, 1932, p. 308.
STAIR: *I.E.S. Trans.*, **27**, 1932, p. 361.

PROJET C. LIGHTING A STAIRWAY

A stairway in a proposed office building is to be lighted in the best possible
way. The stairs are to have the same width, riser height, tread width, and

number of steps as those leading up from the basement of Building —. The corridor is the same width as the stairs and is 9 ft high. The steps are to be of white marble, and the corridor floors are of light-colored terrazzo. Decide on color and finish of walls and ceiling.

Particular attention should be paid to the best possible illumination of the stairs. To be able to descend with ease and safety, it is essential that the edge of each tread be sharply differentiated from the tread beneath it. But since the material is uniform, this can be accomplished only by the skillful use of light and shadow.

References

Am. Architect, November and December, 1934.
LOGAN: *I.E.S. Trans.*, **29**, 1934, p. 686.
SHOEMAKER: *I.E.S. Trans.*, **27**, 1932, p. 308.

PROJET D. LIGHTING A CLASSROOM

Redesign the lighting system for Room — to provide the best possible illumination for seeing. Windows and blackboards will remain as they are. Tables will be fastened permanently in place. Ceiling may be refinished, or a false ceiling may be installed, if desired, to conceal pipes and built-in fixtures.

Two aspects must be considered: elimination of reflections from front blackboard in the daytime, and the best possible illumination of tables and front blackboard at night.

References

Am. Architect, November and December, 1934.
CUTLER: *Magazine of Light*, November, 1933.
LOGAN: *I.E.S. Trans.*, **29**, 1934, p. 686.
SHOEMAKER: *I.E.S. Trans.*, **27**, 1932, p. 308.

PROJET E. LIGHTING AN ART GALLERY

A proposed art gallery 40 ft square with a 15-ft ceiling will be air-conditioned and artificially lighted (no skylights or windows). A long double davenport is to be placed in the center of the room. The walls are to be covered with oil paintings (with or without glass) fastened vertically against the walls.

Design an ideal lighting system to allow maximum visibility of the pictures from all parts of the room and to eliminate direct and reflected glare.

References

Am. Architect, November and December, 1934.
SHOEMAKER: *I.E.S. Trans.*, **27**, 1932, p. 308.
LOGAN: *I.E.S. Trans.*, **29**, 1934, p. 686.

PROJET F. LIGHTING A LIVING ROOM

A modern living room is to be part of a proposed air-conditioned house. One entire end of the room is to be built of glass bricks and provided with

Venetian blinds.   The only other openings are three doors.   Furniture will consist of davenport, easy chairs, radio, built-in book case.   Specify details, finish of walls and ceiling, etc.

Design ideal lighting system to provide (1) low illumination for relaxing and listening to radio, (2) excellent illumination where needed for reading, (3) correct illumination for playing cards.

Special attention is to be paid in (2) to obtaining maximum ease of vision and complete freedom from glare.   If portable floor lamps are used, specify height of bottom of shade above floor, size of lamp, candlepower-distribution curve required for direct and indirect components, position of lamp with reference to printed page.   If permanent lighting is used, specify all details.

References

Decorative Art, Studio Year Book, 1932, 1933, 1934.
Am. Architect, November and December, 1934.
Architectural Forum, December, 1934.
SHOEMAKER: *I.E.S. Trans.*, **27**, 1932, p. 308.

PROJET G.   LIGHTING A BARBER SHOP

The — Barber Shop (select one in your neighborhood) is to be transformed into a modern establishment with the best possible lighting.   Particular attention is to be given to providing ideal seeing conditions for each barber. Specify all details, including finish of walls and ceiling, size of mirrors, etc.

References

LOGAN: *I.E.S. Trans.*, **29**, 1934, p. 686.
STAIR: *I.E.S. Trans.*, **27**, 1932, p. 361.
SHOEMAKER: *I.E.S. Trans.*, **27**, 1932, p. 308.
Am. Architect, November and December, 1934.

PROJET H.   LIGHTING A RAILWAY COACH

A new line of air-conditioned railway coaches is being designed.   General dimensions are standard.   Specify finish of walls and ceilings and size of windows.   Design an ideal lighting system to allow best possible reading conditions at each seat and entire freedom from direct and reflected glare.

References

LOGAN: *I.E.S. Trans.*, **29**, 1934, p. 686.
Am. Architect, November and December, 1934.
SHOEMAKER: *I.E.S. Trans.*, **27**, 1932, p. 308.

Bibliography

GENERAL

1. L. MUMFORD: Technics and Civilization, Harcourt, Brace & Company, New York, 1934.
2. L. MUMFORD: Sticks & Stones, A. & C. Boni, Inc., New York, 1927.
3. L. SULLIVAN: Kindergarten Chats, Scarab Fraternity Press, New York. 1934.

4. S. CHENEY: The New World Architecture, Longmans, Green & Company, New York, 1930.
5. G. A. PLATZ: Die Baukunst der neuesten Zeit, Propyläen-Verlag, Berlin, 1930.
6. H. READ: Art and Industry, Harcourt, Brace & Company, New York, 1935.
7. E. J. KAHN: Design in Art and Industry, Charles Scribner's Sons, New York, 1935.
8. N. BEL GEDDES: Horizons, Little, Brown & Company, Boston, 1932.
9. N. BEL GEDDES: *Fortune*, **2**, July, 1930, p. 51.
10. F. R. S. YORKE: The Modern House, Architectural Press, London, 1934.
11. H. WRIGHT: Housing Urban America, Columbia University Press, New York, 1935.

DIFFUSE AND SPECULAR REFLECTION

12. H. WRIGHT: Photometry of the Diffuse Reflection of Light, *Phil. Mag.*, **49**, 1900, p. 199.
13. L. A. JONES: The Gloss Characteristics of Photographic Papers, *J.O.S.A.*, **6**, 1922, p. 140.
14. WORONKOFF and POKROWSKI: Über die selektive Reflexion des Lichtes, *Zeits. f. Phys.*, **20**, 1924, p. 358.
15. G. I. POKROWSKI: Zur Theorie der diffusen Lichtreflexion, *Zeits. f. Phys.*, **30**, 1924, p. 66.
16. G. I. POKROWSKI: Zur Theorie der diffusen Lichtreflexion, *Zeits. f. Phys.*, II, **35**, 1925, p. 34; III, **35**, 1926, p. 390.
17. D. L. GAMBLE: Reflecting Characteristics of Wall Paints, *I.E.S. Trans.*, **28**, 1933, p. 326.
18. J. M. SLATER: A Recording Goniophotometer, *J.O.S.A.*, **25**, 1935, p. 218.

HUMAN DIMENSIONS

19. PEARSON and LEE: On the Laws of Inheritance in Man, *Biometrika*, **2**, 1903, p. 357.
20. CRIPPS, GREENWOOD, and NEWBOLD: A Biometric Study of the Interrelations of Stature, Stem Length and Weight, *Biometrika*, **14**, 1923, p. 316.
21. E. I. FREESE: Geometry of the Human Figure, *Am. Architect*, July, 1934, p. 57.

APPLICATIONS

22. H. L. LOGAN: Modern Lighting with Control Lenses, *I.E.S. Trans.*, **25**, 1930, p. 859.
23. A. A. BRAINERD: Tailor-made Lighting, *I.E.S. Trans.*, **25**, 1930, p. 867.
24. G. E. SHOEMAKER: Synthetic Lighting, *I.E.S. Trans.*, **27**, 1932, p. 308.
25. STAIR and GRAVES: Louvered Lighting, *I.E.S. Trans.*, **31**, 1936, p. 249.
26. BEGGS and WOODSIDE: Technical Aspects of Architectural Lighting, *I.E.S. Trans.*, **26**, 1931, p. 1007.
27. POTTER and MEAKER: Luminous Architectural Elements, *I.E.S. Trans.*, **26**, 1931, p. 1025.

28. C. S. WOODSIDE: Illumination of Structural Glass, *I.E.S. Trans.*, **29**, 1934, p. 878.

29. LAWALL and POTTER: Design of Opaque Patterns on Luminous Backgrounds, *I.E.S. Trans.*, **30**, 1935, p. 385.

30. E. B. KIRK: The Design of Theater "Down Lights," *I.E.S. Trans.*, **28**, 1933, p. 280.

31. H. L. LOGAN: The Influence of Built-in Lighting Forms on Direct Lighting Methods, *I.E.S. Trans.*, **29**, 1934, p. 686.

32. Modern Interior Lighting: *Am. Architect.*, November and December, 1934.

33. ODAY and PORTER: The Use of Ultraviolet Sources for General Illumination, *I.E.S. Trans.*, **28**, 1933, p. 121.

34. PORTER, EGELER, and STURROCK: Ultraviolet Equipments and Their Applications, *I.E.S. Trans.*, **27**, 1932, p. 23.

35. STURROCK and WALKER: The Heating Effect of Artificial Lighting, *I.E.S. Trans.*, **29**, 1934, p. 23.

36. B. JONES: The Lighting of the Allegheny County Soldiers Memorial, *I.E.S. Trans.*, **6**, 1911, p. 9.

37. STAIR and TATHWELL: Lighting the Replica of the Parthenon, *I.E.S. Trans.*, **25**, 1930, p. 891.

38. C. W. STEDMAN: The Lighting of Severance Hall, *I.E.S. Trans.*, **26**, 1931, p. 351.

39. D. H. HOLDEN: The New Home of the Cleveland Symphony Orchestra, *I.E.S. Trans.*, **26**, 1931, p. 331.

40. L. H. GRAVES: Lighting of the New Waldorf-Astoria Hotel, *I.E.S. Trans.*, **26**, 1931, p. 939.

41. J. L. STAIR: Significant Lighting in Department Stores, *I.E.S. Trans.*, **27**, 1932, p. 361.

42. S. R. MCCANDLESS: Lighting in the Radio City Theaters, *I.E.S. Trans.*, **28**, 1933, p. 665.

43. W. D'A. RYAN: Illumination of a Century of Progress Exposition, *I.E.S. Trans.*, **29**, 1934, p. 107.

44. WOOD and STAHL: Unique Lighting of a Century of Progress, *I.E.S. Trans.*, **29**, 1934, p. 116.

45. C. M. CUTLER: Lighting Ideas from the Fair, *Mag. of Light*, November, 1933.

46. M. REA PAUL: Surfacing Materials for Light Wells, *I.E.S. Trans.*, **28**, 1933, p. 315.

47. Enchanted Tiles, *Fortune* **2**, September, 1930, p. 74.

48. A. J. SWEET: The Lighting of a Swimming Pool, *I.E.S. Trans.*, **22**, 1927, p. 631.

49. Standards of School Lighting, *I.E.S. Trans.*, **28**, 1933, p. 21.

50. I. C. WOOD: Custom-built Lighting Enters the Home, *I.E.S. Trans.*, **27**, 1932, p. 611.

51. T. S. ROGERS: The Home of Tomorrow, *Am. Architect*, March, 1934, p. 23.

52. A. C. DICK: The Home of Tomorrow, *I.E.S. Trans.*, **29**, 1934, p. 455.

53. KETCH, STURROCK, and STALEY: Special Lighting Applications for Industrial Processes, *I.E.S. Trans.*, **28**, 1933, p. 57.

54. G. H. Stickney: Symposium on Office Lighting, *I.E.S. Trans.*, **23**, 1928, p. 51.
55. H. H. Higbie: Illumination of a Large Reading Room, *I.E.S. Trans.*, **21**, 1926, p. 567.
56. R. W. Cost: Modern Lighting in Streamlined Trains, *I.E.S. Trans.*, **30**, 1935, p. 331.
57. A. A. Brainerd: Factory Lighting to Fit the Facts, *I.E.S. Trans.*, **30**, 1935, p. 315.
58. A. L. Powell: Illuminating Eng. Soc. Prize, Beaux-Arts Inst. of Design, *I.E.S. Trans.*, **28**, 1933, p. 204.
59. A. L. Powell: Results of the I.E.S. Beaux-Arts Prize Competition, *I.E.S. Trans.*, **29**, 1934, p. 245.
60. D. W. Atwater: 1935 Prize Award, *I.E.S. Trans.*, **30**, 1935, p. 365.
61. Light in Architecture and Decoration, Illuminating Engineering Society, New York, 1934.
62. J. L. Stair: Lighting à la Mode, *I.E.S. Trans.*, **24**, 1929, p. 947.
63. Brown and Falge: Improved Designs for Stage Lighting Equipment, *I.E.S. Trans.*, **22**, 1927, p. 1144.
64. H. Maisonneuve: Modern Art Lighting, *I.E.S. Trans.*, **24**, 1929, p. 456.
65. J. M. Holmes: Colour in Interior Decoration, Charles Scribner's Sons, New York, 1932.
66. Cutler and Pepper: Modern Color, Harvard University Press, 1923.
67. H. E. Ives: Thomas Young and the Simplification of the Artist's Palette, *Phys. Soc. Proc.*, **46**, 1934, p. 16.
68. F. J. Cadenas: Colorama Lighting, *I.E.S. Trans.*, **25**, 1930, p. 282.
69. W. W. Kantack: Lighting and Decorative Problems, *I.E.S. Trans.*, **31**, 1936, p. 231.

APPENDIX A

SYMBOLS USED IN THE TEXT

Symbol	Meaning	Used in Chapters
a	Radius (ft)	IX, X
b	Cost of power (cents/kw-hr)	VI
c	Velocity of light in free space $= 2.99796$ $\times 10^{10}$ cm/sec	I
c	Cost of lamp + installation charge (cents)	VI
c	Contrast (numeric)	XII
c_{min}	Minimum-perceptible contrast (numeric)	XII
e	Base of Napierian logarithms $=$ $2.7182818 \ldots$	V
e_λ	Spectral radiation factor (numeric)	V, VI
e_i	Total radiation factor (numeric)	V, VI
f	A factor given by Eq. (13.07)	XIII
f_c	Critical frequency of flicker	XII
f_d	$$f_d = \frac{F \text{ on working plane}}{F \text{ emitted by luminaire}}$$ for direct component	XI
f_i, f_h	Corresponding factors for indirect and horizontal components of flux emitted by a luminaire	XI
g	A constant	VI
g_d	Efficiency of luminaire $=$ $$\frac{\text{Total } F \text{ emitted by luminaire}}{F_L}$$ for direct component	XI
g_i, g_h	Corresponding factors for indirect and horizontal components of flux emitted by a luminaire	XI
h	Planck's constant $= 6.547 \times 10^{-27}$ erg-sec	I, VII
h	Height of room, floor to ceiling (ft)	XI
i	Current (amp)	II, VI, VII
i	An integer	II, IV
i	Unit vector in x direction	X
j	An integer	IV
j	Unit vector in y direction	X
k	Unit vector in z direction	X

k_d	Depreciation factor	XI
k_r	Factor which expresses room shape	

$$k_r = \frac{h}{0.90w + 0.10l} \qquad \text{XI}$$

k_u	Coefficient of utilization	XI
$k_1,\ k_2$	Constants of the photochemical reaction in the retina	XII
l	Length of filament (cm)	VI
l	Length of room (ft)	XI
m	Mass (grams)	I, VI, VII

$$m = \frac{\pi \delta}{2\lambda} \cdot \frac{r_0}{z_0} \qquad \text{XII}$$

n	Index of refraction (numeric)	I, IX
n_1	Unit normal vector	X
$p,\ p_i$	Photocell response (amp per watt/sq cm) due to homogeneous radiation of wavelength λ	II
p	Colorimetric purity (numeric)	XIII
q	An integer	I, V
r	A distance $\begin{cases}(\text{cm}) \\ (\text{ft})\end{cases}$	VII, VIII, IX, X, XI, XII, XIV
r_1	$= \sqrt{D^2 + H^2 + W^2}$	IX, X
r_1	A unit vector	X
s	Distance along a curve	IX
t	Time	XII
u	Mounting height of luminaire	VIII
v	Velocity (cm/sec)	I, II, VII
v	Visibility function	III, IV, V, VI, VII, XIII
$w,\ w_i$	Relative effectiveness of homogeneous radiation in producing erythema	II
w	Width of narrow panel (ft)	IX
w	Width of room (ft)	XI
x	An independent variable	V, VI, IX, X
x	Number of molecules of light-sensitive substance associated with one receptor element, expressed in terms of maximum number	XII
x	Unified trichromatic coefficient in C.I.E. system	XIII

$$= \frac{x'}{x' + y' + z'}$$

$\bar{x}$	Trichromatic coefficient, C.I.E. system	XIII
x'	Trichromatic coefficient in C.I.E. system	XIII

$$= \int_0^\infty \bar{x} J_\lambda d\lambda$$

y	A variable	VI, IX, X
y	Unified trichromatic coefficient in C.I.E. system	XIII

$$= \frac{y'}{x' + y' + z'}$$

$\bar{y}$	Trichromatic coefficient, C.I.E. system	XIII
y'	Trichromatic coefficient in C.I.E. system	XIII

$$= \int_0^\infty \bar{y} J_\lambda \, d\lambda$$

z	A variable	IX, X
z	Thickness of filter	VI
z	Unified trichromatic coefficient in C.I.E. system	XIII

$$= \frac{z'}{x' + y' + z'}$$

$\bar{z}$	Trichromatic coefficient, C.I.E. system	XIII
z'	Trichromatic coefficient in C.I.E. system	XIII

$$= \int_0^\infty \bar{z} J_\lambda \, d\lambda$$

A	Floor area (sq ft)	XI
$A_1, A_2 \ldots$	Constants	VI
A_λ	Spectral irradiation (watts/sq cm per micron) of the walls of a Planckian radiator	V
B	Width of luminous panel (in.)	XI
B	Brightness (candles/sq ft of projected area)	App. B
$B_1, B_2 \ldots$	Constants	VI
C_1	First constant of Planck's equation $= 36{,}970$	V
C_2	Second constant of Planck's equation $= 14{,}320$	V
D	Distance (cm or ft)	I, VII, VIII, IX, X, XI, XII, XIV
$D(\lambda)$	Fredholm determinant	X
E	Illumination $\begin{cases} \text{(lightwatts/sq cm)} \\ \text{(lumens/sq cm)} \\ \text{(lumens/sq ft)} \end{cases}$	III, IV, V, VI, VII, VIII, IX, X, XI, XII, XIII, XIV
E	Illumination vector $= iE_x + jE_y + kE_z$	X
E_x	x-component of the illumination vector E	IX, X, XI
E_y	y-component of the illumination vector E	IX, X, XI
E_z	z-component of the illumination vector E	IX, X, XI
E_{av}	Average illumination	VIII, IX, X, XI, XIV

E_G	Illumination at eye due to glare source (lumens/sq ft)	XII
E_{ret}	Retinal illumination	XII
F	Luminous flux $\begin{cases} \text{(lightwatts)} \\ \text{(lumens)} \end{cases}$	III, IV, V, VI, VII, VIII, X, XI
F_L	Lamp lumens	XI
F_d, F_h, F_i	Components of flux from a luminaire (direct component, horizontal component, and indirect component)	XI
G, G_i	Irradiation (watts/sq cm) incident on a surface	II, III, IV, V, VI, VII, XIII
G_λ	Spectral irradiation (watts/sq cm per micron) incident on a surface	II, III, VII, XIII
H	Height of a luminous panel	IX, X
H_m	Mounting height of luminaire above floor (ft)	XI
I	Intensity or candlepower of a luminous source (candles)	VII, VIII, IX, X, XI
I_o	Intensity (candles) normal to the surface	IX, X, XI
J	Radiosity (watts/sq cm) emitted by surface	II, III, V, VI, VII, XIII
J_λ	Spectral radiosity (watts/sq cm per micron wavelength band emitted by a surface)	II, III, V, VI, XIII
$J_{\lambda max}$	Maximum spectral radiosity (watts/sq cm per micron)	V
$J_{\lambda rel}$	Relative spectral radiosity (unity at $\lambda = 0.59\mu$)	V
K	A constant	
$K(x, x_1)$	Kernel of an integral equation	X
L	Luminosity $\begin{cases} \text{(lightwatts/sq cm)} \\ \text{(lumens/sq cm)} \\ \text{(lumens/sq ft)} \end{cases}$	III, IV, V, VI, VI, VIII, IX, X, XI, XII, XIII
L_A	Adapting luminosity (value to which the eye is adapted) (lumens/sq ft)	XII, XIV
L_B	Luminosity of background (lumens/sq ft)	XII
L_O	Luminosity of object (lumens/sq ft)	XII
L_S	Luminosity of the surround (lumens/sq ft)	XII, XIV
$L_0, L_1, L_2 \ldots$	Luminosity coefficients for a surface source having the nonuniform luminosity: $$L = L_0 + L_1 x + L_2 x^2 + \cdots$$	IX, X
£	Life of lamp (hr)	VI
M	A constant	XII
N_1	Unit vector	X
P	Power (watts)	VI
P_r	Radiated power (watts)	VI

Q	Light	App. B
R	Resistance (ohms)	VI
R	Radius of a sphere	VIII, IX, X
$\mathcal{R}$	Resistivity (ohm-cm)	V, VI
S	Surface area (sq cm)	II, III, VI, X
S_c	Contrast sensitivity of the eye	
	$S_c = \dfrac{1}{c_{\min}}$ (numeric)	XII
$S_{1.0}$	Contrast sensitivity for $L_S = L_B$	XII
S_L	Spacing between lamps	XI
S	Sensation	XII
T	Absolute temperature ($°K = °C + 273.1$)	II, III, V, VI
T_c	Color temperature (°K)	V, VI
U	Radiant energy $\begin{cases} \text{(ergs)} \\ \text{(watt-sec)} \end{cases}$	II
V	Voltage (volts)	IV, VI, VII
V_d	Difference in two energy levels (volts)	IV
V_i	Ionization potential (volts)	IV
V_m	Potential corresponding to a metastable level (volts)	IV
V_r	Resonance potential (volts)	IV
W	Width of luminous panel	IX, X
W_p	Work function	II, VII
Z	Atomic number	IV
α	A constant	VI
α_1	A unit vector	X
$d\alpha$	A vector	X
β	An angle subtended by a source	IX, X, XI
γ	An angle subtended by a source	IX, X, XI
δ	Diameter (cm)	VI
δ	Pupil diameter (mm)	XII
ζ	Vaporization factor (grams evaporated per square centimeter per second)	VI
η	Efficiency of energy conversion	II
η_o	Over-all efficacy (lumens/watt)	II, VI
η_l	Luminous efficacy (lightwatts/watt or lumens/watt)	III, IV, V, VI
θ	An angle	I, VII, VIII, IX, X, XI, XII
λ	Wavelength (microns)	I, II, III, IV, V, VI, VII, XII, XIII
λ_d	Dominant wavelength (microns)	XIII
$\lambda_{\max}$	Wavelength (microns) at which a spectroradiometric curve reaches its maximum	V
λ_r	Wavelength of resonance radiation (microns)	IV

ν	Frequency (cycles/sec)	I, IV, VII
ξ	A variable	VII, VIII, IX, X, XII
π	$= 3.14159 \ldots$	
ρ	Reflection factor (numeric)	III, VII, VIII, IX, X, XI, XII, XIII, XIV
$\rho\lambda$	Spectral reflection factor (numeric)	III, V, XIII
σ	Stefan-Boltzmann constant $= 5.709 \times 10^{-12}$.	V, VI
σ	Standard deviation	XIV
$d\sigma$	Element of surface	IX, X, XII
τ	Transmission factor (numeric)	III, VI, XIII
$\tau\lambda$	Spectral transmission factor (numeric)	III, VI, XIII
ϕ	An angle	VIII, IX, X, XI
ψ	An angle	IX, X, XI
ω	An angle	X
Γ	Irradiation evaluated with respect to its ability to produce erythema (erythemalwatts/sq cm)	II
$\Delta_1, \Delta_2, \ldots$	Components of the illumination vector	X
Θ	An angle	X
Υ	Visual acuity	XII
Λ	Surround factor	XII, XIV
Φ	Radiant power or radiant flux (watts)	II, III, IV, V, VI, VII
$\Phi(\omega)$	Flux function	X
Ψ	Erythemal flux	II
$d\Omega$	A solid angle	X

APPENDIX B

PHOTOMETRIC CONCEPTS

Thousands of treatises on photometric concepts are available, but few if any will stand up under critical analysis. Perhaps the present treatment is in the same category, though a serious attempt has been made to examine photometric ideas and to point out some of the more egregious inconsistencies. In the latter part of this appendix will be found a comparison of the various units in use today and conversion factors for changing from one to another.

The Antiquated Photometric Concepts.—To understand the present status of photometric concepts, we must first consider how they originated. The history of the development of photometric units is not unique, being paralleled by the history of most other physical units. In magnetism, for instance, a mathematical development based upon the fictitious "unit magnetic pole" was developed long before the discovery of the connection between electricity and magnetism. A similar development was made in electrostatics, which was originally conceived as a study of the attraction between charged pith balls. As a result of the unfortunate separate development of the electrostatic and the magnetic systems, electrical engineers are yearly wasting a great amount of time changing from one system to the other. In much the same manner, photometric units were developed when light was just "light" and before there was any adequate conception of radiant energy or of the spectrum.

It is rather difficult for us to put ourselves in the position of the early photometrists such as Bouguer or Lambert, who in the eighteenth century originated the concepts that play such an important part in our present photometry. Bouguer's "Essai d'optique" was published in 1729, while Lambert's famous work on photometry[1] appeared in 1760. It was not until the year

[1] J. H. LAMBERT, Photometria siva de mensura gradibus luminis, colorum et umbrae.

1800 that Herschel discovered that the spectrum of the sun extended beyond the visible region, and the *precise* measurement of radiant power did not begin until almost the close of the nineteenth century. "Light" to the early photometrists was a separate entity, an intuitive concept, an "element" as fire, water, and earth were elements to the ancient Greeks. Light was produced by candles, and experiments were performed by moving the candles about in various ways and noting the results. In particular, it was found that if two contiguous parts of the wall were lighted by two candles in such a way that each portion received light from one candle only, an observer could determine equality of illumination with surprising precision. This crude photometer was used in establishing the inverse-square law and the cosine law of illumination.

It was found that some candles gave more light than others, and thus at a somewhat later date it became convenient to specify a standard in terms of which the light-giving properties of all other candles could be expressed. An obvious way of fixing this standard was to specify arbitrarily how it could be reproduced—*i.e.*, to specify the material of which the candle was to be made and its physical size. The property that was measured was called the *intensity*, or *candlepower*. It was an intuitive concept and had no known relation to the units of any other branch of physics. Other concepts were developed as needed, giving the system of units outlined in Table B-I. All were related

TABLE B-I

Concept	Symbol	Unit (English system)	
Intensity...................	I	candle	intuitive concept
Illumination................	E	foot-candle	
Brightness.................	B	{candle/sq ft or lumen/sq ft}	derived concepts
Luminous flux..............	F	lumen	

in a rather obvious geometrical way to the candle. A study of the shadows cast by opaque objects placed near the candle led to the idea of something flowing out from the candle flame in straight lines. This "something" was called *luminous flux*. When this flux fell on a surface, it *illuminated* the surface, the *illumination* being expressible as the luminous flux per unit area. The flux that emanated from the surface per unit of projected area was called *brightness*.

The sole photometric measurement consisted in comparing the brightness of two contiguous surfaces. Owing to the fact that all the candles emitted radiation of essentially the same spectral distribution, the measurement was easily made, and the results were fairly consistent, even when made by different observers. This led to a false idea of the accuracy and importance of the concepts of Table B-I and to the peculiar but prevalent feeling that there is something inviolable about luminous flux and that it expresses a unique visual effect of radiant energy. We shall see that the entire system might have been defined equally well on several fundamentally different bases and that the concepts of Table B-I have at best only a very limited validity. Had more precise measuring methods been available or, in particular, had the sources been of various colors, the whole photometric system might have been built up in quite a different way.

The system of units given in Table B-I has been kept in essentially its pristine state from the eighteenth century to the present time. Candlepower standards and photometers have been improved to permit greater precision, and various physical photometers have been developed. But the method of visual comparison against a standard source has remained the fundamental process used in all important work. As long as light sources had essentially the same spectral energy distribution, such a scheme could be worked in a fairly satisfactory manner, provided one was satisfied with practical results and did not inquire too closely into the nature of what he was measuring. Even the advent of the tungsten-filament lamp with its higher operating temperature brought photometric difficulties, while the present growing importance of gaseous-conduction lamps with their fundamentally different spectra makes the methods of visual comparison almost, if not quite, untenable. To these difficulties is coupled the increased demand for more information than a photometric specification can give. What is the heating effect of the radiation from a given lamp; what is its erythemal effect; how does it affect a photographic film or a photoelectric cell; what sensation of color does the radiation evoke? To answer these questions, we must go to the spectroradiometric curve. Evidently, we are getting rapidly to a place where our antiquated photometric notions must be discarded, and it seems advisable to analyze our concepts and see what can be done to replace them. In the present book, the entire development has been based not on the eighteenth century intuitive concept of "light" but upon the firmly established concept of the spectroradiometric curve. It is true that the precision obtainable in radiometric measurements is still disappointingly low, so that actual photometry may be forced to stick to the old methods for a few years longer. But this does not appear to be an adequate reason why we should continue to force our minds into an eighteenth century mold as regards photometric concepts.

Physical Concepts and Psychological Concepts.—It is largely due to Einstein and his method of treating the concept of simultaneity that we have in modern physics a new spirit which has resulted in a marked improvement in the clarity and exactness of definitions. The principle is essentially this: Every concept must be defined in terms of how it can be measured; concepts that cannot be so defined or that cannot be directly related to measurable quantities are meaningless. As Bridgman says,[2] for example:

What do we mean by the length of an object? We evidently know what we mean by length if we can tell what the length of any and every object is, and for the physicist nothing more is required. To find the length of an object, we have to perform certain physical operations. The concept of length is therefore fixed when the operations by which length is measured are fixed: that is, the concept of length involves as much as and nothing more than the set of operations by which length is determined.. In general, we mean by any concept nothing more than a set of operations; *the concept is synonymous with the corresponding set of operations.*

It would be unwise to claim that the operational method is the "truth" (whatever that may mean) or that it can be applied successfully everywhere—to all mathematics, psychology, and sociology. But in physics, its success has been so marked that its use can hardly be questioned.

[2] P. W. BRIDGMAN, The Logic of Modern Physics, p. 5, The Macmillan Company, New York, 1932.

From the operational standpoint, most of the photometric concepts as defined in the standard definitions are meaningless. One reason for this confusion is that the concepts are complicated by a psychophysiological element which is absent in most branches of science and engineering. The psychophysiology of vision has been investigated most diligently for the past hundred years by biologists, psychologists, and physicists. Yet even the correct basis of an attack has not been agreed upon. The methods of physical science have been marvelously successful in the physical world and are even applicable to such physiological problems as the action of the receptor elements in the retina and the propagation of nervous impulses. Beyond this point in the seeing process, however, we leave the world of physics and enter the world of consciousness, of sensation, in which there is no reason to believe that the methods of physics can ever be applied. We have no way of measuring sensation, in the sense that physical quantities are measured. We have no way of setting up a unit of sensation—a sensation meter stick. We have no way of applying this meter stick to determining how many times one sensation is greater than another. Consequently, there is no possibility of expressing sensation mathematically as a function of stimulus. The Fechner law of logarithmic response is a mere figment of the imagination.[3] We must realize that the difficulty of not being able to measure sensation quantitatively is not a superficial one which, by the improvement in technique and the further development of science, can in the future be eradicated. The trouble is fundamental, is inherent in the very fact that sensation does not reside in the world of physics and thus can never be treated as a physical quantity.

Sensation is an extremely complex thing. Not only are we capable of concentrating at will upon a particular set of nerve messages and relegating the rest into the background of consciousness, but the sensation that is uppermost in consciousness is a subtle blend due to a great number of separate stimuli, some of which may help and others inhibit the sensation that is uppermost. Suppose, for instance, that a luminous spot is projected on the white wall of a room, the radiation being homogeneous of wavelength λ_i and having a certain definite magnitude expressed

---

[3] See J. Guild, The Interpretation of Quantitative Data in Visual Problems, p. 60, Discussion on Vision, Cambridge University Press, 1932.

in watts. The sensation produced by such a colored patch may be analyzed subjectively into *brilliance* and *hue*.[4] But to assume, as is often done, that there is a one-to-one correspondence between these psychological concepts and the physical concepts of radiant power and wavelength is incorrect.[5] If the wavelength is kept constant, for example, and the radiant power is increased, the hue will change as the brilliance changes. At very low values of luminosity, hue disappears entirely, and the sensation is one of gray. At very high values of luminosity, hue also tends to disappear, the sensation being that of a brilliant white. If the magnitude of the stimulus is kept constant, and the wavelength varied, brilliance also varies. If the rest of the room is illuminated, the spectral quality and the quantity of this illumination will be found to alter in a startling manner the sensation caused by the colored spot. Sensation also depends upon previous sensations (fatigue and adaptation effects). Moreover, the sensation is changed by all sorts of obscure physiological effects. As Sir John Parsons[6] says:

It is the custom, incontrovertibly justified by pragmatic sanction, for the physicist to attack his problems by a process of analysis and simplification. Hence it behooves him to remember what the biologist is less likely to overlook, namely, that *animal behavior is the response to the situation as a whole, which can in no case be split up into fragments without profoundly modifying both the whole and the parts.*

Evidently, then, the idea of measuring sensation is utter naïveté.

It may be helpful in our analysis to classify concepts as

1. *Psychological concepts*, such as brilliance, hue, and saturation. Such concepts cannot be defined in terms of operations and have no quantitative significance,

---

[4] Perhaps *saturation* also. I am using these terms to designate psychological concepts as was done by Troland (*J.O.S.A.*, **6**, 1922, p. 527). If one thinks of the sensations evoked by radiant energy, he finds that they can be differentiated in regard to magnitude of sensation (*brilliance*) as red or blue-green or yellow, etc. (*hue*), and with respect to their lack of "paleness" (saturation). The word "*color*" may also be applied to a sensation, though in the present book it is used in its more common meaning of a physical attribute.

[5] E. G. BORING, The Relation of the Attributes of Sensation to the Dimensions of the Stimulus, *Phil. Science*, **2**, 1935, p. 236.

[6] Discussion on Vision, 1932, Cambridge University Press, p. 272.

2. *Physical concepts*, which must be capable of definition in terms of physical operations. Apparently, a characteristic of a physical measurement is that it is essentially independent of the sensuous keenness of the observer. Thus an observer measuring the length of a given steel bar at a given temperature will obtain the same result within small limits each time that he measures it. Any other observer will obtain practically the same result. If one obtains consistently larger readings than the other, we do not take the matter complacently—we say that one of the results is *wrong*.

3. A third class is capable of definition in terms of operations but operations which are dependent upon the observer's senses. Such concepts may be called *psychophysical concepts*. For example, one might wish to set up a method of specifying the ability of any liquid to evoke the sensation of sweetness. There is no way in which he can measure the sensation, but he can develop a new concept dealing with the stimulus. To do this, he sets up an arbitrary standard, perhaps a definite sugar solution One must also define a scale, as by making the new quantity equal numerically to the number of grams of sugar per liter. The psychophysical concept will be defined by a specification of what the observer must do to compare a standard against an unknown by tasting. A sense of equality of sweetness sensation between a standard sample and an unknown will depend to some extent upon who is doing the tasting, particularly if the unknown produces a complex taste, the sweetness component only of which is to be considered. Thus if two observers obtain widely different results for a given unknown, it is no longer permissible to say that one result is wrong, as was done in 2. Each observer makes his own determination, and the results are for him *the correct results*. Thus the psychophysical concept!

To summarize, concepts may be divided into three classes: (1) physical concepts which are quantitative and are independent of the particular observer; (2) psychological concepts which have no quantitative significance; and (3) psychophysical concepts which are quantitative but depend upon the senses of the observer.

Photometric Comparison.—The only concepts developed to date which conceivably can belong to class 3 seem to be the photometric concepts. Indeed, the original method of definition of photometric quantities exhibits a close parallel with the hypothetical example of sweetness. In photometry, an arbitrary physical standard, corresponding to the standard sugar solution, was set up, and a method of comparing the unknown with the standard was specified. "Dilution" was accomplished by moving the photometric screen with respect to the sources, and the results were calculated by use of the inverse-square law.

When two sources of dissimilar spectral composition are compared on the bar photometer, an exact equality of sensation is impossible in general. One recognizes a difference of both *quality* and *quantity* in the sensations produced by the two half-fields. By adjusting the position of the screen with respect to the sources, the quantity difference can be made to disappear, leaving only the difference in quality. This is the position of photometric balance from which the intensity of the unknown is computed. Some photometrists have asserted that such a balance is meaningless unless the quality of the two sensations is also the same. However, by moving the photometric screen, any ordinary observer will find a place where the left half-field is undeniably more brilliant than the right and another place where it is undeniably less brilliant. Consequently, there must be some place between these extremes where the two are equally brilliant, though one must keep in mind that the condition of equality of sensation applies only to the particular observer and the particular conditions. The same result must not be expected with any other observer or with the same observer at a different time or with a photometer having a different-size field or a different length of bar.

Candlepower (and with it, all the derived photometric quantities) is a psychophysical concept, as already defined. This statement seems to be in accord with the expressions of numerous experts. Troland,[7] for instance, classes the photometric quantities as psychophysical. Houstoun[8] says, "The meter-candle is thus a hybrid unit, partly objective and partly subjective." Thus if the photometric quantities are defined in the usual way on the basis of a standard candle and a visual comparison, we must not expect the photometric quantities to behave like the

[7] L. T. TROLAND, *J.O.S.A.*, **6**, 1922, p. 527.

[8] R. A. HOUSTOUN, Vision and Color Vision, p. 2, Longmans, Green & Company, New York, 1932.

familiar physical quantities. Suppose that observer *A* measures the intensity of an unknown gaseous-conduction lamp by direct photometric comparison with a candlepower standard and obtains a value of 157 candles. Another observer *B* makes the same measurement with the same apparatus and obtains 206 candles. Both observers have "normal" vision, and each can duplicate his results to within one per cent approximately. Do we say that one or both are wrong, as we did when there was a discrepancy in the measurement of length? Not at all; for *A* the candlepower *is* 157, for *B* it *is* 206, in accordance with the characteristics of psychophysical quantities and as the only possible interpretation of the foregoing definition of intensity.

Everything seems straightforward and satisfactory. But now arises a peculiar situation. Despite the unanimous assertion that photometric concepts are psychophysical, we find them being used universally as if they were purely physical. One might argue that this difficulty is merely a matter of definition— that others may have a different conception of the word *psychophysical* from that given above. The contention of inconsistency is not based on a definition but on the methods actually being used in determining candlepower. We use a physical standard and make visual comparisons with either a Lummer-Brodhun field or a flicker photometer. Even if we pick a particular observer on the basis of certain tests, and call him *the* standard observer, experience shows that we cannot depend upon the consistency of his results from day to day. Also, basing the standard quantities upon the average of a group of observers merely alters the precision and does not change the fundamental fact that the quantities remain psychophysical.

Yet standardization laboratories apparently see no logical inconsistency in reporting tests in candlepower or lumens to three significant figures, as if they were measurements of mass or length, and with no indication that the result depends in the slightest degree upon the observer. This sort of thing has been fostered by the fact that most sources have had similar spectral-energy distributions, so that the results obtained by various carefully selected individuals were not sufficiently different to be noticeable. The comforting sense of security, however, tends to vanish with the advent of some of the newer light sources. In any case, irrespective of the goodness of the approximation, the specification of a psychophysical quantity as if it were a physical quantity is definitely reprehensible from a logical standpoint.

The Visibility Curve.—Let us now turn to a consideration of the so-called visibility curve. A visibility curve may be obtained by use of the ordinary photometric-comparison screen irradiated by sources of homogeneous radiation. Suppose that the left half-field is irradiated with homogeneous radiation of wavelength 0.554μ and of constant magnitude G_0. This constitutes the standard stimulus.[9] The right half-field is irradiated by homogeneous radiation of a known wavelength λ_i and a variable magnitude G_i. The wavelengths and the values of G are physical quantities measured by the ordinary methods of physics. We now use any chosen wavelength λ_1 for the stimulus on the right half-field, and we adjust the magnitude of this stimulus until a brilliance match is obtained with the standard stimulus of the left half-field. The value of the required irradiation J_1 is then recorded. The wavelength is now changed to other values, and the process repeated. *Visibility*[10] v at wavelength λ_i may be defined by the relation*

$$v = \frac{G_0}{G_i}v_0$$

Values of v plotted against λ give a *visibility curve*, such as that of Fig. 3.02. In practice, several modifications of this procedure have been used in order to reduce or eliminate the psychological difficulty of making a brilliance-match in the presence of large differences in hue, but these modifications need not concern us here.[11] The curves obtained by various observers show variations of considerable magnitude in v, as was noted in Chap. III. Curves representing the average of a number of observers are much more reliable, though the variations are still far from negligible. The values adopted at Geneva[12] in 1924

[9] Strictly speaking, the stimulus is the radiation reaching the eye after being reflected from the photometric screen. The assumption is made, that the two half-fields have identical reflecting characteristics, in which case the stimulus and the irradiation are directly related.

[10] Also called *relative visibility*.

* Chap. III.

[11] See, for instance, Coblentz and Emerson: *Bu. Stds. Sci. Paper* 303, 1917.

[12] *C.I.E. Proc.*, 1924, pp. 67, 232.

were those recommended by Gibson and Tyndall[13] as a result of a study of all available data.

Because of frequent misconceptions as to what *visibility* means, let us consider some of the things that it does *not* mean.

It does *not*
- give a measure of sensation.

- give an indication of the relative amount of radiant power at different wavelengths required to give threshold vision.

- give a measure of seeing ability due to radiation of different wavelengths.

- give a characteristic of any one person or an average of any group of persons.

- apply to any test conditions except those actually used. Any variation in experimental method, such as a change in field size or in the value of the standard irradiation or in the conditions of the surround, may be expected to affect the results.

Evidently, the standard values of visibility give a characteristic of a hypothetical standard observer under a definite set of experimental conditions which have only a somewhat remote bearing upon actual seeing conditions.

Another question now intrudes. How is the standard visibility curve to be used? The I.E.S. standards, based on the C.I.E. definitions and approved by the American Standards Association, do a neat bit of circular defining here which brings us back to the starting point with a net gain of exactly zero. They say:[14]

19. *Visibility Factor.*—The visibility factor for radiation of a particular wavelength is the ratio of the luminous flux at that wavelength to the corresponding radiant flux.

3. *Luminous Flux.*—Luminous flux is the time rate of flow of light.

1. *Light.*—For the purposes of illuminating engineering, *light* is radiant energy evaluated according to its capacity to produce visual sensation.

[13] GIBSON and TYNDALL, Visibility of Radiant Energy, *Bu. Stds. Sci. Paper* 475, 1923.

[14] Illuminating Engineering Nomenclature and Photometric Standards, *I.E.S.*, 1932.

Crittenden[15] appears to voice the opinion of photometrists when he says, "In a sense, the kernel of the whole problem of heterochromatic photometry is found in the standard visibility curve representing the sensibility of the accepted 'normal eye' for radiant energy of different wavelengths, and the commission made a very important step forward in adopting data for such a curve." But the actual method of using the visibility curve is not divulged.

The only way of using the visibility data that seems to me to be consistent with the definition of photometric quantities on the basis of visual comparison is to use the data in selecting standard observers who have visibility curves that agree with the standard curve at all points. Assuming that such standard observers can be found and that they will "hold their calibration," this step will put the photometric concepts upon essentially a physical basis and will eliminate the psychophysical classification inherent in the original scheme. But the idea does not seem practicable.

There is still the possibility of defining all photometric concepts on the basis of the spectroradiometric curve (with ordinates expressed in absolute units) and the standard visibility curve, as has been recommended by a number of investigators, notably Ives.[16] We specify a mathematical process by which the spectroradiometric curve is evaluated with respect to the standard visibility curve. The resultant photometric quantities depend only upon the physical measurements entailed in the determination of the spectroradiometric curve, plus the subsequent arbitrary mathematical manipulation. *All photometric concepts therefore become purely physical concepts, quite independent of the observer.*

This is the idea that was in mind when the standard visibility curve was adopted, though apparently a clear statement to that effect has never been made. It is a canon of physics that a concept shall not be defined in more than one way. Now, according to the standard definitions,[14]

6. *Candle.*—The candle is the unit of luminous intensity. The unit used in the United States is a specified fraction of the average

[15] E. C. CRITTENDEN, Report of Sixth Session I.C.I., *I.E.S. Trans.*, **19**, 1924, p. 613.

[16] H. E. IVES, The Units and Nomenclature of Radiation and Illumination, *Astrophys. J.*, **45**, 1917, p. 39.

horizontal candlepower of a group of 45 carbon-filament lamps preserved at the Bureau of Standards, when the lamps are operated at specified voltages.

The candle is the fundamental unit on which all photometric quantities are based. Thus, we are not at liberty to define the photometric entities *also* on the basis of the spectroradiometric curve; for such a procedure would give two definitions for each photometric concept, one giving a psychophysical quantity, and the other a physical quantity. Alternative possibilities lie before us:

1. Keep the old definitions based on visual comparison against a candlepower standard, in which case the standard visibility curve must be abandoned.

2. Scrap the old definitions and base everything upon physical measurements and a standard method of evaluating these measurements.

There is no middle ground. Any attempt to straddle both 1 and 2 is logically untenable. The second alternative appears to be vastly superior to the first. The adoption of the second alternative would completely eliminate the confusing psychophysical concepts which have caused so much difficulty and would place photometric quantities on a sound physical basis. Even though the actual standardization might require the use of the old methods, pending further developments in the technique of precision radiometry, it seems that philosophically such a step would be decidedly beneficial.

Such a modernization also affects the status of the "standard of light." As long as light remained a separate study, quite divorced from the remainder of physics, a standard of light was necessary. When, however, the radiations that evoke visual sensation were found to be merely a part of a wide spectrum, differing throughout in no respect except as to wavelength, the separate standard of light became unnecessary. Yet an immense amount of time has been devoted to the establishment of candlepower standards. We have had standard sperm candles, the Hefner lamp, the pentane lamp, and many other standard sources, including the Planckian radiator recently developed by the Bureau of Standards.[17] All of these sources give a purely

[17] WENSEL, ROESER, BARBROW, and CALDWELL, The Waidner-Burgess Standard of Light, *Bu. Stds. Res. Paper* 325, 1931.

physical quantity, *viz.*, radiant power.   But such a standard is superfluous, since radiant power is already defined on the basis of the three fundamentals length, mass, and time.[18]

In regard to candlepower standards, Ornstein says:

Envisageant le problème du point de vue physique, il n'y a donc aucune nécessité d'introduire une autre unité que l'unité erg par seconde émis par région définie de longueurs d'onde et par unité d'angle solide. En se plaçant au point de vue physique, les difficultés mentionnées par M. Fleury n'existent pas.   Un étalon de lumière n'a aucun sens; on peut donner un sens à la conservation d'un étalon pour la longueur ou pour la masse, à la fixation d'une résistance électrique par un matériel déterminé.   Mais on est aussi peu fondé à conserver des étalons pour la lumière qu'on le serait a construire et à conserver dans un laboratoire d'étalonnage une machine électrique étalon pour contrôler les mesures et les instruments électriques.

Photometric Definitions on a Physical Basis—the Spectro-radiometric Curve.—Turning to the development of the photo-metric concepts on a physical basis and assuming that the concept of energy is known, we can proceed with other radiometric definitions.

Radiant power, or radiant flux, is defined as the time rate of flow of radiant energy.[14]

When radiant power is incident upon a surface, the latter is said to be *irradiated*.   The *irradiation*[19] G at a given point on a surface is defined as the radiant power incident on the surface at that point per unit area of surface.

If the surface radiates, another concept deals with the radiant power *emitted* per unit area.   Since there seems to be no name for this concept, the author has called it *radiosity J*.   The word is similar to luminosity which denotes the corresponding photo-metric quantity.

The *radiant intensity* I_R of any source in a given direction may be defined by the relation

$$I_R = GD^2 \tag{1}$$

where D = the distance from the source to a small receiving sur-face normal to the direction of energy flow.

[18] For further discussion, see L. S. Ornstein, *Rev. d'optique*, **12**, 1933, p. 387.

[19] "Specific irradiation" might be a better name, as was pointed out by Ives, *loc. cit.*

G = the value of the irradiation of this surface.

The measurements are made at a sufficient distance so that I_R is sensibly independent of distance.

The terms *spectral irradiation* G_λ and *spectral radiosity* J_λ will be used to denote properties of continuous spectra at a particular wavelength λ, per micron wavelength band.

Consideration of how radiometric quantities are measured shows that in all cases the operation consists in introducing a device which absorbs some of the radiant power and converts it into another form, such as thermal, chemical, or electrical power. A photographic plate, photoelectric cell, barrier-layer cell, radiation thermopile, bolometer, or other device may be used. In any case, the response is not due directly to any of the quantities Φ, G, or J but is caused by the portion of the radiant power that is absorbed in the particular energy conversion used. The power absorbed is closely related to the irradiation, and the measuring device may be calibrated to measure irradiation. Radiosity and radiant intensity are never measured directly but are obtained always (from measurements of irradiation) by suitable mathematical processes. The same is true of the total radiant power emitted by a source.

When the value of irradiation is to be measured within a very narrow band of wavelengths, as in obtaining data for a spectroradiometric curve, the same measuring methods may be used, though the determinations are complicated by the interposition of a filter or a prism and optical system between the radiometer and the source. Uncertainties in regard to the exact effect of these intermediate devices may make it convenient to regard the spectroradiometer or filter radiometer as a unit and to calibrate it against a Planckian radiator or other radiation standard.

A *Planckian radiator* may be defined as one whose spectral radiosity is expressible by the equation

$$J_\lambda = \frac{C_1}{\lambda^5} \frac{1}{e^{\frac{C_2}{\lambda T}} - 1} \tag{2}$$

The accepted values [20] for C_1 and C_2 are **36,970** and **14,320**,

[20] R. T. BIRGE, Values of the General Physical Constants, *Phys. Rev. Sup.*, **1**, 1929, p. 1.

G. K. BURGESS, The International Temperature Scale, *Bu. Stds. Res. Paper* 22, 1928.

respectively, if T is in degrees Kelvin, λ is in microns, and J_λ is in watts per square centimeter per micron wavelength band. Actual radiators which follow this law, within the limits of experimental error, are easily constructed in a number of ways. It should be realized that the use of such a device in the calibration of radiometers is not a necessity but merely a convenience, and its use in this way is by no means comparable with its use as a superfluous arbitrary "standard of light."

When a surface is irradiated by unpolarized radiation whose direction of energy flow is normal to the surface, *a complete specification of the irradiation of the surface in the neighborhood of any point is given by the spectroradiometric curve obtained at that point, giving the watts per square centimeter per micron as a function of wavelength.*[21] A knowledge of the spectroradiometric data on irradiation permits the calculation of the erythemal, photoelectric, visual, heating, and other effects. Having such a spectroradiometric curve, one can calculate certain numbers specifying the "color" of the radiation; or knowing the reflecting characteristics of the surface, one can calculate the spectral radiosity of the surface and its radiant intensity.

Though the spectroradiometric data give complete information, they are somewhat cumbersome and inconvenient. When we are interested, as we often are, in only one aspect of the irradiation—in its ability to do one particular thing—it is convenient to be able to specify this particular property by a few numbers, preferably by a single number. In the case of the radiosity of a Planckian radiator, the complete information is implied by the specification of a single number, the temperature. The irradiation of any surface caused by a Planckian radiator requires two numbers, the temperature of the radiator and the value of G_λ at a given wavelength. It is conceivable that two numbers might also be used in specifying the radiation from incandescent lamps. Ornstein[18] has made this suggestion as a substitute for the customary photometric quantities, which would then be abandoned. Such a specification, however, does not seem to help with gaseous-conduction lamps, and trouble might be experienced even in specifying the radiation from incandescent lamps having different types of coiled filaments. Thus, we shall

---

[21] For a line spectrum, the corresponding specification consists of a table of G vs. λ.

continue to use the customary photometric units, but we shall
attempt to develop them in a more logical manner.

Luminous Flux.—We are searching for a way to evaluate
any irradiation with respect to its ability to promote seeing. In
this manner, it will be possible to replace the 30 or more numbers
representing the spectroradiometric curve by a single number.
The question now arises as to what particular aspect of vision
should be used as a criterion. Some of the possibilities are

1. Absolute visual threshold:
    a. Large field.
    b. Point source.
2. Visual acuity:
    a. Photopic.
    b. Scotopic.
3. Contrast sensitivity:
    a. Photopic.
    b. Scotopic.
4. Critical frequency:
    a. Photopic.
    b. Scotopic.
5. Equality of brilliance.
6. Equality of sensation by flicker photometer.

Unfortunately, the results obtained by one method will not agree
with those obtained by another. If we are interested primarily
in the detection of lights at great distances, in beacons, light-
houses, marine signals etc., the absolute threshold is the basis
of comparison, and we must choose some method by which we
can evaluate the spectroradiometric curve with respect to its
ability to excite vision with point sources and low values of
irradiation. Two sources will be said to have the same luminous
intensity if they can be detected at the same distance with dark
surroundings and with dark-adapted eyes.

Such a criterion, though useful in its way, would be worthless
for most purposes. A criterion of equal visual acuity or equal
contrast sensitivity would be more useful with photopic vision.
In particular, the evaluation of radiant power with respect to its
ability to give a definite visual acuity seems promising. We have
seen (Chap. XII) that the curves of visual acuity against log J
are of the same shape for all contrasts and, for foveal vision, are
ideally simple in form. Thus evaluation with respect to foveal
visual acuity would give a very good criterion of how the particular radiation would affect seeing. At present, however, the

data on visual acuity with homogeneous stimuli are entirely inadequate for the establishment of a system of units.

We therefore turn, though somewhat reluctantly, to Nos. 5 and 6, the ordinary methods of visual comparison. Apparently, 5 and 6 do not give the same result, though the differences are small. The criterion used in 5 is that two identical half-fields irradiated by the two sources to be compared shall give a brilliance match. The specification of the photometric quantities in terms of the standard visibility curve has the advantage that the units are approximately those to which we have been accustomed. It must be remembered, however, that these units do not in some mysterious way "evaluate the radiant energy according to its capacity to produce visual sensation," except perhaps in a very narrow sense. The standard visibility curve was obtained under a highly artificial set of conditions which have little connection with ordinary seeing. *The innate complexity of vision makes it impossible to obtain any single criterion which will evaluate radiant energy according to its capacity to produce visual sensation.* An evaluation that applies to photopic vision will be absolutely worthless for scotopic vision as well as for the intermediate region of the Purkinje effect. Size of field, irradiation of field, and magnitude and spectral composition of the irradiation of the surround are some of the multitudinous factors that affect the evaluation. It would seem, therefore, that the evaluation must necessarily be an arbitrary affair. It is not highly important *how* we evaluate the spectroradiometric curve, as long as the method is defined in an unambiguous way and gives results that are reasonable. On this basis, the squandering of time on more precise determinations of the visibility curve with more observers, etc., would be quite unjustified, since no matter how carefully the curve is determined it cannot possibly apply exactly to conditions other than those used in its experimental determination and cannot possibly evaluate radiation on a basis of ordinary visual requirements.

We decide, therefore, to define the photometric quantities in an arbitrary manner from the standard visibility curve:

1. The *photometric* quantities shall be obtained from the corresponding *radiometric* quantities by multiplying the latter (at each wavelength) by the corresponding values of v from the standard C.I.E. visibility curve.

2. Values of vJ_λ (or values of vG_λ) shall be directly additive.

It seems that 2 has always been considered as obviously true, but further consideration leads one to doubt if it is either obvious or true. If, for the sake of definiteness, we consider that the visibility function is obtained by the method outlined in The Visibility Curve of this Appendix, we find that its use as in 1 is confined to the evaluation of simple homogeneous radiations against a standard of wavelength 0.554μ. Suppose that a different λ_0 had been used in obtaining the visibility curve. Have we any justification in assuming that the curve would be the same? We compare two sensations evoked by two different radiations falling on separate patches of the retina. The irradiation of the retina due to the standard remains the same throughout the experiment, and it is customary to assume tacitly that in consequence the *sensation* due to the standard remains constant. Yet we know this to be far from true; the sensation for one half-field is altered by any change in size λ or G of the other half-field. Recent studies on the importance of synaptic conduction in the retina lead to the same conclusion.

What happens if the unknown consists of *two* homogeneous radiations? Photometrists assume that if a balance is obtained with G_o against G_i at λ_i, and another balance is obtained with G_o against G_j at λ_j, it is permissible to use direct addition and to predict that $2G_o$ will balance $G_i + G_j$. But there appears to be no basis for such an assumption. Since, however, the whole photometric system must be set up on an arbitrary basis (because of the complexity of vision which does not allow exact specification of visual effects in terms of a single number), the simplest procedure is to introduce 2. On this basis, any spectroradiometric quantity is changed to the corresponding photometric quantity by multiplying the ordinates of the radiometric curve by the proper values of v and integrating over the resulting curve.

It is customary to call the curve of vJ_λ vs. λ a *luminosity curve*. It seems reasonable, therefore, to call the area under the curve the *luminosity*. In fact, the name has been used by several writers[22] with essentially this meaning, though it has not been universally accepted. The term "radiance" has been used more frequently[16] than luminosity but has obvious disadvantages.

[22] See, for instance, HARDY and PERRIN, The Principles of Optics, p. 19 McGraw-Hill Book Company, Inc., New York, 1932.

Luminosity may be defined, therefore, by the relation

$$L = \int_0^\infty v J_\lambda \, d\lambda \qquad (3)$$

If J_λ is in watts per square centimeter per micron, L is said to be in *lightwatts per square cm.*

Similarly, the curve of irradiation gives the photometric quantity known as *illumination*

$$E = \int_0^\infty v G_\lambda \, d\lambda \quad \text{(lightwatts/sq cm)} \qquad (4)$$

The *luminous flux* is obtained from either L or E,

$$F = \int E \, d\sigma$$

or

$$F = \int L \, d\sigma \quad \text{(lightwatts)} \qquad (5)$$

where $d\sigma$ is a differential area, and the integration is performed over the area in which the flux is desired.   In line spectra or combinations, the integrals in Eqs. (3) and (4) must be taken in the sense of Stieltjes integrals.

The lightwatt appears to be a logical and satisfactory unit of luminous flux, though perhaps the name might be improved. The ordinary unit, however, is the *lumen* which was originally defined from the standard candle.   To express results in lumens, it is necessary merely to make an experimental determination of the relation between the lumen and the lightwatt.   One photometric half-field (say the left one) might be irradiated by homogeneous radiation of wavelength 0.554μ and of constant value, say 10^{-5} watt/sq cm.   The right half-field would be irradiated by a standard candle whose distance from the screen could be varied.   This distance would be adjusted until a photometric brilliance-match was obtained, when the illumination of the right half-field would be calculated by use of the inverse-square law.   The best results of such experiments indicate that balance would be obtained when the illumination of the right half-field was 621×10^{-5} lumen/sq cm.   Thus the conversion factor from lightwatts to lumens is

$$1 \text{ lightwatt} = 621 \text{ lumens}[23]$$

[23] Note that the relation is merely a conversion factor from one unit of luminous flux to another and not the "mechanical equivalent of light,"

There remains the definition of *luminous intensity* as a physical quantity. The standard definition[14] is

5. *Luminous Intensity.*—Luminous intensity, of a source of light, in a given direction, is the solid-angular flux density in the direction in question. Hence, it is the luminous flux on a small surface normal to that direction, divided by the solid angle (in steradians) which the surface subtends at the source of light.

According to the definition, luminous intensity is obtained from two measurements, a measurement of luminous flux incident on a small test surface, and a measurement of the solid angle subtended at the source by this surface. The quotient of these two values, as the solid angle approaches zero, is called the luminous intensity in the direction considered. A limit process is implied here, since we are defining a quantity in a given direction and can expect it to be somewhat different in any other direction. For most sources, with the exception of some projectors, a surface one or two inches in diameter at 10 ft distance is found small enough for practical purposes.

This definition is based upon the divergent light cone of Lambert and has persisted for a great many years despite the obvious fact that it has no significance. In order that there may be a divergent light cone, it is essential that the source be a mathematical point. There are no such sources. But, one may argue, let us take the truncated divergent cone having its apex somewhat behind the actual surface source and bounded by the contour of the source. We are still unable to draw the figure or to see that the definition is anything but absurd. How, for instance, does one measure the solid angle subtended by a 2-in. diameter measuring surface when the source is, say, an ordinary mercury-vapor lamp, even though it be placed a mile away? The same condition obtains even in the intensity measurement of a star.

Or one may arbitrarily fix the apex of the divergent light cone at some point on, behind, or in front of the actual luminous surface. In general, however, a different convention is required for each shape of surface in order that the experimental results

---

as it is often called. "Light" can have no mechanical equivalent, since it is not energy and cannot be expressed in ergs, calories, BTU, or any other energy unit.

shall be consistent, and no criterion is implied in the definition by which we can determine whether our experimental results mean anything.

What is actually done in obtaining candlepower? An analysis shows that no one actually tries to measure either the solid angle or the flux. The sole measured quantities are *illumination* and *distance*. Illumination is measured by placing a receiving surface (such as the target of a bolometer, the disk of a barrier-layer cell, or the test plate of a Macbeth illuminometer) normal to the line on which intensity is to be obtained. Suitable tests can be made, if necessary, to insure that the variation in illumination across the finite test surface does not introduce appreciable error. If illumination is measured at several points along the line, the values of E are found to decrease rapidly as the distance D is increased. But the values of ED^2 are found to approach a constant as D becomes larger. *The limit of these values of ED^2 may be defined as the intensity of the source in this direction,* or

$$I = \lim_{D \to \infty} (ED^2) \tag{6}$$

Note that the new treatment eliminates the ambiguity of the old solid-angle definition and gives a simple operational concept. Nothing whatever is said about "point source." The definition applies equally well to any size of source. Intensity becomes a definite physical property of the source and has nothing whatever to do with the distance at which the source is viewed. There seems to be considerable confusion on this point. In most treatments of the subject, the assumption appears to be made that because the inverse-square law was used in determining the intensity, *therefore* it follows that the intensity can have no meaning except at large distances from the source. In other words, intensity is not a property of the source alone but depends also upon the distance to the observer. We are warned that "strictly speaking, intensity applies only to a mathematical point source. But in practice, other sources are said to possess intensity provided they are viewed at a sufficient distance." It seems to me much better to allow the source to keep its candlepower irrespective of what the observer is doing. The only warning required is that accurate calculations of illumination near the source cannot be made by use of the inverse-square law but require more refined methods. Incidentally, this concept of intensity clears up a confusing detail regarding the specification of brightness in candles per unit of projected area, as will be noted presently.

Reflection and Transmission.—The *spectral reflection factor* ρ_λ of a surface may be defined as the ratio of the total reflected radiant power to the total incident radiant power, the incident power being in the form of homogeneous radiation of wavelength λ. The factor can be written equally well on the basis of unit area, or

$$\rho_\lambda = \frac{J}{G} \tag{7}$$

It will generally depend upon angle of incidence.

The *reflection factor* ρ of a surface may be defined as the ratio of the total reflected luminous flux to the total incident luminous flux. Or, using unit area,

$$\rho = \frac{L}{E} \tag{8}$$

In general, ρ will depend upon the spectral quality of the incident radiation and also upon its angle of incidence. Note that the definition applies to any type of surface, diffusing or otherwise. In any case, the total flux emitted by the reflecting surface in all directions is to be obtained, and this can be done by measurements made in various directions plus an integration or by use of an integrating sphere.

If the surface transmits radiation, a similar pair of quantities applies to the *transmitted* radiation.

The spectral transmission factor τ_λ may be defined as the ratio of the total transmitted radiant power to the total incident radiant power, the incident power being in the form of homogeneous radiation of wavelength λ.

Transmission factor τ may be defined as the ratio of the total transmitted luminous flux to the total incident luminous flux. These definitions give a simple relation between the luminosity of the surface and the illumination. Owing to reflected radiation,

$$L = \rho E \tag{9}$$

and owing to transmitted radiation,

$$L = \tau E \tag{10}$$

These relations are *universally true* by definition, irrespective of the reflecting or transmitting characteristics of the surface, and are in striking contrast to the puzzling relations that enter if one uses the customary concept of brightness instead of the concept of luminosity.

Brightness.—The foregoing treatment puts photometric concepts on a physical foundation. Luminous flux, illumination, luminosity, and luminous intensity have been defined on the basis of the spectroradiometric curve and the standard visibility data. These four quantities are sufficient in all cases. But objections may be raised to the omission of the concept of *brightness*. Brightness was a natural outcome of the old system of visual comparison and seems somewhat foreign to the modern physical concept of photometry. It can be fitted into the modern scheme if it seems advisable to do so; but it introduces and always has introduced a great deal of confusion. One of the several standard definitions[14] is

14. *Brightness.*[14]—Brightness is the quotient of the luminous intensity of a surface measured in a given direction by the area of this surface projected on a plane perpendicular to the direction considered.

After one has digested the statement on page 5 of "Illuminating Nomenclature and Photometric Standards":[14] "Mathematically, a solid angle must have a point at its apex; the definition of luminous intensity therefore applies strictly only to a point source," it is somewhat startling to come across *candle per square foot* and *candle per square meter* on page 7. But this is a trivial criticism which disappears when the operational definition of intensity is used instead of the old solid-angle definition.

The brightness of a given luminous surface at a given point may be measured by placing over the surface a black opaque shield which exposes only a known area A of the luminous surface. The candlepower is then measured in the usual way, and the brightness B of the surface at the point is

$$B = \lim_{D \to \infty} \frac{ED^2}{A \cdot \cos \theta} \tag{11}$$

where θ is the angle between the line of measurement and the normal to the luminous surface at the given point. Evidently, brightness can be defined in a straightforward operational manner. In two respects, however, the concept of brightness appears to be inferior to the concept of luminosity:

1. For brightness, the simple relations Eqs. (9) and (10) do not apply. For a perfectly diffusing surface,[24] the equations are complicated merely by a factor π; but for imperfectly diffusing surfaces, Eqs. (9) and (10) cannot be applied at all.

2. It is a question whether the inclusion of the factor *cos θ* in Eq. (11) does more harm than good. The reason for its inclusion was to make B for a perfectly diffusing surface independent of θ and thus relate B more closely to the sensation of brilliance. But it is now realized that there is no theoretical justification for the cosine law of emission, and apparently no surface has been found that obeys the law even within ordinary photometric precision. The advisability of basing a *definition*, even by implication, upon the properties of a hypothetical surface is questionable. Furthermore, in the whole realm of physics and engineering it seems unlikely that one will encounter another quantity containing *projected* area instead of actual area. Often the word "projected" is omitted, which may cause further confusion.

But the principal objection to the concept of brightness is that it includes too much. The word is used for two distinctly different things—obtained in different ways. The standard definitions continue:

"The brightness of *any* surface, in a specified direction, can also be expressed in terms of the lumens per unit area from a perfectly diffusing surface of equal brightness." In other words, the brightness of any surface can be expressed in terms of brightness of another surface of equal brightness.

Expressed in greater detail:[25]

The unit of brightness is the brightness of a perfect diffuser emitting one lumen per unit area. . . . It will be seen that the brightness of *any* surface whatever, when viewed in a definite direction, can be defined by this method, for to say that such a surface has a brightness of B in

[24] By a *perfectly diffusing surface* is meant one that emits radiation according to the cosine law.

[25] Dept. of Sci. & Ind. Res. *Tech. Paper* 1, 1926, p. 9.

a given direction means that the surface when so viewed has a brightness equal to that of a perfect diffuser emitting B lumens/sq ft.

The definitions seem to require a visual comparison between the unknown and a "perfectly diffusing" surface of known luminosity. Apparently, one sets up a "perfectly diffusing" surface beside the one to be measured and varies the illumination on the former until a brilliance match is obtained. Then the luminosity L of the "perfectly diffusing" surface is measured, and the brightness of the unknown is said to be equal numerically to L. That another visual comparison, with all its attendant difficulties about "normal" observers, etc., should be introduced here is unthinkable on the basis of the modern trend toward physical measurements. The inclusion of the nonexistent perfectly diffusing surface in the definition might prove embarrassing. The standard definitions struggle ahead through more than a page on brightness, going rapidly from bad to worse. Need we follow further?

We have seen several objections to the concept of brightness. The name is used to specify two things which are distinct operationally. The simple relations of Eqs. (9) and (10) do not apply to brightness, except for perfectly diffusing surfaces. The use of the projected area instead of the actual area is likely to cause confusion. The only place where brightness appears to have any advantage over luminosity is in visual research using glossy surfaces. In such a case, brightness is perhaps more closely related to sensation than is luminosity. But since practically all research on vision is conducted with surfaces that are as nearly perfectly diffusing as can be obtained, this consideration does not seem of prime importance.

Colorimetry.—Colorimetry has been developed principally as a method of specifying and classifying the reflecting properties of pigments and dyes. It may be treated as a branch of photometry, as has been done in the present book. In this, as in the previous photometric work, it is necessary to distinguish clearly between the subjective and the objective, between the sensation attributes of *hue, saturation, brilliance, chromaticity,* and the physical quantities such as *dominant wavelength, purity,* and *luminosity.*

We have noted that in the visual comparison of two half-fields, the sensations generally differ both in quality and in quantity. Photometry ordinarily considers only the difference in quantity. Colorimetry considers both quality and quantity. Imagine a modification to be made in our previous apparatus so that instead of getting merely a brilliance match between the two half-fields, we get a complete and perfect match. As a result of an immense amount of experimental work, it is universally agreed that *a perfect match never requires the manipulation of more than three controls.** This is the fundamental fact of colorimetry.

The left half-field may be irradiated by the unknown source, while the right half-field is irradiated from three independent sources (called *primary stimuli*) whose magnitudes can be varied at will. The observer adjusts the three controls and when a perfect match is obtained reads the three component radiosities J_1, J_2, and J_3. A set of three numbers J_1, J_2, and J_3, called the *trichromatic coefficients*, thus specifies the color-matching properties of the given radiation under the standardized conditions of the test as regards field size, field illumination, surround illumination, etc. The three values also depend to some extent upon the observer and are functions of the three primary stimuli.

If a series of homogeneous radiations is used for the left half-field to give stimuli of constant radiosity but variable wavelength, *color-mixture data*, such as those of Fig. 13.07, are obtained. These data can be transformed to any other set of primary stimuli. In particular, for the standard C.I.E. system, the curves of Fig. 13.08 are obtained, giving the *distribution coefficients* $\bar{x}$, $\bar{y}$, and $\bar{z}$ for equal-energy spectrum.

The data of Fig. 13.08 and Appendix G can be utilized to obtain trichromatic coefficients from any spectroradiometric curve. The three coefficients are

$$\left.\begin{array}{l} x' = \displaystyle\int_0^\infty \bar{x} J_\lambda \, d\lambda \\[2mm] y' = \displaystyle\int_0^\infty \bar{y} J_\lambda \, d\lambda \\[2mm] z' = \displaystyle\int_0^\infty \bar{z} J_\lambda \, d\lambda \end{array}\right\} \tag{12}$$

If the luminosity is desired, it is obtained from the second integral, or

$$L = \int_0^\infty \bar{y} J_\lambda \, d\lambda \tag{13}$$

* See Guild, Discussion on Vision, Phys. and Opt. Soc., 1932, p. 2.

It is often advantageous to reduce the number of variables to two, thus allowing a two-dimensional representation—the *color triangle*. The foregoing trichromatic coefficients are expressed in terms of their sum, giving the *unified trichromatic coefficients*

$$\left.\begin{aligned} x = \frac{x'}{x' + y' + z'} \\ y = \frac{y'}{x' + y' + z'} \end{aligned}\right\} \tag{14}$$

The trichromatic method is very useful, though it suffers from the defect that the three numbers are not closely related to the

TABLE OF RADIOMETRIC AND PHOTOMETRIC CONCEPTS

Radiometric			Photometric		
Name	Symbol	Unit	Name	Symbol	Unit
Radiant energy.......	....	Ergs / Watt-sec	Light............	Q	Lumen-sec / Lumen-hr
Radiant power (or radiant flux).......	Φ	Watts	Luminous flux.....	F	Lightwatts / Lumens
Irradiation..........	G	Watts/sq cm	Illumination.......	E	Lumens/sq cm / Lumens/sq ft
Spectral irradiation...	G_λ	Watts/sq cm per micron			
Radiosity...........	J	Watts/sq cm	Luminosity........	L	Lumens/sq cm / Lumens/sq ft
Spectral radiosity.....	J_λ	Watts/sq cm per micron	Brightness........	B	Candles/sq cm / Candles/sq ft
Spectral reflection factor............	ρ_λ	Numeric	Reflection factor...	ρ	Numeric
Spectral transmission factor............	τ_λ	Numeric	Transmission factor	τ	Numeric
Spectral radiation factor...............	e_λ	Numeric			
Total radiation factor.	e_t	Numeric			

Luminous efficacy η_l { lightwatts/radiated watt / lumens/radiated watt

Over-all efficacy η_o { lightwatts/input watt / lumens/input watt

sensation attributes of *hue, saturation,* and *brilliance.* In this respect, the alternate system of specification in terms of *dominant wavelength* (λ_d), *purity* (p), and luminosity (Chap. XIII) is preferable, though this system cannot be obtained directly from the spectroradiometric curve. In a few cases, a specification in terms of *color temperature* (T_c) and luminosity is also possible, though this specification can hardly be recommended.

IDENTITIES

1 finsen ≡ 1 viton/sq cm
1 ft-candle ≡ 1 lumen/sq ft   (illumination)
1 meter-candle ≡ 1 lumen/sq meter ≡ 1 lux   (illumination)
1 lux ≡ 1 lumen/sq meter   (illumination)
1 phot ≡ 1 lumen/sq cm   (illumination)
1 ft-lambert ≡ 1 lumen/sq ft   (brightness)
1 lambert ≡ 1 lumen/sq cm   (brightness)

A perfectly diffusing surface having a brightness of 1 lambert has a luminosity of 1 lumen/sq cm.*
A perfectly diffusing surface having a brightness of 1 ft-lambert has a luminosity of 1 lumen/sq ft.*

CONVERSION FACTORS

1 watt-sec $= 10^7$ ergs
1 micron $= 10^{-4}$ cm
1 lightwatt $= 621$ lumens
1 lumen/sq ft $= 1.076$ milliphots
$= 10.76$ lumens/sq meter
$= 1.076 \times 10^{-3}$ lumen/sq cm
1 lux $= 1$ meter-candle
$= 10^{-4}$ phot
$= 0.0929$ lumen/sq ft
1 phot $= 10^4$ lux $= 929$ lumens/sq ft
1 milliphot $= 10$ meter-candles $= 0.929$ lumen/sq ft
1 millilambert $= 0.929$ foot-lambert
1 ft-lambert $= 1.076$ millilamberts
$= 2.21 \times 10^{-3}$ candle/sq in.
$= 3.43 \times 10^{-4}$ candle/sq cm
1 candle/sq cm $= 3.1416$ lamberts
$= 2919$ ft-lamberts
1 finsen $= 1$ viton/sq cm $= 10^{-5}$ erythemalwatt/sq cm
1 erythemalwatt $= 10^5$ vitons
1 erythemalwatt/sq cm $= 10^5$ vitons/sq cm $= 10^5$ finsens

* True, in general, only for perfectly diffusing surfaces.

APPENDIX C

SPECTRAL RADIOSITY OF A PLANCKIAN RADIATOR

Values computed from the equation

$$J\lambda = \frac{C_1}{\lambda^5} \frac{1}{e^{\frac{C_2}{\lambda T}} - 1} \quad \text{(watt cm}^{-2}\mu^{-1})$$

where $C_1 = 36{,}970$.

$C_2 = 14{,}320$.

λ = wavelength in microns.

T = temperature in degrees Kelvin.

All except last line are *relative* values based upon unity at $\lambda = 0.590\mu$. Tables of Appendix C and Appendix D are based upon the computations of J. F. Skogland, *Bu. Stds. Misc. Pub.* 86, 1929, and Frehafer and Snow, *Bu. Stds. Misc. Pub.* 56, 1925.

RELATIVE RADIOSITY

λ	Temperature, degrees Kelvin										
	1999°	Diff.	2019°	Diff.	2039°	Diff.	2059°	Diff.	2079°	Diff.	2099°
0.32μ	0.00075	+ 9	0.00084	+ 8	0.00092	+10	0.00102	+10	0.00112	+11	0.00123
0.33	0.00128	13	0.00141	14	0.00155	14	169	16	185	17	202
0.34	209	19	228	21	249	22	271	23	294	25	319
0.35	328	29	357	30	387	32	419	34	453	35	488
0.36	505	40	545	42	587	46	633	47	680	51	731
0.37	75	6	81	6	87	6	93	7	0.0100	7	0.0107
0.38	0.0110	7	0.0117	8	0.0125	8	0.0133	9	142	9	151
0.39	156	10	166	11	177	11	188	11	199	12	211
0.40	218	13	231	13	244	14	258	14	272	15	287
0.41	299	16	315	17	332	17	349	17	366	19	385
0.42	402	20	422	20	442	21	463	21	484	23	507
0.43	530	25	555	25	580	25	605	26	631	27	658
0.44	690	29	719	30	749	30	779	30	809	32	841
0.45	886	34	920	34	954	35	989	35	0.1024	36	0.1060
0.46	0.1122	38	0.1160	40	0.1200	40	0.1240	40	0.1280	41	0.1321
0.47	0.1403	44	0.1447	44	0.1491	45	0.1536	45	0.1581	46	0.1627
0.48	0.1735	48	0.1783	49	0.1832	49	0.1881	50	0.1931	50	0.1981
0.49	0.2123	52	0.2175	51	0.2228	53	0.2281	54	0.2335	54	0.2389
0.50	0.2571	56	0.2627	56	0.2683	56	0.2739	57	0.2796	56	0.2852
0.51	0.3084	58	0.3142	59	0.3201	58	0.3259	59	0.3318	59	0.3377
0.52	0.3667	60	0.3727	60	0.3787	59	0.3846	59	0.3905	59	0.3964
0.53	0.4323	59	0.4382	59	0.4441	59	0.4500	58	0.4558	58	0.4616
0.54	0.5058	56	0.5114	56	0.5170	56	0.5226	55	0.5281	55	0.5336
0.55	0.5873	51	0.5924	51	0.5975	51	0.6026	50	0.6076	49	0.6125
0.56	0.6773	45	0.6818	43	0.6861	43	0.6904	41	0.6945	41	0.6986
0.57	0.7760	33	0.7793	32	0.7825	32	0.7857	31	0.7888	31	0.7919
0.58	0.8835	18	0.8853	18	0.8871	18	0.8889	17	0.8906	17	0.8923
0.59	1.0000	0	1.0000	0	1.0000	0	1.0000	0	1.0000	0	1.0000
0.60	1.1256	−22	1.1234	−22	1.1212	−22	1.1190	−21	1.1169	−21	1.1148
0.61	1.2605	50	1.2555	48	1.2507	48	1.2459	46	1.2413	45	1.2368
0.62	1.4044	81	1.3963	79	1.3884	77	1.3807	76	1.3731	74	1.3657
0.63	1.5575	118	1.5457	115	1.5342	113	1.5229	109	1.5120	106	1.5014
0.64	1.7195	160	1.7035	155	1.6880	153	1.6727	148	1.6579	144	1.6435
0.65	1.8903	208	1.8695	201	1.8494	196	1.8298	191	1.8107	185	1.7922
0.66	2.0698	262	2.0436	253	2.0183	246	1.9937	238	1.9699	231	1.9468
0.67	2.2576	321	2.2255	310	2.1945	301	2.1644	292	2.1352	283	2.1069
0.68	2.4534	386	2.4148	373	2.3775	362	2.3413	349	2.3064	337	2.2727
0.69	2.6570	457	2.6113	442	2.5671	427	2.5244	413	2.4831	397	2.4434
0.70	2.8679	536	2.8143	515	2.7628	498	2.7130	480	2.6650	461	2.6189
0.71	3.086	62	3.024	596	2.9644	574	2.9070	553	2.8517	531	2.7986
0.72	3.310	71	3.239	68	3.171	65	3.106	63	3.043	607	2.9823
0.73	3.541	80	3.461	78	3.383	74	3.309	71	3.238	69	3.169
0.74	3.777	90	3.687	87	3.600	84	3.516	80	3.436	76	3.360
0.75	4.019	101	3.918	97	3.821	93	3.728	90	3.638	85	3.553
0.76	4.265	113	4.152	108	4.044	103	3.941	99	3.842	94	3.748
$J_{0.59}$ (watt cm^{-2} μ^{-1})	2.756	354	3.110	389	3.499	429	3.928	472	4.400	518	4.918

λ	2099°	Diff.	2119°	Diff.	2139°	Diff.	2158°	Diff.	2178°	Diff.	2198°
0.32μ	0.00123	+12	0.00135	+13	0.00148	+14	0.00162	+15	0.00177	+15	0.00192
0.33	202	18	220	19	239	20	259	22	281	23	304
0.34	319	27	346	28	374	30	404	32	436	33	469
0.35	488	37	526	40	566	42	608	45	653	47	700
0.36	731	52	783	56	839	58	897	60	957	63	0.0102
0.37	0.0107	7	0.0114	7	0.0121	8	0.0129	8	0.0137	8	145
0.38	151	10	161	10	171	10	181	11	192	11	203
0.39	211	12	223	12	235	13	248	14	262	14	276
0.40	287	15	302	16	318	16	334	17	351	18	369
0.41	385	19	404	19	423	20	443	21	464	21	485
0.42	507	23	530	23	553	24	577	25	602	26	628
0.43	658	27	685	28	713	28	741	29	770	30	800
0.44	841	32	873	32	905	33	938	34	972	34	0.1006
0.45	0.1060	37	0.1097	37	0.1134	38	0.1172	38	0.1210	39	0.1249
0.46	0.1321	42	0.1363	42	0.1405	42	0.1447	43	0.1490	43	0.1533
0.47	0.1627	46	0.1673	46	0.1719	47	0.1766	47	0.1813	48	0.1861
0.48	0.1981	50	0.2031	50	0.2083	50	0.2133	51	0.2184	51	0.2235
0.49	0.2389	54	0.2443	54	0.2497	54	0.2551	54	0.2605	55	0.2660
0.50	0.2852	56	0.2909	57	0.2966	57	0.3023	57	0.3080	56	0.3136
0.51	0.3377	58	0.3435	58	0.3493	59	0.3552	58	0.3610	58	0.3667
0.52	0.3964	59	0.4023	58	0.4081	58	0.4139	58	0.4197	57	0.4254
0.53	0.4616	57	0.4673	57	0.4730	57	0.4787	56	0.4843	56	0.4899
0.54	0.5336	54	0.5390	54	0.5444	53	0.5497	53	0.5550	52	0.5602
0.55	0.6125	49	0.6174	49	0.6223	48	0.6271	47	0.6318	47	0.6365
0.56	0.6986	41	0.7027	41	0.7068	40	0.7108	39	0.7147	39	0.7186
0.57	0.7919	30	0.7949	30	0.7979	29	0.8008	29	0.8037	29	0.8066
0.58	0.8923	17	0.8940	17	0.8957	16	0.8973	17	0.8990	16	0.9006
0.59	1.0000	0	1.0000	0	1.0000	0	1.0000	0	1.0000	0	1.0000
0.60	1.1148	−20	1.1128	−20	1.1108	−19	1.1089	−19	1.1070	−19	1.1051
0.61	1.2368	44	1.2324	43	1.2281	42	1.2239	42	1.2197	40	1.2157
0.62	1.3657	72	1.3585	70	1.3515	69	1.3446	67	1.3379	65	1.3314
0.63	1.5014	104	1.4910	101	1.4809	99	1.4710	96	1.4614	94	1.4520
0.64	1.6435	139	1.6296	136	1.6160	132	1.6028	129	1.5899	126	1.5773
0.65	1.7922	180	1.7742	175	1.7567	170	1.7397	165	1.7232	161	1.7071
0.66	1.9468	225	1.9243	218	1.9025	211	1.8814	205	1.8609	199	1.8410
0.67	2.1069	272	2.0797	264	2.0533	256	2.0277	247	2.0028	242	1.9786
0.68	2.2727	326	2.2401	315	2.2086	305	2.1781	296	2.1485	286	2.1199
0.69	2.4434	383	2.4051	370	2.3681	357	2.3324	347	2.2977	336	2.2641
0.70	2.6189	445	2.5744	429	2.5315	415	2.4900	402	2.4498	388	2.4110
0.71	2.7986	511	2.7475	492	2.6983	475	2.6508	458	2.6050	442	2.5608
0.72	2.9823	582	2.9241	559	2.8682	539	2.8143	521	2.7622	502	2.7120
0.73	3.169	65	3.104	63	3.041	60	2.9801	585	2.9216	564	2.8652
0.74	3.360	74	3.286	70	3.216	68	3.148	65	3.083	63	3.020
0.75	3.553	82	3.471	78	3.393	75	3.318	73	3.246	70	3.176
0.76	3.748	90	3.658	87	3.571	83	3.488	80	3.408	76	3.332
$J_{0.59}$	4.918	567	5.485	620	6.105	641	6.746	734	7.480	798	8.278

λ	2198°	Diff.	2218°	Diff.	2238°	Diff.	2258°	Diff.	2278°	Diff.	2298°
0.32μ	0.00192	+17	0.00209	+18	0.00227	+19	0.00246	+20	0.00266	+22	0.00288
0.33	304	25	329	27	356	28	384	30	414	31	445
0.34	469	35	504	38	542	40	582	42	624	44	668
0.35	700	50	750	52	802	56	858	58	916	61	977
0.36	0.0102	7	0.0109	7	0.0116	7	0.0123	8	0.0131	8	0.0139
0.37	145	9	154	9	163	10	173	10	183	10	193
0.38	203	11	214	12	226	12	238	13	251	13	264
0.39	276	14	290	15	305	15	320	16	336	16	352
0.40	369	18	387	18	405	19	424	19	443	20	463
0.41	485	22	507	22	529	23	552	23	575	24	599
0.42	628	26	654	26	680	27	707	27	734	28	762
0.43	800	30	830	31	861	31	892	32	924	32	956
0.44	0.1006	35	0.0141	35	0.1076	36	0.1112	36	0.1148	37	0.1185
0.45	0.1249	39	0.1288	40	0.1328	40	0.1368	41	0.1409	41	0.1450
0.46	0.1533	44	0.1577	44	0.1621	44	0.1665	45	0.1710	45	0.1755
0.47	0.1861	48	0.1909	48	0.1957	48	0.2005	49	0.2054	49	0.2103
0.48	0.2235	51	0.2286	52	0.2338	52	0.2390	52	0.2442	52	0.2494
0.49	0.2660	54	0.2714	55	0.2769	55	0.2824	55	0.2879	55	0.2934
0.50	0.3136	57	0.3193	57	0.3249	57	0.3306	57	0.3363	57	0.3420
0.51	0.3667	58	0.3725	57	0.3782	58	0.3840	57	0.3897	57	0.3954
0.52	0.4254	57	0.4311	57	0.4368	57	0.4425	57	0.4482	56	0.4538
0.53	0.4899	56	0.4955	55	0.5010	55	0.5065	54	0.5119	54	0.5173
0.54	0.5602	52	0.5654	51	0.5705	51	0.5756	50	0.5806	50	0.5856
0.55	0.6365	46	0.6411	45	0.6456	45	0.6501	45	0.6546	44	0.6590
0.56	0.7186	38	0.7224	38	0.7262	38	0.7300	37	0.7337	36	0.7373
0.57	0.8066	28	0.8094	28	0.8122	28	0.8150	27	0.8177	27	0.8204
0.58	0.9006	16	0.9022	15	0.9037	15	0.9052	14	0.9066	14	0.9080
0.59	1.0000	0	1.0000	0	1.0000	0	1.0000	0	1.0000	0	1.0000
0.60	1.1051	−18	1.1033	−18	1.1015	−18	1.0997	−17	1.0980	−17	1.0963
0.61	1.2157	39	1.2108	39	1.2079	38	1.2041	37	1.2004	36	1.1968
0.62	1.3314	63	1.3251	62	1.3189	61	1.3128	60	1.3068	59	1.3009
0.63	1.4520	91	1.4429	89	1.4340	87	1.4253	85	1.4168	83	1.4085
0.64	1.5773	122	1.5651	119	1.5532	116	1.5416	113	1.5303	110	1.5193
0.65	1.7071	156	1.6915	152	1.6763	147	1.6616	143	1.6473	140	1.6333
0.66	1.8410	193	1.8217	188	1.8029	182	1.7847	177	1.7670	172	1.7498
0.67	1.9786	234	1.9552	226	1.9326	219	1.9107	213	1.8894	208	1.8686
0.68	2.1199	277	2.0921	269	2.0652	261	2.0391	251	2.0140	245	1.9895
0.69	2.2641	325	2.2316	314	2.2002	303	2.1699	294	2.1405	285	2.1120
0.70	2.4110	375	2.3735	362	2.3373	349	2.3024	337	2.2687	326	2.2361
0.71	2.5608	427	2.5181	412	2.4769	399	2.4370	385	2.3985	372	2.3613
0.72	2.7120	484	2.6636	467	2.6169	448	2.5721	432	2.5289	417	2.4872
0.73	2.8652	543	2.8109	522	2.7587	502	2.7085	485	2.6602	466	2.6136
0.74	3.020	607	2.9593	581	2.9012	557	2.8455	536	2.7919	516	2.7403
0.75	3.176	67	3.109	64	3.045	614	2.9836	594	2.9242	572	2.8670
0.76	3.332	74	3.258	70	3.188	68	3.120	65	3.055	619	2.9931
$J_{0.59}$	8.278	867	9.145	940	10.085	1016	11.101	1099	12.200	1186	13.386

λ	2298°	Diff.	2318°	Diff.	2338°	Diff.	2358°	Diff.	2378°	Diff.	2398°
0.32μ	0.00288	+23	0.00311	+23	0.00336	+25	0.00361	+27	0.00388	+29	0.00417
0.33	445	33	478	35	513	37	550	39	589	40	629
0.34	668	46	714	49	763	51	814	53	867	56	923
0.35	977	63	0.0104	6	0.0110	7	0.0117	7	0.0124	8	0.0132
0.36	0.0139	8	147	9	156	9	165	9	174	10	184
0.37	193	11	204	11	215	12	227	12	239	12	251
0.38	264	13	277	14	291	15	306	15	321	15	336
0.39	352	17	369	17	386	18	404	19	423	19	442
0.40	463	20	483	21	504	22	526	22	548	23	571
0.41	599	24	623	25	648	26	674	26	700	26	726
0.42	762	28	790	29	819	30	849	30	879	31	910
0.43	956	33	989	34	0.1023	34	0.1057	34	0.1091	35	0.1126
0.44	0.1185	37	0.1222	38	0.1260	38	0.1298	39	0.1337	39	0.1376
0.45	0.1450	42	0.1492	42	0.1534	43	0.1577	43	0.1620	43	0.1663
0.46	0.1755	46	0.1801	46	0.1847	47	0.1894	47	0.1941	47	0.1988
0.47	0.2103	50	0.2153	49	0.2202	50	0.2252	50	0.2302	51	0.2353
0.48	0.2494	53	0.2547	53	0.2600	53	0.2653	53	0.2706	54	0.2760
0.49	0.2934	55	0.2989	55	0.3044	55	0.3099	55	0.3154	55	0.3209
0.50	0.3420	56	0.3476	57	0.3533	56	0.3589	56	0.3645	56	0.3701
0.51	0.3954	57	0.4011	57	0.4068	56	0.4124	56	0.4180	56	0.4236
0.52	0.4538	56	0.4594	56	0.4650	55	0.4705	55	0.4760	55	0.4815
0.53	0.5173	54	0.5227	53	0.5280	52	0.5332	52	0.5384	52	0.5436
0.54	0.5856	50	0.5906	49	0.5955	49	0.6004	48	0.6052	48	0.6100
0.55	0.6590	44	0.6634	43	0.6677	43	0.6720	43	0.6763	42	0.6805
0 56	0.7373	36	0.7409	36	0.7445	35	0.7480	35	0.7515	34	0.7549
0.57	0.8204	27	0.8231	26	0.8257	25	0.8282	25	0.8307	24	0.8331
0.58	0.9080	14	0.9094	14	0.9108	14	0.9122	13	0.9135	13	0.9148
0.59	1.0000	0	1.0000	0	1.0000	0	1.0000	0	1.0000	0	1.0000
0.60	1.0963	−16	1.0947	−15	1.0932	−16	1.0916	−15	1.0901	−16	1.0885
0.61	1.1968	36	1.1932	36	1.1896	34	1.1862	33	1.1829	33	1.1796
0.62	1.3009	58	1.2951	56	1.2895	55	1.2840	53	1.2787	53	1.2734
0.63	1.4085	81	1.4004	79	1.3925	78	1.3847	76	1.3771	74	1.3697
0.64	1.5193	107	1.5086	105	1.4981	103	1.4878	100	1.4778	98	1.4680
0.65	1.6333	137	1.6196	134	1.6062	130	1.5932	127	1.5805	124	1.5681
0.66	1.7498	168	1.7330	164	1.7166	160	1.7006	156	1.6850	151	1.6699
0.67	1.8686	202	1.8484	197	1.8287	190	1.8097	186	1.7911	181	1.7730
0.68	1.9895	238	1.9657	231	1.9426	225	1.9201	219	1.8982	212	1.8770
0.69	2.1120	276	2.0844	268	2.0576	261	2.0315	253	2.0062	245	1.9817
0.70	2.2361	317	2.2044	307	2.1737	298	2.1439	289	2.1150	281	2.0869
0.71	2.3613	360	2.3253	349	2.2904	338	2.2566	327	2.2239	317	2.1922
0.72	2.4872	404	2.4468	392	2.4076	380	2.3696	368	2.3328	356	2.2972
0.73	2.6136	450	2.5686	437	2.5249	423	2.4826	409	2.4417	396	2.4021
0.74	2.7403	499	2.6904	483	2.6421	467	2.5954	451	2.5503	435	2.5068
0.75	2.8670	551	2.8119	532	2.7587	512	2.7075	494	2.6581	477	2.6104
0.76	2.9931	600	2.9331	582	2.8749	561	2.8188	541	2.7647	521	2.7126
$J_{0.59}$	13.39	127	14.66	138	16.04	147	17.51	159	19.10	169	20.79

λ	2398°	Diff.	2418°	Diff.	2438°	Diff.	2458°	Diff.	2478°	Diff.	2498°
0.32μ	0.00417	+30	0.00447	+31	0.00479	+34	0.00513	+36	0.00549	+38	0.00587
0.33	629	43	672	45	717	47	764	50	814	52	866
0.34	923	56	979	61	0.0104	6	0.0110	7	0.0117	7	0.0124
0.35	0.0132	8	0.0140	8	148	8	156	9	165	9	174
0.36	184	10	194	11	205	11	216	11	227	12	239
0.37	251	13	264	13	277	14	291	14	305	15	320
0.38	336	16	352	16	368	17	385	17	402	18	420
0.39	442	19	461	20	481	20	501	21	522	22	544
0.40	571	23	594	24	618	24	642	24	666	25	691
0.41	726	27	753	28	781	28	809	29	838	29	867
0.42	910	32	942	32	974	32	0.1006	33	0.1039	34	0.1073
0.43	0.1126	36	0.1162	36	0.1198	37	0.1235	37	0.1272	38	0.1310
0.44	0.1376	40	0.1416	40	0.1456	41	0.1497	41	0.1538	42	0.1580
0.45	0.1663	44	0.1707	44	0.1751	45	0.1796	45	0.1841	45	0.1886
0.46	0.1988	47	0.2035	48	0.2083	48	0.2131	49	0.2180	48	0.2228
0.47	0.2353	51	0.2404	51	0.2455	51	0.2506	52	0.2558	51	0.2609
0.48	0.2760	53	0.2813	54	0.2867	53	0.2920	54	0.2974	54	0.3028
0.49	0.3209	55	0.3264	55	0.3319	55	0.3374	56	0.3430	56	0.3486
0.50	0.3701	56	0.3757	56	0.3813	56	0.3869	56	0.3925	56	0.3981
0.51	0.4236	56	0.4292	56	0.4348	56	0.4404	55	0.4459	56	0.4515
0.52	0.4815	55	0.4870	54	0.4924	54	0.4978	53	0.5031	54	0.5085
0.53	0.5436	52	0.5488	51	0.5539	51	0.5590	51	0.5641	50	0.5691
0.54	0.6100	47	0.6147	47	0.6194	47	0.6241	46	0.6287	46	0.6333
0.55	0.6805	41	0.6846	41	0.6887	41	0.6928	40	0.6968	40	0.7008
0.56	0.7549	34	0.7583	34	0.7617	33	0.7650	32	0.7682	32	0.7714
0.57	0.8331	24	0.8355	24	0.8379	24	0.8403	23	0.8426	23	0.8449
0.58	0.9148	13	0.9161	13	0.9174	13	0.9187	13	0.9200	13	0.9213
0.59	1.0000	0	1.0000	0	1.0000	0	1.0000	0	1.0000	0	1.0000
0.60	1.0885	−15	1.0870	−16	1.0854	−15	1.0839	−15	1.0824	−14	1.0810
0.61	1.1796	32	1.1764	32	1.1732	31	1.1701	31	1.1670	30	1.1640
0.62	1.2734	52	1.2682	50	1.2632	49	1.2583	49	1.2534	48	1.2486
0.63	1.3697	73	1.3624	71	1.3553	69	1.3484	68	1.3416	67	1.3349
0.64	1.4680	96	1.4584	93	1.4491	90	1.4401	90	1.4311	88	1.4223
0.65	1.5681	121	1.5560	117	1.5443	114	1.5329	112	1.5217	110	1.5107
0.66	1.6699	147	1.6552	144	1.6408	140	1.6268	136	1.6132	134	1.5998
0.67	1.7730	177	1.7553	171	1.7382	167	1.7215	162	1.7053	158	1.6895
0.68	1.8770	206	1.8564	201	1.8363	196	1.8167	190	1.7977	185	1.7792
0.69	1.9817	238	1.9579	232	1.9347	226	1.9121	219	1.8902	213	1.8689
0.70	2.0869	273	2.0596	264	2.0332	257	2.0075	249	1.9826	242	1.9584
0.71	2.1922	308	2.1614	298	2.1316	289	2.1027	281	2.0746	272	2.0474
0.72	2.2972	344	2.2628	332	2.2296	322	2.1974	313	2.1661	304	2.1357
0.73	2.4021	381	2.3640	369	2.3271	357	2.2914	346	2.2568	336	2.2232
0.74	2.5068	421	2.4647	407	2.4240	394	2.3846	382	2.3464	369	2.3095
0.75	2.6104	461	2.5643	446	2.5197	431	2.4766	416	2.4350	403	2.3947
0.76	2.7126	502	2.6624	483	2.6141	467	2.5674	451	2.5223	437	2.4786
$J_{0.59}$	20.79	182	22.61	194	24.55	207	26.62	221	28.83	235	31.18

λ	2498°	Diff.	2518°	Diff.	2538°	Diff.	2558°	Diff.	2578°	Diff.	2598°
0.32μ	0.00587	+39	0.00626	+42	0.00668	+43	0.00711	+46	0.00757	+47	0.00804
0.33	866	54	920	57	977	63	0.0104	6	0.0110	6	0.0116
0.34	0.0124	7	0.0131	8	0.0139	8	147	8	155	9	164
0.35	174	9	183	10	193	10	203	11	214	11	225
0.36	239	12	251	12	263	13	276	13	289	14	303
0.37	320	15	335	15	350	16	366	16	382	17	399
0.38	420	19	439	19	458	19	477	20	497	20	517
0.39	544	22	566	22	588	23	611	24	635	24	659
0.40	691	26	717	26	743	27	770	28	798	28	826
0.41	867	30	897	30	927	31	958	32	990	32	0.1022
0.42	0.1073	34	0.1107	34	0.1141	35	0.1176	36	0.1212	36	0.1248
0.43	0.1310	38	0.1348	38	0.1386	39	0.1425	40	0.1465	40	0.1505
0.44	0.1580	42	0.1622	42	0.1664	43	0.1707	43	0.1750	44	0.1794
0.45	0.1886	46	0.1932	46	0.1978	47	0.2025	47	0.2072	47	0.2119
0.46	0.2228	49	0.2277	50	0.2327	50	0.2377	50	0.2427	50	0.2477
0.47	0.2609	52	0.2661	52	0.2713	52	0.2765	52	0.2817	53	0.2870
0.48	0.3028	54	0.3082	54	0.3136	54	0.3190	54	0.3244	54	0.3298
0.49	0.3486	55	0.3541	55	0.3596	55	0.3651	55	0.3706	55	0.3761
0.50	0.3981	55	0.4036	56	0.4092	55	0.4147	55	0.4202	55	0.4257
0.51	0.4515	55	0.4570	54	0.4624	54	0.4678	54	0.4732	54	0.4786
0.52	0.5085	53	0.5138	53	0.5191	52	0.5243	52	0.5295	52	0.5347
0.53	0.5691	50	0.5741	50	0.5791	49	0.5840	49	0.5889	48	0.5937
0.54	0.6333	45	0.6378	45	0.6423	45	0.6468	44	0.6512	44	0.6556
0.55	0.7008	39	0.7047	39	0.7086	39	0.7125	38	0.7163	38	0.7201
0.56	0.7714	32	0.7746	32	0.7778	31	0.7809	31	0.7840	31	0.7871
0.57	0.8449	23	0.8472	23	0.8495	22	0.8517	22	0.8539	22	0.8561
0.58	0.9213	12	0.9225	12	0.9237	12	0.9249	12	0.9261	11	0.9272
0.59	1.0000	0	1.0000	0	1.0000	0	1.0000	0	1.0000	0	1.0000
0.60	1.0810	−14	1.0796	−14	1.0782	−13	1.0769	−13	1.0756	−13	1.0743
0.61	1.1640	29	1.1611	29	1.1582	28	1.1554	28	1.1526	28	1.1498
0.62	1.2486	46	1.2440	45	1.2395	45	1.2350	44	1.2306	43	1.2263
0.63	1.3349	65	1.3284	64	1.3220	62	1.3158	61	1.3097	60	1.3037
0.64	1.4223	85	1.4138	83	1.4055	82	1.3973	80	1.3893	78	1.3815
0.65	1.5107	107	1.5000	104	1.4896	102	1.4794	100	1.4694	98	1.4596
0.66	1.5998	130	1.5868	127	1.5741	124	1.5617	121	1.5496	118	1.5378
0.67	1.6895	155	1.6740	151	1.6589	147	1.6442	144	1.6298	141	1.6157
0.68	1.7792	181	1.7611	176	1.7435	171	1.7264	167	1.7097	163	1.6934
0.69	1.8689	207	1.8482	203	1.8279	197	1.8082	192	1.7890	186	1.7704
0.70	1.9584	236	1.9348	229	1.9119	223	1.8896	217	1.8679	211	1.8468
0.71	2.0474	265	2.0209	257	1.9952	250	1.9702	243	1.9459	236	1.9223
0.72	2.1357	295	2.1062	286	2.0776	278	2.0498	270	2.0228	263	1.9965
0.73	2.2232	326	2.1906	316	2.1590	307	2.1283	298	2.0985	289	2.0696
0.74	2.3095	358	2.2737	346	2.2391	336	2.2055	326	2.1729	316	2.1413
0.75	2.3947	390	2.3557	378	2.3179	366	2.2813	355	2.2458	343	2.2115
0.76	2.4786	424	2.4362	410	2.3952	396	2.3556	384	2.3172	371	2.2801
$J_{0.59}$	31.18	250	33.68	266	36.34	282	39.16	300	42.16	317	45.33

λ	2598°	Diff.	2618°	Diff.	2638°	Diff.	2658°	Diff.	2678°	Diff.	2698°
0.32μ	0.00804	+50	0.00854	+52	0.00906	+55	0.00961	+59	0.0102	+ 6	0.0108
0.33	0.0116	7	0.0123	7	0.0130	7	0.0137	8	145	8	153
0.34	164	9	173	9	182	9	191	10	201	10	211
0.35	225	11	236	12	248	12	260	12	272	13	285
0.36	303	14	317	14	331	15	346	16	362	16	378
0.37	399	17	416	18	434	18	452	19	471	19	490
0.38	517	21	538	21	559	22	581	22	603	23	626
0.39	659	24	683	25	708	26	734	26	760	26	786
0.40	826	28	854	29	883	30	913	30	943	30	973
											0.1189
0.41	0.1022	32	0.1054	33	0.1087	34	0.1121	34	0.1155	34	
0.42	0.1248	36	0.1284	37	0.1321	38	0.1359	38	0.1397	38	0.1435
0.43	0.1505	40	0.1545	41	0.1586	41	0.1627	42	0.1669	42	0.1711
0.44	0.1794	44	0.1838	45	0.1883	45	0.1928	45	0.1973	46	0.2019
0.45	0.2119	47	0.2166	48	0.2214	48	0.2262	48	0.2310	49	0.2359
0.46	0.2477	50	0.2527	51	0.2578	51	0.2629	51	0.2680	51	0.2731
0.47	0.2870	53	0.2923	53	0.2976	53	0.3029	53	0.3082	53	0.3135
0.48	0.3298	54	0.3352	55	0.3407	54	0.3461	55	0.3516	54	0.3570
0.49	0.3761	55	0.3816	55	0.3871	55	0.3926	55	0.3981	55	0.4036
0.50	0.4257	55	0.4312	55	0.4367	55	0.4422	55	0.4477	54	0.4531
0.51	0.4786	54	0.4840	54	0.4894	54	0.4948	53	0.5001	53	0.5054
0.52	0.5347	51	0.5398	51	0.5449	51	0.5500	51	0.5551	51	0.5602
0.53	0.5937	48	0.5985	48	0.6033	47	0.6080	47	0.6127	47	0.6174
0.54	0.6556	43	0.6599	43	0.6642	43	0.6685	42	0.6697	42	0.6739
0.55	0.7201	37	0.7238	37	0.7275	37	0.7312	36	0.7348	36	0.7384
0.56	0.7871	30	0.7901	29	0.7930	29	0.7959	29	0.7988	29	0.8017
0.57	0.8561	22	0.8583	21	0.8604	21	0.8625	21	0.8646	20	0.8666
0.58	0.9272	11	0.9283	11	0.9294	11	0.9305	11	0.9316	11	0.9327
0.59	1.0000	0	1.0000	0	1.0000	0	1.0000	0	1.0000	0	1.0000
0.60	1.0743	−13	1.0730	−12	1.0718	−13	1.0705	−12	1.0693	−12	1.0681
0.61	1.1498	27	1.1471	26	1.1445	26	1.1419	25	1.1394	25	1.1369
0.62	1.2263	42	1.2221	41	1.2180	41	1.2139	40	1.2099	39	1.2060
0.63	1.3037	59	1.2978	58	1.2920	57	1.2863	55	1.2808	55	1.2753
0.64	1.3815	77	1.3738	75	1.3663	72	1.3591	71	1.3520	71	1.3449
0.65	1.4596	96	1.4500	93	1.4407	91	1.4316	90	1.4226	88	1.4138
0.66	1.5378	116	1.5262	113	1.5149	111	1.5038	108	1.4930	106	1.4824
0.67	1.6157	137	1.6020	133	1.5887	130	1.5757	129	1.5628	124	1.5504
0.68	1.6934	159	1.6775	155	1.6620	151	1.6469	148	1.6321	144	1.6177
0.69	1.7704	181	1.7523	177	1.7346	173	1.7173	168	1.7005	164	1.6841
0.70	1.8468	205	1.8263	200	1.8063	194	1.7869	191	1.7678	185	1.7493
0.71	1.9223	230	1.8993	224	1.8769	218	1.8551	213	1.8338	207	1.8131
0.72	1.9965	256	1.9709	248	1.9461	240	1.9221	235	1.8986	229	1.8757
0.73	2.0696	281	2.0415	272	2.0143	265	1.9878	257	1.9621	251	1.9370
0.74	2.1413	307	2.1106	297	2.0809	289	2.0520	281	2.0239	273	1.9966
0.75	2.2115	333	2.1782	323	2.1459	314	2.1145	304	2.0841	296	2.0545
0.76	2.2801	360	2.2441	349	2.2092	339	2.1753	329	2.1424	319	2.1105
$J_{0.59}$	45.33	335	48.68	354	52.22	375	55.97	395	59.92	416	64.08

λ	2698°	Diff.	2718°	Diff.	2738°	Diff.	2758°	Diff.	2778°	Diff.	2798°
0.32μ	0.0108	+ 6	0.0114	+ 6	0.0127	+ 7	0.0127	+ 7	0.0134	+ 7	0.0141
0.33	153	8	161	8	169	9	178	9	187	10	197
0.34	211	11	222	11	233	11	244	11	255	12	267
0.35	285	13	298	14	312	14	326	14	340	15	355
0.36	378	16	394	17	411	17	428	17	445	18	463
0.37	490	20	510	20	530	20	550	21	571	22	593
0.38	626	23	649	24	673	24	697	25	722	25	747
0.39	786	27	813	28	841	28	869	29	898	29	927
0.40	973	31	0.1004	32	0.1036	32	0.1068	33	0.1101	33	0.1134
0.41	0.1189	35	0.1224	36	0.1260	36	0.1296	36	0.1332	37	0.1369
0.42	0.1435	39	0.1474	39	0.1513	40	0.1553	40	0.1593	41	0.1634
0.43	0.1711	43	0.1754	43	0.1797	43	0.1840	44	0.1884	44	0.1928
0.44	0.2019	46	0.2065	46	0.2111	47	0.2158	47	0.2205	47	0.2252
0.45	0.2359	49	0.2408	49	0.2457	50	0.2507	50	0.2557	50	0.2607
0.46	0.2731	52	0.2783	51	0.2834	52	0.2886	52	0.2938	53	0.2991
0.47	0.3135	54	0.3189	53	0.3242	54	0.3296	53	0.3349	54	0.3403
0.48	0.3570	55	0.3625	54	0.3679	55	0.3734	54	0.3788	55	0.3843
0.49	0.4036	55	0.4091	55	0.4146	55	0.4201	54	0.4255	54	0.4309
0.50	0.4531	54	0.4585	54	0.4639	54	0.4693	54	0.4747	53	0.4800
0.51	0.5054	52	0.5106	53	0.5159	52	0.5211	52	0.5263	51	0.5314
0.52	0.5602	50	0.5652	50	0.5702	49	0.5751	49	0.5800	49	0.5849
0.53	0.6174	46	0.6220	46	0.6266	46	0.6312	46	0.6358	45	0.6403
0.54	0.6739	41	0.6810	41	0.6851	41	0.6892	41	0.6933	40	0.6973
0.55	0.7384	35	0.7419	35	0.7454	35	0.7489	35	0.7524	34	0.7558
0.56	0.8017	28	0.8045	28	0.8073	28	0.8101	28	0.8129	27	0.8156
0.57	0.8666	20	0.8686	20	0.8706	20	0.8726	19	0.8745	19	0.8764
0.58	0.9327	11	0.9338	11	0.9349	11	0.9360	10	0.9370	9	0.9379
0.59	1.0000	0	1.0000	0	1.0000	0	1.0000	0	1.0000	0	1.0000
0.60	1.0681	−11	1.0670	−12	1.0658	−12	1.0646	−11	1.0635	−11	1.0624
0.61	1.1369	25	1.1344	24	1.1320	24	1.1296	23	1.1273	23	1.1250
0.62	1.2060	38	1.2022	38	1.1984	37	1.1947	36	1.1911	36	1.1875
0.63	1.2753	53	1.2700	52	1.2648	51	1.2597	51	1.2546	49	1.2497
0.64	1.3449	71	1.3378	69	1.3309	67	1.3242	65	1.3177	63	1.3114
0.65	1.4138	86	1.4052	84	1.3968	83	1.3885	81	1.3804	79	1.3725
0.66	1.4824	104	1.4720	101	1.4619	99	1.4520	97	1.4423	94	1.4329
0.67	1.5504	122	1.5382	119	1.5263	116	1.5147	114	1.5033	111	1.4922
0.68	1.6177	141	1.6036	136	1.5898	134	1.5764	131	1.5633	128	1.5505
0.69	1.6841	161	1.6680	156	1.6524	153	1.6371	149	1.6222	146	1.6076
0.70	1.7493	181	1.7312	176	1.7136	172	1.6964	168	1.6796	163	1.6633
0.71	1.8131	201	1.7930	196	1.7734	191	1.7543	186	1.7357	181	1.7176
0.72	1.8757	222	1.8535	216	1.8319	211	1.8108	205	1.7903	199	1.7704
0.73	1.9370	244	1.9126	237	1.8889	231	1.8658	224	1.8434	218	1.8216
0.74	1.9966	265	1.9701	259	1.9442	251	1.9191	244	1.8947	237	1.8710
0.75	2.0545	287	2.0258	279	1.9979	271	1.9708	264	1.9444	256	1.9188
0.76	2.1105	309	2.0796	300	2.0496	292	2.0204	283	1.9921	274	1.9647
$J_{0.59}$	64.08	439	68.47	461	73.08	486	77.94	509	83.03	536	88.39

λ	2798°	Diff.	2818°	Diff.	2838°	Diff.	2858°	Diff.	2878°	Diff.	2898°
0.32μ	0.0141	+ 7	0.0148	+ 8	0.0156	+ 8	0.0164	+ 9	0.0173	+ 9	0.0182
0.33	197	10	207	10	217	10	227	11	238	11	249
0.34	267	12	279	13	292	13	305	14	319	14	333
0.35	355	15	370	16	386	16	402	17	419	17	436
0.36	463	19	482	19	501	19	520	20	540	21	561
0.37	593	22	615	23	638	23	651	24	685	24	709
0.38	747	26	773	27	800	27	827	27	854	28	882
0.39	927	30	957	30	987	31	0.1018	31	0.1049	32	0.1081
0.40	0.1134	34	0.1168	34	0.1202	34	0.1236	35	0.1271	35	0.1306
0.41	0.1369	38	0.1407	38	0.1445	38	0.1483	39	0.1522	39	0.1551
0.42	0.1634	41	0.1675	42	0.1717	42	0.1759	42	0.1801	43	0.1844
0.43	0.1928	44	0.1972	45	0.2017	45	0.2062	46	0.2108	46	0.2154
0.44	0.2252	48	0.2300	48	0.2348	48	0.2396	49	0.2445	49	0.2494
0.45	0.2607	50	0.2657	51	0.2708	51	0.2759	51	0.2810	51	0.2861
0.46	0.2991	52	0.3043	52	0.3095	53	0.3148	53	0.3201	53	0.3254
0.47	0.3403	54	0.3457	54	0.3511	54	0.3565	54	0.3619	54	0.3673
0.48	0.3843	55	0.3898	54	0.3952	55	0.4007	54	0.4061	55	0.4116
0.49	0.4309	54	0.4363	55	0.4418	54	0.4472	54	0.4526	55	0.4581
0.50	0.4800	54	0.4854	53	0.4907	53	0.4960	53	0.5013	53	0.5066
0.51	0.5314	52	0.5366	51	0.5417	51	0.5468	50	0.5518	51	0.5569
0.52	0.5849	49	0.5898	48	0.5946	48	0.5994	48	0.6042	48	0.6090
0.53	0.6403	45	0.6448	44	0.6492	44	0.6536	44	0.6580	44	0.6624
0.54	0.6973	40	0.7013	40	0.7053	40	0.7093	39	0.7132	38	0.7170
0.55	0.7558	34	0.7592	34	0.7626	34	0.7660	33	0.7693	33	0.7726
0.56	0.8156	27	0.8183	27	0.8210	27	0.8237	26	0.8263	26	0.8289
0.57	0.8764	19	0.8783	19	0.8802	19	0.8821	18	0.8839	18	0.8857
0.58	0.9379	10	0.9389	10	0.9399	10	0.9409	9	0.9418	10	0.9428
0.59	1.0000	0	1.0000	0	1.0000	0	1.0000	0	1.0000	0	1.0000
0.60	1.0624	− 11	1.0613	− 11	1.0602	− 10	1.0592	− 10	1.0582	− 11	1.0571
0.61	1.1250	23	1.1227	22	1.1205	22	1.1183	21	1.1162	21	1.1141
0.62	1.1875	35	1.1840	35	1.1805	35	1.1770	33	1.1737	33	1.1704
0.63	1.2497	49	1.2448	48	1.2400	48	1.2352	46	1.2306	45	1.2261
0.64	1.3114	63	1.3051	61	1.2990	60	1.2930	60	1.2870	58	1.2812
0.65	1.3725	77	1.3640	76	1.3572	75	1.3497	73	1.3424	72	1.3352
0.66	1.4329	93	1.4236	91	1.4145	90	1.4055	87	1.3968	86	1.3882
0.67	1.4922	109	1.4813	106	1.4707	104	1.4603	103	1.4500	100	1.4400
0.68	1.5505	125	1.5380	123	1.5257	120	1.5137	117	1.5020	115	1.4905
0.69	1.6076	142	1.5934	139	1.5795	136	1.5659	133	1.5526	130	1.5396
0.70	1.6633	159	1.6474	156	1.6318	152	1.6166	149	1.6017	145	1.5872
0.71	1.7176	177	1.6999	172	1.6827	169	1.6658	165	1.6493	161	1.6332
0.72	1.7704	195	1.7509	190	1.7319	185	1.7134	181	1.6953	177	1.6776
0.73	1.8216	213	1.8003	207	1.7796	202	1.7594	198	1.7396	192	1.7204
0.74	1.8710	231	1.8479	225	1.8254	219	1.8035	213	1.7822	208	1.7614
0.75	1.9188	249	1.8939	243	1.8696	236	1.8460	230	1.8230	224	1.8006
0.76	1.9647	267	1.9380	260	1.9120	254	1.8866	246	1.8620	240	1.8380
$J_{0.59}$	88.39	561	94.00	588	99.88	617	106.05	644	112.49	675	119.24

λ	2898°	Diff.	2918°	Diff.	2938°	Diff.	2958°	Diff.	2978°	Diff.	2998°
0.32μ	0.0182	+ 9	0.0191	+ 9	0.0200	+10	0.0210	+10	0.0220	+10	0.0230
0.33	249	11	260	12	272	12	284	13	297	13	310
0.34	333	14	347	15	362	15	377	16	393	16	409
0.35	436	17	454	18	472	18	490	19	509	19	528
0.36	561	21	582	21	603	22	625	22	647	23	670
0.37	709	25	734	25	759	25	784	26	810	26	836
0.38	882	28	910	29	939	29	968	30	998	31	0.1029
0.39	0.1081	32	0.1113	33	0.1146	33	0.1179	34	0.1213	34	0.1247
0.40	0.1306	36	0.1342	37	0.1379	37	0.1416	38	0.1454	38	0.1492
0.41	0.1551	40	0.1601	41	0.1642	40	0.1682	41	0.1723	42	0.1765
0.42	0.1844	43	0.1887	44	0.1931	44	0.1975	44	0.2019	45	0.2064
0.43	0.2154	47	0.2201	47	0.2248	48	0.2296	47	0.2343	48	0.2391
0.44	0.2494	49	0.2543	50	0.2593	50	0.2643	50	0.2693	50	0.2743
0.45	0.2861	51	0.2912	52	0.2964	52	0.3016	52	0.3068	52	0.3120
0.46	0.3254	53	0.3307	53	0.3360	54	0.3414	53	0.3467	53	0.3520
0.47	0.3673	54	0.3727	54	0.3781	55	0.3836	54	0.3890	54	0.3944
0.48	0.4116	54	0.4170	55	0.4225	54	0.4279	55	0.4334	54	0.4388
0.49	0.4581	54	0.4635	54	0.4689	53	0.4742	54	0.4796	53	0.4849
0.50	0.5066	52	0.5118	52	0.5170	52	0.5222	52	0.5274	52	0.5326
0.51	0.5569	51	0.5620	50	0.5670	49	0.5719	50	0.5769	49	0.5818
0.52	0.6090	47	0.6137	47	0.6184	46	0.6230	46	0.6276	46	0.6322
0.53	0.6624	43	0.6667	43	0.6710	42	0.6752	42	0.6794	42	0.6836
0.54	0.7170	38	0.7208	37	0.7245	37	0.7282	37	0.7319	37	0.7356
0.55	0.7726	32	0.7758	32	0.7790	31	0.7821	31	0.7852	31	0.7883
0.56	0.8289	25	0.8314	25	0.8339	25	0.8364	25	0.8389	24	0.8413
0.57	0.8857	18	0.8875	17	0.8892	17	0.8909	17	0.8926	17	0.8943
0.58	0.9428	9	0.9437	9	0.9446	9	0.9455	9	0.9464	9	0.9473
0.59	1.0000	0	1.0000	0	1.0000	0	1.0000	0	1.0000	0	1.0000
0.60	1.0571	−10	1.0561	−10	1.0551	− 9	1.0542	−10	1.0532	− 9	1.0523
0.61	1.1141	21	1.1120	21	1.1099	20	1.1079	20	1.1059	20	1.1039
0.62	1.1704	32	1.1672	32	1.1640	31	1.1609	30	1.1579	30	1.1549
0.63	1.2269	44	1.2217	43	1.2174	42	1.2132	42	1.2090	42	1.2048
0.64	1.2812	57	1.2755	56	1.2699	55	1.2644	54	1.2590	53	1.2537
0.65	1.3352	70	1.3282	69	1.3213	67	1.3146	67	1.3079	65	1.3014
0.66	1.3882	83	1.3799	83	1.3716	80	1.3636	80	1.3556	77	1.3479
0.67	1.4400	98	1.4302	96	1.4206	94	1.4112	92	1.4020	91	1.3929
0.68	1.4905	112	1.4793	110	1.4683	101	1.4575	106	1.4469	103	1.4366
0.69	1.5396	127	1.5269	124	1.5145	122	1.5023	119	1.4904	116	1.4788
0.70	1.5872	142	1.5730	138	1.5592	136	1.5456	133	1.5323	130	1.5193
0.71	1.6332	157	1.6175	153	1.6022	150	1.5872	147	1.5725	143	1.5582
0.72	1.6776	172	1.6604	168	1.6436	164	1.6272	160	1.6112	157	1.5955
0.73	1.7204	188	1.7016	183	1.6833	178	1.6655	174	1.6481	170	1.6311
0.74	1.7614	203	1.7411	198	1.7213	193	1.7020	188	1.6832	184	1.6648
0.75	1.8006	218	1.7788	213	1.7575	207	1.7368	202	1.7166	197	1.6969
0.76	1.8380	233	1.8147	227	1.7920	221	1.7699	216	1.7483	211	1.7272
$J_{0.59}$	119.2	71	126.3	73	133.6	77	141.3	80	149.3	84	157.7

λ	2998°	Diff.	3018°	Diff.	3038°	Diff.	3058°	Diff.	3078°	Diff.	3098°	Diff.	3118°
0.32μ	0.0230	+11	0.0241	+11	0.0252	+11	0.0263	+12	0.0275	+12	0.0287	+12	0.0299
0.33	310	13	323	14	337	14	351	15	366	15	381	15	396
0.34	409	16	425	17	442	17	459	18	477	18	495	19	514
0.35	528	20	548	20	568	21	589	21	610	22	632	22	654
0.36	670	23	693	24	717	24	741	24	765	26	791	27	818
0.37	836	27	863	28	891	28	919	29	948	29	977	30	0.1007
0.38	0.1029	31	0.1060	31	0.1091	32	0.1123	32	0.1155	33	0.1188	33	0.1221
0.39	0.1247	35	0.1282	35	0.1317	36	0.1353	36	0.1389	36	0.1425	37	0.1462
0.40	0.1492	38	0.1530	39	0.1569	39	0.1608	40	0.1648	40	0.1688	41	0.1729
0.41	0.1765	42	0.1807	42	0.1849	43	0.1892	43	0.1935	44	0.1979	44	0.2023
0.42	0.2064	45	0.2109	46	0.2155	46	0.2201	46	0.2247	47	0.2294	47	0.2341
0.43	0.2391	48	0.2439	48	0.2487	49	0.2536	49	0.2585	49	0.2634	50	0.2681
0.44	0.2743	50	0.2793	51	0.2844	51	0.2895	51	0.2946	52	0.2998	52	0.3050
0.45	0.3120	52	0.3172	53	0.3225	52	0.3277	53	0.3330	53	0.3383	54	0.3437
0.46	0.3520	54	0.3574	54	0.3628	54	0.3682	54	0.3736	54	0.3790	54	0.3844
0.47	0.3944	54	0.3998	55	0.4053	54	0.4107	54	0.4161	54	0.4215	55	0.4270
0.48	0.4388	54	0.4442	54	0.4496	54	0.4550	54	0.4604	54	0.4658	53	0.4711
0.49	0.4849	53	0.4902	53	0.4955	53	0.5008	53	0.5061	53	0.5114	52	0.5166
0.50	0.5326	52	0.5378	51	0.5429	51	0.5480	51	0.5531	51	0.5582	51	0.5633
0.51	0.5818	49	0.5867	49	0.5916	49	0.5965	48	0.6013	48	0.6061	48	0.6109
0.52	0.6322	46	0.6368	45	0.6413	45	0.6458	45	0.6503	45	0.6548	44	0.6592
0.53	0.6836	41	0.6877	41	0.6918	41	0.6959	41	0.7000	40	0.7040	40	0.7080
0.54	0.7356	37	0.7393	36	0.7429	36	0.7465	36	0.7501	35	0.7536	35	0.7571
0.55	0.7883	31	0.7914	30	0.7944	30	0.7974	30	0.8004	29	0.8033	29	0.8062
0.56	0.8413	24	0.8437	23	0.8460	24	0.8484	24	0.8508	23	0.8531	23	0.8554
0.57	0.8943	17	0.8960	16	0.8976	17	0.8993	16	0.9009	16	0.9025	16	0.9041
0.58	0.9473	9	0.9482	8	0.9490	9	0.9499	8	0.9507	9	0.9516	8	0.9524
0.59	1.0000	0	1.0000	0	1.0000	0	1.0000	0	1.0000	0	1.0000	0	1.0000
0.60	1.0523	−10	1.0513	−9	1.0504	−10	1.0494	−9	1.0485	−9	1.0476	−8	1.0468
0.61	1.1039	19	1.1020	19	1.1001	19	1.0982	19	1.0963	18	1.0945	18	1.0927
0.62	1.1549	30	1.1519	30	1.1489	29	1.1460	29	1.1431	28	1.1403	28	1.1375
0.63	1.2048	42	1.2006	40	1.1966	39	1.1927	39	1.1888	38	1.1850	38	1.1812
0.64	1.2537	52	1.2485	52	1.2433	51	1.2382	49	1.2333	49	1.2284	48	1.2236
0.65	1.3014	64	1.2950	63	1.2887	62	1.2825	61	1.2764	60	1.2704	58	1.2646
0.66	1.3479	77	1.3402	74	1.3328	74	1.3254	72	1.3182	71	1.3111	69	1.3042
0.67	1.3929	88	1.3841	87	1.3754	85	1.3669	84	1.3585	82	1.3503	80	1.3423
0.68	1.4366	101	1.4265	99	1.4166	98	1.4068	95	1.3973	93	1.3880	92	1.3788
0.69	1.4788	114	1.4674	112	1.4562	110	1.4452	107	1.4345	105	1.4240	103	1.4137
0.70	1.5193	127	1.5066	124	1.4942	122	1.4820	119	1.4701	117	1.4584	114	1.4470
0.71	1.5582	140	1.5442	137	1.5305	134	1.5171	131	1.5040	128	1.4912	125	1.4787
0.72	1.5955	153	1.5802	150	1.5652	146	1.5506	143	1.5363	140	1.5223	137	1.5086
0.73	1.6311	166	1.6145	163	1.5982	159	1.5823	155	1.5668	151	1.5517	148	1.5369
0.74	1.6648	179	1.6469	175	1.6294	171	1.6123	167	1.5956	163	1.5793	158	1.5635
0.75	1.6969	192	1.6777	187	1.6590	183	1.6407	178	1.6229	174	1.6055	171	1.5884
0.76	1.7272	205	1.7067	199	1.6868	195	1.6673	191	1.6482	185	1.6297	180	1.6117
$J_{0.59}$	157.7	87	166.4	90	175.4	94	184.8	98	194.6	102	204.8	105	215.3

λ	3118°	Diff.	3243°	Diff.	3493°	Diff.	3742°	Diff.	3992°	Diff.	4491°
0.40μ	0.1729	+268	0.1997	+573	0.2570	+631	0.3201	+674	0.3875	+1462	0.5337
0.41	0.2023	286	0.2309	608	0.2917	658	0.3575	689	0.4264	1463	0.5727
0.42	0.2341	303	0.2644	636	0.3280	677	0.3957	696	0.4653	1457	0.6110
0.43	0.2681	322	0.3003	656	0.3659	690	0.4349	709	0.5048	1436	0.6484
0.44	0.3050	330	0.3380	672	0.4052	692	0.4744	699	0.5443	1401	0.6844
0.45	0.3437	338	0.3775	680	0.4455	689	0.5144	686	0.5830	1357	0.7187
0.46	0.3844	341	0.4185	680	0.4865	680	0.5545	664	0.6209	1303	0.7512
0.47	0.4270	339	0.4609	674	0.5283	661	0.5944	640	0.6584	1231	0.7815
0.48	0.4711	336	0.5047	652	0.5699	643	0.6342	605	0.6947	1154	0.8101
0.49	0.5166	328	0.5494	631	0.6125	602	0.6727	570	0.7297	1077	0.8374
0.50	0.5633	313	0.5946	597	0.6543	572	0.7115	528	0.7643	979	0.8622
0.51	0.6109	294	0.6403	559	0.6962	525	0.7487	482	0.7969	882	0.8851
0.52	0.6592	275	0.6867	503	0.7370	478	0.7848	431	0.8279	788	0.9067
0.53	0.7080	246	0.7326	452	0.7778	421	0.8199	373	0.8572	679	0.9251
0.54	0.7571	213	0.7784	389	0.8173	367	0.8540	308	0.8848	578	0.9426
0.55	0.8062	181	0.8243	317	0.8560	296	0.8856	257	0.9113	464	0.9577
0.56	0.8554	138	0.8692	254	0.8946	226	0.9172	191	0.9363	349	0.9712
0.57	0.9041	92	0.9133	174	0.9307	151	0.9458	130	0.9588	229	0.9817
0.58	0.9524	50	0.9574	85	0.9659	79	0.9738	65	0.9803	118	0.9921
0.59	1.0000	00	1.0000	00	1.000	00	1.000	00	1.000	00	1.0000
0.60	1.0468	−48	1.0420	−90	1.033	−80	1.025	−8	1.017	−11	1.0060
0.61	1.0927	97	1.0830	190	1.064	16	1.048	15	1.033	22	1.0110
0.62	1.1375	165	1.1210	290	1.092	23	1.069	21	1.048	33	1.0150
0.63	1.1812	222	1.1590	390	1.120	31	1.089	29	1.060	43	1.0170
0.64	1.2236	276	1.1960	490	1.147	40	1.107	35	1.072	54	1.0180
0.65	1.2646	346	1.2300	590	1.171	48	1.123	41	1.082	64	1.0180
0.66	1.3042	402	1.2640	700	1.194	56	1.138	49	1.089	73	1.0160
0.67	1.3423	463	1.2960	800	1.216	66	1.150	54	1.096	83	1.0130
0.68	1.3788	528	1.3260	900	1.236	74	1.162	60	1.102	92	1.0100
0.69	1.4137	597	1.3540	1010	1.253	80	1.173	66	1.107	101	1.0060
0.70	1.4470	660	1.3810	1110	1.270	88	1.182	73	1.109	109	1.0000
0.71	1.4787	727	1.4060	1210	1.285	96	1.189	78	1.111	116	0.9950
0.72	1.5086	796	1.4290	1310	1.298	102	1.196	84	1.112	124.2	0.9878
$J_{0.59}$	215.3	754	290.7	2062	496.9	2926	789.5	3965	1186.0	11498	2335.8

λ	4491°	Diff.	4990°	Diff.	5489°	Diff.	5987°	Diff.	6486°	Diff.	6985°
0.40μ	0.5337	+1537	0.6874	+1677	0.8451	+1589	1.0040	+154	1.158	+149	1.307
0.41	0.5727	1510	0.7237	1522	0.8759	1511	1.0270	143	1.170	140	1.310
0.42	0.6110	1472	0.7582	1459	0.9041	1419	1.0460	134	1.180	129	1.309
0.43	0.6484	1420	0.7904	1382	0.9286	1334	1.0620	125	1.187	118	1.305
0.44	0.6844	1353	0.8197	1308	0.9505	1245	1.0750	115	1.190	109	1.299
0.45	0.7187	1263	0.8470	1228	0.9698	1142	1.0840	106	1.190	97	1.287
0.46	0.7512	1209	0.8721	1138	0.9859	1051	1.0910	96	1.187	89	1.276
0.47	0.7815	1135	0.8950	1047	0.9997	953	1.0950	87	1.182	78	1.260
0.48	0.8101	1049	0.9150	950	1.0100	880	1.0980	76	1.174	70	1.244
0.49	0.8374	953	0.9327	863	1.0190	770	1.0960	68	1.164	62	1.226
0.50	0.8622	857	0.9479	771	1.0250	680	1.0930	60	1.153	54	1.207
0.51	0.8851	767	0.9618	672	1.0290	59	1.088	52	1.140	46	1.186
0.52	0.9067	660	0.9727	583	1.0310	51	1.082	43	1.125	40	1.165
0.53	0.9251	566	0.9817	493	1.0310	42	1.073	36	1.109	33	1.142
0.54	0.9426	457	0.9883	407	1.0290	35	1.064	30	1.094	26	1.120
0.55	0.9577	364	0.9941	319	1.0260	27	1.053	23	1.076	21	1.097
0.56	0.9712	264	0.9976	244	1.0220	19	1.041	17	1.058	14	1.072
0.57	0.9817	181	0.9998	152	1.0150	14	1.029	10	1.039	9	1.048
0.58	0.9921	79	1.000	9	1.0090	6	1.015	5	1.020	5	1.025
0.59	1.0000	00	1.000	0	1.0000	00	1.000	0	1.000	0	1.000
0.60	1.0060	−23	0.9983	−84	0.9899	−46	0.9853	−67	0.9796	−36	0.9760
0.61	1.0110	78	0.9933	129	0.9804	111	0.9693	91	0.9602	79	0.9523
0.62	1.0150	261	0.9889	195	0.9694	153	0.9541	145	0.9396	99	0.9297
0.63	1.0170	344	0.9826	256	0.9570	197	0.9373	174	0.9199	140	0.9059
0.64	1.0180	412	0.9768	319	0.9449	244	0.9205	215	0.8990	160	0.8830
0.65	1.0180	487	0.9693	370	0.9323	294	0.9029	242	0.8787	189	0.8598
0.66	1.0160	559	0.9601	409	0.9192	332	0.8860	268	0.8592	214	0.8378
0.67	1.0130	618	0.9512	457	0.9055	367	0.8688	294	0.8394	241	0.8153
0.68	1.0100	684	0.9416	504	0.8912	391	0.8521	327	0.8194	257	0.7937
0.69	1.0060	738	0.9322	548	0.8774	426	0.8348	359	0.7999	269	0.7730
0.70	1.0000	789	0.9211	583	0.8628	457	0.8171	362	0.7809	288	0.7521
0.71	0.9950	848	0.9102	624	0.8478	478	0.8000	374	0.7626	304	0.7322
0.72	0.9878	893	0.8985	655	0.8330	499	0.7831	393	0.7438	317	0.7121
$J_{0.59}$	2336	1687	4023	2265	6288	2844	9132	3424	12556	3971	16527

λ	6985°	Diff.	7983°	Diff.	8981°	Diff.	9979°	Diff.	11,980°	Diff.	13,970°
0.40μ	1.307	+280	1.587	+251	1.838	+223	2.061	+376	2.437	+292	2.729
0.41	1.310	256	1.566	227	1.793	201	1.994	332	2.326	257	2.583
0.42	1.309	234	1.543	205	1.748	178	1.926	295	2.221	221	2.442
0.43	1.305	211	1.516	185	1.701	159	1.860	258	2.118	203	2.311
0.44	1.299	190	1.489	164	1.653	141	1.794	225	2.019	168	2.187
0.45	1.287	173	1.460	145	1.605	124	1.729	198	1.927	143	2.070
0.46	1.276	153	1.429	128	1.557	107	1.664	172	1.836	126	1.962
0.47	1.260	136	1.396	113	1.509	95	1.604	147	1.751	106	1.857
0.48	1.244	119	1.363	98	1.461	81	1.542	128	1.670	91	1.761
0.49	1.226	104	1.330	84	1.414	70	1.484	107	1.591	77	1.668
0.50	1.207	88	1.295	73	1.368	59	1.427	91	1.518	64	1.582
0.51	1.186	76	1.262	61	1.323	49	1.372	76	1.448	52	1.500
0.52	1.165	62	1.227	52	1.279	40	1.319	62	1.381	44	1.425
0.53	1.142	51	1.193	42	1.235	33	1.268	51	1.319	33	1.352
0.54	1.120	40	1.160	32	1.192	26	1.218	39	1.257	28	1.285
0.55	1.097	31	1.128	24	1.152	20	1.172	29	1.201	19	1.220
0.56	1.072	23	1.095	17	1.112	15	1.127	20	1.147	14	1.161
0.57	1.048	14	1.062	12	1.074	8	1.082	13	1.095	9	1.104
0.58	1.025	6	1.031	5	1.036	4	1.040	6	1.046	4	1.050
0.59	1.000	0	1.000	0	1.000	0	1.000	0	1.000	0	1.000
0.60	0.9760	−73	0.9687	−38	0.9649	−48	0.9601	−39	0.9562	−38	0.9524
0.61	0.9523	124	0.9399	94	0.9305	63	0.9242	95	0.9147	73	0.9074
0.62	0.9297	186	0.9111	135	0.8976	84	0.8892	150	0.8742	94	0.8648
0.63	0.9059	227	0.8832	168	0.8664	125	0.8539	169	0.8370	123	0.8247
0.64	0.8830	273	0.8557	193	0.8364	146	0.8218	212	0.8006	143	0.7863
0.65	0.8598	309	0.8289	221	0.8068	169	0.7899	231	0.7668	160	0.7508
0.66	0.8378	348	0.8030	246	0.7784	177	0.7607	262	0.7345	174	0.7171
0.67	0.8153	368	0.7785	273	0.7512	199	0.7313	276	0.7037	188	0.6849
0.68	0.7937	403	0.7534	283	0.7251	210	0.7041	298	0.6743	193	0.6550
0.69	0.7730	426	0.7304	305	0.6999	225	0.6774	306	0.6468	211	0.6257
0.70	0.7521	441	0.7080	324	0.6756	235	0.6521	316	0.6205	215	0.5990
0.71	0.7322	462	0.6860	337	0.6523	240	0.6283	330	0.5953	225	0.5728
0.72	0.7121	477	0.6644	347	0.6297	249	0.6048	338	0.5710	227	0.5483
$J_{0.59}$	16.53 × 10³	944	25.97 × 10³	1119	37.16 × 10³	1264	49.80 × 10³	2875	78.55 × 10³	3189	110.44 × 10³

λ	13,970°	Diff.	15,970°	Diff.	17,960°	Diff.	19,960°	Diff.	21,950°	Diff.	23,950°
0.40μ	2.729.	+236	2.965	+187	3.152	+153	3.305	+131	3.436	+107	3.543
0.41	2.583	201	2.784	165	2.949	132	3.081	111	3.192	91	3.283
0.42	2.442	179	2.621	138	2.759	115	2.874	95	2.969	77	3.046
0.43	2.311	152	2.463	121	2.584	96	2.680	84	2.764	65	2.829
0.44	2.187	133	2.320	101	2.421	83	2.504	73	2.577	54	2.631
0.45	2.070	114	2.184	86	2.270	71	2.341	60	2.401	48	2.449
0.46	1.962	95	2.057	75	2.132	60	2.192	51	2.243	40	2.283
0.47	1.857	83	1.940	63	2.003	50	2.053	43	2.096	34	2.130
0.48	1.761	68	1.829	54	1.883	42	1.925	37	1.962	27	1.989
0.49	1.668	59	1.727	44	1.771	39	1.808	30	1.838	22	1.860
0.50	1.582	48	1.630	38	1.668	29	1.697	24	1.721	20	1.741
0.51	1.500	40	1.540	31	1.571	24	1.595	21	1.616	15	1.631
0.52	1.425	31	1.456	25	1.481	19	1.500	18	1.518	11	1.529
0.53	1.352	26	1.378	20	1.398	15	1.413	13	1.426	9	1.435
0.54	1.285	19	1.304	16	1.320	11	1.331	11	1.342	7	1.349
0.55	1.220	15	1.235	11	1.246	9	1.255	8	1.263	5	1.268
0.56	1.161	9	1.170	8	1.178	7	1.185	5	1.190	4	1.194
0.57	1.104	5	1.109	5	1.114	4	1.118	5	1.123	1	1.124
0.58	1.050	4	1.054	1	1.055	2	1.057	2	1.059	1	1.060
0.59	1.000	0	1.000	0	1.000	0	1.000	0	1.000	0	1.000
0.60	0.9524	−30	0.9494	−22	0.9472	−12	0.9460	0	0.9460	−20	0.9440
0.61	0.9074	56	0.9028	42	0.8986	22	0.8964	14	0.8950	28	0.8922
0.62	0.8648	72	0.8576	49	0.8527	32	0.8495	27	0.8468	31	0.8437
0.63	0.8247	87	0.8160	55	0.8105	52	0.8053	27	0.8026	41	0.7985
0.64	0.7867	92	0.7775	62	0.7693	50	0.7643	38	0.7605	44	0.7561
0.65	0.7508	109	0.7399	87	0.7312	58	0.7254	49	0.7205	40	0.7165
0.66	0.7171	120	0.7051	91	0.6960	65	0.6895	47	0.6848	51	0.6797
0.67	0.6849	130	0.6719	94	0.6625	73	0.6552	56	0.6496	47	0.6449
0.68	0.6550	138	0.6412	98	0.6314	79	0.6235	55	0.6180	56	0.6124
0.69	0.6257	140	0.6117	101	0.6016	85	0.5931	54	0.5877	59	0.5818
0.70	0.5990	146	0.5844	113	0.5731	81	0.5650	63	0.5587	55	0.5532
0.71	0.5728	146	0.5582	116	0.5466	86	0.5380	62	0.5318	56	0.5262
0.72	0.5483	153	0.5330	110	0.5220	92	0.5128	60	0.5068	59	0.5009
$J_{0.59}$	110.4 × 10³	344	144.8 × 10³	358	180.6 × 10³	373	217.9 × 10³	379	255.8 × 10³	389	294.7 × 10³

APPENDIX D

ORDINATES OF THE LUMINOSITY CURVE FOR A PLANCKIAN RADIATOR

$C_2 = 14,320.$ Relative Values for a Maximum of Unity at Each Temperature

Based on computations of J. F. Skogland, *Bu. Stds. Misc. Pub.* 86

λ	1999°	Diff.	2079°	Diff.	2158°	Diff.	2238°	Diff.	2318°	Diff.	2398°
0.40μ	^{4}12	+2	^{4}14	+3	^{4}17	+3	^{4}20	+4	^{4}24	+4	^{4}28
0.41	47	10	57	11	68	13	81	14	95	15	^{3}110
0.42	^{3}209	41	^{3}250	46	^{3}296	49	^{3}345	53	^{3}398	57	455
0.43	799	146	945	157	^{2}1102	167	^{2}1269	177	^{2}1446	187	^{2}1633
0.44	^{2}2062	339	^{3}2401	362	2763	385	3145	397	3542	415	3957
0.45	^{2}4374	649	5023	682	5705	709	6414	733	7147	754	7901
0.46	8747	1165	9912	1208	^{1}1112	124	^{1}1236	127	^{1}1363	129	^{1}1492
0.47	^{1}1660	197	^{1}1857	201	2058	204	2262	207	2469	208	2677
0.48	3135	330	3465	332	3797	334	4131	333	4464	332	4796
0.49	5739	530	6269	527	6796	523	7319	517	7836	508	8344
0.50	0.1079	87	0.1166	85	0.1251	83	0.1334	82	0.1416	79	0.1495
0.51	0.2016	138	0.2154	134	0.2288	130	0.2418	126	0.2544	121	0.2665
0.52	0.3383	194	0.3577	187	0.3764	178	0.3942	170	0.4112	162	0.4274
0.53	0.4843	227	0.5070	215	0.5285	203	0.5488	191	0.5679	180	0.5859
0.54	0.6270	231	0.6501	215	0.6716	200	0.6916	186	0.7102	173	0.7275
0.55	0.7595	206	0.7801	189	0.7990	173	0.8163	158	0.8321	144	0.8465
0.56	0.8758	159	0.8917	141	0.9058	125	0.9183	110	0.9293	97	0.9390
0.57	0.9600	90	0.9690	75	0.9765	62	0.9827	50	0.9877	40	0.9917
0.58	0.9988	11	0.9999	0	0.9999	−10	0.9989	−17	0.9972	−22	0.9950
0.59	0.9838	−69	0.9769	−73	0.9696	76	0.9620	78	0.9542	78	0.9464
0.60	0.9231	136	0.9095	133	0.8962	129	0.8833	126	0.8707	122	0.8585
0.61	0.8239	181	0.8058	173	0.7885	164	0.7721	155	0.7566	148	0.7418
0.62	0.6954	203	0.6751	189	0.6562	177	0.6385	165	0.6220	154	0.6066
0.63	0.5363	192	0.5171	178	0.4993	164	0.4829	151	0.4678	141	0.4537
0.64	0.3910	166	0.3744	151	0.3593	138	0.3455	127	0.3328	116	0.3212
0.65	0.2629	129	0.2500	115	0.2385	104	0.2281	96	0.2185	87	0.2098
0.66	0.1641	90	0.1551	81	0.1470	73	0.1397	65	0.1332	59	0.1273
0.67	^{1}9388	570	^{1}8818	506	^{1}8312	449	^{1}7863	402	^{1}7461	364	^{1}7097
0.68	5420	360	5060	317	4743	281	4462	249	4213	223	3990
0.69	2832	205	2627	188	2449	157	2292	138	2154	123	2031
0.70	1528	117	1411	103	1308	90	1218	79	1139	70	1069
0.71	^{2}8421	692	^{2}7729	598	^{2}7131	522	^{2}6609	455	^{2}6154	401	^{2}5753
0.72	4517	394	4123	338	3785	293	3492	254	3238	224	3014
0.73	2392	219	2173	188	1985	162	1823	140	1683	122	1561
0.74	1227	118	1109	101	1008	86	^{3}922	74	^{3}848	64	^{3}784
0.75	^{3}626	62	^{3}564	54	^{3}510	45	465	39	426	34	392
0.76	333	35	298	30	268	25	243	21	222	19	203
Sum =	10.4645		10.4811		10.4966		10.5108		10.5236		10.5351
Max at	0.5818μ		0.5806		0.5794		0.5782		0.5770		0.5758

Note.—Superscript refers to number of zeros after decimal point. Thus ^{4}12 means 0.000012.

λ	2398°	Diff.	2478°	Diff.	2558°	Diff.	2638°	Diff.	2718°	Diff.	2798°
0.40μ	$^{4}28$	+5	$^{4}33$	+5	$^{4}38$	+5	$^{4}43$	+5	$^{4}48$	+6	$^{4}54$
0.41	$^{3}110$	15	$^{3}125$	16	$^{3}141$	17	$^{3}158$	19	$^{3}177$	20	$^{3}197$
0.42	455	60	515	63	578	66	644	68	712	71	783
0.43	$^{2}1633$	196	$^{2}1829$	204	$^{2}2033$	210	$^{2}2243$	216	$^{2}2459$	222	$^{2}2681$
0.44	3957	429	4386	442	4828	452	5280	460	5740	468	6208
0.45	7901	771	8672	783	9455	795	$^{1}1013$	81	$^{1}1106$	81	$^{1}1187$
0.46	$^{1}1492$	132	$^{1}1622$	132	$^{1}1754$	132	1886	132	2018	132	2150
0.47	2677	208	2885	208	3093	208	3301	206	3507	205	3712
0.48	4796	329	5125	326	5451	322	5773	317	6090	312	6402
0.49	$^{8}344$	499	8843	491	9334	481	9815	475	0.1029	45	0.1074
0.50	0.1495	77	0.1572	75	0.1647	73	0.1720	71	0.1791	68	0.1859
0.51	0.2665	116	0.2781	112	0.2893	107	0.3000	104	0.3104	100	0.3204
0.52	0.4274	154	0.4428	147	0.4575	141	0.4716	134	0.4850	127	0.4977
0.53	0.5859	169	0.6028	159	0.6187	151	0.6338	142	0.6480	134	0.6614
0.54	0.7275	161	0.7436	150	0.7586	138	0.7724	128	0.7852	120	0.7972
0.55	0.8465	131	0.8596	119	0.8715	109	0.8824	99	0.8923	91	0.9014
0.56	0.9390	86	0.9476	75	0.9551	66	0.9617	58	0.9675	51	0.9726
0.57	0.9917	29	0.9946	22	0.9968	16	0.9984	10	0.9994	5	0.9999
0.58	0.9950	−27	0.9923	−32	0.9891	−35	0.9856	−37	0.9819	−39	0.9780
0.59	0.9464	79	0.9385	79	0.9306	79	0.9227	78	0.9149	76	0.9073
0.60	0.8585	118	0.8467	114	0.8353	109	0.8244	106	0.8138	103	0.8035
0.61	0.7418	141	0.7277	133	0.7144	127	0.7017	120	0.6897	115	0.6782
0.62	0.6066	145	0.5921	136	0.5785	128	0.5657	121	0.5536	114	0.5422
0.63	0.4537	130	0.4407	121	0.4286	112	0.4174	106	0.4068	99	0.3969
0.64	0.3212	107	0.3105	99	0.3006	92	0.2914	85	0.2829	78	0.2751
0.65	0.2098	80	0.2018	72	0.1946	66	0.1880	62	0.1818	57	0.1761
0.66	0.1273	53	0.1220	49	0.1171	45	0.1126	41	0.1085	37	0.1048
0.67	$^{1}7097$	329	$^{1}6768$	299	$^{1}6469$	272	$^{1}6197$	248	$^{1}5949$	226	$^{1}5723$
0.68	3990	201	3789	182	3607	164	3443	149	3294	135	3159
0.69	2031	109	1922	99	1823	90	1733	80	1653	73	1580
0.70	1069	61	1008	555	$^{2}9525$	498	$^{2}9027$	448	$^{2}8579$	405	$^{2}8174$
0.71	$^{2}5753$	353	$^{2}5400$	315	5085	281	4804	253	4551	228	4323
0.72	3014	195	2819	173	2646	154	2492	139	2353	125	2228
0.73	1561	107	1454	95	1359	83	1276	74	1202	67	1135
0.74	$^{3}784$	56	$^{3}728$	50	678	44	634	39	595	34	561
0.75	392	30	362	26	336	23	313	20	293	17	276
0.76	203	16	187	13	174	12	162	11	151	10	141

Sum =	10.5351		10.5447		10.5532		10.5606		10.5667		10.5719
Max at	0.5758μ		0.5747		0.5736		0.5725		0.5715		0.5705

λ	2798°	Diff.	2878°	Diff.	2958°	Diff.	3038°	Diff.	3118°
0.40μ	^{4}54	+6	^{4}60	+7	^{4}67	+7	^{4}74	+6	^{4}80
0.41	^{3}197	20	^{3}217	21	^{3}238	22	^{3}260	22	^{3}282
0.42	783	73	856	75	931	77	^{2}1008	78	^{2}1086
0.43	^{2}2681	227	^{2}2908	231	^{2}3139	235	3374	237	3611
0.44	6208	476	6684	481	7165	483	7648	488	8136
0.45	^{1}1187	82	^{1}1269	82	^{1}1351	83	^{1}1434	81	^{1}1515
0.46	2150	132	2282	132	2414	132	2546	129	2675
0.47	3712	203	3915	200	4115	197	4312	196	4508
0.48	6402	308	6710	303	7013	294	7307	288	7595
0.49	0.1074	45	0.1119	44	0.1163	43	0.1206	41	0.1247
0.50	0.1859	66	0.1925	64	0.1989	62	0.2051	59	0.2110
0.51	0.3204	96	0.3300	92	0.3392	88	0.3480	84	0.3564
0.52	0.4977	121	0.5098	116	0.5214	110	0.5324	105	0.5429
0.53	0.6614	127	0.6741	120	0.6861	112	0.6973	106	0.7079
0.54	0.7972	113	0.8085	106	0.8191	96	0.8287	90	0.8377
0.55	0.9014	84	0.9098	76	0.9174	68	0.9242	63	0.9305
0.56	0.9726	45	0.9771	39	0.9810	33	0.9843	28	0.9871
0.57	0.9999	1	1.0000	−2	0.9998	−5	0.9993	−9	0.9984
0.58	0.9780	−41	0.9739	42	0.9697	42	0.9655	45	0.9610
0.59	0.9073	75	0.8998	74	0.8924	72	0.8852	71	0.8781
0.60	0.8035	98	0.7937	95	0.7842	92	0.7750	88	0.7662
0.61	0.6782	108	0.6674	104	0.6570	100	0.6470	95	0.6375
0.62	0.5422	107	0.5315	101	0.5214	96	0.5118	91	0.5027
0.63	0.3969	92	0.3877	87	0.3790	82	0.3708	77	0.3631
0.64	0.2751	73	0.2678	69	0.2609	65	0.2544	60	0.2484
0.65	0.1761	53	0.1708	49	0.1659	47	0.1612	43	0.1569
0.66	0.1048	35	0.1013	324	^{1}9806	299	^{1}9507	279	^{1}9228
0.67	^{1}5723	209	^{1}5514	193	5321	175	5146	164	4982
0.68	3159	124	3035	114	2921	105	2816	97	2719
0.69	1580	67	1513	61	1452	56	1396	52	1344
0.70	^{2}8174	369	^{2}7805	335	^{2}7470	307	^{2}7163	281	^{2}6882
0.71	4323	206	4117	187	3930	172	3758	156	3602
0.72	2228	112	2116	101	2015	94	1921	84	1837
0.73	1135	60	1075	54	1021	49	^{3}972	45	^{3}927
0.74	^{3}561	31	^{3}530	28	^{3}502	26	476	22	454
0.75	276	16	260	14	246	13	233	13	220
0.76	141	9	132	7	125	7	118	6	112
Sum =	10.5719		10.5767		10.5805		10.5824		10.5834
Max at	0.5705μ		0.5696		0.5687		0.5678		0.5669

APPENDIX E

ILLUMINATION FROM RECTANGULAR SOURCE OF UNIFORM LUMINOSITY
On Plane Parallel to Source

$$E_z/L$$

γ	$\beta = 5°$	10°	15°	20°	25°	30°	35°	40°	45°
5°	^{2}2412	^{4}4787	^{7}7091	^{2}9290	^{1}1135	^{1}1326	^{1}1498	^{1}1650	^{1}1782
10	4787	^{2}9503	^{1}1408	^{1}1845	2256	2635	2978	3282	3545
15	7091	^{1}1408	2086	2735	3346	3910	4422	4877	5271
20	^{2}9290	1845	2735	3588	4391	5136	5813	6416	6941
25	^{1}1135	2256	3346	4391	5379	6297	7134	7883	^{1}8537
30	1326	2635	3910	5136	6297	7379	8371	^{1}9261	0.1004
35	1498	2978	4422	5813	7134	8371	^{1}9508	0.1053	0.1144
40	1650	3282	4877	6416	7883	^{1}9261	0.1053	0.1169	0.1271
45	1782	3545	5271	6941	^{1}8537	0.1004	0.1144	0.1271	0.1385
50	1893	3767	5604	7385	^{1}9092	0.1071	0.1222	0.1360	0.1485
55	1983	3947	5875	7748	^{1}9548	0.1126	0.1286	0.1434	0.1568
60	2053	4088	6087	8033	^{1}9908	0.1169	0.1338	0.1494	0.1636
65	2105	4192	6244	8245	0.1018	0.1202	0.1377	0.1539	0.1688
70	2140	4264	6353	8391	0.1036	0.1225	0.1404	0.1571	0.1726
75	2162	4308	6420	8482	0.1048	0.1239	0.1421	0.1592	0.1749
80	2174	4331	6455	8530	0.1054	0.1247	0.1430	0.1602	0.1762
85	2178	4340	6469	8548	0.1056	0.1250	0.1433	0.1606	0.1767
90	^{1}2179	^{1}4341	^{1}6470	^{1}8551	0.1057	0.1250	0.1434	0.1607	0.1768

$$E_z/L$$

γ	$\beta = 50°$	55°	60°	65°	70°	75°	80°	85°	90°
5°	^{1}1893	^{1}1983	^{1}2053	^{1}2105	^{1}2140	^{1}2162	^{1}2174	^{1}2178	^{1}2179
10	3767	3947	4088	4192	4264	4308	4331	4340	4341
15	5604	5875	6087	6244	6353	6420	6455	6469	6470
20	7385	7748	8033	^{1}8245	^{1}8391	^{1}8482	^{1}8530	^{1}8548	^{1}8551
25	^{1}9092	^{1}9548	^{1}9908	0.1018	0.1036	0.1048	0.1054	0.1056	0.1057
30	0.1071	0.1126	0.1169	0.1202	0.1225	0.1239	0.1247	0.1250	0.1250
35	0.1222	0.1286	0.1338	0.1377	0.1404	0.1421	0.1430	0.1433	0.1434
40	0.1360	0.1434	0.1494	0.1539	0.1571	0.1592	0.1602	0.1606	0.1607
45	0.1485	0.1568	0.1636	0.1688	0.1726	0.1749	0.1762	0.1767	0.1768
50	0.1594	0.1687	0.1764	0.1823	0.1866	0.1894	0.1909	0.1914	0.1915
55	0.1687	0.1790	0.1874	0.1941	0.1990	0.2022	0.2040	0.2047	0.2048
60	0.1764	0.1874	0.1967	0.2042	0.2098	0.2135	0.2156	0.2164	0.2165
65	0.1823	0.1941	0.2042	0.2142	0.2187	0.2230	0.2254	0.2264	0.2266
70	0.1866	0.1990	0.2098	0.2187	0.2256	0.2306	0.2335	0.2347	0.2349
75	0.1894	0.2022	0.2135	0.2230	0.2306	0.2362	0.2397	0.2412	0.2415
80	0.1909	0.2040	0.2156	0.2254	0.2335	0.2397	0.2438	0.2458	0.2462
85	0.1914	0.2047	0.2164	0.2264	0.2347	0.2412	0.2458	0.2484	0.2490
90	0.1915	0.2048	0.2165	0.2266	0.2349	0.2415	0.2462	0.2490	0.2500

NOTE.—Superscript indicates number of zeros after the decimal point.

ILLUMINATION FROM RECTANGULAR SOURCE OF UNIFORM LUMINOSITY
On Plane Perpendicular to Source
E_y/L

γ	$\beta = 5°$	10°	15°	20°	25°	30°	35°	40°	45°
5°	^{3}11	^{3}21	^{3}31	^{3}41	^{3}50	^{3}58	^{3}65	^{3}72	^{3}78
10	^{3}42	^{3}83	^{2}123	^{2}161	^{2}197	^{2}230	^{2}260	^{2}287	^{2}310
15	^{3}93	^{2}184	^{2}273	^{2}358	^{2}438	^{2}513	^{2}580	^{2}640	^{2}692
20	^{2}162	322	478	^{2}627	^{2}768	^{2}899	^{1}1019	^{1}1125	^{1}1219
25	248	492	^{2}730	^{2}960	^{1}1177	^{1}1380	1566	1733	1880
30	347	^{2}689	^{1}1024	^{1}1347	1654	1943	2209	2450	2663
35	456	^{2}908	1350	1778	2188	2574	2933	3260	3552
40	573	^{1}1141	1698	2240	2762	3256	3720	4146	4530
45	694	1382	2059	2721	3360	3971	4548	5085	5573
50	814	1623	2422	3204	3965	4698	5396	6051	6656
55	^{2}931	1858	2775	3677	4559	5414	6236	7016	7746
60	^{1}1041	2078	3107	4123	5122	6097	7042	7950	8810
65	1140	2277	3408	4529	5636	6724	7787	8819	^{1}9811
70	1226	2450	3669	4881	6084	7272	^{1}8443	^{1}9590	0.1071
75	1296	2590	3881	5169	6450	7722	^{1}8984	0.1023	0.1146
80	1347	2693	4038	5381	6721	8057	^{1}9388	0.1071	0.1202
85	1378	2756	4134	5512	6888	8264	^{1}9638	0.1101	0.1238
90	^{1}1389	^{1}2778	^{1}4167	^{1}5556	^{1}6944	^{1}8333	^{1}9722	0.1111	0.1250

E_y/L

γ	$\beta = 50°$	55°	60°	65°	70°	75°	80°	85°	90°
5°	^{3}83	^{3}87	^{3}90	^{3}92	^{3}93	^{3}94	^{3}95	^{3}95	^{3}95
10	^{2}329	^{2}345	^{2}357	^{2}367	^{2}373	^{2}377	^{2}379	^{2}380	^{2}380
15	^{2}736	^{2}772	^{2}801	^{2}822	^{2}836	^{2}845	^{2}850	^{2}852	^{2}852
20	^{1}1298	^{1}1363	^{1}1414	^{1}1452	^{1}1479	^{1}1495	^{1}1504	^{1}1507	^{1}1508
25	2005	2108	2191	2252	2295	2322	2336	2342	2342
30	2846	2999	3121	3213	3278	3318	3340	3348	3349
35	3806	4020	4192	4324	4417	4476	4508	4519	4521
40	4868	5155	5390	5571	5701	5785	5829	5846	5849
45	6008	6384	6695	6939	7116	7232	7295	7319	7322
50	7201	7680	8084	8406	^{1}8646	^{1}8804	^{1}8891	^{1}8925	^{1}8930
55	8415	^{1}9013	^{1}9527	^{1}9947	0.1027	0.1048	0.1061	0.1065	0.1066
60	^{1}9613	0.1034	0.1099	0.1153	0.1195	0.1225	0.1242	0.1249	0.1250
65	0.1075	0.1163	0.1242	0.1310	0.1366	0.1407	0.1432	0.1442	0.1443
70	0.1178	0.1280	0.1376	0.1461	0.1534	0.1590	0.1626	0.1642	0.1645
75	0.1266	0.1382	0.1493	0.1597	0.1690	0.1767	0.1822	0.1848	0.1853
80	0.1332	0.1461	0.1586	0.1707	0.1821	0.1924	0.2007	0.2056	0.2066
85	0.1375	0.1511	0.1646	0.1780	0.1912	0.2040	0.2159	0.2252	0.2282
90	0.1389	0.1528	0.1667	0.1806	0.1944	0.2083	0.2222	0.2361	0.2500

NOTE.—Superscript indicates number of zeros after the decimal point.

APPENDIX F

ILLUMINATION FACTOR

(Used in calculating E_{av}. See p. 352)

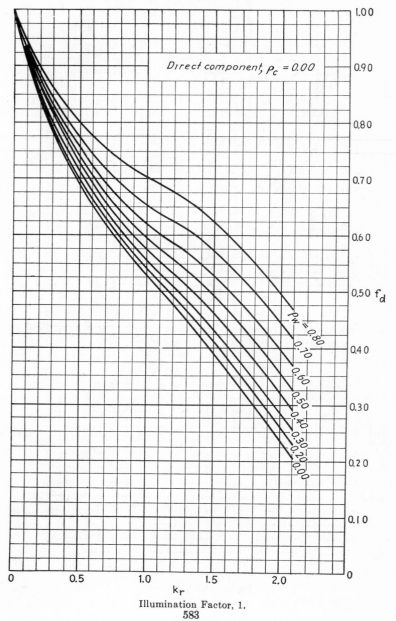

Direct component, $\rho_c = 0.00$

$\rho_w = 0.80$
0.70
0.60
0.50
0.40
0.30
0.20
0.00

k_r

f_d

Illumination Factor, 1.

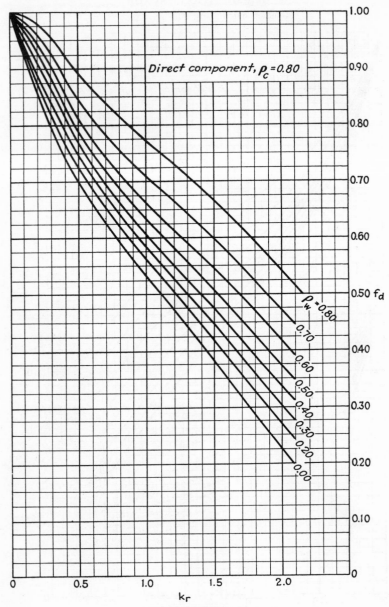

Illumination Factor, 2.

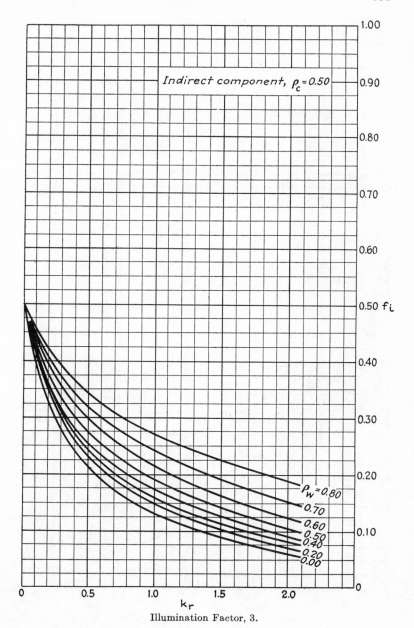

Illumination Factor, 3.

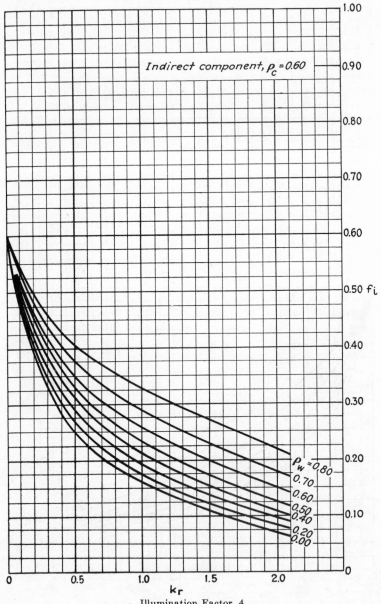

Illumination Factor, 4.

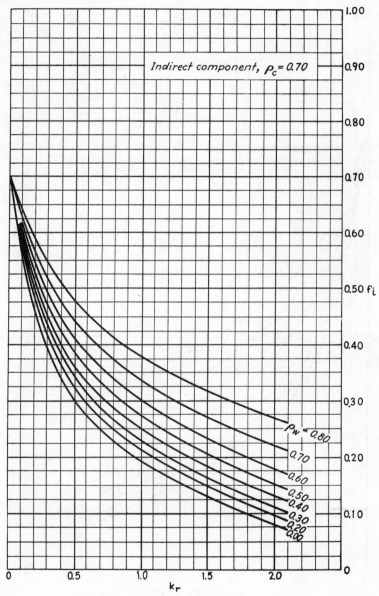

Illumination Factor, 5.

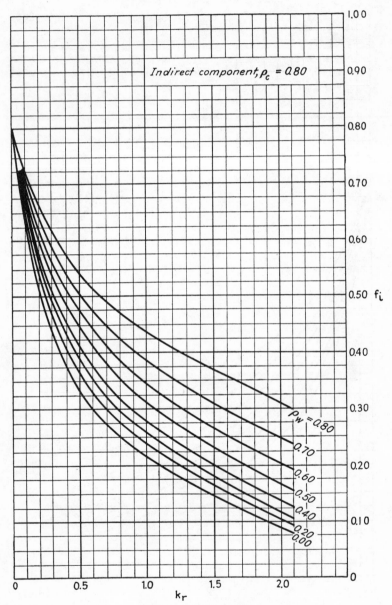

Indirect component, $\rho_c = 0.80$

$\rho_w = 0.80$
0.70
0.60
0.50
0.40
0.20
0.00

f_i

k_r

Illumination Factor, 6.

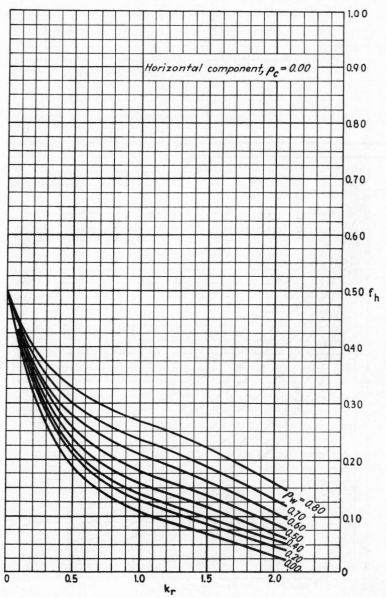

Illumination Factor, 7.

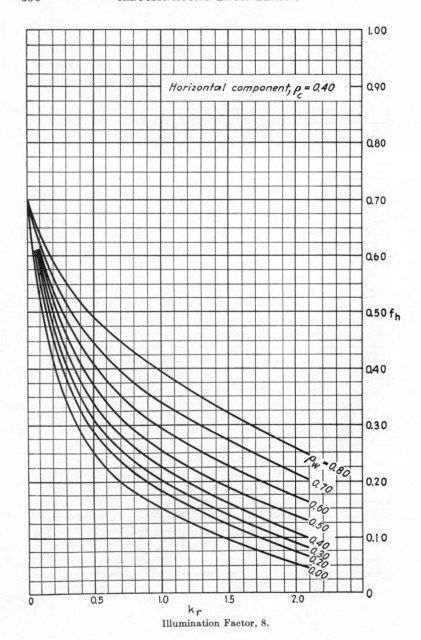

Illumination Factor, 8.

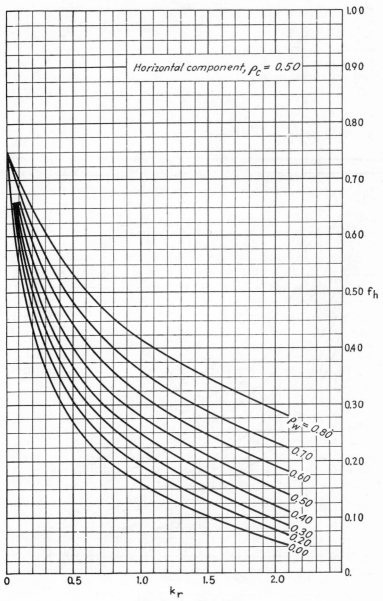

Illumination Factor, 9.

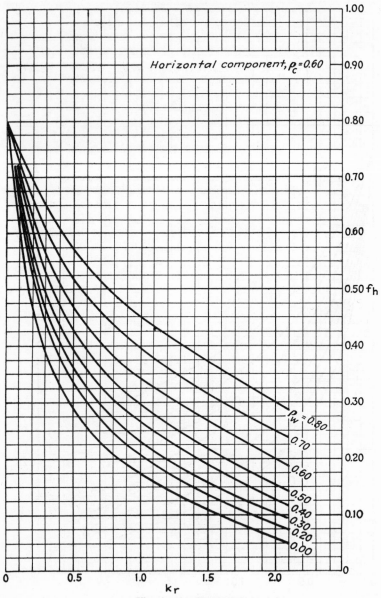

Illumination Factor, 10.

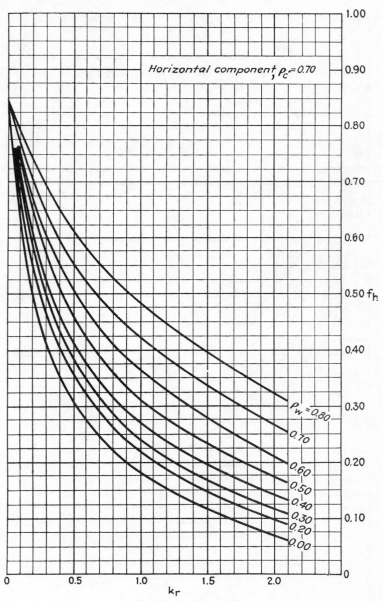

Illumination Factor, 11.

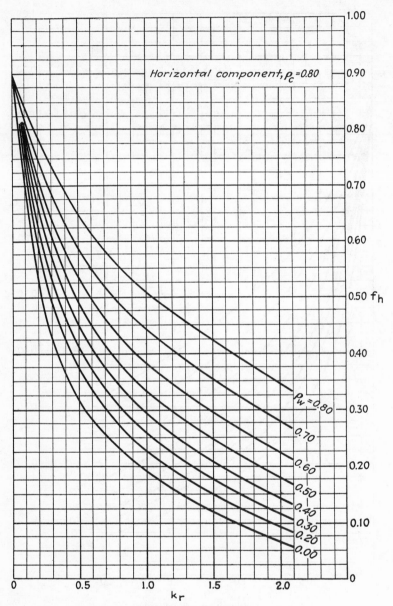

Illumination Factor, 12.

APPENDIX G

DISTRIBUTION COEFFICIENTS FOR EQUAL-ENERGY SPECTRUM
(From *Compte Rendu, C.I.E.*, 1932, p. 25)

λ	Red ($\bar{x}$)	Green ($\bar{y}$)	Blue ($\bar{z}$)
0.380μ	0.0014	0.0000	0.0065
0.385	0.0022	0.0001	0.0105
0.390	0.0042	0.0001	0.0201
0.395	0.0076	0.0002	0.0362
0.400	0.0143	0.0004	0.0679
0.405	0.0232	0.0006	0.1102
0.410	0.0435	0.0012	0.2074
0.415	0.0776	0.0022	0.3713
0.420	0.1344	0.0040	0.6456
0.425	0.2148	0.0073	1.0391
0.430	0.2839	0.0116	1.3856
0.435	0.3285	0.0168	1.6230
0.440	0.3483	0.0230	1.7471
0.445	0.3481	0.0298	1.7826
0.450	0.3362	0.0380	1.7721
0.455	0.3187	0.0480	1.7441
0.460	0.2908	0.0600	1.6692
0.465	0.2511	0.0739	1.5281
0.470	0.1954	0.0910	1.2876
0.475	0.1421	0.1126	1.0419
0.480	0.0956	0.1390	0.8130
0.485	0.0580	0.1693	0.6162
0.490	0.0320	0.2080	0.4652
0.495	0.0147	0.2586	0.3533
0.500	0.0049	0.3230	0.2720
0.505	0.0024	0.4073	0.2123
0.510	0.0093	0.5030	0.1582
0.515	0.0291	0.6082	0.1117
0.520	0.0633	0.7100	0.0782
0.525	0.1096	0.7932	0.0573
0.530	0.1655	0.8620	0.0422
0.535	0.2257	0.9149	0.0298
0.540	0.2904	0.9540	0.0203
0.545	0.3597	0.9803	0.0134

DISTRIBUTION COEFFICIENTS FOR EQUAL-ENERGY SPECTRUM.—(Continued)

λ	Red ($\bar{x}$)	Green ($\bar{y}$)	Blue ($\bar{z}$)
0.550μ	0.4334	0.9950	0.0087
0.555	0.5121	1.0002	0.0057
0.560	0.5945	0.9950	0.0039
0.565	0.6784	0.9786	0.0027
0.570	0.7621	0.9520	0.0021
0.575	0.8425	0.9154	0.0018
0.580	0.9163	0.8700	0.0017
0.585	0.9786	0.8163	0.0014
0.590	1.0263	0.7570	0.0011
0.595	1.0567	0.6949	0.0010
0.600	1.0622	0.6310	0.0008
0.605	1.0456	0.5668	0.0006
0.610	1.0026	0.5030	0.0003
0.615	0.9384	0.4412	0.0002
0.620	0.8544	0.3810	0.0002
0.625	0.7514	0.3210	0.0001
0.630	0.6424	0.2650	0.0000
0.635	0.5419	0.2170	
0.640	0.4479	0.1750	
0.645	0.3608	0.1382	
0.650	0.2835	0.1070	
0.655	0.2187	0.0816	
0.660	0.1649	0.0610	
0.665	0.1212	0.0446	
0.670	0.0874	0.0320	
0.675	0.0636	0.0232	
0.680	0.0468	0.0170	
0.685	0.0329	0.0119	
0.690	0.0227	0.0082	
0.695	0.0158	0.0057	
0.700	0.0114	0.0041	
0.705	0.0081	0.0029	
0.710	0.0058	0.0021	
0.715	0.0041	0.0015	
0.720	0.0029	0.0010	
0.725	0.0020	0.0007	
0.730	0.0014	0.0005	
0.735	0.0010	0.0004	
0.740	0.0007	0.0003	
0.745	0.0005	0.0002	
0.750	0.0003	0.0001	
0.755	0.0002	0.0001	
0.760	0.0002	0.0001	
0.765	0.0001	0.0000	
0.770	0.0001		
0.775	0.0000		
0.780	0.0000		

INDEX

597

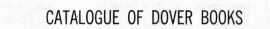
CATALOGUE OF DOVER BOOKS

ENGINEERING AND TECHNOLOGY

General and mathematical

ENGINEERING MATHEMATICS, Kenneth S. Miller. A text for graduate students of engineering to strengthen their mathematical background in differential equations, etc. Mathematical steps very explicitly indicated. Contents: Determinants and Matrices, Integrals, Linear Differential Equations, Fourier Series and Integrals, Laplace Transform, Network Theory, Random Function . . . all vital requisites for advanced modern engineering studies. Unabridged republication. Appendices: Borel Sets; Riemann-Stieltjes Integral; Fourier Series and Integrals. Index. References at Chapter Ends. xii + 417pp. 6 x 8½.   S1121 Paperbound **$2.00**

MATHEMATICAL ENGINEERING ANALYSIS, Rufus Oldenburger. A book designed to assist the research engineer and scientist in making the transition from physical engineering situations to the corresponding mathematics. Scores of common practical situations found in all major fields of physics are supplied with their correct mathematical formulations—applications to automobile springs and shock absorbers, clocks, throttle torque of diesel engines, resistance networks, capacitors, transmission lines, microphones, neon tubes, gasoline engines, refrigeration cycles, etc. Each section reviews basic principles of underlying various fields: mechanics of rigid bodies, electricity and magnetism, heat, elasticity, fluid mechanics, and aerodynamics. Comprehensive and eminently useful. Index. 169 problems, answers. 200 photos and diagrams. xiv + 426pp. 5⅜ x 8½.   S919 Paperbound **$2.00**

MATHEMATICS OF MODERN ENGINEERING, E. G. Keller and R. E. Doherty. Written for the Advanced Course in Engineering of the General Electric Corporation, deals with the engineering use of determinants, tensors, the Heaviside operational calculus, dyadics, the calculus of variations, etc. Presents underlying principles fully, but purpose is to teach engineers to deal with modern engineering problems, and emphasis is on the perennial engineering attack of set-up and solve. Indexes. Over 185 figures and tables. Hundreds of exercises, problems, and worked-out examples. References. Two volume set. Total of xxxiii + 623pp. 5⅜ x 8.
S734 Vol I Paperbound **$1.85**
S735 Vol II Paperbound **$1.85**
The set **$3.70**

MATHEMATICAL METHODS FOR SCIENTISTS AND ENGINEERS, L. P. Smith. For scientists and engineers, as well as advanced math students. Full investigation of methods and practical description of conditions under which each should be used. Elements of real functions, differential and integral calculus, space geometry, theory of residues, vector and tensor analysis, series of Bessel functions, etc. Each method illustrated by completely-worked-out examples, mostly from scientific literature. 368 graded unsolved problems. 100 diagrams. x + 453pp. 5⅝ x 8⅜.   S220 Paperbound **$2.00**

THEORY OF FUNCTIONS AS APPLIED TO ENGINEERING PROBLEMS, edited by R. Rothe, F. Ollendorff, and K. Pohlhausen. A series of lectures given at the Berlin Institute of Technology that shows the specific applications of function theory in electrical and allied fields of engineering. Six lectures provide the elements of function theory in a simple and practical form, covering complex quantities and variables, integration in the complex plane, residue theorems, etc. Then 5 lectures show the exact uses of this powerful mathematical tool, with full discussions of problem methods. Index. Bibliography. 108 figures. x + 189pp. 5⅜ x 8.
S733 Paperbound **$1.35**

Aerodynamics and hydrodynamics

AIRPLANE STRUCTURAL ANALYSIS AND DESIGN, E. E. Sechler and L. G. Dunn. Systematic authoritative book which summarizes a large amount of theoretical and experimental work on structural analysis and design. Strong on classical subsonic material still basic to much aeronautic design . . . remains a highly useful source of information. Covers such areas as layout of the airplane, applied and design loads, stress-strain relationships for stable structures, truss and frame analysis, the problem of instability, the ultimate strength of stiffened flat sheet, analysis of cylindrical structures, wings and control surfaces, fuselage analysis, engine mounts, landing gears, etc. Originally published as part of the CALCIT Aeronautical Series. 256 Illustrations. 47 study problems. Indexes. xi + 420pp. 5⅜ x 8½.
S1043 Paperbound **$2.25**

FUNDAMENTALS OF HYDRO- AND AEROMECHANICS, L. Prandtl and O. G. Tietjens. The well-known standard work based upon Prandtl's lectures at Goettingen. Wherever possible hydrodynamics theory is referred to practical considerations in hydraulics, with the view of unifying theory and experience. Presentation is extremely clear and though primarily physical, mathematical proofs are rigorous and use vector analysis to a considerable extent. An Engineering Society Monograph, 1934. 186 figures. Index. xvi + 270pp. 5⅜ x 8.
S374 Paperbound **$1.85**

FLUID MECHANICS THROUGH WORKED EXAMPLES, D. R. L. Smith and J. Houghton. Advanced text covering principles and applications to practical situations. Each chapter begins with concise summaries of fundamental ideas. 163 fully worked out examples applying principles outlined in the text. 275 other problems, with answers. Contents: The Pressure of Liquids on Surfaces; Floating Bodies; Flow Under Constant Head in Pipes; Circulation; Vorticity; The Potential Function; Laminar Flow and Lubrication; Impact of Jets; Hydraulic Turbines; Centrifugal and Reciprocating Pumps; Compressible Fluids; and many other items. Total of 438 examples. 250 line illustrations. 340pp. Index. 6 x 8⅞.   S981 Clothbound **$6.00**

THEORY OF SHIP MOTIONS, S. N. Blagoveshchensky. The only detailed text in English in a rapidly developing branch of engineering and physics, it is the work of one of the world's foremost authorities—Blagoveshchensky of Leningrad Shipbuilding Institute. A senior-level treatment written primarily for engineering students, but also of great importance to naval architects, designers, contractors, researchers in hydrodynamics, and other students. No mathematics beyond ordinary differential equations is required for understanding the text. Translated by T. & L. Strelkoff, under editorship of Louis Landweber, Iowa Institute of Hydraulic Research, under auspices of Office of Naval Research. Bibliography. Index. 231 diagrams and illustrations. Total of 649pp. 5⅜ x 8½.   Vol. I: S234 Paperbound **$2.00**
Vol. II: S235 Paperbound **$2.00**

THEORY OF FLIGHT, Richard von Mises. Remains almost unsurpassed as balanced, well-written account of fundamental fluid dynamics, and situations in which air compressibility effects are unimportant. Stressing equally theory and practice, avoiding formidable mathematical structure, it conveys a full understanding of physical phenomena and mathematical concepts. Contains perhaps the best introduction to general theory of stability. "Outstanding," Scientific, Medical, and Technical Books. New introduction by K. H. Hohenemser. Bibliographical, historical notes. Index. 408 illustrations. xvi + 620pp. 5⅜ x 8⅜.   S541 Paperbound **$2.95**

THEORY OF WING SECTIONS, I. H. Abbott, A. E. von Doenhoff. Concise compilation of subsonic aerodynamic characteristics of modern NASA wing sections, with description of their geometry, associated theory. Primarily reference work for engineers, students, it gives methods, data for using wing-section data to predict characteristics. Particularly valuable: chapters on thin wings, airfoils; complete summary of NACA's experimental observations, system of construction families of airfoils. 350pp. of tables on Basic Thickness Forms, Mean Lines, Airfoil Ordinates, Aerodynamic Characteristics of Wing Sections. Index. Bibliography. 191 illustrations. Appendix. 705pp. 5⅜ x 8.   S558 Paperbound **$3.25**

WEIGHT-STRENGTH ANALYSIS OF AIRCRAFT STRUCTURES, F. R. Shanley. Scientifically sound methods of analyzing and predicting the structural weight of aircraft and missiles. Deals directly with forces and the distances over which they must be transmitted, making it possible to develop methods by which the minimum structural weight can be determined for any material and conditions of loading. Weight equations for wing and fuselage structures. Includes author's original papers on inelastic buckling and creep buckling. "Particularly successful in presenting his analytical methods for investigating various optimum design principles," AERONAUTICAL ENGINEERING REVIEW. Enlarged bibliography. Index. 199 figures. xiv + 404pp. 5⅝ x 8⅜.   S660 Paperbound **$2.45**

Electricity

TWO-DIMENSIONAL FIELDS IN ELECTRICAL ENGINEERING, L. V. Bewley. A useful selection of typical engineering problems of interest to practicing electrical engineers. Introduces senior students to the methods and procedures of mathematical physics. Discusses theory of functions of a complex variable, two-dimensional fields of flow, general theorems of mathematical physics and their applications, conformal mapping or transformation, method of images, freehand flux plotting, etc. New preface by the author. Appendix by W. F. Kiltner. Index. Bibliography at chapter ends. xiv + 204pp. 5⅜ x 8½.   S1118 Paperbound **$1.50**

FLUX LINKAGES AND ELECTROMAGNETIC INDUCTION, L. V. Bewley. A brief, clear book which shows proper uses and corrects misconceptions of Faraday's law of electromagnetic induction in specific problems. Contents: Circuits, Turns, and Flux Linkages; Substitution of Circuits; Electromagnetic Induction; General Criteria for Electromagnetic Induction; Applications and Paradoxes; Theorem of Constant Flux Linkages. New Section: Rectangular Coil in a Varying Uniform Medium. Valuable supplement to class texts for engineering students. Corrected, enlarged edition. New preface. Bibliography in notes. 49 figures. xi + 106pp. 5⅜ x 8.   S1103 Paperbound **$1.25**

INDUCTANCE CALCULATIONS: WORKING FORMULAS AND TABLES, Frederick W. Grover. An invaluable book to everyone in electrical engineering. Provides simple single formulas to cover all the more important cases of inductance. The approach involves only those parameters that naturally enter into each situation, while extensive tables are given to permit easy interpolations. Will save the engineer and student countless hours and enable them to obtain accurate answers with minimal effort. Corrected republication of 1946 edition. 58 tables. 97 completely worked out examples. 66 figures. xiv + 286pp. 5⅜ x 8½.   S974 Paperbound **$1.85**

Optical design, lighting

THE SCIENTIFIC BASIS OF ILLUMINATING ENGINEERING, Parry Moon, Professor of Electrical Engineering, M.I.T. Basic, comprehensive study. Complete coverage of the fundamental theoretical principles together with the elements of design, vision, and color with which the lighting engineer must be familiar. Valuable as a text as well as a reference source to the practicing engineer. Partial contents: Spectroradiometric Curve, Luminous Flux, Radiation from Gaseous-Conduction Sources, Radiation from Incandescent Sources, Incandescent Lamps, Measurement of Light, Illumination from Point Sources and Surface Sources, Elements of Lighting Design. 7 Appendices. Unabridged and corrected republication, with additions. New preface containing conversion tables of radiometric and photometric concepts. Index. 707-item bibliography. 92-item bibliography of author's articles. 183 problems. xxiii + 608pp. 5⅜ x 8½.   S242 Paperbound **$2.85**

OPTICS AND OPTICAL INSTRUMENTS: AN INTRODUCTION WITH SPECIAL REFERENCE TO PRACTICAL APPLICATIONS, B. K. Johnson. An invaluable guide to basic practical applications of optical principles, which shows how to set up inexpensive working models of each of the four main types of optical instruments—telescopes, microscopes, photographic lenses, optical projecting systems. Explains in detail the most important experiments for determining their accuracy, resolving power, angular field of view, amounts of aberration, all other necessary facts about the instruments. Formerly "Practical Optics." Index. 234 diagrams. Appendix. 224pp. 5⅜ x 8.   S642 Paperbound **$1.65**

APPLIED OPTICS AND OPTICAL DESIGN, A. E. Conrady. With publication of vol. 2, standard work for designers in optics is now complete for first time. Only work of its kind in English; only detailed work for practical designer and self-taught. Requires, for bulk of work, no math above trig. Step-by-step exposition, from fundamental concepts of geometrical, physical optics, to systematic study, design, of almost all types of optical systems. Vol. 1: all ordinary ray-tracing methods; primary aberrations; necessary higher aberration for design of telescopes, low-power microscopes, photographic equipment. Vol. 2: (Completed from author's notes by R. Kingslake, Dir. Optical Design, Eastman Kodak.) Special attention to high-power microscope, anastigmatic photographic objectives. "An indispensable work," J., Optical Soc. of Amer. "As a practical guide this book has no rival," Transactions, Optical Soc. Index. Bibliography. 193 diagrams. 852pp. 6⅛ x 9¼.   Vol. 1 S366 Paperbound **$2.95**
                                                                     Vol. 2 S612 Paperbound **$2.95**

Miscellaneous

THE MEASUREMENT OF POWER SPECTRA FROM THE POINT OF VIEW OF COMMUNICATIONS ENGINEERING, R. B. Blackman, J. W. Tukey. This pathfinding work, reprinted from the "Bell System Technical Journal," explains various ways of getting practically useful answers in the measurement of power spectra, using results from both transmission theory and the theory of statistical estimation. Treats: Autocovariance Functions and Power Spectra; Direct Analog Computation; Distortion, Noise, Heterodyne Filtering and Pre-whitening; Aliasing; Rejection Filtering and Separation; Smoothing and Decimation Procedures; Very Low Frequencies; Transversal Filtering; much more. An appendix reviews fundamental Fourier techniques. Index of notation. Glossary of terms. 24 figures. XII tables. Bibliography. General index. 192pp. 5⅜ x 8.   S507 Paperbound **$1.85**

CALCULUS REFRESHER FOR TECHNICAL MEN, A. Albert Klaf. This book is unique in English as a refresher for engineers, technicians, students who either wish to brush up their calculus or to clear up uncertainties. It is not an ordinary text, but an examination of most important aspects of integral and differential calculus in terms of the 756 questions most likely to occur to the technical reader. The first part of this book covers simple differential calculus, with constants, variables, functions, increments, derivatives, differentiation, logarithms, curvature of curves, and similar topics. The second part covers fundamental ideas of integration, inspection, substitution, transformation, reduction, areas and volumes, mean value, successive and partial integration, double and triple integration. Practical aspects are stressed rather than theoretical. A 50-page section illustrates the application of calculus to specific problems of civil and nautical engineering, electricity, stress and strain, elasticity, industrial engineering, and similar fields.—756 questions answered. 566 problems, mostly answered. 36 pages of useful constants, formulae for ready reference. Index. v + 431pp. 5⅜ x 8.   T370 Paperbound **$2.00**

METHODS IN EXTERIOR BALLISTICS, Forest Ray Moulton. Probably the best introduction to the mathematics of projectile motion. The ballistics theories propounded were coordinated with extensive proving ground and wind tunnel experiments conducted by the author and others for the U.S. Army. Broad in scope and clear in exposition, it gives the beginnings of the theory used for modern-day projectile, long-range missile, and satellite motion. Six main divisions: Differential Equations of Translatory Motion of a projectile; Gravity and the Resistance Function; Numerical Solution of Differential Equations; Theory of Differential Variations; Validity of Method of Numerical Integration; and Motion of a Rotating Projectile. Formerly titled: "New Methods in Exterior Ballistics." Index. 38 diagrams. viii + 259pp. 5⅜ x 8½.   S232 Paperbound **$1.75**

Technological, historical

A DIDEROT PICTORIAL ENCYCLOPEDIA OF TRADES AND INDUSTRY, Manufacturing and the Technical Arts in Plates Selected from "L'Encyclopédie ou Dictionnaire Raisonné des Sciences, des Arts, et des Métiers" of Denis Diderot. Edited with text by C. Gillispie. This first modern selection of plates from the high point of 18th century French engraving is a storehouse of valuable technological information to the historian of arts and science. Over 2000 illustrations on 485 full-page plates, most of them original size, show the trades and industries of a fascinating era in such great detail that the processes and shops might very well be reconstructed from them. The plates teem with life, with men, women, and children performing all of the thousands of operations necessary to the trades before and during the early stages of the industrial revolution. Plates are in sequence, and show general operations, closeups of difficult operations, and details of complex machinery. Such important and interesting trades and industries are illustrated as sowing, harvesting, bee-keeping, cheesemaking, operating windmills, milling flour, charcoal burning, tobacco processing, indigo, fishing, arts of war, salt extraction, mining, smelting, casting iron, steel, extracting mercury, zinc, sulphur, copper, etc., slating, tinning, silverplating, gilding, making gunpowder, cannons, bells, shoeing horses, tanning, papermaking, printing, dyeing, and more than 40 other categories. Professor Gillispie, of Princeton, supplies a full commentary on all the plates, identifying operations, tools, processes, etc. This material, presented in a lively and lucid fashion, is of great interest to the reader interested in history of science and technology. Heavy library cloth. 920pp. 9 x 12.   T421 Two volume set **$18.50**

CHARLES BABBAGE AND HIS CALCULATING ENGINES, edited by P. Morrison and E. Morrison. Babbage, leading 19th century pioneer in mathematical machines and herald of modern operational research, was the true father of Harvard's relay computer Mark I. His Difference Engine and Analytical Engine were the first machines in the field. This volume contains a valuable introduction on his life and work; major excerpts from his autobiography, revealing his eccentric and unusual personality; and extensive selections from "Babbage's Calculating Engines," a compilation of hard-to-find journal articles by Babbage, the Countess of Lovelace, L. F. Menabrea, and Dionysius Lardner. 8 illustrations, Appendix of miscellaneous papers. Index. Bibliography. xxxviii + 400pp. 5⅜ x 8.   T12 Paperbound **$2.00**

HISTORY OF HYDRAULICS, Hunter Rouse and Simon Ince. First history of hydraulics and hydrodynamics available in English. Presented in readable, non-mathematical form, the text is made especially easy to follow by the many supplementary photographs, diagrams, drawings, etc. Covers the great discoveries and developments from Archimedes and Galileo to modern giants—von Mises, Prandtl, von Karman, etc. Interesting browsing for the specialist; excellent introduction for teachers and students. Discusses such milestones as the two-piston pump of Ctesibius, the aqueducts of Frontius, the anticipations of da Vinci, Stevin and the first book on hydrodynamics, experimental hydraulics of the 18th century, the 19th-century expansion of practical hydraulics and classical and applied hydrodynamics, the rise of fluid mechanics in our time, etc. 200 illustrations. Bibliographies. Index. xii + 270pp. 5¾ x 8.
S1131 Paperbound **$2.00**

BRIDGES AND THEIR BUILDERS, David Steinman and Sara Ruth Watson. Engineers, historians, everyone who has ever been fascinated by great spans will find this book an endless source of information and interest. Dr. Steinman, recipient of the Louis Levy medal, was one of the great bridge architects and engineers of all time, and his analysis of the great bridges of history is both authoritative and easily followed. Greek and Roman bridges, medieval bridges, Oriental bridges, modern works such as the Brooklyn Bridge and the Golden Gate Bridge, and many others are described in terms of history, constructional principles, artistry, and function. All in all this book is the most comprehensive and accurate semipopular history of bridges in print in English. New, greatly revised, enlarged edition. 23 photographs, 26 line drawings. Index. xvii + 401pp. 5⅜ x 8.   T431 Paperbound **$2.00**

Prices subject to change without notice.

Dover publishes books on art, music, philosophy, literature, languages, history, social sciences, psychology, handcrafts, orientalia, puzzles and entertainments, chess, pets and gardens, books explaining science, intermediate and higher mathematics, mathematical physics, engineering, biological sciences, earth sciences, classics of science, etc. Write to:

Dept. catrr.
Dover Publications, Inc.
180 Varick Street, N.Y. 14, N.Y.